MEANS UNIT PRICE ESTIMATING METHODS

Standards & Procedures for Using Unit Price Cost Data

Second Edition

Senior Editor
Phillip R. Waier, P.E.

Illustrator
Carl W. Linde

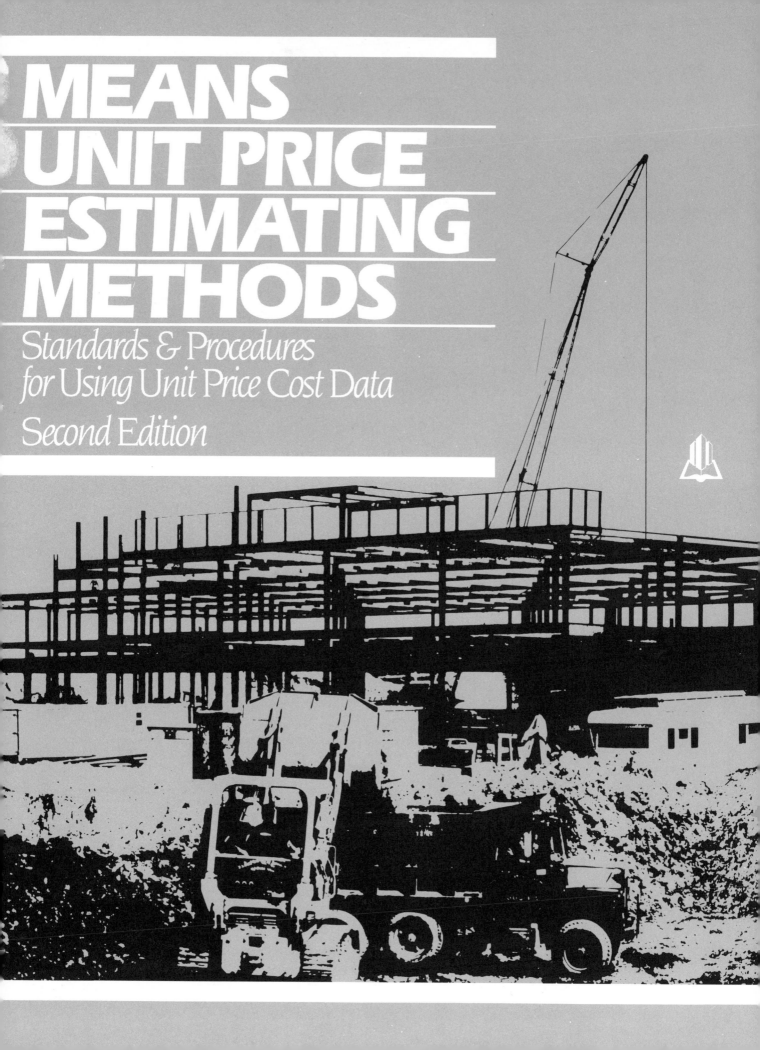

MEANS
UNIT PRICE
ESTIMATING
METHODS

Standards & Procedures
for Using Unit Price Cost Data

Second Edition

R.S. MEANS COMPANY, INC.
A Southam Company

CONSTRUCTION PUBLISHERS & CONSULTANTS
100 Construction Plaza
P.O. Box 800
Kingston, MA 02364-0800
(617) 585-7880

Copyright 1993

The editors for the second edition were Phillip Waier, Mary Greene, Edward Damphousse, and Rory Woolsey. Production was managed by Helen Marcella, and coordinated by Marion E. Schofield. Composition was supervised by Joan C. Marshman. The book and jacket were designed by Norman R. Forgit.

10 9 8 7 6 5 4 3 2 1

Library of Congress Cataloging in Publication Data

ISBN 0-87629-315-1

TABLE OF CONTENTS

FOREWORD

In addition to collecting and publishing construction cost data for over 50 years, Means has also developed a popular series of estimating and other construction reference books. *Means Unit Price Estimating* was one of the first, a response to customers who sought information on how to create unit price estimates, division by division, and how to use published costs most effectively. The book has been used by novice and practiced estimators to build and enhance their skills.

This book explains and demonstrates the methods and procedures of Unit Price Estimating, from the plans and specifications to the estimate summary. All aspects of the estimate, including the site visit, the quantity takeoff, pricing and bidding, are covered in detail. A complete sample estimate is presented to demonstrate the application of these estimating practices.

All construction costs used as examples in this book are from the 1993 edition of *Means Building Construction Cost Data*. Many pages, tables and charts from the annual cost guide are reproduced in order to show the origin and development of the cost data used in the estimating examples. *Means Building Construction Cost Data* is the leading source of thorough and up-to-date costs for the construction industry.

This book follows the logical progression of the estimating process. Initial chapters include analysis of the plans and specifications, the site visit, and evaluation of collected site data. The quantity takeoff, determination of costs, and final pricing are thoroughly covered, reflecting the importance and required attention to detail for each procedure. Also included are some strategies and principles that may be applied upon completion of the estimate. In addition, the format and origin of costs in *Means Building Construction Cost Data* are explained.

The final section of the book is devoted to a detailed discussion of estimating for each CSI MasterFormat division. A sample building project estimate is carried out, by division, to the estimate summary. This process demonstrates the proven estimating techniques described in the book. These are the techniques used by a majority of construction estimators and represent sound estimating practice.

Features of this new second edition include the fully updated sample estimate, as well as a new focus on computer estimating. An entirely new chapter provides an overview of the available computer estimating products and their capabilities, from the most basic to quite sophisticated programs. The use of published cost data and its integration into these systems is also covered.

Further enhancements to the original book include an expanded Appendix, with reference tables on a selection of commonly used construction materials.

It is the editors' intention that the new features of the second edition, combined with the proven methods established in the first, will provide readers with a comprehensive course in unit price estimating.

INTRODUCTION

Estimates are an important part of everyday life. We estimate the amount of food required to feed our family for a week or travel time to a desired destination. The preparation of a construction estimate requires the same kind of analysis. In general, we have to determine the amount of materials needed to complete a project, and the time required to install those materials, before assigning a cost to both.

Each estimate contains three interdependent variables:

- Quantity
- Quality
- Cost

Construction documentation in the form of plans and specifications dictates the quality and quantities of materials required. Cost is then determined based on these two elements. If a specific cost/budget must be maintained, then either the quantity or quality of the components is adjusted to meet the cost requirement.

Unit Price Estimating

What is the correct or accurate cost of a given construction project? Is it the total price the owner pays the contractor? Might not another reputable contractor perform the same work for a different cost, whether higher or lower? In fact, there isn't one *correct* estimated cost for a given project. There are too many variables in construction. At best, the estimator can determine a close approximation of what the final costs will be. The resulting accuracy of the approximation is affected by the amount of detail provided, the amount of time spent on the estimate, and the skill of the estimator. The estimator's skill is based on his or her working knowledge of how buildings are constructed. The estimator's creativity may lead to significant differences between estimates prepared by equally qualified individuals. Using a new method to accomplish a particular work activity (in the form of a new piece of equipment or new methodology) may significantly impact final costs.

The accuracy is determined by the cost accountant at the end of the project. If the project was completed in the allotted time and the profit met the expectation provided in the estimate, then it was accurate.

It is apparent that building construction estimating is not as simple as blindly applying material and labor prices and arriving at a magic figure. The purpose of this text is to make the estimating process easier and more organized for the experienced estimator, and to provide less experienced estimators with a basis for sound estimating practice.

Who Uses Unit Price Estimates?

A unit price estimate is the most detailed and accurate type of construction estimate. It is used by architects, engineers, contractors, and many owners/facilities managers in their daily activities.

Architects/Engineers

Design professionals perform unit price estimates for the following reasons.

- To evaluate change orders. When a change order is required, the A/E requests a proposal from the contractor. The proposal is usually supported by a detailed estimate. The A/E may perform a unit price estimate to validate or dispute the costs before approving the change.
- To verify a schedule of payments. Periodically, it may be necessary to validate a contractor's schedule of payments (the cost related to various elements of work) for invoicing purposes.

Contractors

Most of the estimates a contractor performs are unit price. Except in the early design stages, owners usually require "hard number" estimates (the price for which the contractor will execute a contract to do the work). Therefore, the contractor must perform the most accurate type of estimate – a unit price estimate. Any binding estimate is usually a unit price estimate.

Facilities Manager

When facilities managers/owners want an accurate estimate on which to base an authorization for expenditure or a loan application, a unit price estimate may be prepared. Owners (or their representatives) also evaluate contractors' proposals for work or change orders to ongoing projects based on unit price estimates.

When accuracy is required, a unit price estimate is the answer.

Chapter 1
ESTIMATE TYPES

Chapter 1

ESTIMATE TYPES

Construction estimators use four basic types of estimates. These types may be referred to by different names and may not be recognized by all as definitive, but most estimators will agree that each type has its place in the construction estimating process. The type of estimate performed is related to the amount of design information available. As the project proceeds through the various stages of design (from schematic design to design development to contract documents), the type of estimate changes and the accuracy of the estimate increases. Figure 1.1 graphically demonstrates the relationship of required time versus resulting accuracy for these four basic estimate types.

1. **Order of Magnitude Estimate:** The order of magnitude estimate could be loosely described as an educated guess. It is also known as a "napkin estimate," because it is often the result of a conversation between a contractor (or developer) and a client/owner over lunch or dinner, in which an estimate is created on the nearest piece of paper, usually a napkin. Order of Magnitude Estimates can be completed in a matter of minutes. Accuracy is plus or minus 20%.

2. **Square Foot and Cubic Foot Estimates:** This type of estimate is most often useful when only the proposed size and use of a planned building is known. Very little information is required. Performing a breakout for this type of estimate enables the designer and estimator to adjust components for the proposed use of the structure (hospital, factory, school, apartments), type of foundation (slab on grade, spread footing, piles), and superstructure (steel, concrete, or a combination) and to focus the cost more closely to the final price. Accuracy of the square foot estimate is plus or minus 15%.

3. **Systems (or Assemblies) Estimate:** A systems estimate is best used as a budgetary tool in the planning stages of a project. Accuracy is expected at plus or minus 10%.

4. **Unit Price Estimate:** Working drawings and full specifications are required to complete a unit price estimate. It is the most accurate of the four types but is also the most time-consuming. Used primarily for bidding purposes, accuracy is plus or minus 5%.

Order of Magnitude Estimates

The Order of Magnitude Estimate can be completed with only a minimum of information. The proposed use and size of the planned structure should be known and may be the only requirement. The "units" to describe the structure can be very general, and need not be well-defined. For example: "An office building for a small service company in a suburban industrial park will cost about $500,000." This type of statement (or estimate) can be made after a few minutes of thought used to draw upon experience and to make comparisons with similar projects from the past. While this rough figure might be appropriate for a project in one region of the country, an adjustment may be required for a change of location and for cost changes over time (price changes, inflation, etc.).

Figure 1.2, from *Means Building Construction Cost Data*, shows examples of a different approach to the Order of Magnitude Estimate. This format is based on unit of use. Please note at the bottom of the categories "Hospitals" and "Housing" that costs are given "per bed or person," "per rental unit," and "per apartment." This data does not require that details of the proposed project be known in order to determine rough costs; the only required information is the intended use of the building and its approximate size. What is lacking in accuracy (plus or minus 20%) is more than compensated by the minimal time required to complete the Order of Magnitude Estimate – a matter of minutes.

Square Foot and Cubic Foot Estimates

The use of Square Foot and Cubic Foot Estimates is most appropriate prior to the preparation of plans or preliminary drawings, when budgetary parameters are being analyzed and established. Please refer again to Figure 1.2 and note that costs for each type of project are presented first as "Total project costs" by square foot and by cubic foot. These costs are then broken down into different construction components, and then into the relationship of each component to the project as a whole, in terms of costs per square foot. This breakdown enables the designer, planner or estimator to adjust certain components according to the unique requirements of the proposed project.

Historical data for square foot costs of new construction are plentiful (see *Means Building Construction Cost Data*, Division 17). However, the best source of

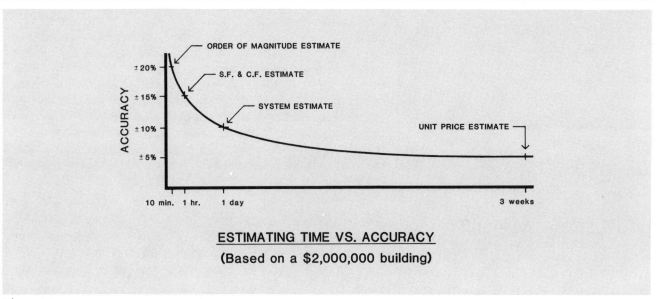

ESTIMATING TIME VS. ACCURACY
(Based on a $2,000,000 building)

Figure 1.1

square foot costs is the estimator's own cost records for similar projects, adjusted to the parameters of the project in question. While helpful for preparing preliminary budgets, Square Foot and Cubic Foot Estimates can also be useful as checks against other, more detailed estimates. While slightly more time is required than with Order of Magnitude Estimates, a greater accuracy (plus or minus 15%) is achieved due to more specific definition of the project. A Square Foot Estimate is consistent with the amount of design information available at the schematic design phase.

Systems (or Assemblies) Estimates

Rising design and construction costs in recent years have made budgeting and cost efficiency increasingly important in the early stages of building projects. Never before has the estimating process had such a crucial role in the initial planning. Unit Price Estimating, because of the time and detailed information required, is not suited as a budgetary or planning tool. A faster and more cost-effective method is needed for the planning phase of a building project; this is the "Systems," or "Assemblies Estimate." A Systems Estimate is usually prepared when the architect completes the design development plans.

The Systems method is a logical, sequential approach which reflects how a building is constructed. Twelve "Uniformat" divisions organize building construction into major components that can be used in Systems Estimates. These Uniformat divisions are listed below:

Systems Estimating Divisions:

Division 1 — Foundations

Division 2 — Substructures

Division 3 — Superstructures

Division 4 — Exterior Closure

Division 5 — Roofing

Division 6 — Interior Construction

Division 7 — Conveying Systems

Division 8 — Mechanical

Division 9 — Electrical

Division 10 — General Conditions and Profit

Division 11 — Special

Division 12 — Site Work

Each division is further broken down into systems. Each of these systems incorporates several different items into an assemblage that is commonly used in building construction. Figure 1.3 is an example of a typical system, in this case "Drywall Partitions/Stud Framing" (see *Means Assemblies Cost Data*).

In the Systems format, a construction component may appear in more than one division. For example, concrete is found in Division 1 - Foundations, as well as in Divisions 2, 3, 5 and 12 (see list above). Conversely, each division may incorporate many different areas of construction, and the labor of different trades.

A great advantage of the Systems Estimate is that the estimator/designer is able to substitute one system for another during design development and can quickly determine the cost differential. The owner can then anticipate accurate budgetary requirements before final details and dimensions are established.

171 | S.F., C.F. and % of Total Costs

		171 000	S.F. & C.F. Costs	UNIT	UNIT COSTS			% OF TOTAL			
					1/4	MEDIAN	3/4	1/4	MEDIAN	3/4	
410	0010	**GARAGES, PARKING**		S.F.	18.70	24.25	42.40				410
	0020	Total project costs		C.F.	1.67	2.14	3.51				
	2720	Plumbing		S.F.	.47	.65	1.02	2.20%	3%	3.80%	
	2900	Electrical			.79	1.19	1.92	4.20%	5.40%	7.20%	
	3100	Total: Mechanical & Electrical		↓	1.36	1.84	2.99	6.80%	8.70%	10.90%	
	3200										
	9000	Per car, total cost		Car	7,300	8,100	11,500				
	9500	Total: Mechanical & Electrical		"	465	640	960				
430	0010	**GYMNASIUMS**		S.F.	50.90	65.90	81.50				430
	0020	Total project costs		C.F.	2.48	3.40	4.41				
	1800	Equipment		S.F.	1.13	2.29	4.68	2%	3.30%	6.70%	
	2720	Plumbing			3.12	4.19	5.20	5.30%	7.20%	8.30%	
	2770	Heating, ventilating, air conditioning			3.19	5.55	8.75	7.20%	9.70%	13.30%	
	2900	Electrical			4.12	4.98	6.70	6.50%	8.20%	10.30%	
	3100	Total: Mechanical & Electrical		↓	7.80	12.65	17.70	16.40%	20.70%	26.20%	
	3500	See also division 114-801 & 114-805									
460	0010	**HOSPITALS**		S.F.	106	127	176				460
	0020	Total project costs		C.F.	8	10.05	13.60				
	1120	Roofing		S.F.	1.97	2.52	6.33	1.20%	2%	3%	
	1800	Equipment			2.66	5	8.60	1.60%	3.90%	5.90%	
	2720	Plumbing			9.20	11.95	16.05	7.20%	9.10%	10.70%	
	2770	Heating, ventilating, air conditioning			10.35	17.25	23.75	7.90%	13.80%	16.70%	
	2900	Electrical			11.05	14.95	22.60	9.80%	12%	15%	
	3100	Total: Mechanical & Electrical		↓	31.65	41.70	62.95	26.50%	34%	39.90%	
	9000	Per bed or person, total cost		Bed	26,400	52,400	71,600				
	9900	See also division 117-001		"							
480	0010	**HOUSING For the Elderly**		S.F.	51.60	65.05	80.55				480
	0020	Total project costs		C.F.	3.66	5.10	6.45				
	0100	Sitework		S.F.	3.58	5.50	8.05	5.80%	8%	12%	
	0500	Masonry			1.20	5.40	8.45	2.10%	6.50%	10.90%	
	1120	Roofing			1.02	1.80	3.25	1.30%	2.10%	3.20%	
	1140	Dampproofing			.29	.40	.84	.30%	.40%	.70%	
	1350	Glass & glazing			.28	.54	1.02	.30%	.60%	1.10%	
	1530	Drywall		↓	3.12	3.85	6.55	3.80%	4.10%	4.50%	
	1540	Floor covering		S.F.	.94	1.21	1.89	.90%	1.40%	2%	
	1570	Tile & marble			.40	.58	.85	.40%	.60%	.70%	
	1580	Painting			1.69	2.31	2.77	2%	2.60%	3%	
	1800	Equipment			1.22	1.65	2.68	1.80%	3.20%	4.40%	
	2510	Conveying systems			1.23	1.65	2.24	1.70%	2.20%	2.80%	
	2720	Plumbing			3.84	5.27	6.85	8.20%	9.60%	10.70%	
	2730	Heating, ventilating, air conditioning			1.78	2.72	3.75	3.20%	5.60%	6.80%	
	2900	Electrical			3.81	5.25	7.05	7.40%	8.90%	10.60%	
	2910	Electrical incl. electric heat			3.58	8.30	9.85	9.60%	11.10%	13.30%	
	3100	Total: Mechanical & Electrical		↓	9.40	13.20	16.90	18.30%	21.70%	24.70%	
	9000	Per rental unit, total cost		Unit	46,300	54,500	60,400				
	9500	Total: Mechanical & Electrical		"	8,900	11,100	13,200				
500	0010	**HOUSING Public (Low Rise)**		S.F.	40.85	57.45	75.45				500
	0020	Total project costs		C.F.	3.34	4.54	5.60				
	0100	Sitework		S.F.	5.10	7.45	12.40	8%	11.70%	16.10%	
	1800	Equipment			1.15	1.87	3.07	2.10%	2.90%	4.60%	
	2720	Plumbing			2.89	4.06	5.10	6.80%	9%	11.50%	
	2730	Heating, ventilating, air conditioning			1.54	2.99	3.19	4.20%	6%	6.40%	
	2900	Electrical			2.57	3.69	5.25	5%	6.50%	8.10%	
	3100	Total: Mechanical & Electrical		↓	7.55	11.15	15.25	14.90%	19.20%	23.40%	
	9000	Per apartment, total cost		Apt.	45,300	50,200	62,800				
	9500	Total: Mechanical & Electrical		"	7,400	10,200	12,700				

Figure 1.2

Final design details of the building project are required for a Unit Price Estimate. The Systems method does not require such details, but the estimators who use it must have a solid background knowledge of construction materials and methods, Building Code requirements, design options, and budgetary restrictions.

The Systems Estimate should not be used as a substitute for the Unit Price Estimate. While the Systems approach can be an invaluable tool in the planning stages of a project, it should be supported by Unit Price Estimating when greater accuracy is required.

Unit Price Estimates

The Unit Price Estimate is the most accurate and detailed of the four estimate types and therefore takes the most time to complete. Detailed working drawings and specifications (contract documents) must be available to the unit price estimator. All decisions regarding the building's materials and methods must be made in order to complete this type of estimate. There are fewer variables, and the estimate can therefore be more accurate. The working drawings and specifications are needed to determine the quantities of materials, equipment, and labor. Current and accurate costs for these items (unit prices) are also necessary. These costs can come from different sources. Wherever possible the estimator should use prices based on experience or cost figures from similar projects. If no records are available, prices may be determined instead from an up-to-date industry source book such as *Means Building Construction Cost Data*.

Because of the detail involved and the need for accuracy, Unit Price Estimates require a great deal of time and expense to complete properly. For this reason, Unit Price Estimating is best suited for construction bidding. It can also be effective for determining certain detailed costs in conceptual budgets or during design development.

Most construction specification manuals and cost reference books such as *Means Building Construction Cost Data* divide all unit price information into the sixteen MasterFormat divisions as adopted by the Construction Specifications Institute:

MasterFormat Construction Index Divisions:

Division 1 — General Requirements

Division 2 — Site Work

Division 3 — Concrete

Division 4 — Masonry

Division 5 — Metals

Division 6 — Wood and Plastics

Division 7 — Thermal and Moisture Protection

Division 8 — Doors and Windows

Division 9 — Finishes

Division 10 — Specialties

Division 11 — Equipment

Division 12 — Furnishings

Division 13 — Special Construction

Division 14 — Conveying Systems

Wood Stud Framing

Metal Stud Framing

The Drywall Partitions/Stud Framing Systems are defined by type of drywall and number of layers, type and spacing of stud framing, and treatment on the opposite face. Components include taping and finishing.

Cost differences between regular and fire resistant drywall are negligible, and terminology is interchangeable. In some cases fiberglass insulation is included for additional sound deadening.

System Components	QUANTITY	UNIT	COST PER S.F.		
			MAT.	INST.	TOTAL
SYSTEM 6.1-510-1250 DRYWALL PARTITION,5/8" F.R.1 SIDE,5/8" REG.1 SIDE,2"X4"STUDS,16" O.C.					
Gypsum plasterboard, nailed/screwed to studs, 5/8"F.R. fire resistant	1.000	S.F.	.23	.29	.52
Gypsum plasterboard, nailed/screwed to studs, 5/8" regular	1.000	S.F.	.21	.29	.50
Taping and finishing joints	2.000	S.F.	.16	.58	.74
Framing, 2 x 4 studs @ 16" O.C., 10' high	1.000	S.F.	.31	.61	.92
Total			.91	1.77	2.68

6.1-510 Drywall Partitions/Wood Stud Framing

	FACE LAYER	BASE LAYER	FRAMING	OPPOSITE FACE	INSULATION	COST PER S.F.		
						MAT.	INST.	TOTAL
1200	5/8" FR drywall	none	2 x 4, @ 16" O.C.	same	0	.93	1.77	2.70
1250				5/8" reg. drywall	0	.91	1.77	2.68
1300				nothing	0	.62	1.19	1.81
1400		1/4" SD gypsum	2 x 4 @ 16" O.C.	same	1-1/2" fiberglass	1.60	2.72	4.32
1450				5/8" FR drywall	1-1/2" fiberglass	1.43	2.39	3.82
1500				nothing	1-1/2" fiberglass	1.12	1.81	2.93
1600		resil. channels	2 x 4 @ 16", O.C.	same	1-1/2" fiberglass	1.47	3.44	4.91
1650				5/8" FR drywall	1-1/2" fiberglass	1.37	2.75	4.12
1700				nothing	1-1/2" fiberglass	1.06	2.17	3.23
1800		5/8" FR drywall	2 x 4 @ 24" O.C.	same	0	1.32	2.22	3.54
1850				5/8" FR drywall	0	1.09	1.93	3.02
1900				nothing	0	.78	1.35	2.13
1950		5/8" FR drywall	2 x 4, 16" O.C.	same	0	1.39	2.35	3.74
1955				5/8" FR drywall	0	1.16	2.06	3.22
2000				nothing	0	.85	1.48	2.33
2010		5/8" FR drywall	staggered, 6" plate	same	0	1.71	2.96	4.67
2015				5/8" FR drywall	0	1.48	2.67	4.15
2020				nothing	0	1.17	2.09	3.26
2200		5/8" FR drywall	2 rows-2 x 4 16"O.C.	same	2" fiberglass	2.13	3.24	5.37
2250				5/8" FR drywall	2" fiberglass	1.90	2.95	4.85
2300				nothing	2" fiberglass	1.59	2.37	3.96
2400	5/8" WR drywall	none	2 x 4, @ 16" O.C.	same	0	1.09	1.77	2.86
2450				5/8" FR drywall	0	1.01	1.77	2.78
2500				nothing	0	.70	1.19	1.89
2600		5/8" FR drywall	2 x 4, @ 24" O.C.	same	0	1.48	2.22	3.70
2650				5/8" FR drywall	0	1.17	1.93	3.10
2700				nothing	0	.86	1.35	2.21

Figure 1.3

Division 15 — Mechanical

Division 16 — Electrical

This method of organizing the various components of construction provides a standard of uniformity that is widely used by construction industry professionals — architects, engineers, material suppliers, and contractors. An example page from *Means Building Construction Cost Data* is shown in Figure 1.4. This page lists various types of formwork. (Please note that the heading "031 Concrete Formwork" denotes the MasterFormat subdivision classification for these items in Division 3 - Concrete.) Each page contains a wealth of information useful in Unit Price Estimating. The type of work to be performed is described in detail: typical crew makeup, daily output, and separate costs for material and installation. Total costs are extended to include the installing contractor's overhead and profit.

Figure 1.5 is a Means' "Condensed Estimate Summary" form. This form can be used after each division has been separately estimated. It serves as a checklist to ensure that estimators have included all divisions, and is a concise means for determining the total costs of the Unit Price Estimate. Please note at the top of the form these items: Total Area, Total Volume, Cost per Square Foot, and Cost per Cubic Foot. This information can prove valuable when the estimator needs Order of Magnitude, or Square Foot and Cubic Foot Estimates for budgeting. This data will also serve as a cross-check for similar projects in the future.

A fifth type of estimate, more accurate than unit price, warrants mention: the Scheduling Estimate. This type involves the application of realistic manpower allocation. A complete Unit Price Estimate is a prerequisite for the preparation of a Scheduling Estimate. A thorough discussion of Scheduling Estimating is beyond the scope of this book, but a brief discussion is included in Chapter Five, and a complete discussion may be found in *Means Scheduling Manual*, 3rd edition, by F. William Horsley.

031 | Concrete Formwork

		031 100	Struct C.I.P. Formwork	CREW	DAILY OUTPUT	MAN-HOURS	UNIT	1993 BARE COSTS				TOTAL INCL O&P	
								MAT.	LABOR	EQUIP.	TOTAL		
158	5000	Spread footings, 1 use			305	.105		1.07	2.32	.08	3.47	4.92	
	5050	2 use			371	.086		.62	1.91	.07	2.60	3.75	
	5100	3 use			401	.080		.47	1.77	.06	2.30	3.36	
	5150	4 use			414	.077		.39	1.71	.06	2.16	3.19	
	6000	Supports for dowels, plinths or templates, 2' x 2'			25	1.280	Ea.	2.95	28.50	.99	32.44	49	
	6050	4' x 4' footing			22	1.455		6.35	32	1.12	39.47	58.50	
	6100	8' x 8' footing			20	1.600		12.90	35.50	1.23	49.63	71	
	6150	12' x 12' footing			17	1.882		21	41.50	1.45	63.95	90	
	7000	Plinths, 1 use			250	.128	SFCA	1.64	2.84	.10	4.58	6.35	
	7100	4 use			270	.119		.46	2.63	.09	3.18	4.73	
162	0010	FORMS IN PLACE, GRADE BEAM 1 use R031 -050	C-2	530	.091		1.25	2.07	.06	3.38	4.70	162
	0050	2 use			580	.083		.75	1.89	.06	2.70	3.86	
	0100	3 use			600	.080		.57	1.83	.05	2.45	3.56	
	0150	4 use			605	.079		.48	1.82	.05	2.35	3.44	
166	0010	FORMS IN PLACE, MAT FOUNDATION 1 use			290	.166	SFCA	1.37	3.79	.11	5.27	7.60	166
	0050	2 use			310	.155		.78	3.54	.11	4.43	6.55	
	0100	3 use			330	.145		.56	3.33	.10	3.99	5.95	
	0120	4 use			350	.137		.46	3.14	.09	3.69	5.55	
170	0010	**FORMS IN PLACE, SLAB ON GRADE**											170
	1000	Bulkhead forms with keyway, 1 use, 2 piece	C-1	510	.063	L.F.	.45	1.39	.05	1.89	2.73	
	1050	3 piece (see also edge forms)			400	.080		.56	1.77	.06	2.39	3.47	
	1100	4 piece			350	.091		.74	2.03	.07	2.84	4.07	
	1400	Bulkhead forms w/keyway, 1 piece expanded metal, left in place											
	1410	In lieu of 2 piece form	C-1	1,375	.023	L.F.	.80	.52	.02	1.34	1.71	
	1420	In lieu of 3 piece form			1,200	.027		.80	.59	.02	1.41	1.83	
	1430	In lieu of 4 piece form			1,050	.030		.80	.68	.02	1.50	1.97	
	2000	Curb forms, wood, 6" to 12" high, on grade, 1 use			215	.149	SFCA	1.40	3.30	.11	4.81	6.80	
	2050	2 use			250	.128		.78	2.84	.10	3.72	5.40	
	2100	3 use			265	.121		.56	2.67	.09	3.32	4.92	
	2150	4 use			275	.116		.45	2.58	.09	3.12	4.64	
	3000	Edge forms, to 6" high, 4 use, on grade			600	.053	L.F.	.25	1.18	.04	1.47	2.18	
	3050	7" to 12" high, 4 use, on grade			435	.074	SFCA	.74	1.63	.06	2.43	3.43	
	3500	For depressed slabs, 4 use, to 12" high			300	.107	L.F.	.53	2.36	.08	2.97	4.38	
	3550	To 24" high			175	.183		.68	4.05	.14	4.87	7.25	
	4000	For slab blockouts, 1 use to 12" high			200	.160		.54	3.54	.12	4.20	6.30	
	4050	To 24" high			120	.267		.68	5.90	.21	6.79	10.25	
	4100	Plastic (extruded) edge forms, to 6" high, multiple use, on grade		800	.040		.15	.89	.03	1.07	1.59	
	5000	Screed, 24 ga. metal key joint											
	5020	Wood, incl. wood stakes, 1" x 3"	C-1	900	.036	L.F.	.32	.79	.03	1.14	1.62	
	5050	2" x 4"			900	.036	*	.92	.79	.03	1.74	2.28	
170	6000	Trench forms in floor, 1 use	C-1	160	.200	SFCA	1.71	4.43	.15	6.29	9	170
	6050	2 use			175	.183		.93	4.05	.14	5.12	7.55	
	6100	3 use			180	.178		.68	3.94	.14	4.76	7.10	
	6150	4 use			185	.173		.55	3.83	.13	4.51	6.75	
174	0010	FORMS IN PLACE, STAIRS (Slant length x width), 1 use R031 -050	C-2	165	.291	S.F.	2.50	6.65	.20	9.35	13.40	174
	0050	2 use			170	.282		1.45	6.45	.19	8.09	11.95	
	0100	3 use			180	.267		1.10	6.10	.18	7.38	11	
	0150	4 use			190	.253		.93	5.80	.17	6.90	10.25	
	1000	Alternate pricing method (0.7 L.F./S.F.), 1 use			100	.480	LF Rsr	3.59	11	.33	14.92	21.50	
	1050	2 use			105	.457		2.15	10.45	.31	12.91	19.10	
	1100	3 use			110	.436		1.67	10	.30	11.97	17.80	
	1150	4 use			115	.417		1.46	9.55	.28	11.29	16.90	
	2000	Stairs, cast on sloping ground (length x width), 1 use			220	.218	S.F.	1.83	4.99	.15	6.97	10	
	2100	4 use			240	.200	*	1.07	4.58	.14	5.79	8.55	

Figure 1.4

MEANS CONDENSED ESTIMATE SUMMARY

	SHEET NO.
PROJECT	ESTIMATE NO.
LOCATION	TOTAL AREA/VOLUME	DATE
ARCHITECT	COST PER S.F./C.F.	NO. OF STORIES
PRICES BY:	EXTENSIONS BY:	CHECKED BY:

DIV.	DESCRIPTION	MATERIAL	LABOR	EQUIPMENT	SUBCONTRACT	TOTAL
1.0	General Requirements					
2.0	Site Work					
3.0	Concrete					
4.0	Masonry					
5.0	Metals					
6.0	Carpentry					
7.0	Moisture & Thermal Protection					
8.0	Doors, Windows, Glass					
9.0	Finishes					
10.0	Specialties					
11.0	Equipment					
12.0	Furnishings					
13.0	Special Construction					
14.0	Conveying Systems					
15.0	Mechanical					
16.0	Electrical					
	Subtotals					
	Sales Tax %					
	Overhead %					
	Subtotal					
	Profit %					
	Contingency %					
	Adjustments					
	TOTAL BID					

Figure 1.5

Chapter 2

BEFORE STARTING THE ESTIMATE

Chapter 2
BEFORE STARTING THE ESTIMATE

The "Invitation to Bid" — To the contractor, this can mean the prospect of weeks of hard work with only a chance of bidding success. It can also mean the opportunity to obtain a contract for a successful and lucrative building project. It is not uncommon for the contractor to bid ten or more jobs in order to win just one. The success rate most often depends upon estimating accuracy and thus, the preparation, organization and care that go into the estimating process.

The first step before starting the estimate is to obtain copies of the plans and specifications in *sufficient quantities*. Most estimators mark up plans with colored pencils and make numerous notes and references. For one trade to estimate from plans that have been used by another is difficult at best and may easily lead to errors. Most often two complete sets are provided by the architect. More sets must be purchased, if needed.

The estimator should be aware of and note any instructions to bidders, which may be included in the specifications or in a separate document. To avoid future confusion, the bid due date, time and place should be clearly stated and understood upon receipt of the construction documents (plans and specifications). The due date should be marked on a calendar and a schedule. Completion of the estimate should be made as soon as possible, to avoid confusion at the last minute.

If bid security, or a bid bond, is required, then time must be allowed and arrangements made, especially if the bonding capability or capacity of a contractor has not previously been established.

All pre-bid meetings with the owner or architect should be attended, preferably *after* a review of the plans and specifications. Important points are often brought up at such meetings and details clarified. Attendance by all bidders is important, not only to show the owner an interest in the project, but also to ensure equal and competitive bidding. It is to the estimator's advantage to examine and review the plans and specifications before any such meetings and before the initial site visit. It is important to become familiar with the project as soon as possible.

In recent years, specifications, or project manuals, have become massive volumes containing a wealth of information. This author cannot stress enough the importance of reading all contract documents thoroughly. They exist to protect all parties involved in the construction process. The contract documents are written so that the estimators will be bidding equally and competitively, ensuring that all items in a project are included. The contract documents protect the designer (the architect or engineer) by ensuring that all work is supplied and installed as specified. The owner also benefits from thorough and complete construction documents, being guaranteed a measure of quality control and a complete job. Finally, the contractor benefits because the scope of work is well-defined, eliminating the gray areas of what is implied but not stated. "Extras" are more readily avoided. Change orders, if required, are accepted with less argument if the original contract documents are complete, well-stated, and most importantly, read by all concerned parties. Appendix A of this book contains a reproduction of a SPEC-AID, an R.S. Means Co., Inc. publication. This document was created not only to assist designers and planners when developing project specifications, but also as an aid to the estimator. The sections, arranged by MasterFormat division, list thousands of components and variables of the building construction process. The estimator can use this form as a means of documenting a project's requirements, and as a checklist to be sure that all items have been included.

During the first review of the specifications, all items to be priced should be identified and noted. All work to be subcontracted should be examined for "related work" required from other trades. Such work is usually referenced and described in a thorough project specification. "Work by others" or "Not in Contract" should be clearly defined as well as delineated on the drawings. Certain materials are often specified by the designer and purchased by the owner to be installed (labor only) by the contractor. These items should be noted and the responsibilities of each party clearly understood.

The General Conditions, Supplemental Conditions and Special Conditions sections of the specifications should be examined carefully. These sections describe the items that have a direct bearing on the proposed project, but may not be part of the actual physical construction. An office trailer, temporary utilities, and testing are examples of these kinds of items. Also included in these sections is information regarding completion dates, payment requirements (e.g., retainage), allowances, alternates, and other important project requirements. All of these requirements have a significant bearing on the ultimate costs of the project and must be known and understood prior to performing the estimate. A more detailed discussion of General Conditions is included in Chapter 9.

While analyzing the plans and specifications, the estimator should evaluate the different portions of the project to determine which areas warrant the most attention. For example, if a building is to have a steel framework with a glass and aluminum frame skin, then more time should be spent estimating Division 5 — Metals, and Division 8 — Doors and Windows than Division 6 — Wood and Plastics.

Figures 2.1 and 2.2 are charts showing the relative percentage of different construction components by MasterFormat Divisions and Systems Division, respectively. These charts have been developed to represent the average percentages for new construction as a whole. All commonly used building types are included. The estimator should determine, for a given project, the relative proportions of each component, and time should be allocated accordingly. Using the percentages in Figure 2.1, a 10% error in Division 6 would result in approximately a 0.2% error in the project as a whole, while a 10% error in Division

15 would result in an approximate 2% error overall. Thus, more time and care should be given to estimating those areas which contribute more to the cost of the project.

When the overall scope of the work has been identified, the drawings should be examined to confirm the information in the specifications. This is the time to clarify details while reviewing the general content. The estimator should note which sections, elevations and detail drawings are for which plans. At this point and throughout the whole estimating process, the estimator should note and list any discrepancies between the plans and specifications, as well as any possible omissions. It is often stated in bid documents that bidders are obliged to notify the owner or architect/engineer of any such discrepancies.

Component Contribution of Divisions and Subdivisions

NO.	DIVISION	%	NO.	DIVISION	%	NO.	DIVISION	%
016	CONTRACTOR EQUIPMENT*	6.5%	051	Structural Metal Framing	2.2%	092	Lath, Plaster & Gypsum Board	5.1%
022	Earthwork	1.6	052,053	Metal Joists & Decking	1.5	093,094	Tile & Terrazzo	1.0
023	Tunneling, Piles & Caissons	0.7	055	Metal Fabrications	2.6	095	Acoustical Treat. & Wood Flooring	0.8
025	Paving & Surfacing	0.8	5	METALS	6.3	096	Flooring & Carpet	1.3
026,027	Utilities, Sewerage & Drainage	0.6	061	Rough Carpentry	1.7	099	Painting & Wall Coverings	2.2
028	Site Improvements	0.1	062	Finish Carpentry	0.1	9	FINISHES	10.4
029	Landscaping	1.1	6	WOOD & PLASTICS	1.8	10-14	DIVISIONS 10-14	8.7
2	SITE WORK	4.9	071	Waterproofing & Dampproofing	0.7	151-153	Plumbing: Piping & Fixtures	5.4
031	Concrete Formwork	5.8	072	Insulation & Fireproofing	0.6	154	Fire Protection	2.7
032	Concrete Reinforcing	2.4	073	Shingles	0.3	155	Heating	7.2
033	Cast in Place Concrete	9.5	074,075	Roofing & Siding	3.0	156,157	Air Conditioning & Ventilation	4.4
034	Precast Concrete	0.3	076	Flashing & Sheet Metal	0.2	15	MECHANICAL	19.7
035	Cementitious Decks	0.1	7	THERMAL & MOISTURE PROT.	4.8	16	ELECTRICAL	9.6
3	CONCRETE	18.1	081-083	Doors & Frames	1.5		TOTAL (Div. 1-16)	100.0%
041	Mortar & Masonry Accessories	0.3	085	Windows	2.5			
042	Unit Masonry	9.2	088,089	Glazing & Glazed Curtain Walls	1.8	* Percentage for contractor equipment is		
044	Stone	0.4	8	DOORS & WINDOWS	5.8	spread among divisions and included		
4	MASONRY	9.9				above for information only		

Figure 2.1

Table 13.1-011 Labor, Material and Equipment Cost Distribution for Weighted Average Listed by System Division

Division No.	Building System	Percentage	Division No.	Building System	Percentage
1 & 2	Foundation & Substructure	9.6%	7	Conveying	5.1%
3	Superstructure	17.2%	8	Mechanical	19.7%
4	Exterior Closure	15.7%	9	Electric	9.6%
5	Roofing	3.2%	11	Equipment	3.6%
6	Interior Construction	12.0%	12	Site Work	4.3%
				Total weighted index (Div. 1-12)	100.0%

Figure 2.2

When so notified, the designer will most often issue an addendum to the contract documents in order to properly notify all parties concerned and to ensure equal and competitive bidding.

Once familiar with the contract documents, the estimator should notify appropriate subcontractors and vendors to solicit bids. Those subcontractors whose work is affected by the site conditions should accompany the estimator on the job site visit. At least one such visit (and often two or more) is extremely important, especially in cases of renovation and remodeling where existing conditions can have a significant effect on the cost of a project. During the site visit, the estimator should take notes, and possibly photographs, of all information pertinent to the construction and therefore to the project estimate. Pre-printed forms, such as the Job Site Analysis shown in Figures 2.3 and 2.4, can be useful to ensure that all items are included. Please note that most aspects of site work are included, in addition to such items as utilities, taxes, material and labor availability. This kind of form can be very helpful as a checklist to prevent the omission of items which may be less obvious. If unusual site conditions exist or if questions arise during the takeoff, a second site visit is recommended.

In some areas, questions are likely to arise that cannot be answered clearly by the plans and specifications. Certain items may be omitted, or there may be conflicts or discrepancies within the contract documents. It is crucial that the owner or responsible party be notified quickly (usually in writing) so that these questions may be resolved before causing unnecessary problems. A proper estimate cannot be completed until all such questions are answered.

Perhaps the best way for an estimator to approach a project is to begin with a clear mind and a clear desk. Clutter and confusion in either case can have detrimental effects on the efficiency and accuracy of the estimate.

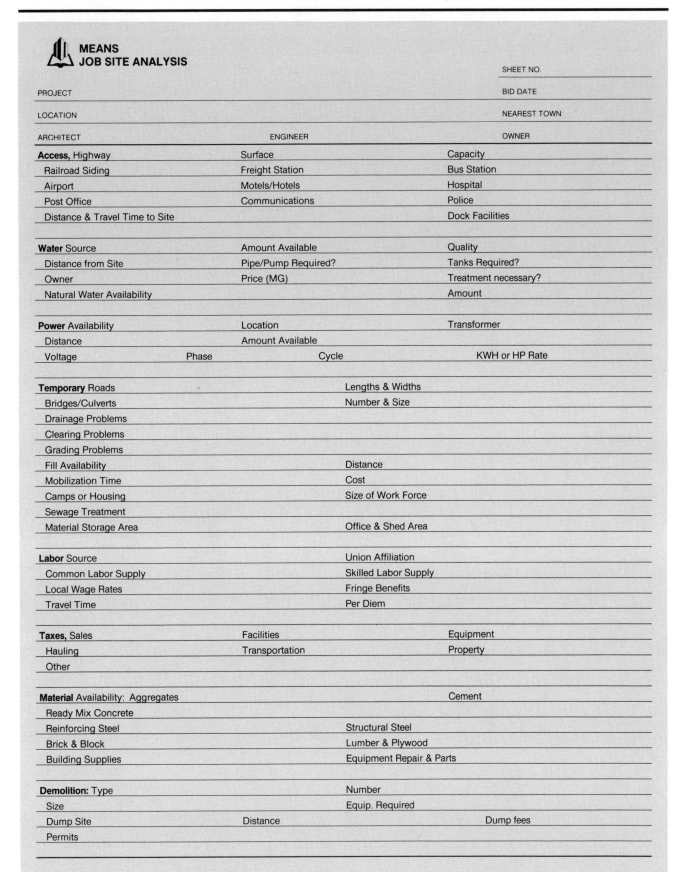

MEANS
JOB SITE ANALYSIS

			SHEET NO.
PROJECT			BID DATE
LOCATION			NEAREST TOWN
ARCHITECT	ENGINEER		OWNER

Access, Highway	Surface	Capacity
Railroad Siding	Freight Station	Bus Station
Airport	Motels/Hotels	Hospital
Post Office	Communications	Police
Distance & Travel Time to Site		Dock Facilities

Water Source	Amount Available	Quality
Distance from Site	Pipe/Pump Required?	Tanks Required?
Owner	Price (MG)	Treatment necessary?
Natural Water Availability		Amount

Power Availability	Location	Transformer
Distance	Amount Available	
Voltage Phase	Cycle	KWH or HP Rate

Temporary Roads	Lengths & Widths
Bridges/Culverts	Number & Size
Drainage Problems	
Clearing Problems	
Grading Problems	
Fill Availability	Distance
Mobilization Time	Cost
Camps or Housing	Size of Work Force
Sewage Treatment	
Material Storage Area	Office & Shed Area

Labor Source	Union Affiliation
Common Labor Supply	Skilled Labor Supply
Local Wage Rates	Fringe Benefits
Travel Time	Per Diem

Taxes, Sales	Facilities	Equipment
Hauling	Transportation	Property
Other		

Material Availability: Aggregates		Cement
Ready Mix Concrete		
Reinforcing Steel	Structural Steel	
Brick & Block	Lumber & Plywood	
Building Supplies	Equipment Repair & Parts	

Demolition: Type	Number	
Size	Equip. Required	
Dump Site	Distance	Dump fees
Permits		

Figure 2.3

19

Clearing: Area   Timber   Diameter   Species

    Brush Area   Burn on Site   Disposal Area

    Saleable Timber   Useable Timber   Haul

    Equipment Required

Weather: Mean Temperatures

    Highs   Lows

    Working Season Duration   Bad Weather Allowance

    Winter Construction

    Average Rainfall   Wet Season   Dry Season

    Stream or Tide Conditions

    Haul Road Problems

    Long Range Weather

Soils: Job Borings Adequate?   Test Pits

    Additional Borings Needed   Location   Extent

    Visible Rock

    U.S. Soil & Agriculture Maps

    Bureau of Mines Geological Data

    Conty/State Agriculture Agent

    Tests Required

    Ground Water

Construction Plant Required

    Alternate Method

    Equipment Available

    Rental Equipment   Location

Miscellaneous: Contractor Interest

    Sub Contractor Interest

    Material Fabricator Availability

    Possible Job Delays

    Political Situation

    Construction Money Availability

    Unusual Conditions

Summary

Figure 2.4

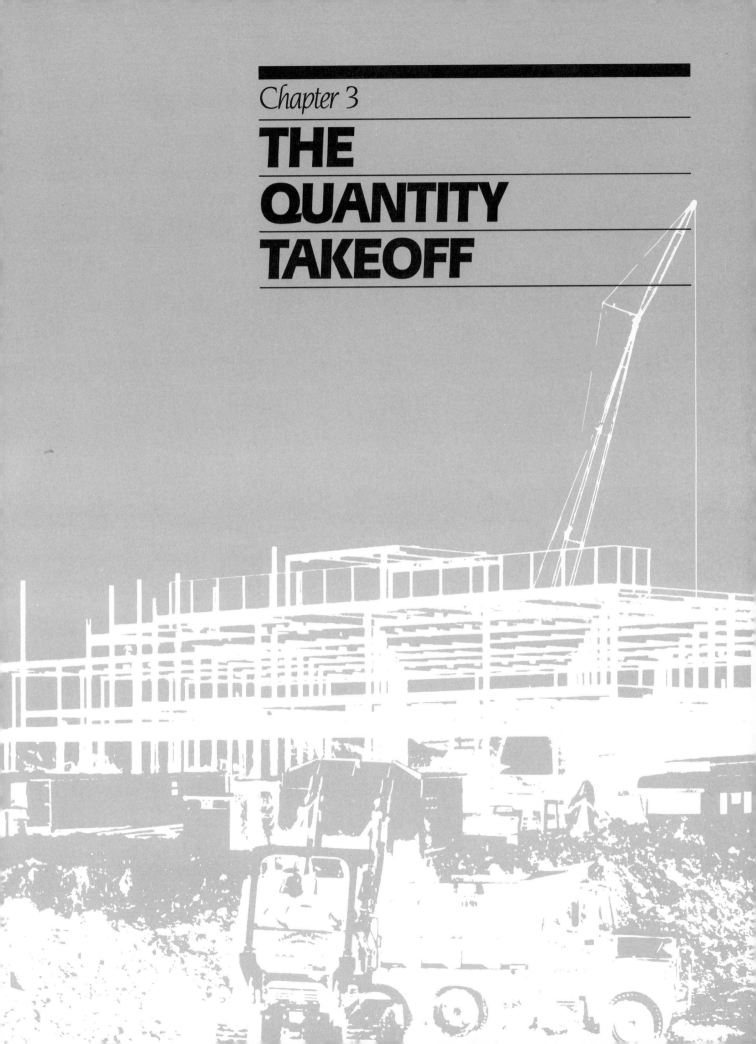

Chapter 3
THE QUANTITY TAKEOFF

Chapter 3

THE QUANTITY TAKEOFF

Traditionally, quantities are taken off, or surveyed from the drawings in sequence as the building would be built. Recently, however, the sequence of takeoff and estimating is more often based on the sixteen divisions of the CSI MasterFormat. A thorough and detailed discussion, by MasterFormat division, is included in Chapter 9.

Quantities may be taken off by one person if the project is not too large and time allows. For larger projects, the plans are often split into several disciplines (or divisions) and the work assigned to two or more estimators. In this case a project leader is assigned to coordinate and assemble the estimate.

When working with the plans during the quantity takeoff, consistency is the most important consideration. If each job is approached in the same manner, a pattern will develop, such as moving from the lower floors to the top, clockwise or counterclockwise. The choice of method is not important, but consistency is. The purpose of being consistent is to avoid duplications as well as omissions and errors. Pre-printed forms provide an excellent means for developing consistent patterns. Figures 3.1 and 3.2 are examples of such forms. The Quantity Sheet (Figure 3.1) is designed purely for quantity takeoff. Note that one set of dimensions can be used for up to four different items. A good example of the use of this form is shown in Chapter 9, Figure 9.37. Figure 3.2, a Consolidated Estimate sheet, is designed to be used for both quantity takeoff and pricing on one form.

Every contractor might benefit from designing custom forms which would be appropriate for specific uses. If employees within the same company all use the same types of forms, then communication, interaction and coordination of the estimating process will proceed more smoothly. One estimator will be able to understand the work of another. R.S. Means has published two books completely devoted to forms and their use, entitled *Means Forms for Building Construction Professionals* and *Means Forms for Contractors*. Forms, with examples and instructions for use, are included in each book.

If approached logically and systematically, there are a number of short cuts which can help to save time without sacrificing accuracy. Abbreviations simply save the time of writing things out. An abbreviations list, similar to that in the back of *Means Building Construction Cost Data*, might be posted in a conspicuous place, providing a consistent pattern of definitions for use within an office.

MEANS QUANTITY SHEET

			SHEET NO.	
PROJECT			ESTIMATE NO.	
LOCATION		ARCHITECT	DATE	
TAKE OFF BY		EXTENSIONS BY:	CHECKED BY:	

DESCRIPTION	NO.	DIMENSIONS		UNIT		UNIT		UNIT		UNIT

Figure 3.1

Figure 3.2

25

Figure 3.2

25

All dimensions — whether printed, measured, or calculated — that can be used for determining quantities for more than one item should be listed on a separate sheet and posted for easy reference. Posted gross dimensions can also be used to quickly check for order of magnitude errors.

Measurements should be converted to decimal equivalents before calculations are performed to extend the quantities. A chart similar to that shown in Figure 3.3 serves as a quick reference for such conversions. Whether converting from feet and inches to decimals, or from cubic feet to cubic yards, use good judgment and common sense to determine significant digits. Rounding off, or decreasing the number of significant digits, should be done only when it will not statistically affect the resulting product.

The estimator must use good judgment to determine when rounding is appropriate. An overall two or three percent variation in a competitive market can often be the difference between getting or losing a job, or between profit or no profit. The estimator should establish rules for rounding to achieve a consistent level of precision. As a general rule, it is best to not round numbers until the final summary of quantities. The final summary is also the time to convert units (square feet of paving to square yards, linear feet of lumber to board feet, etc.).

Figure 3.4 illustrates an example of the effects of premature rounding. If all items of a project were similarly rounded up for "safety," total project costs may include an unwarranted, or at least unaccountable allowance. An extra 5% may remove a bid from the competition.

Be sure to quantify and include "labor only" items that are not shown on plans. Such items may or may not be indicated in the specifications and might include cleanup, special labor for handling materials, etc.

Conversion of Inches to Decimal Parts per Foot												
	0	1″	2″	3″	4″	5″	6″	7″	8″	9″	10″	11″
0	0	.08	.17	.25	.33	.42	.50	.58	.67	.75	.83	.92
1/8″	.01	.09	.18	.26	.34	.43	.51	.59	.68	.76	.84	.93
1/4″	.02	.10	.19	.27	.35	.44	.52	.60	.69	.77	.85	.94
3/8″	.03	.11	.20	.28	.36	.45	.53	.61	.70	.78	.86	.95
1/2″	.04	.12	.21	.29	.37	.46	.54	.62	.71	.79	.87	.96
5/8″	.05	.14	.22	.30	.39	.47	.55	.64	.72	.80	.89	.97
3/4″	.06	.15	.23	.31	.40	.48	.56	.65	.73	.81	.90	.98
7/8″	.07	.16	.24	.32	.41	.49	.57	.66	.74	.82	.91	.99

Figure 3.3

In general, the quantity takeoff should be organized so that information gathered can be used to future advantage. Scheduling can be made easier if items are taken off and listed by construction phase, or by floor. Material purchasing will similarly benefit.

Units for each item should be consistent throughout the whole project — from takeoff to cost control. In this way, the original estimate can be equitably compared to progress and final cost reports more easily. It will be easier to keep track of a job.

The following list is a summation of the suggestions just mentioned plus a few more rules which will be helpful during the quantity takeoff:

- Use pre-printed forms.
- Transfer carefully and make clear notations of sums carried from one sheet to the next.
- List dimensions consistently.
- Use printed dimensions, otherwise measure dimensions carefully if the scale is known and accurate.
- Add printed dimensions for a single entry.
- Convert feet and inches to decimal feet.
- Do not round off until the final summary of quantities.
- Mark drawings as quantities are determined.
- Be alert for changes in scale, or notes such as "N.T.S." (not to scale).
- Include required items which may not appear in the plans and specs.
- Use building symmetry to avoid repetitive takeoffs.

Effect of Rounding Off Measurements at Quantity Takeoff		Actual	Rounded Off	% Difference
	Length of partition	96'-8"	100'	3.4%
	Height of partition	11'-9"	12'	2.1%
	Total S.F.	1135.87 S.F.	1200 S.F.	5.6%
	Cost ($3.83/S.F.)	$4350.38	$4596.00	5.6%
	+15% overhead	$5002.94	$5285.40	5.6%
	+10% profit	$5503.23	$5813.94	5.6%
	Total cost difference (incl. (O&P): $310.71			

Figure 3.4

And perhaps the five most important points:

- Write legibly.
- Be organized.
- Use common sense.
- Be consistent.
- Add explanatory notes to the estimate to provide an audit trail.

Chapter 4
PRICING THE ESTIMATE

Chapter 4
PRICING THE ESTIMATE

When the quantities have been determined, then prices, or unit costs, must be applied in order to determine the total costs. Depending upon the chosen estimating method (and thus the degree of accuracy required) and the level of detail, these unit costs may be direct or bare costs, or may include overhead, profit or contingencies. In Unit Price Estimating, the unit costs most commonly used are "bare," or "unburdened." Items such as overhead and profit are usually added to the total direct costs on the bottom line, at the time of the estimate summary.

Sources of Cost Information

One of the most difficult aspects of the estimator's job is determining accurate and reliable bare cost data. Sources for such data are varied, but can be categorized in terms of their relative reliability. The most reliable source of any cost information is the accurate, up-to-date, well-kept records of the estimator's own company. There is no better cost for a particular construction item than the *actual* cost to the contractor of that item from another recent job, modified (if necessary) to meet the requirements of the project being estimated.

Bids from *responsible* subcontractors are the second most reliable source of cost data. Any estimating inaccuracies are essentially absorbed by the subcontractor. A subcontract bid is a known, fixed cost, prior to the project. Whether the price is "right" or "wrong" does not matter (as long as it is a responsible bid with no gross errors). The bid is what the appropriate portion of the work will cost. The prime contractor does not have to estimate the work of subcontractors, except for possible verification of the quote.

Quotations by vendors for material costs are, for the same reasons, as reliable as subcontract bids. In this case, however, the estimator must apply estimated labor costs. Thus the "installed" price for a particular item may be more variable. Whenever possible, all price quotations from vendors or subcontractors should be obtained in writing. Qualifications and exclusions should be clearly stated. Inclusions should be checked to be sure that they are complete and as specified. One way to ensure that these requirements are met is to prepare a form on which all subcontractors and vendors must submit quotations. This form can ask all appropriate questions and provide a consistent source of information for the estimator.

The above procedures are ideal, but often in the realistic haste of estimating and bidding, quotations are received orally, either in person or by telephone or fax. The importance of gathering all pertinent information is heightened because omissions are more likely. A pre-printed form, such as the one shown in Figure 4.1, can be extremely useful to ensure that all required information and qualifications are obtained and understood. How often has the subcontractor stated, "I didn't know that I was supposed to include that?" With the help of such forms, the appropriate questions are asked and answered. An example of the use of this form is shown in Figure 9.34.

If the estimator has no cost records for a particular item and is unable to obtain a quotation, then the next most reliable source of price information is current unit price cost books such as *Means Building Construction Cost Data*. Means presents all such data in the form of national averages; these figures must be adjusted to local conditions. This procedure will be explained in Chapter 7. In addition to being a source of primary costs, unit price books can be useful as a reference or cross-check for verifying costs obtained elsewhere.

Lacking cost information from any of the above-mentioned sources, the estimator may have to rely on data from old books or adjusted records from an old project. While these types of costs may not be very accurate, they may be better than the final alternative – guesswork.

No matter which source of cost information is used, the system and sequence of pricing should be the same as that used for the quantity takeoff. This consistent approach should continue through both accounting and cost control during construction of the project.

Types of Costs

Unit price estimates for building construction may be organized according to the 16 divisions of the CSI MasterFormat. Within each division, the components or individual construction items are identified, listed, and priced. This kind of definition and detail is necessary to complete an accurate estimate. In addition, each "item" can be broken down further into material, labor and equipment components.

All costs included in a Unit Price Estimate can be divided into two types: direct and indirect. Direct costs are those directly linked to the physical construction of a project – those costs without which the project could not be completed. The material, labor and equipment costs just mentioned, as well as subcontract costs, are all direct costs. These may also be referred to as "bare," or "unburdened" costs.

Indirect costs are usually added to the estimate at the summary stage and are most often calculated as a percentage of the direct costs. They include such items as sales tax on materials, overhead, profit and contingencies, etc. It is the indirect costs that generally account for the greatest variation in estimating.

Types of Costs in a Construction Estimate

Direct Costs	Indirect Costs
Material	Taxes
Labor	Overhead
Equipment	Profit
Subcontractors	Contingencies
Project Overhead	

Direct Costs

On the list above, Project Overhead has been listed as a direct cost. Project Overhead represents those costs of a construction project which are usually included in Division 1 – General Requirements. Typical items are the job site office trailer, supervisory labor costs, daily and final cleanup, and temporary

MEANS
TELEPHONE QUOTATION

DATE _____

PROJECT _____

TIME _____

FIRM QUOTING _____

PHONE ( ) _____

ADDRESS _____

BY _____

ITEM QUOTED _____

RECEIVED BY _____

WORK INCLUDED	AMOUNT OF QUOTATION

DELIVERY TIME **TOTAL BID**

DOES QUOTATION INCLUDE THE FOLLOWING: If ☐ NO is checked, determine the following:

STATE & LOCAL SALES TAXES	☐ YES	☐ NO	MATERIAL VALUE
DELIVERY TO THE JOB SITE	☐ YES	☐ NO	WEIGHT
COMPLETE INSTALLATION	☐ YES	☐ NO	QUANTITY
COMPLETE SECTION AS PER PLANS & SPECIFICATIONS	☐ YES	☐ NO	DESCRIBE BELOW

EXCLUSIONS AND QUALIFICATIONS

ADDENDA ACKNOWLEDGEMENT   **TOTAL ADJUSTMENTS**

ADJUSTED TOTAL BID

ALTERNATES

ALTERNATE NO. _____

ALTERNATE NO. _____

ALTERNATE NO. _____

ALTERNATE NO. _____

ALTERNATE NO. _____

ALTERNATE NO. _____

ALTERNATE NO. _____

Figure 4.1

heat and power. While these items may not be directly part of the physical structure, the project could not be completed without them. Project Overhead, like all other direct costs, can be separated into material, labor and equipment components. Figures 4.2 and 4.3 are examples of a form that can help ensure that all appropriate costs are included. Project Overhead will be further discussed below and in Chapter 9.

Material: When quantities have been carefully taken off, estimates of material cost can be very accurate. In order to maintain a high level of accuracy, the unit prices for materials must be reliable and current. The most reliable source of material costs is a quotation from a vendor for the particular job in question. Ideally, the vendor should have access to the plans and specifications for verification of quantities and specified products.

Material pricing appears relatively simple and straightforward. There are, however, certain considerations that the estimator must address when analyzing material quotations. The reputation of the vendor is a significant factor. Can the vendor "deliver," both figuratively and literally? Often estimators may choose not to rely on a "competitive" lower price from an unknown vendor, but will instead use a slightly higher price from a known, reliable vendor. Experience is the best judge for such decisions.

There are many questions that the estimator should ask. How long is the price guaranteed? At the end of that period, is there an escalation clause? Does the price include delivery or sales tax, if required? Note that most of these questions are addressed on the form in Figure 4.1. But more information should be obtained to ensure that a quoted price is accurate and competitive.

The estimator must be sure that the quotation or obtained price is for the materials as per plans and specifications. Architects and engineers may write into the specifications that: a) the particular type or brand of product must be used with no substitution, b) the particular type or brand of product is recommended, but alternate brands may be accepted *upon approval*, or c) no particular type or brand is specified. Depending upon the options, the estimator may be able to find an acceptable, less expensive alternative. In some cases, these substitutions can substantially lower the cost of a project.

When the estimator has received material quotations, there are still other considerations which should have a bearing on the final choice of a vendor. Lead time – the amount of time between order and delivery – must be determined and considered. It does not matter how competitive or low a quote is if the material cannot be delivered to the job site on time. If a delivery date is promised, is there a guarantee, or a penalty clause for late delivery?

The estimator should also determine if there are any unusual payment requirements. Cash flow for a company can be severely affected if a large material purchase, thought to be payable in 30 days (90 days 10 years ago!) is delivered C.O.D. Truck drivers may not allow unloading until payment has been received. Such requirements must be determined during the estimating stage so that the cost of borrowing money, if necessary, can be included.

If unable to obtain the quotation of a vendor from whom the material would be purchased, the estimator has other sources for obtaining material prices. These include, in order of reliability:

1. Current price lists from manufacturer's catalogues. Be sure to check that the list is for "contractor prices."
2. Cost records from previous jobs. Historical costs must be updated for present conditions.

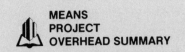

MEANS PROJECT OVERHEAD SUMMARY

SHEET NO.

PROJECT _____

ESTIMATE NO.

LOCATION _____ ARCHITECT _____ DATE _____

QUANTITIES BY: _____ PRICES BY: _____ EXTENSIONS BY: _____ CHECKED BY: _____

DESCRIPTION	QUANTITY	UNIT	MATERIAL/EQUIPMENT		LABOR		TOTAL COST	
			UNIT	TOTAL	UNIT	TOTAL	UNIT	TOTAL
Job Organization: Superintendent								
Project Manager								
Timekeeper & Material Clerk								
Clerical								
Safety, Watchman & First Aid								
Travel Expense: Superintendent								
Project Manager								
Engineering: Layout								
Inspection/Quantities								
Drawings								
CPM Schedule								
Testing: Soil								
Materials								
Structural								
Equipment: Cranes								
Concrete Pump, Conveyor, Etc.								
Elevators, Hoists								
Freight & Hauling								
Loading, Unloading, Erecting, Etc.								
Maintenance								
Pumping								
Scaffolding								
Small Power Equipment/Tools								
Field Offices: Job Office								
Architect/Owner's Office								
Temporary Telephones								
Utilities								
Temporary Toilets								
Storage Areas & Sheds								
Temporary Utilities: Heat								
Light & Power								
Water								
PAGE TOTALS								

Figure 4.2

DESCRIPTION	QUANTITY	UNIT	MATERIAL/EQUIPMENT		LABOR		TOTAL COST	
			UNIT	TOTAL	UNIT	TOTAL	UNIT	TOTAL
Total Brought Forward								
Winter Protection: Temp. Heat/Protection								
Snow Plowing								
Thawing Materials								
Temporary Roads								
Signs & Barricades: Site Sign								
Temporary Fences								
Temporary Stairs, Ladders & Floors								
Photographs								
Clean Up								
Dumpster								
Final Clean Up								
Punch List								
Permits: Building								
Misc.								
Insurance: Builders Risk								
Owner's Protective Liability								
Umbrella								
Unemployment Ins. & Social Security								
Taxes								
City Sales Tax								
State Sales Tax								
Bonds								
Performance								
Material & Equipment								
Main Office Expense								
Special Items								
TOTALS:								

Figure 4.3

3. Reputable and current annual unit price cost books, such as *Means Building Construction Cost Data*. Such books usually represent national averages and must be factored to local markets.

No matter which price source is used, the estimator must be sure to include any costs over the actual cost of the material. The above-mentioned concerns regarding vendor quotations should also be taken into consideration.

Labor: In order to determine the labor cost for each unit of construction, the estimator must know two pieces of information: first, the labor rate (hourly wage or salary) of the worker, and second, how many units this worker can produce or install in a given time period — in other words, the output or productivity. Wage rates are known going into a project but productivity may be very hard to determine. The best source of labor productivity (and therefore labor costs) is the estimator's well-kept records from previous projects.

To estimators working for contractors, construction labor rates for employers will be known, well-documented and constantly updated. Estimators for owners, architects, or engineers must determine labor rates from outside sources. Unit price cost books, such as *Means Building Construction Cost Data*, provide national average union labor rates by trade and base the unit costs for labor on these averages. Figure 4.4 shows national average *union* rates for the construction industry (based on January 1, 1993). Figure 4.5 lists national average open shop (*non-union*) rates, again based on January 1, 1993.

If more accurate rates are required, the estimator has alternate sources. Union locals can provide rates (as well as negotiated increases) for a particular location. This source requires the estimator to call the union hall for each trade. Employer bargaining groups can usually provide labor cost data, but this data may not be continually updated. R.S. Means Co., Inc. publishes *Means Labor Rates for the Construction Industry* on an annual basis. This book lists the labor rates by trade for over 300 U.S. and Canadian cities. Other sources of wage rate information are the published Federal prevailing wage rates, known as *Davis Bacon Wages*, and the state prevailing wage rates. These rates are the minimum rate that must be paid to workers on Federal- or State-funded projects.

The above sources are for union rates. Determination of "open shop" labor rates is much more difficult. There are often organizations in larger cities representing open shop contractors. These organizations may have records of local pay scales, but ultimately the wage rates are determined by each contractor.

Unit labor costs are the least predictable of all costs for building projects. It is important to determine as accurately as possible both the prevailing wages and the productivity. If there are no company records for productivity, cost data books, such as *Means Building Construction Cost Data*, and productivity reference books, such as *Means Man-Hour Standards*, can be invaluable. Included with the listing for each individual construction item is the designation of typical crew make-up, together with the productivity or output — the amount of work that the crew will produce. Figure 4.6, a typical page from *Means Man-Hour Standards*, includes this data and indicates the required number of man-hours for each "unit" of work for the designated task.

The estimator who has neither company records nor the sources described above must put together the appropriate crews and determine the expected output or productivity. This type of estimating should only be attempted based upon strong experience and considerable exposure to construction methods and practices.

		A		B	C	D	E	F	G	H	I
		Base Rate Incl. Fringes		Workers' Comp. Ins.	Average Fixed Overhead	Overhead	Profit	Total Overhead & Profit		Rate with O & P	
Abbr.	Trade	Hourly	Daily					%	Amount	Hourly	Daily
Skwk	Skilled Workers Average (35 trades)	$24.10	$192.80	17.6%	16.8%	13.0%	10.0%	57.4%	$13.85	$37.95	$303.60
	Helpers Average (5 trades)	18.10	144.80	18.8		11.0		56.6	10.25	28.35	226.80
	Foreman Average, Inside ($.50 over trade)	24.60	196.80	17.6		13.0		57.4	14.10	38.70	309.60
	Foreman Average, Outside ($2.00 over trade)	26.10	208.80	17.6		13.0		57.4	15.00	41.10	328.80
Clab	Common Building Laborers	18.55	148.40	19.2		11.0		57.0	10.55	29.10	232.80
Asbe	Asbestos Workers	26.15	209.20	16.7		16.0		59.5	15.55	41.70	333.60
Boil	Boilermakers	26.80	214.40	10.5		16.0		53.3	14.30	41.10	328.80
Bric	Bricklayers	24.05	192.40	16.8		11.0		54.6	13.15	37.20	297.60
Brhe	Bricklayer Helpers	18.85	150.80	16.8		11.0		54.6	10.30	29.15	233.20
Carp	Carpenters	23.35	186.80	19.2		11.0		57.0	13.30	36.65	293.20
Cefi	Cement Finishers	23.05	184.40	11.4		11.0		49.2	11.35	34.40	275.20
Elec	Electricians	26.70	213.60	7.3		16.0		50.1	13.40	40.10	320.80
Elev	Elevator Constructors	27.25	218.00	8.1		16.0		50.9	13.85	41.10	328.80
Eqhv	Equipment Operators, Crane or Shovel	24.95	199.60	11.7		14.0		52.5	13.10	38.05	304.40
Eqmd	Equipment Operators, Medium Equipment	24.10	192.80	11.7		14.0		52.5	12.65	36.75	294.00
Eqlt	Equipment Operators, Light Equipment	23.10	184.80	11.7		14.0		52.5	12.15	35.25	282.00
Eqol	Equipment Operators, Oilers	20.25	162.00	11.7		14.0		52.5	10.65	30.90	247.20
Eqmm	Equipment Operators, Master Mechanics	25.55	204.40	11.7		14.0		52.5	13.40	38.95	311.60
Glaz	Glaziers	23.50	188.00	13.9		11.0		51.7	12.15	35.65	285.20
Lath	Lathers	23.20	185.60	12.6		11.0		50.4	11.70	34.90	279.20
Marb	Marble Setters	24.15	193.20	16.8		11.0		54.6	13.20	37.35	298.80
Mill	Millwrights	24.35	194.80	11.6		11.0		49.4	12.05	36.40	291.20
Mstz	Mosaic and Terrazzo Workers	23.70	189.60	9.9		11.0		47.7	11.30	35.00	280.00
Pord	Painters, Ordinary	21.75	174.00	15.0		11.0		52.8	11.50	33.25	266.00
Psst	Painters, Structural Steel	22.55	180.40	52.0		11.0		89.8	20.25	42.80	342.40
Pape	Paper Hangers	21.95	175.60	15.0		11.0		52.8	11.60	33.55	268.40
Pile	Pile Drivers	23.50	188.00	29.5		16.0		72.3	17.00	40.50	324.00
Plas	Plasterers	22.80	182.40	15.6		11.0		53.4	12.20	35.00	280.00
Plah	Plasterer Helpers	19.05	152.40	15.6		11.0		53.4	10.15	29.20	233.60
Plum	Plumbers	27.40	219.20	8.7		16.0		51.5	14.10	41.50	332.00
Rodm	Rodmen (Reinforcing)	25.85	206.80	34.4		14.0		75.2	19.45	45.30	362.40
Rofc	Roofers, Composition	21.25	170.00	32.6		11.0		70.4	14.95	36.20	289.60
Rots	Roofers, Tile and Slate	21.30	170.40	32.6		11.0		70.4	15.00	36.30	290.40
Rohe	Roofer Helpers (Composition)	15.25	122.00	32.6		11.0		70.4	10.75	26.00	208.00
Shee	Sheet Metal Workers	26.65	213.20	12.4		16.0		55.2	14.70	41.35	330.80
Spri	Sprinkler Installers	29.00	232.00	9.4		16.0		52.2	15.15	44.15	353.20
Stpi	Steamfitters or Pipefitters	27.45	219.60	8.7		16.0		51.5	14.15	41.60	332.80
Ston	Stone Masons	24.15	193.20	16.8		11.0		54.6	13.20	37.35	298.80
Sswk	Structural Steel Workers	26.00	208.00	40.1		14.0		80.9	21.05	47.05	376.40
Tilf	Tile Layers (Floor)	23.50	188.00	9.9		11.0		47.7	11.20	34.70	277.60
Tilh	Tile Layer Helpers	18.70	149.60	9.9		11.0		47.7	8.90	27.60	220.80
Trlt	Truck Drivers, Light	19.15	153.20	15.2		11.0		53.0	10.15	29.30	234.40
Trhv	Truck Drivers, Heavy	19.45	155.60	15.2		11.0		53.0	10.30	29.75	238.00
Sswl	Welders, Structural Steel	26.00	208.00	40.1		14.0		80.9	21.05	47.05	376.40
Wrck	*Wrecking	18.55	148.40	40.6	↓	11.0	↓	78.4	14.55	33.10	264.80

*Not included in Averages.

Figure 4.4

UNION

Abbr.	Trade	A Base Rate Incl. Fringes		B Workers' Comp. Ins.	C Average Fixed Overhead	D Overhead	E Profit	F Total Overhead & Profit	G	H Rate with O & P	I
		Hourly	Daily					%	Amount	Hourly	Daily
Skwk	Skilled Workers Average (35 trades)	$15.65	$125.20	17.6%	16.8%	27.0%	10.0%	71.4%	$11.15	$26.80	$214.40
	Helpers Average (5 trades)	11.75	94.00	18.8		25.0		70.6	8.30	20.05	160.40
	Foreman Average, Inside ($.50 over trade)	16.15	129.20	17.6		27.0		71.4	11.55	27.70	221.60
	Foreman Average, Outside ($2.00 over trade)	17.65	141.20	17.6		27.0		71.4	12.60	30.25	242.00
Clab	Common Building Laborers	12.05	96.40	19.2		25.0		71.0	8.55	20.60	164.80
Asbe	Asbestos Workers	17.00	136.00	16.7		30.0		73.5	12.50	29.50	236.00
Boil	Boilermakers	17.40	139.20	10.5		30.0		67.3	11.70	29.10	232.80
Bric	Bricklayers	15.65	125.20	16.8		25.0		68.6	10.75	26.40	211.20
Brhe	Bricklayer Helpers	12.25	98.00	16.8		25.0		68.6	8.40	20.65	165.20
Carp	Carpenters	15.20	121.60	19.2		25.0		71.0	10.80	26.00	208.00
Cefi	Cement Finishers	15.00	120.00	11.4		25.0		63.2	9.50	24.50	196.00
Elec	Electricians	17.35	138.80	7.3		30.0		64.1	11.10	28.45	227.60
Elev	Elevator Constructors	17.70	141.60	8.1		30.0		64.9	11.50	29.20	233.60
Eqhv	Equipment Operators, Crane or Shovel	16.20	129.60	11.7		28.0		66.5	10.75	26.95	215.60
Eqmd	Equipment Operators, Medium Equipment	15.65	125.20	11.7		28.0		66.5	10.40	26.05	208.40
Eqlt	Equipment Operators, Light Equipment	15.00	120.00	11.7		28.0		66.5	10.00	25.00	200.00
Eqol	Equipment Operators, Oilers	13.15	105.20	11.7		28.0		66.5	8.75	21.90	175.20
Eqmm	Equipment Operators, Master Mechanics	16.60	132.80	11.7		28.0		66.5	11.05	27.65	221.20
Glaz	Glaziers	15.30	122.40	13.9		25.0		65.7	10.05	25.35	202.80
Lath	Lathers	15.10	120.80	12.6		25.0		64.4	9.70	24.80	198.40
Marb	Marble Setters	15.70	125.60	16.8		25.0		68.6	10.75	26.45	211.60
Mill	Millwrights	15.85	126.80	11.6		25.0		63.4	10.05	25.90	207.20
Mstz	Mosaic and Terrazzo Workers	15.40	123.20	9.9		25.0		61.7	9.50	24.90	199.20
Pord	Painters, Ordinary	14.15	113.20	15.0		25.0		66.8	9.45	23.60	188.80
Psst	Painters, Structural Steel	14.65	117.20	52.0		25.0		103.8	15.20	29.85	238.80
Pape	Paper Hangers	14.25	114.00	15.0		25.0		66.8	9.50	23.75	190.00
Pile	Pile Drivers	15.30	122.40	29.5		30.0		86.3	13.20	28.50	228.00
Plas	Plasterers	14.80	118.40	15.6		25.0		67.4	10.00	24.80	198.40
Plah	Plasterer Helpers	12.40	99.20	15.6		25.0		67.4	8.35	20.75	166.00
Plum	Plumbers	17.80	142.40	8.7		30.0		65.5	11.65	29.45	235.60
Rodm	Rodmen (Reinforcing)	16.80	134.40	34.4		28.0		89.2	15.00	31.80	254.40
Rofc	Roofers, Composition	13.80	110.40	32.6		25.0		84.4	11.65	25.45	203.60
Rots	Roofers, Tile and Slate	13.85	110.80	32.6		25.0		84.4	11.70	25.55	204.40
Rohe	Roofer Helpers (Composition)	9.90	79.20	32.6		25.0		84.4	8.35	18.25	146.00
Shee	Sheet Metal Workers	17.30	138.40	12.4		30.0		69.2	11.95	29.25	234.00
Spri	Sprinkler Installers	18.85	150.80	9.4		30.0		66.2	12.50	31.35	250.80
Stpi	Steamfitters or Pipefitters	17.85	142.80	8.7		30.0		65.5	11.70	29.55	236.40
Ston	Stone Masons	15.70	125.60	16.8		25.0		68.6	10.75	26.45	211.60
Sswk	Structural Steel Workers	16.90	135.20	40.1		28.0		94.9	16.05	32.95	263.60
Tilf	Tile Layers (Floor)	15.30	122.40	9.9		26.0		61.7	9.45	24.75	198.00
Tilh	Tile Layer Helpers	12.15	97.20	9.9		25.0		61.7	7.50	19.65	157.20
Trlt	Truck Drivers, Light	12.45	99.60	15.2		25.0		67.0	8.35	20.80	166.40
Trhv	Truck Drivers, Heavy	12.65	101.20	15.2		25.0		67.0	8.50	21.15	169.20
Sswl	Welders, Structural Steel	16.90	135.20	40.1		28.0		94.9	16.05	32.95	263.60
Wrck	*Wrecking	12.05	96.40	40.6	▼	25.0	▼	92.4	11.15	23.20	185.60

*Not included in Averages.

Figure 4.5

NON UNION

051 200	Structural Steel	CREW	MAKEUP	DAILY OUTPUT	MAN-HOURS	UNIT
230	**LIGHTGAGE FRAMING**					
0400	Angle framing, 4" and larger	E-4	1 Struc. Steel Foreman	3,000	.011	Lb.
			3 Struc. Steel Workers			
			1 Gas Welding Machine			
0450	Less than 4" angles			1,800	.018	Lb.
0600	Channel framing, 8" and larger			3,500	.009	Lb.
0650	Less than 8" channels	↓	↓	2,000	.016	Lb.
1000	Continuous slotted channel framing system, minimum	2 Sswk	2 Struc. Steel Workers	2,400	.007	Lb.
1200	Maximum	"	"	1,600	.010	Lb.
1302	Lightgage framing, cross bracing, rods, 3/4" diameter	E-3	1 Struc. Steel Foreman	700	.034	Lb.
			1 Struc. Steel Worker			
			1 Welder			
			1 Gas Welding Machine			
			1 Torch, Gas & Air			
1310	7/8" diameter			700	.034	Lb.
1320	1" diameter			700	.034	Lb.
1330	Angle, 5" x 5" x 3/8"			2,800	.009	Lb.
1350	Hanging lintels, average	↓	↓	850	.028	Lb.
1380	Roof frames, 3'-0" square, 5' span	E-2	1 Struc. Steel Foreman	4,200	.013	Lb.
			4 Struc. Steel Workers			
			1 Equip. Oper. (crane)			
			1 Equip. Oper. Oiler			
			1 Crane, 90 Ton			
1400	Tie rod, not upset, 1-1/2" to 4" diameter, with turnbuckle	2 Sswk	2 Struc. Steel Workers	800	.020	Lb.
1420	No turnbuckle			700	.023	Lb.
1500	Upset, 1-3/4" to 4" diameter, with turnbuckle			800	.020	Lb.
1520	No turnbuckle			700	.023	Lb.
1600	Tubular aluminum framing for window wall, minimum			600	.027	Lb.
1800	Maximum	↓	↓	500	.032	Lb.
232	**LINTELS** Plain steel angles, under 500 lb.	1 Bric	1 Bricklayer	500	.016	Lb.
0100	500 to 1000 lb.			600	.013	Lb.
0200	1000 to 2000 lb.			600	.013	Lb.
0300	2000 to 4000 lb.			600	.013	Lb.
2000	Steel angles, 3-1/2" x 3", 1/4" thick, 2'-6" long			50	.160	Ea.
2100	4'-6" long			45	.178	Ea.
2500	3-1/2" x 3-1/2" x 5/16", 5'-0" long			44	.182	Ea.
2600	4" x 3-1/2", 1/4" thick, 5'-0" long			40	.200	Ea.
2700	9'-0" long			35	.229	Ea.
2800	4" x 3-1/2" x 5/16", 7'-0" long			38	.211	Ea.
2900	5" x 3-1/2" x 5/16", 10'-0" long	↓	↓	35	.229	Ea.
235	**PRE-ENGINEERED STEEL BUILDINGS** For Hangars see 131-211					
0100	Building shell above the foundations with 26 ga. colored					
0111	Roofing and siding, minimum	E-2	1 Struc. Steel Foreman	1,800	.031	SF Flr.
			4 Struc. Steel Workers			
			1 Equip. Oper. (crane)			
			1 Equip. Oper. Oiler			
			1 Crane, 90 Ton			
0200	Maximum	"	"	1,000	.056	SF Flr.
0800	Accessory items: add to the basic building cost above					
1000	Eave overhang, 2' wide, 26 ga., with soffit	E-2	1 Struc. Steel Foreman	360	.156	L.F.
			4 Struc. Steel Workers			
			1 Equip. Oper. (crane)			
			1 Equip. Oper. Oiler			
			1 Crane, 90 Ton			
1200	4' wide, without soffit			300	.187	L.F.
1300	With soffit			250	.224	L.F.

Figure 4.6

Equipment: Over recent years, construction equipment has become much more sophisticated, not only because of the incentive of reduced labor costs, but also as a response to new, highly technological construction methods and materials. As a result, equipment costs represent an increasing percentage of total project costs in building construction. Estimators must carefully address the equipment and all related expenses. Costs for equipment can be divided into two categories.

1. Rental, lease or ownership costs. These costs may be determined based on hourly, daily, weekly, monthly or annual increments. These fees or payments only buy the "right" to use the equipment.
2. Operating costs. Once the "right" of use is obtained, costs are incurred for actual use, or operation. These costs include fuel, lubrication, maintenance and parts.

Equipment costs as described above do not include the operator's wages. However, some cost books and suppliers may include the operator in the quoted price for equipment as an "operated" rental cost. The estimator must be aware of what is and what is not included.

Quotations for equipment rental or lease costs can be obtained from local dealers and suppliers, or even from manufacturers. These costs can fluctuate and should be updated regularly. Ownership costs must be determined within a company. There are many considerations beyond the up-front purchase price; these facts must be taken into account when figuring the cost of owning equipment. Interest rates and amortization schedules should be studied prior to the purchase. Insurance costs, storage fees, maintenance, taxes and licenses, all added together, can become a significant percentage of the cost of owning equipment. These costs must be anticipated prior to purchase in order to properly manage the ownership.

When purchasing equipment, the owner should be aware of some basic principles of accounting (or hire a good accountant). In particular, various methods of depreciation (a way of quantifying loss of value to the owner over time) can have varied effects at tax time.

Figure 4.7 shows the effects of three "textbook" examples of depreciation methods: "Straight Line," "Sum of Years Digit," and "Declining Balance." Notice that different dollar amounts are depreciated in different years. These are very simplistic examples. A tax planning strategy should be developed in order to determine the appropriate and most advantageous method. An accountant should be consulted due to the current, complicated, ever-changing tax laws. The possibilities of accelerated methods, investment tax credits and other incentives should also be considered.

Equipment ownership costs apply to both leased and owned equipment. The operating costs of equipment, whether rented, leased or owned, are available from the following sources (listed in order of reliability):

1. The company's own records.
2. Annual cost books containing equipment operating costs, such as *Means Building Construction Cost Data*.
3. Manufacturers' estimates.
4. Textbooks dealing with equipment operating costs.

These operating costs consist of fuel, lubrication, expendable parts replacement, and minor maintenance. For financial analysis purposes, the equipment ownership and operating costs should be listed separately. In this way, the decision to rent, lease or purchase can be decided project by project.

There are two commonly used methods for including equipment costs in a construction estimate. The first is to include the equipment as a part of the construction task for which it is used. In this case, costs are included in each line item as a separate unit price. The advantage of this method is that costs are allocated to the division or task that actually incurs the expense. As a result, more accurate records can be kept for each construction component. The disadvantage of this method occurs in the pricing of equipment (e.g., tower crane, personnel hoist, etc.) that may be used by many different trades for different tasks. Duplication of costs can occur in this instance.

The second method for including equipment costs in the estimate is to keep all such costs separate and to include them in Division I as a part of Project Overhead. The advantage of this method is that all equipment costs are grouped together, and that items used by all trades are included (without duplication). The disadvantage is that for future estimating purposes, equipment costs will be known only by job and not by unit of construction. Under these circumstances, omissions can easily occur.

Whichever method is used, the estimator must be consistent, and must be sure that all equipment costs are included, but not duplicated. The estimating method should be the same as that chosen for cost monitoring and accounting, so that the data will be available for future projects.

Subcontractors: In essence, subcontractor quotations should be solicited and analyzed in the same way as material quotes. A primary concern is that the bid covers the work as per plans and specifications, and that all appropriate work alternates and allowances are included. Any exclusions should be clearly stated and explained. If the bid is received orally, a form such as that in Figure 4.1 will help to ensure that all is included. Oral bids/quotes should be followed up by fax and hard copy confirmation. Any unique scheduling or payment requirements must be noted and evaluated prior to submission of the prime bid. Such requirements could affect or restrict the normal progress of the project, and should therefore be known in advance.

Depreciation Strategies for Equipment — Based upon a $15,000 Purchase Price with No Allowance for Salvage	Methods of Depreciation		
Year	Straight Line	Sum of Years Digit	Declining Balance
1	$ 3,000	$ 5,000	$ 6,000.00
2	3,000	4,000	3,600.00
3	3,000	3,000	2,160.00
4	3,000	2,000	1,296.00
5	3,000	1,000	777.60
Total	$15,000	$15,000	$13,833.60

Figure 4.7

The estimator should note how long the subcontract bid will be honored. This time period usually varies from 30 to 90 days and is often included as a condition in complete bids. The general contractor may have to define the time limits of the prime bid based upon certain subcontractors. The estimator must also note any escalation clauses that may be included in subcontractor bids.

Reliability is another factor to be considered when soliciting and evaluating subcontractor bids. Reliability cannot be measured or priced until the project is actually under construction. Most general contractors stay with the same subcontractors for just this reason. A certain unspoken communication exists in these established relationships and usually has a positive effect on the performance of the work. Such familiarity, however, can often erode the competitive nature of bidding. To be competitive with the prime bid, the estimator should always obtain comparison subcontract prices, whether these prices come from another subcontractor or are prepared by the estimator.

The estimator should question and verify the bonding capability and capacity of unfamiliar subcontractors. Taking such action may be necessary when bidding in a new location. Other than word of mouth, these inquiries may be the only way to confirm subcontractor reliability.

For major subcontract items such as mechanical, electrical, and conveying systems, it may be necessary to make up spreadsheets in order to tabulate inclusions and omissions. This procedure ensures that all cost considerations are included in the "adjusted" quotation. Time permitting, the estimator should make a takeoff and price these major subcontract items to compare with the subcontractor bids. If time does not permit a detailed takeoff, the estimator should at least budget the work. A Systems Estimate is ideal for this purpose.

Project Overhead: Project overhead includes those items as specified in Division 1 — General Requirements. It also includes those items required for the actual construction of the project, but not necessarily applicable to another specific MasterFormat division. As seen in Figures 4.2 and 4.3, project overhead covers items from project supervision to cleanup, from temporary utilities to permits. All may not agree that certain items (such as equipment or scaffolding) should be included as Project Overhead, and might prefer to list such items in another division. Ultimately, it is not important *where* each item is incorporated into the estimate, but that *every item is included somewhere*, and not in two locations.

Project overhead often includes time-related items; equipment rental, supervisory labor, and temporary utilities are examples. The cost for these items depends upon the duration of the project. A preliminary schedule should, therefore, be developed *prior* to completion of the estimate so that time-related items can be properly counted. This will be further discussed in Chapter 5.

Bond requirements for a project are usually specified in the General Conditions portion of the specification. Costs for bonds are based on total project costs and are determined at the estimate summary stage. A discussion of different types of bonds is included below.

Indirect Costs

The direct costs of a project must be itemized, tabulated and totalled before the indirect costs can be applied to the estimate. The indirect costs are almost always defined as a percentage of direct costs and include:

1. Sales Tax (if required)
2. Office or Operating Overhead (vs. Project Overhead)
3. Profit
4. Contingencies
5. Bonds (often included as Project Overhead)

Sales Tax: Sales tax varies from state to state and often from city to city within a state (see Figure 4.8). Larger cities may have a sales tax in addition to the state sales tax. Some localities also impose separate sales taxes on labor and equipment.

When bidding takes place in unfamiliar locations, the estimator should check with local agencies regarding the amount and the method of payment of sales tax. Local authorities may require owners to withhold payments to out-of-state contractors until payment of all required sales tax has been verified. Sales tax is often taken for granted or even omitted and, as can be seen in Figure 4.8, can be as much as 7.25% of material costs. Indeed, this can represent a significant portion of the project's total cost. Conversely, some clients and/or their projects may be tax exempt. If this fact is unknown to the estimator, a large dollar amount for sales tax might be needlessly included in a bid.

Office or Operating Overhead: Office overhead, or the cost of doing business, is perhaps one of the main reasons why so many contractors are unable to realize a profit, or even to stay in business. If a contractor does not know the costs of operating the business, then, more than likely, these costs will not be recovered. Many companies survive, and even turn a profit, by simply adding a certain percentage for overhead to each job, without knowing how the percentage is derived or what is included. When annual volume changes significantly, whether by increase or decrease, the previously used percentage for overhead may no longer be valid. Often when such a volume change

R010-090 Sales Tax by State

State sales tax on materials is tabulated below (5 states have no sales tax). Many states allow local jurisdictions, such as a county or city, to levy additional sales tax.

Some projects may be sales tax exempt, particularly those constructed with public funds.

State	Tax (%)	State	Tax (%)	State	Tax (%)	State	Tax (%)
Alabama	4	Illinois	6.25	Montana	0	Rhode Island	7
Alaska	0	Indiana	5	Nebraska	5	South Carolina	5
Arizona	5	Iowa	4	Nevada	6.75	South Dakota	4
Arkansas	4.5	Kansas	4.25	New Hampshire	0	Tennessee	5.5
California	7.25	Kentucky	6	New Jersey	7	Texas	6.25
Colorado	3	Louisiana	4	New Mexico	5	Utah	5
Connecticut	6	Maine	5	New York	4	Vermont	5
Delaware	0	Maryland	5	North Carolina	4	Virginia	3.5
District of Columbia	6	Massachusetts	5	North Dakota	4	Washington	6.5
Florida	6	Michigan	4	Ohio	5	West Virginia	6
Georgia	4	Minnesota	6	Oklahoma	4.5	Wisconsin	5
Hawaii	4	Mississippi	6	Oregon	0	Wyoming	3
Idaho	5	Missouri	4.225	Pennsylvania	6	Average	4.56%

Figure 4.8

44

occurs, the owner finds that the company is not doing as well as before and cannot determine the reasons. Chances are, overhead costs are not being fully recovered. As an example, Figure 4.9 lists office costs and expenses for a "typical" construction company for a year. It is assumed that the anticipated annual volume of the company is $10 million. Each of the items is described briefly below.

Owner: This includes only a reasonable base salary and does not include profits.

Engineer/Estimator: Since the owner is primarily on the road getting business, this is the person who runs the daily operation of the company and is responsible for estimating.

Assistant Estimator: This person is the "number cruncher," performing most quantity takeoffs and some pricing.

Project Manager: This is the person who runs the projects from the office and acts as the liaison between the owner and the field.

General Superintendent: The general super's post is perhaps the most important position in the company. This person is responsible for the day-to-day progress of all projects – the nuts and bolts. All field personnel are handled by this person.

Bookkeeper/Office Manager: This is the overworked, underpaid person who actually runs the company. Every company must have one.

Secretary/Receptionist: This is the assistant to the person who actually runs the company.

Office Worker Insurance & Taxes: These costs are for main office personnel only and, for this example, are calculated as 38% of the total salaries based on the following breakdown:

Workers' Compensation	6%
FICA	8%
Unemployment	4%
Medical & other insurance	10%
Profit sharing, pension, etc.	10%
	38%

Physical Plant Expenses: Whether the office, warehouse and yard are rented or owned, roughly the same costs are incurred. Telephone and utility costs will vary depending on the size of the building and the type of business. Office equipment includes items such as copy machine rental, typewriters, etc.

Professional Services: Accountant fees are primarily for quarterly audits and year-end statements. Legal fees go towards collecting and contract disputes. Advertising includes the Yellow Pages, promotional materials, etc.

Miscellaneous: There are many expenses that could be placed in this category. Included in the example are just a few.

Uncollected Receivables: This amount can vary greatly, often depending upon the overall economic climate. Depending upon the timing of "uncollectables," cash flow can be severely restricted and can cause serious financial problems, even for large companies. Sound cash planning and anticipation of such possibilities can help to prevent severe repercussions.

While the office example used here is feasible within the industry, keep in mind that it is hypothetical and that conditions and costs vary from company to company.

ANNUAL MAIN OFFICE EXPENSES

Salaries

Owner	$ 80,000
Engineer/Estimator	50,000
Assistant Estimator	35,000
Project Manager	60,000
General Superintendent	50,000
Bookkeeper/Office Manager	28,000
Secretary/Receptionist	18,000

Office Worker Benefits

Workers' Compensation		
FICA & Unemployment	38% of	121,980
Medical Insurance	Salaries	
Miscellaneous Benefits		

Physical Plant

Office & Warehouse (Rental)	30,000
Utilities	2,400
Telephone	3,000
Office Equipment	3,500
Office Supplies	2,000
Auto & Truck (4 vehicles)	24,000

Professional Services

Accounting	4,000
Legal	2,000
Advertising	4,000

Miscellaneous

Dues	1,500
Seminars & Travel	2,500
Entertainment & Gifts	3,000
Uncollected Receivables (1%)	$100,000
TOTAL ANNUAL EXPENSES	**$624,880**

Figure 4.9

In order for this company to stay in business without losses (profit is not yet a factor), not only must all direct construction costs be paid, but an additional $624,880 must be recovered during the year in order to operate the office. Remember that the anticipated volume is $10 million for the year. Office overhead costs, therefore, will be approximately 6.3% of annual volume for this example. The most common method for recovering these costs is to apply this percentage to each job over the course of the year. The percentage may be applied in two ways:

1. Office overhead applied as a percentage of total project costs. This is probably the most commonly used method and is appropriate where material and labor costs are not separated.
2. Office overhead applied as a percentage of labor costs only. This method requires that labor and material costs be estimated separately. As a result, material handling charges are also more easily applied.

The second method described above allows for more precision in the estimate. This method assumes that office expenses are more closely related to labor costs than to total project costs. For example, assume that two companies have the same total annual volume. Company A builds projects that are material-intensive (90% materials, 10% labor). Company B builds projects that are very labor-intensive (10% materials, 90% labor). In order to manage the large labor force, the office (and overhead) expense of Company B will be much greater than that of Company A. As a result, the applicable overhead percentage of B is greater than that of A based on equal annual volumes. For argument's sake, the overhead percentage of *total costs* for Company A is 3%, for Company B, 10%. If company A then gets projects that are more labor-intensive, an allowance of 3% becomes too low and costs will not be recovered. Likewise, if Company B starts to build material-intensive projects, 10% will be too high an overhead figure and bids may no longer be competitive. Office overhead may be more precisely recovered if it is figured as a percentage of labor costs, rather than total costs. In order to do this, a company must determine the ratio of material to labor costs from its historical records. In the example of Figure 4.9, assume that for this company, the ratio is 50/50. Total annual labor costs would be anticipated to be $4,437,500, as calculated below. As a percentage of labor, office overhead will be:

Annual Volume	$10,000,000
Anticipated Overhead (6.3%)	- 625,000
Anticipated Profit (3%)	- 500,000
Total Bare Costs	8,875,000
Labor (50% of Bare Costs)	$ 4,437,500

$$\frac{\$624,880}{\$4,437,500} = 14\%$$

By applying this overhead percentage (14%) to labor costs, the company is assured of recovering office expenses even if the ratio of material to labor changes significantly.

The estimator must also remember that if volume changes significantly, then the percentage for office overhead should be recalculated for current conditions. The same is true if there are changes in office staff. Remember that salaries are the major portion of office overhead costs. It should be noted that a percentage is commonly applied to material costs, for handling, in addition to and regardless of the method of recovering office overhead costs. This percentage is more easily calculated if material costs are estimated and listed separately.

Profit: Determining a fair and reasonable percentage to be included for profit is not an easy task. This responsibility is usually left to the owner or chief estimator. Experience is crucial in anticipating what profit the market will bear. The economic climate, competition, knowledge of the project, and familiarity with the architect or owner, all affect the way in which profit is determined. Chapter 6 will show one way to mathematically determine profit margin based on historical bidding information. As with all facets of estimating, experience is the key to success.

Contingencies: Like profit, contingencies can be difficult to quantify. Especially appropriate in preliminary budgets, the addition of a contingency is meant to protect the contractor as well as to give the owner a realistic estimate of project costs.

A contingency percentage should be based on the number of "unknowns" in a project. This percentage should be inversely proportional to the amount of planning detail that has been done for the project. If complete plans and specifications are supplied, and the estimate is thorough and precise, then there is little need for a contingency. Figure 4.10, from *Means Building Construction Cost Data*, lists suggested contingency percentages that may be added to an estimate based on the stage of planning and development.

As an estimate is priced and each individual item is rounded up or "padded," this is, in essence, adding a contingency (see Figure 3.4). This method can cause problems, however, because the estimator can never be quite sure of what is the actual cost and what is the "padding," or safety margin for each item. At the summary, the estimator cannot determine exactly how much has been included as a contingency for the whole project. A much more accurate and controllable approach is the precise pricing of the estimate and the addition of one contingency amount at the bottom line.

Bonds: Bonding requirements for a project will be specified in Division 1 — General Requirements, and will be included in the construction contract. Various types of bonds may be required. Listed below are a few common types:

Bid Bond. A form of bid security executed by the bidder or principle and by a surety (bonding company) to guarantee that the bidder will enter into a contract within a specified time and furnish any required Performance or Labor and Material Payment bonds.

Completion Bond. Also known as "Construction" or "Contract" bond. The guarantee by a surety that the construction contract will be completed and that it will be clear of all liens and encumbrances.

Labor and Material Payment Bond. The guarantee by a surety to the owner that the contractor will pay for all labor and materials used in the performance of the contract as per the construction documents. The claimants under the bond are those having direct contracts with the contractor or any subcontractor.

Performance and Payment Bond. (1) A guarantee that a contractor will perform a job according to the terms of the contracts. (2) A bond of the contractor in which a surety guarantees to the owner that the work will be performed in accordance with the contract documents. Except where prohibited by statute, the performance bond is frequently combined with the labor and material payment bond. The payment bond guarantees that the

		010 000	Overhead	CREW	DAILY OUTPUT	MAN-HOURS	UNIT	1993 BARE COSTS MAT.	LABOR	EQUIP.	TOTAL	TOTAL INCL O&P	
004	0011	**ARCHITECTURAL FEES** R010 -010											004
	0020	For new construction											
	0060	Minimum					Project					4.90%	
	0090	Maximum										16%	
	0100	For alteration work, to $500,000, add to fee										50%	
	0150	Over $500,000, add to fee										25%	
012	0010	**CONSTRUCTION COST INDEX** (Appendix) for 162 major U.S. and											012
	0020	Canadian cities, total cost, min. (Greensboro, NC)					%					77%	
	0050	Average										100%	
	0100	Maximum (New York, NY)										133.40%	
014	0010	**CONSTRUCTION ECONOMIES** For bricklaying R042 -100											014
016	0010	**CONSTRUCTION MANAGEMENT FEES** $1,000,000 job, minimum					Project					4.50%	016
	0050	Maximum										7.50%	
	0300	$5,000,000 job, minimum										2.50%	
	0350	Maximum										4%	
018	0010	**CONSTRUCTION TIME** Requirements R010 -020											018
020	0010	**CONTINGENCIES** Allowance to add at conceptual stage					Project					15%	020
	0050	Schematic stage										10%	
	0100	Preliminary working drawing stage										7%	
	0150	Final working drawing stage										2%	
022	0010	**CONTRACTOR EQUIPMENT** See division 016 R016 -410											022
024	0010	**CREWS** For building construction, see How To Use This Book											024
028	0010	**ENGINEERING FEES** Educational planning consultant, minimum R010 -030					Project					.50%	028
	0100	Maximum					"					2.50%	
	0200	Electrical, minimum					Contrct					4.10%	
	0300	Maximum										10.10%	
	0400	Elevator & conveying systems, minimum										2.50%	
	0500	Maximum										5%	
	0600	Food service & kitchen equipment, minimum										8%	
	0700	Maximum										12%	
	0800	Landscaping & site development, minimum										2.50%	
	0900	Maximum										6%	
	1000	Mechanical (plumbing & HVAC), minimum										4.10%	
	1100	Maximum										10.10%	
	1200	Structural, minimum					Project					1%	
	1300	Maximum					"					2.50%	
034	0010	**FIELD OFFICE EXPENSE**											034
	0100	Office equipment rental, average					Month	140			140	154	
	0120	Office supplies, average					"	250			250	275	
	0125	Office trailer rental, see division 015-904											
	0140	Telephone bill; avg. bill/month incl. long dist.					Month	235			235	259	
	0160	Field office lights & HVAC					"	78			78	86	
036	0010	**FIELD PERSONNEL** Clerk average					Week		230		225	350	036
	0100	Field engineer, minimum							535		520	810	
	0120	Average							715		695	1,080	
	0140	Maximum							805		780	1,215	
	0160	General purpose laborer, average							740		720	1,120	
	0180	Project manager, minimum							1,015		985	1,535	
	0200	Average							1,135		1,100	1,715	
	0220	Maximum							1,285		1,250	1,945	
	0240	Superintendent, minimum							965		935	1,460	
	0260	Average							1,070		1,040	1,620	

Figure 4.10a

010 | Overhead and Miscellaneous Data

010 000 | Overhead

			CREW	DAILY OUTPUT	MAN-HOURS	UNIT	1993 BARE COSTS				TOTAL INCL O&P	
							MAT.	LABOR	EQUIP.	TOTAL		
036	0280	Maximum				Week		1,200		1,170	1,825	036
	0290	Timekeeper, average				↓		625		605	940	
038	0010	**HISTORICAL COST INDEXES** Back to 1943										038
040	0010	**INSURANCE** Builders risk, standard, minimum	R010 -040			Job					.22%	040
	0050	Maximum									.59%	
	0200	All-risk type, minimum	R010 -050								.25%	
	0250	Maximum				↓					.62%	
	0400	Contractor's equipment floater, minimum	R010 -060			Value •					.50%	
	0450	Maximum									1.50%	
	0600	Public liability, average				Job					1.55%	
	0800	Workers' compensation & employer's liability, average										
	0850	by trade, carpentry, general				Payroll		19.24%				
	0900	Clerical						.59%				
	0950	Concrete						17.88%				
	1000	Electrical						7.26%				
	1050	Excavation						11.72%				
	1100	Glazing						13.93%				
	1150	Insulation						16.70%				
	1200	Lathing						12.58%				
	1250	Masonry						16.77%				
	1300	Painting & decorating						15%				
	1350	Pile driving						29.54%				
	1400	Plastering						15.59%				
	1450	Plumbing						8.71%				
	1500	Roofing						32.62%				
	1550	Sheet metal work (HVAC)						12.37%				
	1600	Steel erection, structural						40.08%				
	1650	Tile work, interior ceramic						9.85%				
	1700	Waterproofing, brush or hand caulking						8.55%				
	1800	Wrecking						40.56%				
	2000	Range of 35 trades in 50 states, excl. wrecking, minimum						2.50%				
	2100	Average						17.60%				
	2200	Maximum				↓		143.50%				
042	0010	**JOB CONDITIONS** Modifications to total										042
	0020	project cost summaries										
	0100	Economic conditions, favorable, deduct				Project					2%	
	0200	Unfavorable, add									5%	
	0300	Hoisting conditions, favorable, deduct									2%	
	0400	Unfavorable, add									5%	
	0500	General Contractor management, experienced, deduct									2%	
	0600	Inexperienced, add									10%	
	0700	Labor availability, surplus, deduct									1%	
	0800	Shortage, add									10%	
	0900	Material storage area, available, deduct									1%	
	1000	Not available, add									2%	
	1100	Subcontractor availability, surplus, deduct									5%	
	1200	Shortage, add									12%	
	1300	Work space, available, deduct									2%	
	1400	Not available, add				↓					5%	
046	0010	**LABOR INDEX** (Appendix) For 162 major U.S. and Canadian cities										046
	0020	Minimum (El Paso, TX)				%		59.70%				
	0050	Average						100%				
	0100	Maximum (New York, NY)				↓		155.20%				
048	0010	**MAIN OFFICE EXPENSE** Average for General Contractors	R010 -050									048
	0020	As a percentage of their annual volume										

Figure 4.10b

contractor will pay all subcontractors and material suppliers. Figure 4.11 shows typical average rates for performance and payment bonds for building and roadway construction projects.

Surety Bond. A legal instrument under which one party agrees to answer to another party for the debt, default or failure to perform of a third party.

The Paperwork

At the pricing stage of the estimate, there is typically a large amount of paperwork that must be assembled, analyzed and tabulated. Generally, the information contained in this paperwork is covered by the following major categories:

- Quantity Takeoff sheets for all general contractor items (Figure 3.1)
- Material supplier written quotations
- Material supplier telephone quotations (Figure 4.1)
- Subcontractor written quotations
- Equipment supplier quotations
- Cost Analysis or Consolidated Cost Analysis sheets (Figures 4.12 and 4.13)
- Estimate Summary sheet (Figures 4.14, 4.15 and 4.16)

A system is needed to efficiently handle this mass of paperwork and to ensure that everything will get transferred (and only once) from the Quantity Takeoff to the Cost Analysis sheets. Some general rules for this procedure are:

- Write on only one side of any document where possible.
- Code each sheet with a large division number in a consistent place, preferably near one of the upper corners.

Construction Contract Amount	Ordinary Building Class "B" Rate	Preferred Building Rate
First $ 100,000	$ 25.00 per M	$11.50
Next 400,000	15.00 per M	11.50
Next 2,000,000	10.00 per M	8.00
Next 2,500,000	7.50 per M	6.50
Next 2,500,000	7.00 per M	6.00
Over 7,500,000	6.50 per M	5.50

Performance and Payment Bond Rates

The table shows examples of performance bond rates for jobs scheduled to be completed in about 24 months. The preferred rates are rates which are offered to contractors that the bonding company considers financially sound and capable of doing the work.

Contractors should prequalify through a bonding company agency before submitting a bid on a contract which requires a bond. This is only an example. Costs will vary by company, location and project type.

Figure 4.11

- Use Telephone Quotation forms for uniformity in recording prices received from any source, not only telephone quotes.
- Document the source of every quantity and price.
- Keep each type of document in its pile (Quantities, Material, Subcontractors, Equipment) filed in order by division number.
- Keep the entire estimate in one or more compartmented folders.
- When an item is transferred to the Cost Analysis sheet, check it off.
- If gross subcontractor quantities are known, pencil in the resultant unit prices to serve as a guide for future projects.

All subcontract costs should be properly noted and listed separately. These costs contain the subcontractor's markups, and will be treated differently from other direct costs when the estimator calculates the general contractor's overhead, profit and contingency allowance.

After all the unit prices, subcontractor prices, and allowances have been entered on the Cost Analysis sheets, the costs are extended. In making the extensions, ignore the cents column and round all totals to the nearest dollar. In a column of figures, the cents will average out and will not be of consequence. Indeed, for budget-type estimates, the extended figures could be rounded to the nearest $10, or even $100, with the loss of only a small amount of precision. Finally, each subdivision is added and the results checked, preferably by someone other than the person doing the extensions.

It is important to check the larger items for order of magnitude errors. If the total subdivision costs are divided by the building area, the resultant square foot cost figures can be used to quickly pinpoint areas that are out of line with expected square foot costs.

The takeoff and pricing method as discussed has been to utilize a Quantity Sheet for the material takeoff (see Figure 3.1), and to transfer the data to a Cost Analysis form for pricing the material, labor, and subcontractor items (see Figure 4.12).

An alternative to this method is a consolidation of the takeoff task and pricing on a single form. An example, the Consolidated Cost Analysis form, is shown in Figure 4.13. The same sequences and recommendations for completing the Quantity Sheet and Cost Analysis form are to be followed when using the Consolidated Cost Analysis form to price the estimate.

The Estimate Summary

When the pricing of all direct costs is complete, the estimator has two choices: all further price changes and adjustments can be made on the Cost Analysis or Consolidated Estimate sheets, *or* total costs for each subdivision can be transferred to an Estimate Summary sheet so that all further price changes, until bid time, will be done on one sheet.

Unless the estimate has a limited number of items, it is recommended that costs be transferred to an Estimate Summary sheet. This step should be double-checked since an error of transposition may easily occur. Pre-printed forms can be useful. A plain columnar form, however, may suffice.

MEANS
COST ANALYSIS

SHEET NO.

ESTIMATE NO.

PROJECT

ARCHITECT

DATE

TAKE OFF BY: QUANTITIES BY: PRICES BY: EXTENSIONS BY: CHECKED BY:

DESCRIPTION	SOURCE/DIMENSIONS			QUANTITY	UNIT	MATERIAL		LABOR		EQUIPMENT		SUB./TOTAL	
						UNIT COST	TOTAL	UNIT COST	TOTAL	UNIT COST	TOTAL	UNIT COST	TOTAL

Figure 4.12

53

Figure 4.13

If a company has certain standard listings that are used repeatedly, it would save valuable time to have a custom Estimate Summary sheet printed with the items that need to be listed. The Estimate Summary in Figures 4.14 and 4.15 is an example of a commonly used form. The printed MasterFormat division and subdivision headings act as a checklist to ensure that all required costs are included. Figure 4.16 is a Condensed Estimate Summary form. Appropriate column headings or categories for any Estimate Summary form are:

1. Material
2. Labor
3. Equipment
4. Subcontractor
5. Total

As items are listed in the proper columns, each category is added and appropriate markups applied to the total dollar values. Generally, the sum of each column has different percentages added near the end of the estimate for the indirect costs:

1. Sales Tax
2. Overhead
3. Profit
4. Contingencies

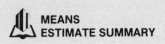

**MEANS
ESTIMATE SUMMARY**

SHEET NO. _____

PROJECT _____

ESTIMATE NO. _____

LOCATION _____

TOTAL AREA/VOLUME _____

DATE _____

ARCHITECT _____

COST PER S.F./C.F. _____

NO. OF STORIES _____

PRICES BY: _____

EXTENSIONS BY: _____

CHECKED BY: _____

DIV.	DESCRIPTION	MATERIAL	LABOR	EQUIPMENT	SUBCONTRACT	TOTAL
1.0	**General Requirements**					
	Insurance, Taxes, Bonds					
	Equipment & Tools					
	Design, Engineering, Supervision					
2.0	**Site Work**					
	Site Preparation, Demolition					
	Earthwork					
	Caissons & Piling					
	Drainage & Utilities					
	Paving & Surfacing					
	Site Improvements, Landscaping					
3.0	**Concrete**					
	Formwork					
	Reinforcing Steel & Mesh					
	Foundations					
	Superstructure					
	Precast Concrete					
4.0	**Masonry**					
	Mortar & Reinforcing					
	Brick, Block, Stonework					
5.0	**Metal**					
	Structural Steel					
	Open-Web Joists					
	Steel Deck					
	Misc. & Ornamental Metals					
	Fasteners, Rough Hardware					
6.0	**Carpentry**					
	Rough					
	Finish					
	Architectural Woodwork					
7.0	**Moisture & Thermal Protection**					
	Water & Dampproofing					
	Insulation & Fireproofing					
	Roofing & Sheet Metal					
	Siding					
	Roof Accessories					
8.0	**Doors, Windows, Glass**					
	Doors & Frames					
	Windows					
	Finish Hardware					
	Glass & Glazing					
	Curtain Wall & Entrances					
	PAGE TOTALS					

Figure 4.14

DIV.	DESCRIPTION	MATERIAL	LABOR	EQUIPMENT	SUBCONTRACT	TOTAL
	Totals Brought Forward					
9.0	**Finishes**					
	Studs & Furring					
	Lath, Plaster & Stucco					
	Drywall					
	Tile, Terrazzo, Etc.					
	Acoustical Treatment					
	Floor Covering					
	Painting & Wall Coverings					
10.0	**Specialties**					
	Bathroom Accessories					
	Lockers					
	Partitions					
	Signs & Bulletin Boards					
11.0	**Equipment**					
	Appliances					
	Dock					
	Kitchen					
12.0	**Furnishings**					
	Blinds					
	Seating					
13.0	**Special Construction**					
	Integrated Ceilings					
	Pedestal Floors					
	Pre Fab Rooms & Bldgs.					
14.0	**Conveying Systems**					
	Elevators, Escalators					
	Pnuematic Tube Systems					
15.0	**Mechanical**					
	Pipe & Fittings					
	Plumbing Fixtures & Appliances					
	Fire Protection					
	Heating					
	Air Conditioning & Ventilation					
16.0	**Electrical**					
	Raceways					
	Conductors & Grounding					
	Boxes & Wiring Devices					
	Starters, Boards & Switches					
	Transformers & Bus Duct					
	Lighting					
	Special Systems					
	Subtotals					
	Sales Tax %					
	Overhead %					
	Subtotal					
	Profit %					
	Adjustments/Contingency					
	TOTAL BID					

Figure 4.15

MEANS CONDENSED ESTIMATE SUMMARY

SHEET NO.						
PROJECT				ESTIMATE NO.		
LOCATION		TOTAL AREA/VOLUME		DATE		
ARCHITECT		COST PER S.F./C.F.		NO. OF STORIES		
PRICES BY:		EXTENSIONS BY:		CHECKED BY:		

DIV.	DESCRIPTION	MATERIAL	LABOR	EQUIPMENT	SUBCONTRACT	TOTAL
1.0	General Requirements					
2.0	Site Work					
3.0	Concrete					
4.0	Masonry					
5.0	Metals					
6.0	Carpentry					
7.0	Moisture & Thermal Protection					
8.0	Doors, Windows, Glass					
9.0	Finishes					
10.0	Specialties					
11.0	Equipment					
12.0	Furnishings					
13.0	Special Construction					
14.0	Conveying Systems					
15.0	Mechanical					
16.0	Electrical					
	Subtotals					
	Sales Tax %					
	Overhead %					
	Subtotal					
	Profit %					
	Contingency %					
	Adjustments					
	TOTAL BID					

Figure 4.16

58

PRE-BID
SCHEDULING

Chapter 5
PRE-BID SCHEDULING

The need for planning and scheduling is clear once the contract is signed and work commences on the project. However, some scheduling is also important during the bidding stage for the following reasons:

1. To determine if the project can be completed in the allotted or specified time.
2. To determine the time requirements for general conditions items, such as supervision, field office, and watchman.
3. To determine when the building will be enclosed in order to anticipate possible temporary heat and power requirements.

The schedule produced prior to bidding may be a simple bar chart or network diagram that includes overall quantities, probable delivery times and available manpower. Network scheduling methods, such as the Critical Path Method (CPM) and the Precedence Chart simplify prebid scheduling because they do not require scaled diagrams.

In the CPM Diagram, the activity is represented by the arrow. The Precedence Diagram, on the other hand, shows the activity in a node with arrows used to denote precedence relationships between the activities. The precedence arrows may be used in different configurations to represent the sequential relationships between activities. Examples of CPM and Precedence Diagrams are shown in Figures 5.1 and 5.2, respectively. In both systems, duration times are indicated along each path. The sequence of activities requiring the most total time represents the shortest possible time in which those activities may be completed.

For example, in Figure 5.1, activities A, B, and C require 20 successive days for completion before activity G can begin. Activity paths for D and E, and for F are shorter and can be easily fit into the 20 day sequence. Therefore, this 20 day sequence is the shortest possible time for completion of these activities before activity G can begin.

Past experience or a prepared rough schedule may suggest that the allotted time specified in the bidding documents is insufficient to complete the required work. In such cases, a more comprehensive schedule should be produced prior to bidding; this schedule should include the calculations for added overtime or premium time work costs required to meet the completion date.

The following simple example is of a 100' x 200', four-story flat plate building with a basement and 25' square bays. It is based on the data listed below.

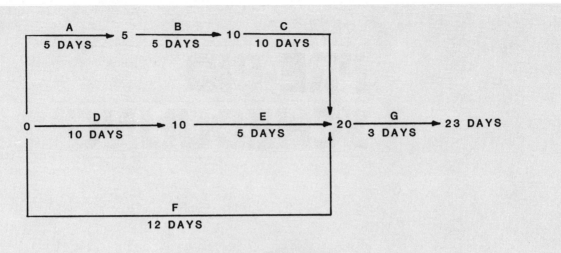

C.P.M. DIAGRAM

Figure 5.1

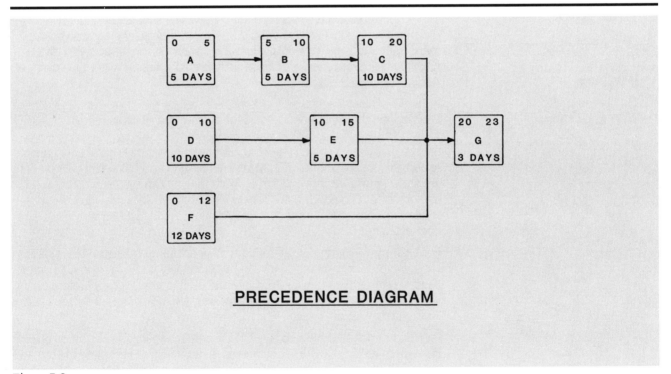

PRECEDENCE DIAGRAM

Figure 5.2

Description	Quantity Output	Duration
Earthwork:		
Bulk Excavation	7228 C.Y. / 1000 C.Y./Day	7 Days
Footing Excavation	1300 C.Y. / 200 C.Y./Day	7 Days
Backfill Bulk	1300 C.Y. / 240 C.Y./Day	5 Days
Backfill Footings	770 C.Y. / 240 C.Y./Day	3 Days
Forms:		
Spread and Continuous Footings	5894 S.F. / 400 S.F./Day	15 Days
Walls and Pilasters	10,176 S.F. / 600 S.F./Day	17 Days

Figure 5.3 shows a preliminary schedule for excavation and the foundation. Note that a one day duration time has been added to the estimated time to complete the forming operation for both the footings and walls. The established duration time to excavate, form, reinforce and place the concrete for the foundation is 32 days, not including a factor for weather.

Our next major category on the schedule is the poured-in-place concrete structure. Because of the large amount of formwork required, a rough schedule

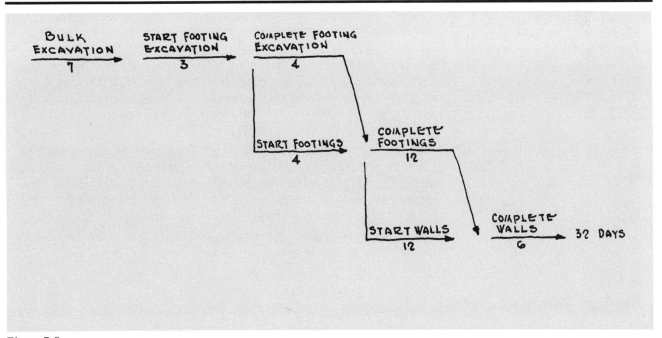

Figure 5.3

may help to produce a more reliable quotation. The most efficient and economical quantity of the forms and number of uses can be determined. Assume the specifications require seven days curing time for the concrete slabs before the forms may be stripped and the slabs reshored. Also assume a twelve man carpenter crew is available with additional laborers to support the carpenters. Durations for each task are developed from derived quantities, productivity rates and assumed crew sizes. The calculations are shown in Figure 5.4.

A preliminary schedule may be developed to determine the minimum time requirements for forming, reinforcing and placing the concrete. The schedule will also help determine how many sets of forms are required for the most efficient use in the specified curing time. Figure 5.5 is an example of this kind of preliminary schedule.

Repeating the cycle for the roof slab and assuming that one set of floor forms (enough for one floor of the building) is available, the structure would take approximately sixty-eight working days to complete with no allowance for weather. A *quick*, rough estimate of time to erect the same structure may be derived by using the formula below. Exercise care when using the quick method to estimate the duration times of activities that may be overlapped or done concurrently. Crew output is the product of the output per man per day times the number of men.

$$\frac{\text{Form Area}}{\text{Crew Output}} + \frac{\text{Final Reinf.}}{\text{Duration}} + \frac{\text{Final Conc.}}{\text{Duration}} = \text{Total Duration}$$

$$\frac{25{,}060 \text{ SFCA}}{1080 \text{ S.F./Day}} + \frac{75{,}200 \text{ SFCA}}{1680 \text{ S.F./Day}} + 2 \text{ Days} + 1 \text{ Day} = 71 \text{ Days}$$

$$\text{(first floor)} \qquad\qquad \text{(upper floors)}$$

Only the final reinforcing and concrete durations are included because previous durations are not limiting activities. If the same formula is applied to the foundations, approximate total duration time can be determined as follows:

$$\frac{5894 \text{ SFCA}}{400 \text{ S.F./Day}} + \frac{10{,}176 \text{ SFCA}}{600 \text{ S.F./Day}} + 1 \text{ Day} + 1 \text{ Day} = 34 \text{ Days}$$

To complete the schedule, probable duration times are derived from the estimated quantities for the remaining divisions of the estimate. The precedence format works well for the preliminary schedules because of the advantage of using arrow placement to show precedence relationships between activities. The relationships between activity nodes (rectangles) can be shown with the arrow configurations as in Figure 5.6.

The computations used in precedence schedules can become complicated. Finish-to-start connectors with lag times are convenient and make calculations easier. The polygons on the diagram are used to show logical delivery times for materials, allowing adequate turn-around time for shop drawings.

Once the preliminary schedule has been developed using a no-scale network diagram depicting activity dependencies, a simple bar chart for the project can be drawn to condense the information.

55'	50'	50'	45'

100'

| 1A | 1B | 1C | 1D |

Placement Plan

Duration Derivation

Columns Each

Forms $\dfrac{90 \text{ sfca Ea}}{60 \text{ sfca/day x 12 Carp}} = .125$ days Ea (1st use)

Reinforcing $\dfrac{.13 \text{ tons Ea}}{.375 \text{ tons/day x 4 Rdmn}} = .087$ days Ea

Concrete $\dfrac{1.67 \text{ cy Ea}}{11.5 \text{ cy/day x 8 men}} = .018$ days Ea

Slab Forms 1st Floor

"1A" Slab Form 5500 sfca
      Edge Form 168 sfca

$\dfrac{5668 \text{ sfca}}{90 \text{ sfca/day x 12 Carp}} = 5$ days

"1B & 1C" Slab Form 5000 sfca
           Edge Form 158 sfca

$\dfrac{5158 \text{ sfca}}{90 \text{ sfca/day x 12 Carp}} = 4.78$ days

Columns 10 Ea x .125 days Ea $= \dfrac{1.25 \text{ days}}{6.0 \text{ days}}$

"1D" Slab Form 4500 sfca
      Edge Form 150 sfca

$\dfrac{4650 \text{ sfca}}{90 \text{ sfca/day x 12 Carp}} = 4.3$ days

Columns 10 Ea x .125 days Ea $= \dfrac{1.25 \text{ days}}{6.0 \text{ days}}$

Reinforcing @ 2.8 psf

"1A" $\dfrac{5500 \text{ sf x 2.8 psf}}{2000}$ $\dfrac{7.7 \text{ tons}}{.7 \text{ tons/day x 5 Rdmn}} = 2$ days

"1B & 1C" $\dfrac{5000 \text{ sf x 2.8 psf}}{2000}$ $\dfrac{7.0 \text{ tons}}{.7 \text{ tons/day} = 5 \text{ Rdmn}} = 2$ days

"1D" $\dfrac{4500 \text{ sf x 2.8 psf}}{2000}$ $\dfrac{6.3 \text{ tons}}{.7 \text{ tons/day x 5 Rdmn}} = 2$ days

Concrete (Average)

$\dfrac{150 \text{ cy}}{16.5 \text{ cy/day x 9 men}} = 1$ day

2nd & 3rd Floors & Roof

Forms "A" $\dfrac{5668 \text{ sfca}}{140 \text{ sfca/day x 12 Carp}} = 4$ days

"B & C" $\dfrac{5158 \text{ sfca}}{140 \text{ sfca/day x 12 Carp}} = 3$ days

"D" $\dfrac{4650 \text{ sfca}}{140 \text{ sfca/day x 12 Carp}} = 3$ days

Reinforcing and concrete placement durations are the same as the 1st floor.

Figure 5.4

Figure 5.5

Figure 5.6

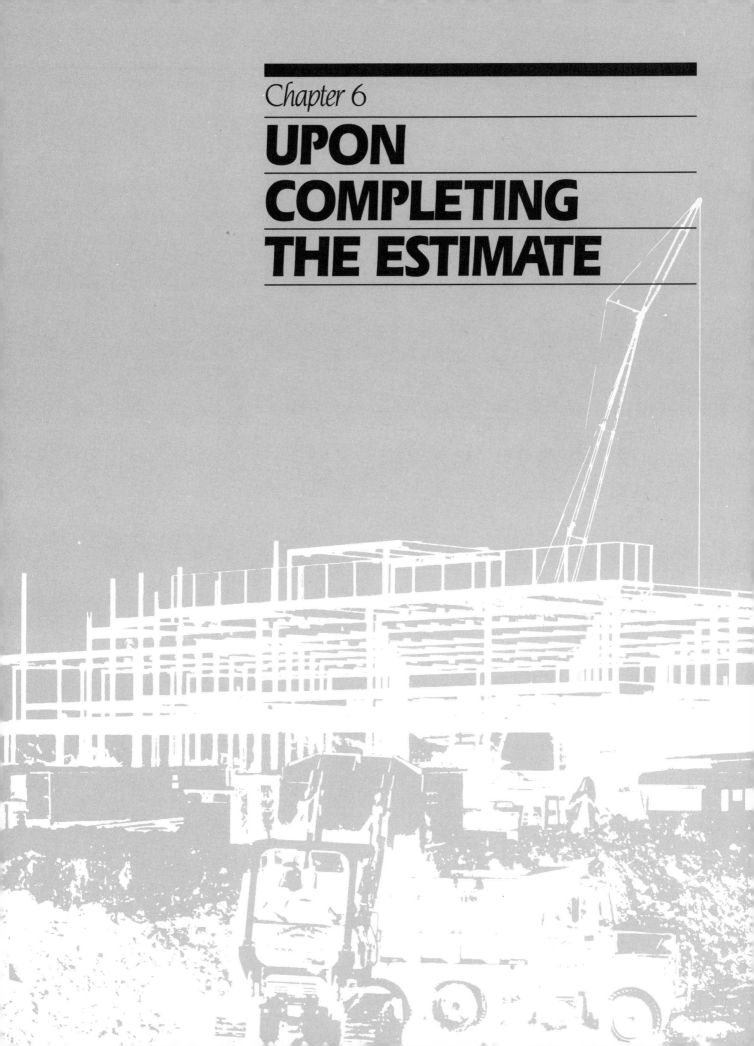

Chapter 6

UPON COMPLETING THE ESTIMATE

Chapter 6

UPON COMPLETING THE ESTIMATE

Bidding Strategies

The goal of most contractors is to make as much money as possible on each job, but more importantly, to maximize return on investment on an annual basis. This means making more money by taking fewer jobs at a higher profit.

One measure of successful bidding is how much money is "left on the table," the difference between the low bid and next lowest bid. The contractor who consistently takes jobs by a wide margin below the next bidder, is obviously not making as much money as possible. Information on competitive public bidding is accessible. Thus, the amount of money left on the table is easily determined and can be the basis for fine-tuning a future bidding strategy.

Since a contractor cannot physically bid every type of job in a geographic area, a selection process must determine which projects should be bid. This selective process should begin with an analysis of the strengths and weaknesses of the contractor. The following items that must be considered as objectively as possible are:

- Individual strengths of the company's top management.
- Management experience with the type of construction involved, from top management to project superintendents.
- Cost records adequate for the appropriate type of construction.
- Bonding capability and capacity.
- Size of projects with which the company is "comfortable."
- Geographic area that can be managed effectively.
- Unusual corporate assets such as:
  - Specialized equipment availability
  - Reliable and timely cost control systems
  - Strong balance sheet

Market Analysis

Most contractors tend to concentrate on one, or a few, fairly specialized types of construction. From time to time, the company should step back and examine the total picture of the industry they are serving. During this process, the following items should be carefully analyzed.

- Historical trend of the market segment.
- Expected future trend of the market segment.
- Geographic expectations of the market segment.
- Historical and expected competition among other builders.
- Risk involved in the particular market segment.
- Typical size of projects in this market.
- Expected return on investment from the market segment.

If several of these areas are experiencing a downturn, then it might be appropriate to examine an alternate market.

Certain steps should be taken to develop a bid strategy for a particular market. The first is to obtain the bid results of jobs in the prospective geographic area. These results should be set up on a tabular basis. This is fairly easy to do in public jobs since the bid results are normally published (or at least available) from the agency responsible for the project. In private work this step is very difficult, since the bid results are not normally divulged by the owner.

For example, assume a public market where all bid prices and the total number of bidders is known. For each "type" of market sector, create a chart showing the percentage left on the table versus the total number of bidders. When the median figure (percent left on the table) for each number of bidders is connected with a smooth curve, the usual shape of the curve is shown in Figure 6.1.

The exact shape and magnitude of the amounts left on the table will depend on how much risk is involved with that type of work. If the percentages left on the table are high, then the work can be assumed be very risky; if the percentages are low, the work is probably not too risky.

Bidding Analysis

If a company has been bidding in a particular market, certain information should be collected and recorded as a basis for a bidding analysis. The percentage left on the table should be tabulated, along with the number of bidders for the projects in that market on which the company was the low bidder. By probability, half the bids should be above the median line and half below. (See Figure 6.1.) If more than half are below the line, the company is doing well; if more than half are above, the bidding strategy should be examined. Once the bidding track record for the company has been established, the next step is to reduce the historical percentage left on the table. One method is to create a chart showing, for instance, the last ten jobs on which the company

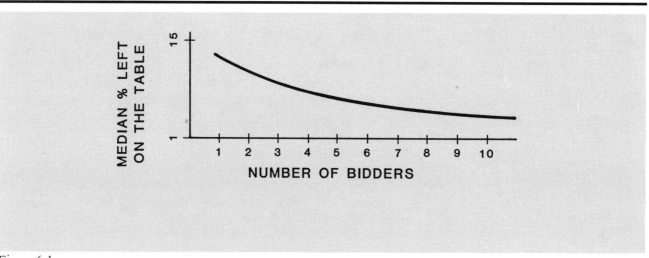

Figure 6.1

70

was low bidder and the dollar spread between the low and second lowest bid. Next, rank the percentage differences from one to ten (one being the smallest and ten being the largest left on the table). An example is shown in Figure 6.2.

The company's "costs" ($17,170,000) are derived from the company's low bid ($18,887,000) assuming a 10% profit ($1,717,000). The "second bid" is the next lowest bid. The "difference" is the dollar amount between the low bid and the second bid. The differences are then ranked based on the percentage of job "costs" left on the table for each.

$$\text{Median \% Difference} = \frac{5.73 + 6.44}{2} = 6.09\%$$

From Figure 6.2, the median percentage left on the table is 6.09%. To maximize the potential returns on a series of competitive bids, a useful formula for pricing profit is needed. The following formula has proven effective.

$$\text{Normal Profit \%} + \frac{\text{Median \% Difference}}{2} = \text{Adjusted Profit \%}$$

$$10.00 + \frac{6.09}{2} = 13.05\%$$

Now apply this adjusted profit % to the same list of ten jobs as shown in Figure 6.3. Note that the job "costs" remain the same, but that the low bids have been revised. Compare the bottom line results of Figure 6.2 to those of Figure 6.3 based on the two profit margins, 10% and 13.05%, respectively.

Job No.	"Cost"	Low Bid	Second Bid	Difference	% Diff.	% Rank	Profit (Assumed at 10%)
1	$ 918,000	$ 1,009,800	$1,095,000	$ 85,200	9.28	10	$ 91,800
2	1,955,000	2,150,500	2,238,000	87,500	4.48	3	195,500
3	2,141,000	2,355,100	2,493,000	137,900	6.44	6	214,100
4	1,005,000	1,105,500	1,118,000	12,500	1.24	1	100,500
5	2,391,000	2,630,100	2,805,000	174,900	7.31	8	239,100
6	2,782,000	3,060,200	3,188,000	127,800	4.59	4	278,200
7	1,093,000	1,202,300	1,282,000	79,700	7.29	7	109,300
8	832,000	915,200	926,000	10,800	1.30	2	83,200
9	2,372,000	2,609,200	2,745,000	135,800	5.73	5	237,200
10	1,681,000	1,849,100	2,005,000	155,900	9.27	9	168,100
	$17,170,000	$18,887,000		$1,008,000			$1,717,000 = 10% of Cost

Figure 6.2

Total volume *drops* from $18,887,000 to $17,333,900.

Net profits *rise* from $1,717,000 to $2,000,900.

Profits rise while volume drops. If the original volume is maintained or even increased, profits would rise even faster. Note how this occurs. By determining a reasonable increase in profit margin, the company has, in effect, raised all bids. By doing so, the company loses two jobs to the second bidder (jobs 4 and 8 in Figure 6.3).

A positive effect of this volume loss is reduced exposure to risk. Since the profit margin is higher, the remaining eight jobs collectively produce more profit than the ten jobs based on the original, lower profit margin. From where did this money come? The money "left on the table" has been reduced from $1,008,000 to $517,100. The whole purpose is to systematically lessen the dollar amount difference between the low bid and the second low bid. This is a hypothetical approach based upon a number of assumptions:

- Bidding must be done within the same market in which data for the analysis was gathered.
- Economic conditions should be stable from the time the data is gathered until the analysis is used in bidding. If conditions change, use of such an analysis should be reviewed.
- Each contractor must make roughly the same number of bidding mistakes. For higher numbers of jobs in the sample, this requirement becomes more probable.
- The company must bid additional jobs if total annual volume is to be maintained or increased. Likewise, if net total profit margin is to remain constant, fewer jobs need be bid.

Job No.	Company's "Cost"	Revised Low Bid	Second Bid	Adj. Diff.	Profit [10% + 3.05%]		Total
1	$ 918,000	$ 1,037,800	$1,095,000	$ 57,200	$ 91,800 +	$28,000	$ 119,800
2	1,955,000	2,210,100	2,238,000	27,900	195,500 +	59,600	225,100
3	2,141,000	2,420,400	2,493,000	72,600	214,100 +	65,300	279,400
4	(1,005,000)	(1,136,100)	1,118,000 (L)	—	100,500 +	30,600	0
5	2,391,000	2,703,000	2,805,000	102,000	239,100 +	72,900	312,000
6	2,782,000	3,145,100	3,188,000	42,900	278,200 +	84,900	363,100
7	1,093,000	1,235,600	1,282,000	46,400	109,300 +	33,300	142,600
8	(832,000)	(940,600)	926,000 (L)	—	83,200 +	25,400	0
9	2,372,000	2,681,500	2,745,000	63,500	237,200 +	72,300	309,500
10	1,681,000	1,900,400	2,005,000	104,600	168,100 +	51,300	219,400
	$15,333,000	$17,333,900		$517,100			$2,000,900

Figure 6.3

Even though the accuracy of this strategy is based on these criteria, the concept is valid and can be applied, with appropriate and reasonable judgment, to many bidding situations.

Cost Control and Analysis

An internal accounting system should be used by the contractor to logically allocate and track the gathered costs of a construction project. With this information, a cost analysis can be made about each cost center. The cost centers of a project are the major items of construction (e.g., concrete) that can be subdivided by component. This subdivision should coincide with the system and methods of the quantity takeoff. The major purposes of cost control and analysis are:

- To provide management with a system to monitor costs and progress.
- To provide cost feedback to the estimator(s).
- To determine the costs of change orders.
- To be used as a basis for submitting payment requisitions to the owner or his representative.
- To manage cash flow.

A cost control system should be established that is uniform throughout the company and from job to job. The various costs are then consistently allocated. The cost control system might be simplified with a code that provides a different designation for each part of a component cost. The following information should be recorded for each component cost.

- Labor charges in dollars and man-hours, summarized from weekly time cards, are distributed by code.
- Equipment rental costs are derived from purchase orders or from weekly charges from an equipment company.
- Material charges are determined from purchase orders.
- Appropriate subcontractor charges are allocated.
- Job overhead items may be listed separately or by component.
- Quantities completed to date must also be recorded in order to determine unit costs.

Each component of costs – labor, materials and equipment – is now calculated on a unit basis by dividing the quantity to date (percentage complete) into the component cost to date. This procedure establishes the actual unit costs to date. The remaining quantities of each component to be completed should be estimated at a unit cost approximating the costs to date. The actual costs to date and the predicted costs are added together to represent the anticipated costs at the end of the project. Typical forms that may be used to develop a cost control system are shown in Figures 6.4 to 6.7.

The analysis of cost centers serves as a useful management tool, providing information on a current basis. Immediate attention is attracted to any center that is operating at a loss. Management can concentrate on this item in an attempt to make it profitable or to minimize the expected loss.

The estimating department can use the unit costs developed in the field as background information for future bidding purposes. Particularly useful are unit labor costs and unit man-hours (productivity) for the separate components. Current unit man-hours and labor costs should be integrated into the accumulated historical data.

Frequently, items are added to or deleted from the contract. Accurate cost records are an excellent basis for determining cost changes that result from change orders and requests for additional work.

**MEANS
PERCENTAGE
COMPLETE ANALYSIS**

PAGE

PROJECT   ARCHITECT   DATE

LOCATION   BY   FROM   TO

NO.	DESCRIPTION	ACTUAL OR ESTIMATED	TOTAL PROJECT	THIS PERIOD			PERCENT TOTAL TO DATE										
				QUANTITY	%	QUANTITY	10	20	30	40	50	60	70	80	90	100
		ACTUAL														
		ESTIMATED														
		ACTUAL														
		ESTIMATED														
		ACTUAL														
		ESTIMATED														
		ACTUAL														
		ESTIMATED														
		ACTUAL														
		ESTIMATED														
		ACTUAL														
		ESTIMATED														
		ACTUAL														
		ESTIMATED														
		ACTUAL														
		ESTIMATED														
		ACTUAL														
		ESTIMATED														
		ACTUAL														
		ESTIMATED														
		ACTUAL														
		ESTIMATED														
		ACTUAL														
		ESTIMATED														
		ACTUAL														
		ESTIMATED														
		ACTUAL														
		ESTIMATED														
		ACTUAL														
		ESTIMATED														
		ACTUAL														
		ESTIMATED														
		ACTUAL														
		ESTIMATED														
		ACTUAL														
		ESTIMATED														
		ACTUAL														
		ESTIMATED														
		ACTUAL														
		ESTIMATED														
		ACTUAL														
		ESTIMATED														
		ACTUAL														
		ESTIMATED														
		ACTUAL														
		ESTIMATED														

Figure 6.4

**MEANS
JOB PROGRESS REPORT**

SHEET _____ OF _____

JOB NO. _____

PROJECT

LOCATION

YEARS

WORK ITEM	QUANTITY, $, OR %	BEGINNING BALANCE	MONTHS											ENDING BALANCE
	DATE													
	YEAR													

Figure 6.5

MEANS
MATERIAL COST RECORD

			SHEET NO.
			DATE FROM
PROJECT			DATE TO
LOCATION			BY

DATE	NUMBER	VENDOR/DESCRIPTION	QTY.	UNIT PRICE				QTY.	UNIT PRICE				QTY.	UNIT PRICE			

Figure 6.6

76

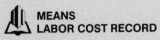

MEANS
LABOR COST RECORD

SHEET NO.

DATE FROM:

PROJECT

DATE TO:

LOCATION

BY:

DATE	CHARGE NO.	DESCRIPTION	HOURS	RATE	AMOUNT	HOURS	RATE	AMOUNT	HOURS	RATE	AMOUNT

Figure 6.7

Cost records require the determination of completed quantities in order to calculate unit costs. These calculations are used to determine the percent completion of each cost center. This percentage is used to calculate the billing of completed items for payment requisitions.

A cost system is only as good as the people responsible for coding and recording the required information. Simplicity is the key word. Do not try to break down the code into very small items unless there is a specific need. Continuous updating of costs is important so that operations which are not in control can be immediately brought to the attention of management.

Productivity and Efficiency

When using a cost control system such as the one described above, the derived unit costs should reflect standard practices. Productivity should be based on a five day, eight hour per day (during daylight hours) work week unless a company's requirements are particularly and normally unique. Installation costs should be derived using normal minimum crew sizes, under normal weather conditions, during the normal construction season. Costs and productivity should also be based on familiar types of construction.

All unusual costs incurred or expected should be separately recorded for each component of work. For example, an overtime situation might occur on every job and in the same proportion. In this case, it would make sense to carry the unit price adjusted for the added cost of premium time. Likewise, unusual weather delays, strike activity or owner/architect delays should have separate, identifiable cost contributions; these are applied as isolated costs to the activities affected by the delays. This procedure serves two purposes:

- To identify and separate the cost contribution of the delay so that job estimates will not automatically include an allowance for these "non-typical" delays, and
- To serve as a basis for an extra compensation claim and or as justification for reasonable extension of the job.

The use of long-term overtime on almost any construction job is counter-productive; that is, the longer the period of overtime, the lower the actual production rate. There have been numerous studies conducted which come up with slightly different numbers, but all have the same conclusion.

As illustrated in Figure 6.8, there can be a difference between the actual payroll cost per hour and the *effective* cost per hour for overtime work. This is due to the reduced production efficiency with the increase in weekly hours beyond 40. This difference between actual and effective cost is for overtime over a prolonged period. Short-term overtime does not result as great a reduction in efficiency, and in such cases, cost premiums would approach the payroll costs rather than the effective hourly costs listed in Figure 6.8. As the total hours per week are increased on a regular basis, more time is lost by absenteeism and the accident rate increases.

As an example, assume a project where workers are working 6 days a week, 10 hours per day. From Figure 6.8 (based on productivity studies), the actual productive hours are 51.1 hours. This represents a theoretical production efficiency of 51.1/60 or 85.2%.

Depending upon the locale, overtime work is paid at time and a half or double time. In both cases, the overall *actual* payroll cost (including regular and overtime hours) is determined as follows:

For time and a half:

$$\frac{40 \text{ reg. hrs.} + (20 \text{ overtime hrs. x } 1.5)}{60 \text{ hrs.}} = 1.167$$

Based on 60 hours, the payroll cost per hour will be 116.7% of the normal rate at 40 hours per week.

For double time:

$$\frac{40 \text{ reg. hrs.} + (20 \text{ overtime hrs. x } 2)}{60 \text{ hrs.}} = 1.33$$

Payroll cost will be 133% of the normal rate.

However, because the actual productive hours (and thus production efficiency) are reduced to 51.1 hours, the *effective* cost of overtime is:

For time and a half:

$$\frac{40 \text{ reg. hrs.} + (20 \text{ overtime hrs. x } 1.5)}{51.1 \text{ hrs.}} = 1.37$$

Payroll cost will be 137% of the normal rate.

For double time:

$$\frac{40 \text{ reg. hrs.} + (20 \text{ overtime hrs. x } 2)}{51.1 \text{ hrs.}} = 1.566$$

Efficiency and Cost Effects of Prolonged Overtime Work								
Days per Week	Hours per Day	Total Hours Worked	Actual Productive Hours	Production Efficiency	Payroll Cost per Hour Overtime After 40 Hrs.		Effective Cost per Hour Overtime After 40 Hrs.	
					@ 1-1/2 times	@ 2 times	@ 1-1/2 times	@ 2 times
	8	40	40.0	100.0%	100.0%	100.0%	100.0%	100.0%
	9	45	43.4	96.5	105.6	111.1	109.4	115.2
5	10	50	46.5	93.0	110.0	120.0	118.3	129.0
	11	55	49.2	89.5	113.6	127.3	127.0	142.3
	12	60	51.6	86.0	116.7	133.3	135.7	155.0
	8	48	46.1	96.0	108.3	116.7	112.8	121.5
	9	54	48.9	90.6	113.0	125.9	124.7	139.1
6	10	60	51.1	85.2	116.7	133.3	137.0	156.6
	11	66	52.7	79.8	119.7	139.4	149.9	174.6
	12	72	53.6	74.4	122.2	144.4	164.2	194.0
	8	56	48.8	87.1	114.3	128.6	131.1	147.5
	9	63	52.2	82.8	118.3	136.5	142.7	164.8
7	10	70	55.0	78.5	121.4	142.9	154.5	181.8
	11	77	57.1	74.2	124.0	148.1	167.3	199.6
	12	84	58.7	69.9	126.2	152.4	180.6	218.1

Figure 6.8

Payroll cost will be 156.6% of the normal rate.

Thus, when figuring overtime, the actual cost per unit of work will be higher than the apparent overtime payroll dollar increase, due to the reduced productivity of the longer work week. These calculations are true only for those pay costs which are determined by hours worked. Costs which are applied weekly or monthly, such as some fringe benefits, will not be similarly affected.

Retainage and Cash Flow

The majority of construction projects have some percentage of retainage held back by the owner until the job is complete. This retainage can range from 5% to as high as 15% or 20% in unusual cases. The most typical retainage is 10%. Since the profit on a given job may be less than the amount of withheld retainage, the contractor must wait longer before a positive cash flow is achieved than if there were no retainage.

Figures 6.9 and 6.10 are graphic and tabular representations of the projected cash flow for a small project. With this kind of projection, the contractor is able to anticipate cash needs throughout the course of the job. Note that at the eleventh of May, before the second payment is received, the contractor has paid out about $25,000 more than has been received. This is the maximum amount of cash (on hand or financed) that is required for the whole project. At this stage of planning, the contractor can determine if there will be adequate cash available or if a loan is needed. In the latter case, the expense of interest could be anticipated and included in the estimate. On larger projects, the projection of cash flow becomes crucial, because unexpected interest expense can quickly erode profit margin.

The General Conditions section of the specifications usually explains the responsibilities of both the owner and the contractor with regard to billing and payments. Even the best planning and projections are contingent upon the owner paying requisitions as anticipated. There is an almost unavoidable adversary relationship between contractor and owner regarding payment during the construction process. However, it is in the best interest of the owner that the contractor be solvent so that delays, complications, and difficulties can be avoided prior to final completion of the project. The interest of both parties is best served if information is shared and communication is open. Both are working toward the same goal: the timely and successful completion of the project.

Life Cycle Costs

Life cycle costing is a valuable method of evaluating the total costs of an economic unit during its entire life. Regardless of whether the unit is a piece of excavating machinery or a manufacturing building, life cycle costing gives the owner an opportunity to look at the economic consequences of a decision. Today, the initial cost of a unit is often not the most important; the operation and maintenance costs of some building types far exceed the initial outlay. Hospitals, for example, may have operating costs within a three-year period that exceed the original construction costs.

Estimators are in the business of initial costs. But what about the other costs that affect any owner: taxes, fuel, inflation, borrowing, estimated salvage at the end of the facility's lifespan, and expected repair or remodeling costs. These costs that may occur at a later date need to be evaluated in advance. The thread that ties all of these costs together is the time value of money. The value of money today is quite different from what it will be tomorrow. $1,000 placed in a savings bank at 5% interest will, in four years, have increased to $1,215.50. Conversely, if $1,000 is needed four years from now, then $822.70 should be

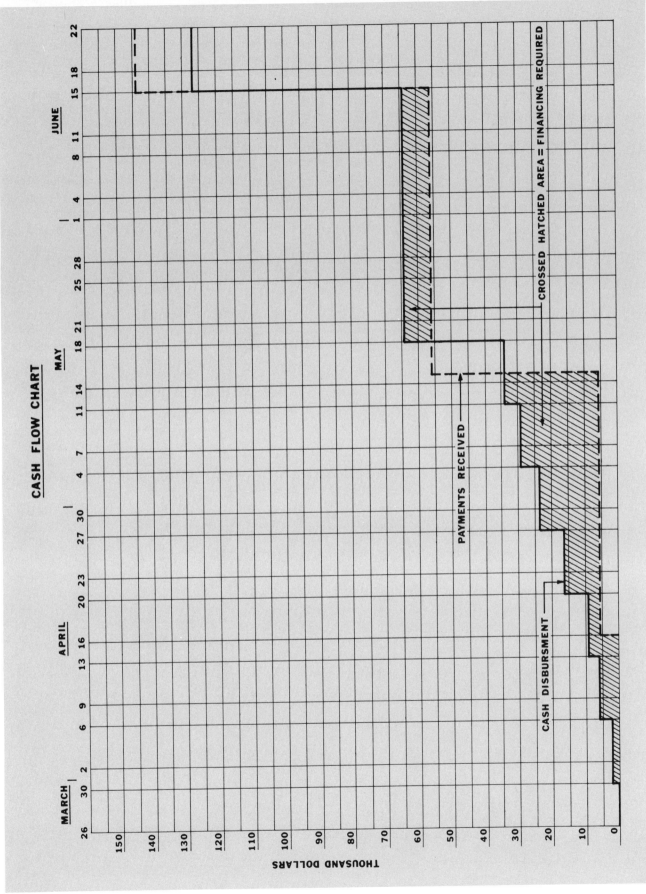

Figure 6.9

Date	Item	Payroll Incl. Taxes (1)	Workers' Comp. (2)	Monthly Billing (3)	Retainage (4)	Subs Billing + Payment (5)	Retainage (6)	Materials Incl. Taxes (7)	Equip. Incl. Taxes (8)	Payments (9)	Accumulated Costs $ (10)
3-30	Payroll	1926	148								− 1926
3-30	Monthly Billing			4558	506	708	777				
4-6	Payroll	3246	253								− 5172
4-13	Payroll	4197	311								− 9369
4-16	Payment									4558	− 4811
4-20	Pay Subs					708					− 5519
4-20	Pay Materials							515			− 6504
4-20	Pay Equipment								965		− 6999
4-20	Payroll	3827	275								− 10826
4-27	Payroll	4525	335								− 15351
4-30	Monthly Billing			51330	5704	5245	582				
5-4	Payroll	5525	508								− 20876
5-11	Payroll	3531	370								− 24407
5-15	Payment									51330	− 26923
5-18	Payroll	2613	243								+ 24310
5-18	Pay Subs					5245					+ 19065
5-18	Pay Materials							22118			+ 30653
5-18	Pay Equipment								779		− 3832
6-1	Final Billing			88883	9896	48915	5435				+ 85051
6-15	Payment									88883	+ 36136
	Pay Subs					48915					+ 23451
	Pay Materials							12685			+ 227113
	Pay Equipment								738		
		$ 29590	$ 2441	$ 144771	$ 16086	$ 54860	$ 6094	$ 35318	$ 2482	$ 144771	

General Conditions
Permit — 150 @ $3.00 — 450
Supervision—Carpenter Foreman 35 days @ $170 — 5950
Temp. Power + Water — 200
Temp. Office + Storage 6 wks @ $30 — 180
Clean Up Labor 2 days @ $122 — 244
7024

Cash — 22715
Retainage — 16086
38799
Pay Workers Comp — 2441
36358
Pay Subs Retainage — 6094
30264
Gen. Conditions — 7024
23240

Figure 6.10

82

placed in an account today. Another way of saying the same thing is that at 5% interest, the value of $1,000 four years from now is only worth $822.70 today.

Using interest and time, future costs are equated to the present by means of a present worth formula. Standard texts in engineering economics have outlined different methods for handling interest and time. A present worth evaluation could be used, or all costs might be converted into an equivalent, uniform annual cost method.

As an example, assume that an excavating machine is purchased for $20,000. Hourly gas and oil charges will be $6.20. A major overhaul of the engine will be needed in three years at a cost of $4,000. After six years, the trade-in value will be $1,500. What is the total *present worth* of the machine over its six-year life if money is borrowed at 12%?

First Cost of the Machine:

Purchase Price =	$20,000.00
Total present worth of Operating and Maintenance @ $6.20/hour = 1,500 hours x $6.20 = $9,300/year x 4.111 (present worth of a uniform series of payment for six years) =	38,232.30
Present worth of a major overhaul three years from now = $4,000 x .7118 (time/value factor) =	2,847.20
Present worth of the salvage at the end of six years = $1,500 x 0.5066 (time/value factor) =	+ 759.90
The Total Present Worth of the Tractor	$61,839.40

If we consider the uniform annual costs of the machine, then (at 12% interest) the following happens:

The uniform annual cost of the initial investment ($20,000) x .24323 (capital recovery factor) =	$ 4,864.60
The uniform maintenance and operating costs =	9,300.00
The uniform cost of motor repair in the third year is the present worth times the capital recovery factor, $2,847 x .24323 =	692.52
The equivalent uniform cost of the salvage, $1,500 x .12323 (sinking fund factor) =	+ 184.85
Total Equivalent Uniform Annual Costs	$15,041.97

This is the same as if the total present worth was multiplied by the capital recovery factor: $61,839.40 x .24323 = $15,041.20. If the machine is used 1,500 hours per year, then the hourly base operating cost is approximately $10 per hour.

Another benefit of life cycle costing is having the ability to compare the equivalent uniform costs between two different machines. This comparison can help with the decision to rent or purchase.

Life cycle costs are not always determined easily. The initial investment and the operating costs can be estimated, and maintenance costs can be determined from past experience with similar machines; but anticipating a motor overhaul precisely or knowing the projected salvage price is difficult. Interest rates and time factors are critical in determining life cycle costs. By varying the time intervals and/or the interest rate when comparing the alternatives, a good investment might appear poor, or vice versa. It is therefore essential that realistic, accurate rates be used.

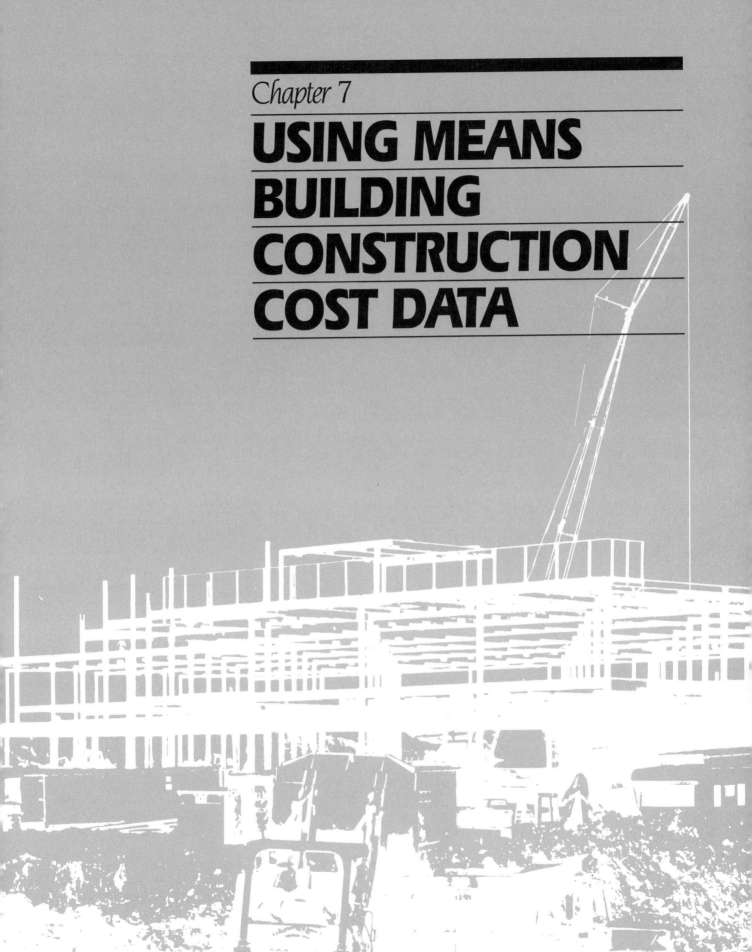

Chapter 7

USING MEANS BUILDING CONSTRUCTION COST DATA

Chapter 7

USING MEANS BUILDING CONSTRUCTION COST DATA

Users of *Means Building Construction Cost Data* are chiefly interested in obtaining quick, reasonable, average prices for building construction items. This is the primary purpose of the annual book — to eliminate guesswork when pricing unknowns. Many people use the cost data, whether for bids or verification of quotations or budgets, without being fully aware of how the prices are obtained and derived. Without this knowledge, this vast resource is not being used to its fullest advantage. In addition to the basic cost data, the book also contains a wealth of information to aid the estimator, the contractor, the designer and the owner to better plan and manage building construction projects. Productivity data is provided in order to assist with scheduling. National labor rates are analyzed. Tables and charts for location and time adjustments are included and help the estimator to tailor the prices to a specific location. And ultimately, the book is a list of line items for over 20,000 individual components of construction. This information, outlined in the CSI MasterFormat divisions, provides an invaluable checklist to the construction professional to assure that all required items are included in a project.

Format & Data

The major portion of *Means Building Construction Cost Data* is the Unit Price section. This is the primary source of unit cost data and is organized according to the 16 divisions of the MasterFormat. This index was developed by representatives of all parties concerned with the building construction industry and has been adopted by the American Institute of Architects (AIA), the Associated General Contractors of America, Inc. (AGC) and the Construction Specifications Institute, Inc. (CSI).

The MasterFormat Divisions:

Division 1 — General Requirements

Division 2 — Site Work

Division 3 — Concrete

Division 4 — Masonry

Division 5 — Metals

Division 6 — Wood and Plastics

Division 7 — Thermal and Moisture Protection

Division 8 — Doors and Windows

Division 9 — Finishes

Division 10 — Specialties

Division 11 — Equipment

Division 12 — Furnishings

Division 13 — Special Construction

Division 14 — Conveying Systems

Division 15 — Mechanical

Division 16 — Electrical

In addition to the sixteen MasterFormat divisions of the Unit Price section, Division 17, Square Foot and Cubic Foot Costs, presents consolidated data from over ten thousand actual reported construction projects and provides information based on total project costs as well as costs for major components. Following Division 17 is the Reference Section, which provides supporting cost, design and reference information for the Unit Price section. Individual materials and construction methods are presented in depth and detail in this section. Also included in this section are Change Orders, Crew Tables, City Cost Index, Abbreviations, and finally, the book index.

The prices as presented in *Means Building Construction Cost Data* are national averages. Material and equipment costs are developed through annual contact with manufacturers, dealers, distributors and contractors throughout the United States. Means' staff of engineers is constantly updating prices and keeping abreast of changes and fluctuations within the industry. Labor rates are the national average of each trade as determined from union agreements from thirty major U.S. cities. Throughout the calendar year, as new wage agreements are negotiated, labor costs should be factored accordingly.

There are various factors and assumptions on which the costs, as presented in *Means Building Construction Cost Data*, have been based:

Quality — The costs are based on methods, materials and workmanship in accordance with U.S. Government standards and represent good, sound construction practice.

Overtime — The costs as presented include *no* allowance for overtime. If overtime or premium time is anticipated, labor costs must be factored accordingly.

Productivity — The daily output figures are based on an eight hour workday, during daylight hours. The chart in Figure 6.8 shows that as the number of hours worked per day (over eight) increases, and as the days per week (over five) increase, production efficiency decreases (See Chapter 6).

Size of Project — Costs in *Means Building Construction Cost Data* are based on commercial and industrial buildings which cost $500,000 and up. Large residential projects are also included.

Local Factors — Weather conditions, season of the year, local union restrictions, and unusual building code requirements can all have a significant impact on construction costs. The availability of a skilled labor force, sufficient materials and even adequate energy and utilities will also affect costs.

These factors vary in impact and are not dependent upon location. They must be reviewed for each project in every area.

In the presentation of prices in *Means Building Construction Cost Data*, certain rounding rules are employed to make the numbers easy to use without significantly affecting accuracy. The rules are used consistently and are as follows:

Prices From...	Rounded to the nearest...
$.01 to $5.00	$.01
$5.01 to $20.00	$.05
$20.01 to $100.00	$.50
$100.01 to $300.00	$1.00
$300.01 to $1,000.00	$5.00
$1,000.01 to $10,000.00	$25.00
$10,000.01 to $50,000.00	$100.00
$50,000.01 and above	$500.00

Unit Price Section

The Unit Price section of *Means Building Construction Cost Data* contains a great deal of information in addition to the unit cost for each construction component. Figure 7.1 is a typical page, showing costs for brick veneer. Note that prices are included for more than ten types of brick and ten bonding patterns and course types. In addition, each type and bond is priced per thousand brick as well as per square foot of wall area. The information and cost data is broken down and itemized in this way to provide not only for the most detailed pricing possible, but also to accommodate different methods of quantity takeoff and estimating.

Within each individual line item, there is a description of the construction component, information regarding typical crews designated to perform the work, and the daily output of each crew. Costs are presented bare, or unburdened, as well as with markups for overhead and profit. Figure 7.2 is a graphic representation of how to use the Unit Price section as presented in *Means Building Construction Cost Data*.

Line Numbers

Every construction item in the Means unit price cost data books has a unique line number. This line number acts as an address so that each item can be quickly located and/or referenced. The numbering system is based on the MasterFormat classification by division. In Figure 7.2, note the bold number in reverse type, 031. This number represents the MEANS subdivision, in this case, Formwork, of the MasterFormat Division 3 — Concrete. All 16 MasterFormat divisions are organized in this manner. Within each subdivision, the data is broken down into major classifications. These major classifications are listed alphabetically and are designated by bold type for both numbers and descriptions. Each item, or line, is further defined by an individual number. As shown in Figure 7.2, the full line number for each item consists of: MasterFormat Division — MEANS subdivision — a major classification number — an item line number. Each full line number describes a unique construction

042 | Unit Masonry

042 550 | Masonry Veneer

			DAILY OUTPUT	MAN-HOURS	UNIT	1993 BARE COSTS				TOTAL INCL O&P	
			CREW			MAT.	LABOR	EQUIP.	TOTAL		
554	0010	**BRICK VENEER** Scaffolding not included, truck load lots									554
	0015	MATERIAL COSTS INCLUDE A 3% BRICK WASTE ALLOWANCE									
	0020	4" thk., sel. common, 8" x 2-2/3" x 4" @ $265 per M (6.75/S.F.)	D-8	1.50	26.667	M	300	585		885	1,225
	0050	Standard 8" x 2-2/3" x 4", running bond, red face, $295 per M		1.50	26.667		335	585		920	1,275
	0100	Full header every 6th course (7.88/S.F.) R042 -120		1.45	27.586		335	605		940	1,300
	0150	English, full header every 2nd course (10.13/S.F.)		1.40	28.571		335	630		965	1,325
	0200	Flemish, alternate header every course (9.00/S.F.) R042 -180		1.40	28.571		335	630		965	1,325
	0250	Flemish, alt. header every 6th course (7.13/S.F.)		1.45	27.586		335	605		940	1,300
	0300	Full headers throughout (13.50/S.F.) R042 -500		1.40	28.571		335	630		965	1,325
	0350	Rowlock course (13.50/S.F.)		1.35	29.630		335	650		985	1,375
	0400	Rowlock stretcher (4.50/S.F.) R042 -550		1.40	28.571		335	630		965	1,325
	0450	Soldier course (6.75/S.F.)		1.40	28.571		335	630		965	1,325
	0500	Sailor course (4.50/S.F.)		1.30	30.769		335	675		1,010	1,425
	0601	Running bond, buff or gray face, (6.75/S.F.) $375 per M		1.50	26.667		415	585		1,000	1,350
	0700	Glazed face, 8" x 2-2/3" x 4" @ $1030 per M, running bond		1.40	28.571		1,100	630		1,730	2,175
	0750	Full header every 6th course (7.88/S.F.)		1.35	29.630		1,100	650		1,750	2,200
	1000	Jumbo, 12" x 4" x 6" $1010/M (3.00/S.F.)		1.30	30.769		1,150	675		1,825	2,300
	1051	Norman, 12" x 2-2/3" x 4" $570/M (4.50/S.F.)		1.45	27.586		625	605		1,230	1,625
	1100	Norwegian, 12" x 3-1/5" x 4" at $640 per M (3.75/S.F.)		1.40	28.571		700	630		1,330	1,750
	1150	Economy, 8" x 4" x 4" at $520 per M (4.50 per S.F.)		1.40	28.571		565	630		1,195	1,600
	1201	Engineer, 8" x 3-1/5" x 4", $410/M (5.63/S.F.)		1.45	27.586		450	605		1,055	1,425
	1251	Roman, 12" x 2" x 4", $590/M (6.00/S.F.)		1.50	26.667		645	585		1,230	1,625
	1300	S.C.R. 12" x 2-2/3" x 6" $795/M (4.50/S.F.)		1.40	28.571		880	630		1,510	1,950
	1350	Utility, 12" x 4" x 4" $850/M (3.00/S.F.)		1.35	29.630		920	650		1,570	2,000
	1360	For less than truck load lots, add					10				
	1400	For battered walls, add						30%			
	1450	For corbels, add						60%			
	1500	For curved walls, add						30%			
	1550	For pits and trenches, deduct						20%			
	1999	Alternate method of figuring by square foot									
	2000	Standard, sel. common, 8" x 2-2/3" x 4", $265 per M (6.75/S.F.)	D-8	230	.174	S.F.	2.04	3.82		5.86	8.15
	2020	Stnd, 8" x 2-2/3" x 4", running bond, red, (6.75/S.F.), $295/M		220	.182		2.24	3.99		6.23	8.65
	2050	Full header every 6th course (7.88/S.F.)		185	.216		2.62	4.75		7.37	10.25
	2100	English, full header every 2nd course (10.13/S.F.)		140	.286		3.37	6.30		9.67	13.40
	2150	Flemish, alternate header every course (9.00/S.F.)		150	.267		2.99	5.85		8.84	12.35
	2200	Flemish, alt. header every 6th course (7.13/S.F.)		205	.195		2.37	4.29		6.66	9.25
	2250	Full headers throughout (13.50/S.F.)		105	.381		4.49	8.35		12.84	17.90
	2300	Rowlock course (13.50/S.F.)		100	.400		4.49	8.80		13.29	18.55
	2350	Rowlock stretcher (4.50/S.F.)		310	.129		1.50	2.83		4.33	6.05
	2400	Soldier course (6.75/S.F.)		200	.200		2.24	4.39		6.63	9.25
	2450	Sailor course (4.50/S.F.)		290	.138		1.50	3.03		4.53	6.35
	2600	Running bond, buff or gray face at $375 per M (6.75/S.F.)		220	.182		2.80	3.99		6.79	9.30
	2700	Glazed face, brick at $1030 per M, running bond		210	.190		7.35	4.18		11.53	14.55
	2750	Full header every 6th course (7.88/S.F.)		170	.235		8.60	5.15		13.75	17.45
	3000	Jumbo, 12" x 4" x 6" running bond @ $1010 per M (3.00/S.F.)		435	.092		3.41	2.02		5.43	6.85
	3050	Norman, 12" x 2-2/3" x 4" running bond, $570/M (4.50/S.F.)		320	.125		2.82	2.75		5.57	7.35
	3100	Norwegian, 12" x 3-1/5" x 4" at $640 per M (3.75/S.F.)		375	.107		2.62	2.34		4.96	6.50
	3150	Economy, 8" x 4" x 4" at $520 per M (4.50/S.F.)		310	.129		2.55	2.83		5.38	7.20
	3200	Engineer, 8" x 3-1/5" x 4" at $410 per M (5.63/S.F.)		260	.154		2.54	3.38		5.92	8.05
	3250	Roman, 12" x 2" x 4" at $590 per M (6.00/S.F.)		250	.160		3.87	3.52		7.39	9.70
	3300	SCR, 12" x 2-2/3" x 6" at $795 per M (4.50/S.F.)		310	.129		3.96	2.83		6.79	8.75
	3350	Utility, 12" x 4" x 4" at $850 per M (3.00/S.F.)		450	.089		2.76	1.95		4.71	6.05
	3400	For cavity wall construction, add						15%			
	3450	For stacked bond, add						10%			
	3500	For interior veneer construction, add						15%			
	3550	For curved walls, add						30%			

Figure 7.1

element. For example, in Figure 7.1, the line number for Norman brick veneer, running bond (per square foot) is 042-554-3050.

Line Description

Each line has a text description of the item for which costs are listed. The description may be self-contained and all inclusive. If indented items are delineations (by size, color, material, etc.) or breakdowns of previously described items. An index is provided in the back of *Means Building Construction Cost Data* to aid in locating particular items.

Crew

For each construction element, (each line item), a minimum typical crew is designated as appropriate to perform the work. The crew may include one or more trades, foremen, craftsmen and helpers, and any equipment required for proper installation of the described item. If an individual trade installs the item using only hand tools, the smallest efficient number of tradesmen will be indicated (1 Carp, 2 Carp, etc.). Abbreviations for trades are shown in Figure 7.3. If more than one trade is required to install the item and/or if powered equipment is needed, a crew number will be designated (B-5, D-3, etc.) A complete listing of crews is presented following the Reference Section in the back of *Means Building Construction Cost Data* (see Figure 7.4). Each crew breakdown contains the following components:

1. Number and type of workers designated.
2. Number, size, and type of any equipment required.
3. Hourly labor costs listed two ways: bare (base rate including fringe benefits) and including installing contractor's overhead and profit (billing rate). See Figure 7.3.
4. Daily equipment costs, based on the weekly equipment rental cost divided by 5, plus the hourly operating cost, times 8 hours. This cost is listed two ways: as a bare cost and with a 10% markup to cover handling and management costs.
5. Labor and equipment are broken down further: cost per man-hour for labor, and cost per man-hour for the equipment.
6. The total daily labor man-hours for the crew.
7. The total bare costs per day for the crew, including equipment.
8. The total daily cost of the crew including the installing contractor's overhead and profit.

The total daily cost of the craftsmen involved or the total daily crew indicated is used to calculate the unit installation cost for each item (for both bare costs and cost including overhead and profit).

The crew designation does not mean that this is the only crew that can perform the work. Crew size and content have been developed and chosen based on practical experience and feedback from contractors and represent a labor and equipment makeup commonly found in the industry. The most appropriate crew for a given task is best determined based on particular project requirements. Unit costs may vary if crew sizes or content are significantly changed.

Figure 7.5 is a page from Division 016 of *Means Building Construction Cost Data*. This type of page lists the equipment costs used in the presentation and calculation of the crew costs and unit price data. Rental costs are shown as daily, weekly, and monthly rates. The Hourly Operating Cost represents the cost of fuel, lubrication and routine maintenance. The column on the right in

031 | Concrete Formwork

031 100 | Struct C.I.P. Formwork

				CREW	DAILY OUTPUT	MAN-HOURS	UNIT	1993 BARE COSTS				TOTAL INCL O&P	
								MAT.	LABOR	EQUIP.	TOTAL		
158	5000	Spread footings, 1 use	R031 -050	C-1	305	.105	SFCA	1.07	2.32	.08	3.47	4.92	158
	5050	2 use			371	.086		.62	1.91	.07	2.60	3.75	
	5100	3 use			401	.080		.47	1.77	.06	2.30	3.36	
	5150	4 use			414	.077		.39	1.71	.06	2.16	3.19	

Description

Crew C1 will install 305 SFCA of spread footing forms per 8 hour day.

Line Numbers (031 158 5000)

Each unit price line item has been assigned a unique 10-digit code based on the 5-digit CSI MASTERFORMAT classification.

MASTERFORMAT Mediumscope
MASTERFORMAT Division

031 100
031 158 5000

Means Subdivision
Means Major Classification
Means Individual Line Number

Crew No.	Bare Costs		Incl. Subs O & P		Cost Per Man-Hour	
Crew C-1	Hr.	Daily	Hr.	Daily	Bare Costs	Incl. O&P
3 Carpenters	$23.35	$560.40	$36.65	$879.60	$22.15	$34.76
1 Building Laborer	18.55	148.40	29.10	232.80		
3 Power Tools		24.60		27.05	.77	.85
32 M.H., Daily Totals		$733.40		$1139.45	$22.92	$35.61

Productivity: Daily Output (305)/ Man-Hours (.105)

The "Daily Output" represents the typical number of units the designated crew will install in a normal 8-hour day. To find out the number of days the given crew would require to complete the installation, divide your quantity by the daily output. For example:

Quantity	÷	Daily Output	=	Duration
1000 SFCA	÷	305 SFCA/ Crew Day	=	3.28 Crew Days

The "Man-Hours" figure represents the number of man-hours required to install one unit of work. To find out the number of man-hours required for your particular task, multiply the quantity of the item times the number of man-hours shown. For example:

Quantity	x	Productivity Rate	=	Duration
1000 SFCA	x	.105 Man-Hours/ SFCA	=	105 Man-Hours

Bare Costs:

Mat. (Bare Material Cost) (1.07)

This figure for the unit material cost for the line item is the "bare" material cost with no overhead and profit allowances included. *Costs shown reflect national average material prices for January of the current year and include delivery to the job site. No sales taxes are included.*

Labor (2.32)

The unit labor cost is derived by multiplying bare man-hour costs for Crew C-1 by man-hour units. In this case, the bare man-hour cost is found in the Crew Section under C-1. (If a trade is listed, the hourly labor cost—the wage rate—is found on the inside back cover.)

Man-Hour Cost Crew C-1	x	Man-Hour Units	=	Labor
$22.15	x	.105	=	$2.32

Equip. (Equipment) (.08)

Equipment costs for each crew are listed in the description of each crew. The unit equipment cost is derived by multiplying the bare equipment hourly cost by the man-hour units.

Equipment Cost Crew C-1	x	Man-Hour Units	=	Equip.
$0.77	x	.105	=	$0.08

Total (3.47)

The total of the bare costs is the arithmetic total of the three previous columns: mat., labor, and equip.

Material	+	Labor	+	Equip.	=	Total
$1.07	+	$2.32	+	$.08	=	$3.47

Total Costs Including O&P

The figure in this column is the sum of three components: the bare material cost plus 10%; the bare labor cost plus overhead and profit (per the labor rate table on the inside back cover or, if a crew is listed, from the crew listings); and the bare equipment cost plus 10%.

Material is Bare Material cost + 10% = $1.07 + $0.11	=	$1.18
Labor for Crew C-1 = Man-Hour Cost ($34.76) x Man-Hour Units (.105)	=	$3.65
Equip. is Bare Equip. Cost + 10% = $0.08 + $0.01	=	$0.09
Total	=	$4.92

Figure 7.2

Abbr.	Trade	Base Rate Incl. Fringes		Workers' Comp. Ins.	Average Fixed Over-head	Over-head	Profit	Total Overhead & Profit		Rate with O & P	
		A		**B**	**C**	**D**	**E**	**F**	**G**	**H**	**I**
		Hourly	Daily	Ins.		head		%	Amount	Hourly	Daily
Skwk	Skilled Workers Average (35 trades)	$24.10	$192.80	17.6%	16.8%	13.0%	10.0%	57.4%	$13.85	$37.95	$303.60
	Helpers Average (5 trades)	18.10	144.80	18.8		11.0		56.6	10.25	28.35	226.80
	Foreman Average, Inside ($.50 over trade)	24.60	196.80	17.6		13.0		57.4	14.10	38.70	309.60
	Foreman Average, Outside ($2.00 over trade)	26.10	208.80	17.6		13.0		57.4	15.00	41.10	328.80
Clab	Common Building Laborers	18.55	148.40	19.2		11.0		57.0	10.55	29.10	232.80
Asbe	Asbestos Workers	26.15	209.20	16.7		16.0		59.5	15.55	41.70	333.60
Boil	Boilermakers	26.80	214.40	10.5		16.0		53.3	14.30	41.10	328.80
Bric	Bricklayers	24.05	192.40	16.8		11.0		54.6	13.15	37.20	297.60
Brhe	Bricklayer Helpers	18.85	150.80	16.8		11.0		54.6	10.30	29.15	233.20
Carp	Carpenters	23.35	186.80	19.2		11.0		57.0	13.30	36.65	293.20
Cefi	Cement Finishers	23.05	184.40	11.4		11.0		49.2	11.35	34.40	275.20
Elec	Electricians	26.70	213.60	7.3		16.0		50.1	13.40	40.10	320.80
Elev	Elevator Constructors	27.25	218.00	8.1		16.0		50.9	13.85	41.10	328.80
Eqhv	Equipment Operators, Crane or Shovel	24.95	199.60	11.7		14.0		52.5	13.10	38.05	304.40
Eqmd	Equipment Operators, Medium Equipment	24.10	192.80	11.7		14.0		52.5	12.65	36.75	294.00
Eqlt	Equipment Operators, Light Equipment	23.10	184.80	11.7		14.0		52.5	12.15	35.25	282.00
Eqol	Equipment Operators, Oilers	20.25	162.00	11.7		14.0		52.5	10.65	30.90	247.20
Eqmm	Equipment Operators, Master Mechanics	25.55	204.40	11.7		14.0		52.5	13.40	38.95	311.60
Glaz	Glaziers	23.50	188.00	13.9		11.0		51.7	12.15	35.65	285.20
Lath	Lathers	23.20	185.60	12.6		11.0		50.4	11.70	34.90	279.20
Marb	Marble Setters	24.15	193.20	16.8		11.0		54.6	13.20	37.35	298.80
Mill	Millwrights	24.35	194.80	11.6		11.0		49.4	12.05	36.40	291.20
Mstz	Mosaic and Terrazzo Workers	23.70	189.60	9.9		11.0		47.7	11.30	35.00	280.00
Pord	Painters, Ordinary	21.75	174.00	15.0		11.0		52.8	11.50	33.25	266.00
Psst	Painters, Structural Steel	22.55	180.40	52.0		11.0		89.8	20.25	42.80	342.40
Pape	Paper Hangers	21.95	175.60	15.0		11.0		52.8	11.60	33.55	268.40
Pile	Pile Drivers	23.50	188.00	29.5		16.0		72.3	17.00	40.50	324.00
Plas	Plasterers	22.80	182.40	15.6		11.0		53.4	12.20	35.00	280.00
Plah	Plasterer Helpers	19.05	152.40	15.6		11.0		53.4	10.15	29.20	233.60
Plum	Plumbers	27.40	219.20	8.7		16.0		51.5	14.10	41.50	332.00
Rodm	Rodmen (Reinforcing)	25.85	206.80	34.4		14.0		75.2	19.45	45.30	362.40
Rofc	Roofers, Composition	21.25	170.00	32.6		11.0		70.4	14.95	36.20	289.60
Rots	Roofers, Tile and Slate	21.30	170.40	32.6		11.0		70.4	15.00	36.30	290.40
Rohe	Roofer Helpers (Composition)	15.25	122.00	32.6		11.0		70.4	10.75	26.00	208.00
Shee	Sheet Metal Workers	26.65	213.20	12.4		16.0		55.2	14.70	41.35	330.80
Spri	Sprinkler Installers	29.00	232.00	9.4		16.0		52.2	15.15	44.15	353.20
Stpi	Steamfitters or Pipefitters	27.45	219.60	8.7		16.0		51.5	14.15	41.60	332.80
Ston	Stone Masons	24.15	193.20	16.8		11.0		54.6	13.20	37.35	298.80
Sswk	Structural Steel Workers	26.00	208.00	40.1		14.0		80.9	21.05	47.05	376.40
Tilf	Tile Layers (Floor)	23.50	188.00	9.9		11.0		47.7	11.20	34.70	277.60
Tilh	Tile Layer Helpers	18.70	149.60	9.9		11.0		47.7	8.90	27.60	220.80
Trlt	Truck Drivers, Light	19.15	153.20	15.2		11.0		53.0	10.15	29.30	234.40
Trhv	Truck Drivers, Heavy	19.45	155.60	15.2		11.0		53.0	10.30	29.75	238.00
Sswl	Welders, Structural Steel	26.00	208.00	40.1		14.0		80.9	21.05	47.05	376.40
Wrck	*Wrecking	18.55	148.40	40.6	▼	11.0	▼	78.4	14.55	33.10	264.80

*Not included in Averages.

Figure 7.3

CREWS

Crew No.	Bare Costs Hr.	Bare Costs Daily	Incl. Subs O & P Hr.	Incl. Subs O & P Daily	Cost Per Man-Hour Bare Costs	Cost Per Man-Hour Incl. O&P
Crew B-25	Hr.	Daily	Hr.	Daily	Bare Costs	Incl. O&P
1 Labor Foreman	$20.55	$164.40	$32.25	$258.00	$20.25	$31.47
7 Laborers	18.55	1038.80	29.10	1629.60		
3 Equip. Oper. (med.)	24.10	578.40	36.75	882.00		
1 Asphalt Paver, 130 H.P		1145.00		1259.50		
1 Tandem Roller, 10 Ton		223.80		246.20		
1 Roller, Pneumatic Wheel		231.40		254.55	18.18	20.00
88 M.H., Daily Totals		$3381.80		$4529.85	$38.43	$51.47

Crew No.	Hr.	Daily	Hr.	Daily	Bare Costs	Incl. O&P
Crew B-25B	Hr.	Daily	Hr.	Daily	Bare Costs	Incl. O&P
1 Labor Foreman	$20.55	$164.40	$32.25	$258.00	$20.57	$31.91
7 Laborers	18.55	1038.80	29.10	1629.60		
4 Equip. Oper. (medium)	24.10	771.20	36.75	1176.00		
1 Asphalt Paver, 130 H.P.		1145.00		1259.50		
2 Rollers, Steel Wheel		447.60		492.35		
1 Roller, Pneumatic Wheel		231.40		254.55	19.00	20.90
96 M.H., Daily Totals		$3798.40		$5070.00	$39.57	$52.81

Crew No.	Hr.	Daily	Hr.	Daily	Bare Costs	Incl. O&P
Crew B-26	Hr.	Daily	Hr.	Daily	Bare Costs	Incl. O&P
1 Labor Foreman (outside)	$20.55	$164.40	$32.25	$258.00	$20.81	$32.73
6 Building Laborers	18.55	890.40	29.10	1396.80		
2 Equip. Oper. (med.)	24.10	385.60	36.75	588.00		
1 Rodman (reinf.)	25.85	206.80	45.30	362.40		
1 Cement Finisher	23.05	184.40	34.40	275.20		
1 Grader, 30,000 Lbs.		557.40		613.15		
1 Paving Mach. & Equip.		1238.00		1361.80	20.40	22.44
88 M.H., Daily Totals		$3627.00		$4855.35	$41.21	$55.17

Crew No.	Hr.	Daily	Hr.	Daily	Bare Costs	Incl. O&P
Crew B-27	Hr.	Daily	Hr.	Daily	Bare Costs	Incl. O&P
1 Labor Foreman (outside)	$20.55	$164.40	$32.25	$258.00	$19.05	$29.89
3 Building Laborers	18.55	445.20	29.10	698.40		
1 Berm Machine		62.00		68.20	1.94	2.13
32 M.H., Daily Totals		$671.60		$1024.60	$20.99	$32.02

Crew No.	Hr.	Daily	Hr.	Daily	Bare Costs	Incl. O&P
Crew B-28	Hr.	Daily	Hr.	Daily	Bare Costs	Incl. O&P
2 Carpenters	$23.35	$373.60	$36.65	$586.40	$21.75	$34.13
1 Building Laborer	18.55	148.40	29.10	232.80		
24 M.H., Daily Totals		$522.00		$819.20	$21.75	$34.13

Crew No.	Hr.	Daily	Hr.	Daily	Bare Costs	Incl. O&P
Crew B-29	Hr.	Daily	Hr.	Daily	Bare Costs	Incl. O&P
1 Labor Foreman (outside)	$20.55	$164.40	$32.25	$258.00	$19.99	$31.09
4 Building Laborers	18.55	593.60	29.10	931.20		
1 Equip. Oper. (crane)	24.95	199.60	38.05	304.40		
1 Equip. Oper. Oiler	20.25	162.00	30.90	247.20		
1 Gradall, 3 Ton, 1/2 C.Y.		587.60		646.35	10.49	11.54
56 M.H., Daily Totals		$1707.20		$2387.15	$30.48	$42.63

Crew No.	Hr.	Daily	Hr.	Daily	Bare Costs	Incl. O&P
Crew B-30	Hr.	Daily	Hr.	Daily	Bare Costs	Incl. O&P
1 Equip. Oper. (med.)	$24.10	$192.80	$36.75	$294.00	$21.00	$32.08
2 Truck Drivers (heavy)	19.45	311.20	29.75	476.00		
1 Hyd. Excavator, 1.5 C.Y.		724.60		797.05		
2 Dump Trucks, 16 Ton		775.60		853.15	62.51	68.76
24 M.H., Daily Totals		$2004.20		$2420.20	$83.51	$100.84

Crew No.	Hr.	Daily	Hr.	Daily	Bare Costs	Incl. O&P
Crew B-32	Hr.	Daily	Hr.	Daily	Bare Costs	Incl. O&P
1 Highway Laborer	$18.55	$148.40	$29.10	$232.80	$22.71	$34.84
3 Equip. Oper. (med.)	24.10	578.40	36.75	882.00		
1 Grader, 30,000 Lbs.		557.40		613.15		
1 Tandem Roller, 10 Ton		223.80		246.20		
1 Dozer, 200 H.P.		832.00		915.20	50.41	55.45
32 M.H., Daily Totals		$2340.00		$2889.35	$73.12	$90.29

Crew No.	Hr.	Daily	Hr.	Daily	Bare Costs	Incl. O&P
Crew B-32A	Hr.	Daily	Hr.	Daily	Bare Costs	Incl. O&P
1 Laborer	$18.55	$148.40	$29.10	$232.80	$22.25	$34.20
2 Equip. Oper. (medium)	24.10	385.60	36.75	588.00		
1 Grader, 30,000 Lbs.		557.40		613.15		
1 Roller, Vibratory, 29,000 Lbs.		366.00		402.60	38.48	42.32
24 M.H., Daily Totals		$1457.40		$1836.55	$60.73	$76.52

Crew No.	Hr.	Daily	Hr.	Daily	Bare Costs	Incl. O&P
Crew B-32B	Hr.	Daily	Hr.	Daily	Bare Costs	Incl. O&P
1 Laborer	$18.55	$148.40	$29.10	$232.80	$22.25	$34.20
2 Equip. Oper. (medium)	24.10	385.60	36.75	588.00		
1 Dozer, 200 H.P.		832.00		915.20		
1 Roller, Vibratory, 29,000 Lbs.		366.00		402.60	49.92	54.91
24 M.H., Daily Totals		$1732.00		$2138.60	$72.17	$89.11

Crew No.	Hr.	Daily	Hr.	Daily	Bare Costs	Incl. O&P
Crew B-32C	Hr.	Daily	Hr.	Daily	Bare Costs	Incl. O&P
1 Labor Foreman	$20.55	$164.40	$32.25	$258.00	$21.66	$33.45
2 Laborers	18.55	296.80	29.10	465.60		
3 Equip. Oper. (medium)	24.10	578.40	36.75	882.00		
1 Grader, 30,000 Lbs.		557.40		613.15		
1 Roller, Steel Wheel		223.80		246.20		
1 Dozer, 200 H.P.		832.00		915.20	33.61	36.97
48 M.H., Daily Totals		$2652.80		$3380.15	$55.27	$70.42

Crew No.	Hr.	Daily	Hr.	Daily	Bare Costs	Incl. O&P
Crew B-33	Hr.	Daily	Hr.	Daily	Bare Costs	Incl. O&P
1 Equip. Oper. (med.)	$24.10	$192.80	$36.75	$294.00	$22.51	$34.56
.5 Building Laborer	18.55	74.20	29.10	116.40		
.25 Equip. Oper. (med.)	24.10	48.20	36.75	73.50		
14 M.H., Daily Totals		$315.20		$483.90	$22.51	$34.56

Crew No.	Hr.	Daily	Hr.	Daily	Bare Costs	Incl. O&P
Crew B-33A	Hr.	Daily	Hr.	Daily	Bare Costs	Incl. O&P
1 Equip. Oper. (med.)	$24.10	$192.80	$36.75	$294.00	$22.51	$34.56
.5 Building Laborer	18.55	74.20	29.10	116.40		
.25 Equip. Oper. (med.)	24.10	48.20	36.75	73.50		
1 Scraper, Towed, 7 C.Y.		65.80		72.40		
1 Dozer, 300 H.P.		926.60		1019.25		
.25 Dozer, 300 H.P.		231.65		254.80	87.43	96.18
14 M.H., Daily Totals		$1539.25		$1830.35	$109.94	$130.74

Crew No.	Hr.	Daily	Hr.	Daily	Bare Costs	Incl. O&P
Crew B-33B	Hr.	Daily	Hr.	Daily	Bare Costs	Incl. O&P
1 Equip. Oper. (med.)	$24.10	$192.80	$36.75	$294.00	$22.51	$34.56
.5 Building Laborer	18.55	74.20	29.10	116.40		
.25 Equip. Oper. (med.)	24.10	48.20	36.75	73.50		
1 Scraper, Towed, 10 C.Y.		180.40		198.45		
1 Dozer, 300 H.P.		926.60		1019.25		
.25 Dozer, 300 H.P.		231.65		254.80	95.62	105.18
14 M.H., Daily Totals		$1653.85		$1956.40	$118.13	$139.74

Figure 7.4

Figure 7.5 is the Crew's Equipment Cost. These figures represent the costs as included in the bare daily crew costs and are calculated as follows:

Line number:	016-408-1910
Equipment:	Grader, self-propelled, 30,000 lb.
Rent per Week:	$2,175
Hourly Operating Cost:	$15.30

$$\frac{\text{Weekly rental}}{5 \text{ days per week}} + (\text{Hourly Oper. Cost} \times 8 \text{ hrs./day}) = \frac{\text{Crews Equipment}}{\text{Cost}}$$

$$\frac{\$2,175}{5} + (\$15.30 \times 8) = \$557.40$$

The Crew's Equipment Cost is basically the daily cost of equipment. This figure is based on rental by the week. Note how the equipment costs in the example above are used in developing the crew cost for Crew B-26 in Figure 7.4. The daily equipment costs, including overhead and profit, contain a 10% fee added to the bare costs to cover the handling and overhead associated with use of the equipment.

The daily output represents the number of units that the designated minimum crew will install in one 8 hour day. (See "Units" section.) These figures have been determined from construction experience under actual working conditions. With a designation of the appropriate crew and determination of the daily output, the unit costs for installation are easily calculated:

$$\frac{\text{Daily Crew Cost (\$/day)}}{\text{Daily Output (units/day)}} = \text{Unit Installation Cost (\$/unit)}$$

The man-hours per unit can also be easily determined using the data provided. A man-hour is the equivalent of one worker working for one hour, and is a relative indicator of productivity. To calculate man-hours per unit:

$$\frac{\text{Total Daily Crew Man-hours}}{\text{Daily Output}} = \frac{\text{Man-hours/Day}}{\text{Units/Day}} = \text{Man-hours per Unit}$$

The resulting units of productivity can be very useful as an aid for scheduling. Manpower allocations are more readily determined and time durations can be calculated based on crew size.

Unit

The unit column (see Figures 7.1 and 7.2) defines the component for which the costs have been calculated. It is this "unit" on which Unit Price Estimating is based. The units, as used, represent standard estimating and quantity takeoff procedures. However, the estimator should always check to be sure that the units taken off are the same as those priced. Note in Figure 7.1 that the same items are priced based on two very different units — per thousand brick and per square foot. A list of standard abbreviations is included at the back of Means Building Construction Cost Data.

Bare Costs

The four columns listed under "Bare Costs" — "Material," "Labor," "Equip.," and "Total" represent the actual cost of construction items to the contractor. In other words, bare costs are those which *do not* include the overhead and profit of the installing contractor, whether a subcontractor or a general contracting company using its own crews.

016 400 | Equipment Rental

			UNIT	HOURLY OPER. COST	RENT PER DAY	RENT PER WEEK	RENT PER MONTH	CREW EQUIPMENT COST	
408	0010	**EARTHWORK EQUIPMENT RENTAL** Without operators	R016 -410						408
	0040	Aggregate spreader, push type 8' to 12' wide	Ea.	1	90	270	810	62	
	0050	Augers for truck or trailer mounting, vertical drilling	R022						
	0060	4" to 36" diam., 54 H.P., gas, 10' spindle travel	-220 Ea.	13.95	510	1,530	4,600	417.60	
	0070	14' spindle travel	R022	15.15	565	1,700	5,100	461.20	
	0075	Auger, truck mounted, vertical drilling, to 25' depth	-240	41.90	2,050	6,170	18,500	1,569	
	0080	Auger, horizontal boring machine, 12" to 36" diameter, 45 H.P.	R022	6.40	298	895	2,675	230.20	
	0090	12" to 48" diameter, 65 H.P.	-250	11.15	595	1,785	5,350	446.20	
	0100	Backhoe, diesel hydraulic, crawler mounted, 1/2 C.Y. cap.	R023	9.90	435	1,300	3,900	339.20	
	0120	5/8 C.Y. capacity	-620	14.05	435	1,300	3,900	372.40	
	0140	3/4 C.Y. capacity		15.45	550	1,650	4,950	453.60	
	0150	1 C.Y. capacity		20	690	2,075	6,225	575	
	0200	1-1/2 C.Y. capacity		23.70	890	2,675	8,025	724.60	
	0300	2 C.Y. capacity		39.85	1,075	3,250	9,750	968.80	
	0320	2-1/2 C.Y. capacity		54	2,175	6,500	19,500	1,732	
	0340	3-1/2 C.Y. capacity		71.50	2,650	7,925	23,800	2,157	
	0350	Gradall type, truck mounted, 3 ton @ 15' radius, 5/8 C.Y.		23.70	665	1,990	5,975	587.60	
	0370	1 C.Y. capacity		26.15	1,000	3,010	9,025	811.20	
	0400	Backhoe-loader, wheel type, 40 to 45 H.P., 5/8 C.Y. capacity	Ea.	6.55	198	595	1,775	171.40	
	0450	45 H.P. to 60 H.P., 3/4 C.Y. capacity		7.70	232	695	2,075	200.60	
	0460	80 H.P., 1-1/4 C.Y. capacity		11.55	315	950	2,850	282.40	
	0470	112 H.P.,1-3/4 C.Y. loader, 1/2 C.Y. backhoe		13.95	340	1,020	3,050	315.60	
	0500	Brush chipper, gas engine, 6" cutter head, 35 H.P.		3.65	107	320	960	93.20	
	0550	12" cutter head, 130 H.P.		11.45	162	485	1,450	188.60	
	0600	15" cutter head, 165 H.P.		14.20	168	505	1,525	214.60	
	0750	Bucket, clamshell, general purpose, 3/8 C.Y.		.73	55	165	495	38.85	
	0800	1/2 C.Y.		.90	65	195	585	46.20	
	0850	3/4 C.Y.		.98	73.50	220	660	51.85	
	0900	1 C.Y.		1.25	86.50	260	780	62	
	0950	1-1/2 C.Y.		1.50	117	350	1,050	82	
	1000	2 C.Y.		1.70	130	390	1,175	91.60	
	1010	Bucket, dragline, medium duty, 1/2 C.Y.		.26	30.50	92	276	20.50	
	1020	3/4 C.Y.		.50	45	135	405	31	
	1030	1 C.Y.		.52	49.50	148	445	33.75	
	1040	1-1/2 C.Y.		.70	63.50	190	570	43.60	
	1050	2 C.Y.		.77	81.50	245	735	55.15	
	1070	3 C.Y.		1.35	112	335	1,000	77.80	
	1200	Compactor, roller, 2 drum, 2000 lb., operator walking		1.65	110	330	990	79.20	
	1250	Rammer compactor, gas, 1000 lb. blow		.36	35.50	107	320	24.30	
	1300	Vibratory plate, gas, 13" plate, 1000 lb. blow		.46	28.50	86	258	20.90	
	1350	24" plate, 5000 lb. blow		1.65	53.50	160	480	45.20	
	1750	Extractor, piling, see lines 2500 to 2750							
	1860	Grader, self-propelled, 25,000 lb.	Ea.	13.30	545	1,630	4,900	432.40	
	1910	30,000 lb.		15.30	725	2,175	6,525	557.40	
	1920	40,000 lb.		16.50	700	2,100	6,300	552	
	1930	55,000 lb.		32	1,250	3,775	11,300	1,011	
	1950	Hammer, pavement demo., hyd., gas, self-prop., 1000 to 1250 lb.		16.20	375	1,120	3,350	353.60	
	2000	Diesel 1300 to 1500 lb.		8.25	415	1,250	3,750	316	
	2050	Pile driving hammer, steam or air, 4150 ft.-lb. @ 225 BPM		1.65	240	720	2,150	157.20	
	2100	8750 ft.-lb. @ 145 BPM		2.95	350	1,050	3,150	233.60	
	2150	15,000 ft.-lb. @ 60 BPM		3.75	410	1,225	3,675	275	
	2200	24,450 ft.-lb. @ 111 BPM		4.25	500	1,500	4,500	334	
	2250	Leads, 15,000 ft.-lb. hammers	L.F.		1.67	5	15	1	
	2300	24,450 ft.-lb. hammers and heavier	"	.03	1.75	5.25	15.75	1.30	
	2350	Diesel type hammer , 22,400 ft.-lb.	Ea.	5.25	400	1,200	3,600	282	
	2400	41,300 ft.-lb.		8.75	645	1,940	5,825	458	
	2450	141,000 ft.-lb.		17.20	1,250	3,750	11,300	887.60	
	2500	Vib. elec. hammer/extractor, 200 KW diesel generator, 34 H.P.		8	560	1,685	5,050	401	

Figure 7.5

Material: Material costs are based on the national average contractor purchase price delivered to the job site. Delivered costs are assumed to be within a 20 mile radius of metropolitan areas. No sales tax is included in the material prices because of variations from state to state.

The prices are based on large quantities that would normally be purchased for projects costing $500,000 and up. Prices for small quantities must be adjusted accordingly. If more current costs for materials are available for the appropriate location, it is recommended that adjustments be made to the unit costs to reflect any cost difference.

Labor: The unit cost for labor of an item is calculated as shown previously (see "Daily Output"). The daily labor cost of the designated crew is divided by the number of units that the crew will install in one day.

Equipment: The unit cost for equipment is calculated by dividing the daily bare equipment cost by the daily output.

The labor rates used to determine the bare installation costs are shown for 35 standard trades in Figure 7.3, under the column "Base Rate Including Fringes". This rate includes a worker's actual hourly wage plus employer-paid benefits (health insurance, vacation, pension, etc.). The labor rates used are *national average* union rates based on trade union agreements (as of January 1 of the current year) from 30 major cities in the United States. As new wage agreements are negotiated within a calendar year, labor costs should be adjusted.

Total Bare Costs: This column simply represents the arithmetic sum of the bare material, labor and equipment costs. This total is the average cost to the contractor for the particular item of construction, supplied and installed, or "in place". No overhead and/or profit is included.

Total Including Overhead and Profit

The prices in the "Total Including Overhead and Profit" column might also be called the "billing rate." These prices are, on the average, what the installing contractor would charge for the particular item of work. The term "installing contractor" can refer to either a subcontractor or a general contractor. In effect, this rate reflects the amount the subcontractor would charge to the general contractor or what the general contractor would charge the owner for work performed by the general contractor's own employees. The general contractor normally adds a percentage to subcontractor prices (commonly 10%) for supervision and management.

The "Total Including Overhead and Profit" costs are determined by adding the following two calculations:

1. Bare materials and equipment — increased by 10% for handling. See Figure 7.2.
2. Bare daily crew labor costs — increased to include overhead and profit, then divided by the daily output. See Figures 7.2 and 7.4.

In order to increase crew cost to include overhead and profit, labor and equipment costs are treated separately. 10% is added to the bare equipment cost for handling, management, etc. Labor costs are increased, depending upon trade by percentages for overhead and profit (as shown in Figure 7.3). The resulting rates are listed in the right hand columns of Figure 7.3. Note that the percentage increase for overhead and profit for the average skilled worker is 57.4% of the base rate. The following items are included in the increase for overhead and profit, as shown in Figure 7.3.

Workers' Compensation and Employer's Liability:

Workers' Compensation and Employer's Liability Insurance rates vary from state to state and are tied into the construction trade safety records in that particular state. Rates also vary by trade according to the hazard involved. (See Figures 7.6 and 7.7.) The proper authorities will most likely keep the contractor well informed of the rates and obligations.

State and Federal Unemployment Insurance:

The employer's tax rate is adjusted by a merit-rating system according to the number of former employees applying for benefits. Contractors who find it possible to offer a maximum of steady employment can enjoy a reduction in the unemployment tax rate.

General Requirements | R010 | Overhead and Miscellaneous Data

R010-060 Workers' Compensation Insurance Rates by Trade

The table below tabulates the national averages for Workers' Compensation insurance rates by trade and type of building. The average "Insurance Rate" is multiplied by the "% of Building Cost" for each trade. This produces the "Workers' Compensation

Cost" by % of total labor cost, to be added for each trade by building type to determine the weighted average Workers' Compensation rate for the building types analyzed.

Trade	Insurance Rate (% Labor Cost)		% of Building Cost			Workers' Compensation		
	Range	Average	Office Bldgs.	Schools & Apts.	Mfg.	Office Bldgs.	Schools & Apts.	Mfg.
Excavation, Grading, etc.	5.3% to 33.8%	11.7%	4.8%	4.9%	4.5%	.56%	.57%	.53%
Piles & Foundations	5.9 to 63.8	29.5	7.1	5.2	8.7	2.09	1.53	2.57
Concrete	5.9 to 38.6	17.9	5.0	14.8	3.7	.90	2.65	.66
Masonry	5.7 to 66.9	16.8	6.9	7.5	1.9	1.16	1.26	.32
Structural Steel	5.9 to 143.5	40.1	10.7	3.9	17.6	4.29	1.56	7.06
Miscellaneous & Ornamental Metals	4.7 to 26.0	12.9	2.8	4.0	3.6	.36	.52	.46
Carpentry & Millwork	5.9 to 53.7	19.2	3.7	4.0	0.5	.71	.77	.10
Metal or Composition Siding	5.9 to 50.1	17.1	2.3	0.3	4.3	.39	.05	.74
Roofing	5.9 to 85.9	32.6	2.3	2.6	3.1	.75	.85	1.01
Doors & Hardware	3.3 to 34.6	11.2	0.9	1.4	0.4	.10	.16	.04
Sash & Glazing	5.9 to 32.7	13.9	3.5	4.0	1.0	.49	.56	.14
Lath & Plaster	5.9 to 37.4	15.6	3.3	6.9	0.8	.51	1.08	.12
Tile, Marble & Floors	4.5 to 28.4	9.9	2.6	3.0	0.5	.26	.30	.05
Acoustical Ceilings	4.7 to 31.8	12.6	2.4	0.2	0.3	.30	.03	.04
Painting	4.8 to 45.1	15.0	1.5	1.6	1.6	.23	.24	.24
Interior Partitions	5.9 to 53.7	19.2	3.9	4.3	4.4	.75	.83	.84
Miscellaneous Items	2.9 to 130.6	18.0	5.2	3.7	9.7	.94	.67	1.75
Elevators	2.4 to 17.0	8.1	2.1	1.1	2.2	.17	.09	.18
Sprinklers	2.5 to 23.0	9.4	0.5	–	2.0	.05	–	.19
Plumbing	2.7 to 16.7	8.7	4.9	7.2	5.2	.43	.63	.45
Heat., Vent., Air Conditioning	4.8 to 32.2	12.4	13.5	11.0	12.9	1.67	1.36	1.60
Electrical	2.7 to 12.5	7.3	10.1	8.4	11.1	.74	.61	.81
Total	2.5% to 143.5%	–	100.0%	100.0%	100.0%	17.85%	16.32%	19.90%
Overall Weighted Average 18.02%								

Figure 7.6

Employer-Paid Social Security (FICA):
The tax rate is adjusted annually by the federal government. It is a percentage of an employee's salary up to a maximum annual contribution.

Builder's Risk and Public Liability:
These insurance rates vary according to the trades involved and the state in which the work is done.

Overhead: The column listed as "Sub's Overhead" provides percentages to be added for office or operating overhead. This is the cost of doing business. The percentages are presented as national averages by trade as shown in Figure 7.3. Note that the operating overhead costs are applied to *labor only* in *Means Building Construction Cost Data*. A detailed discussion of operating, or office overhead and its application is included in Chapter 4.

Profit: This percentage is the fee added by the contractor to offer both a return on investment and an allowance to cover the risk involved in the type

Workers' Compensation Insurance Rates by States

The table below lists the weighted average Workers' Compensation base rate for each state with a factor comparing this with the national average of 17.6%.

State	Weighted Average	Factor	State	Weighted Average	Factor	State	Weighted Average	Factor
Alabama	20.4%	116	Kentucky	14.4%	82	North Dakota	13.0%	74
Alaska	18.7	106	Louisiana	24.0	136	Ohio	10.6	60
Arizona	17.3	98	Maine	20.3	115	Oklahoma	15.4	88
Arkansas	12.4	70	Maryland	10.4	59	Oregon	26.6	151
California	16.4	93	Massachusetts	26.7	152	Pennsylvania	15.9	90
Colorado	23.3	132	Michigan	18.4	105	Rhode Island	16.8	95
Connecticut	24.2	138	Minnesota	32.8	186	South Carolina	8.6	49
Delaware	10.8	61	Mississippi	11.4	65	South Dakota	12.4	70
District of Columbia	21.0	119	Missouri	9.9	56	Tennessee	11.1	63
Florida	26.5	151	Montana	36.6	208	Texas	21.7	123
Georgia	14.2	81	Nebraska	11.0	63	Utah	11.4	65
Hawaii	15.5	88	Nevada	16.2	92	Vermont	11.7	66
Idaho	14.1	80	New Hampshire	19.7	112	Virginia	8.2	47
Illinois	24.7	140	New Jersey	8.2	47	Washington	12.6	72
Indiana	6.4	36	New Mexico	18.8	107	West Virginia	10.8	61
Iowa	11.9	68	New York	14.3	81	Wisconsin	13.6	77
Kansas	11.1	63	North Carolina	8.4	48	Wyoming	5.6	32
Weighted Average for U.S. is			16.0% of payroll = 100 %					

Rates in the following table are the base or manual costs per $100 of payroll for Workers' Compensation in each state. Rates are usually applied to straight time wages only and not to premium time wages and bonuses.

The weighted average skilled worker rate for 35 trades is 17.6%. For bidding purposes, apply the full value of Workers' Compensation directly to total labor costs, or if labor is 32%, materials 48% and overhead and profit 20% of total cost, carry 32/80 x 17.6% = 7.0% of cost (before overhead and profit) into overhead. Rates vary not only from state to state but also with the experience rating of the contractor.

Rates are the most current available at the time of publication.

Figure 7.7

of construction being bid. The profit percentage may vary from 4% on large, straightforward projects to as much as 25% on smaller, high-risk jobs. Profit percentages are directly affected by economic conditions, the expected number of bidders, and the estimated risk involved in the project. For estimating purposes, *Means Building Construction Cost Data* assumes 10% as a reasonable average profit factor.

Square Foot and Cubic Foot Costs

Division 17 in *Building Construction Cost Data* has been developed to facilitate the preparation of rapid preliminary budget estimates. The cost figures in this division are derived from more than 10,000 actual building projects contained in the R.S. Means data bank of construction costs and include the contractor's overhead and profit. The prices shown *do not* include architectural fees or land costs. Costs for new projects are added to the files each year, while projects over ten years old are discarded. For this reason, certain costs may not show a uniform, annual progression. In no case are all subdivisions of a project listed.

These projects were located throughout the United States and reflect differences in square foot and cubic foot costs due to differences in both labor and material costs, plus differences in the owners' requirements. For instance, a bank in a large city would have different features and costs than one in a rural area. This is true of all the different types of buildings analyzed. All individual cost items were computed and tabulated separately. Thus, the sum of the median figures for Plumbing, H.V.A.C. and Electrical will not normally add up to the total Mechanical and Electrical costs arrived at by separate analysis and tabulation of the projects.

The data and prices presented (as shown in Figure 7.8) are listed as square foot or cubic foot costs and as a percentage of total costs. Each category tabulates the data in a similar manner. The median, or middle figure, is listed. This means that 50% of all projects had lower costs, and 50% had higher costs than the median figure. Figures in the "1/4" column indicate that 25% of the projects had lower costs and 75% had higher costs.

Similarly, figures in the "3/4" column indicate that 75% had lower costs and 25% of the projects had higher costs.

The costs and figures represent all projects and do not take into account project size. As a rule, larger buildings (of the same type and relative location) will cost less to build per square foot than similar buildings of a smaller size. This cost difference is due to economies of scale as well as a lower exterior envelope-to-floor area ratio. A conversion is necessary to adjust project costs based on size relative to the norm. Figure 7.9 lists typical sizes (by square foot) and typical ranges of sizes for different building types.

Figure 7.10 is an Area Conversion Scale that can be used to adjust costs based on project size. For example, a proposed mid-rise office building is to be 34,000 square feet. From Figure 7.9, the typical size is 52,000 square feet. A size factor is calculated:

$$\frac{\text{Proposed Building Area}}{\text{Typical Building Area}} = \frac{34,000 \text{ S.F.}}{52,000 \text{ S.F.}} = 0.65$$

The size factor, applied to the Area Conversion Scale, indicates a cost multiplier of 1.06.

Cost Multiplier x Median Cost = Converted Cost

1.06 x $67.80 = $71.87

171 000 | S.F. & C.F. Costs	UNIT	UNIT COSTS			% OF TOTAL		
		1/4	MEDIAN	3/4	1/4	MEDIAN	3/4
520 0010 **JAILS**	S.F.	114	137	169				**520**
0020 Total project costs	C.F.	8.95	11.90	14.80			
1800 Equipment	S.F.	4.64	12.30	20.60	3.80%	8.90%	14.80%
2720 Plumbing		10.90	14.35	16.10	7%	9.60%	12%
2770 Heating, ventilating, air conditioning		7.80	13.60	21.35	6.40%	9.40%	15.80%
2900 Electrical		11.60	15	19	7.90%	10.50%	13.80%
3100 Total: Mechanical & Electrical	↓	28.70	39.25	54.05	25.30%	30.60%	35.70%
530 0010 **LIBRARIES**	S.F.	67.20	83.40	104				**530**
0020 Total project costs	C.F.	4.72	5.75	7.35			
0500 Masonry	S.F.	3.76	6.80	13.05	4%	6.70%	10.70%
1800 Equipment		.95	2.49	4.10	1.10%	2.80%	4.80%
2720 Plumbing		2.75	3.75	5.10	3.60%	4.50%	5.50%
2770 Heating, ventilating, air conditioning		6.40	9.70	12.60	8.40%	10.90%	13.60%
2900 Electrical		6.80	8.85	11.35	8.40%	10.90%	12.10%
3100 Total: Mechanical & Electrical	↓	14.15	19	28.35	17.40%	23.10%	28.30%
550 0010 **MEDICAL CLINICS**	S.F.	65.10	80.30	99.10				**550**
0020 Total project costs	C.F.	4.97	6.55	8.50			
1800 Equipment	S.F.	1.73	3.69	5.60	1.80%	4.80%	6.80%
2720 Plumbing		4.53	6.20	8.40	6.20%	8.40%	10%
2770 Heating, ventilating, air conditioning		5.45	6.85	10.35	6.60%	9%	11.60%
2900 Electrical		5.70	7.80	10.35	8.10%	9.90%	11.90%
3100 Total: Mechanical & Electrical	↓	14.05	18.10	25.50	19%	24.40%	29.70%
3500 See also division 117-001							
570 0010 **MEDICAL OFFICES**	S.F.	60	76.10	93.60				**570**
0020 Total project costs	C.F.	4.61	6.35	8.50			
1800 Equipment	S.F.	2.04	4.05	5.80	3%	5.80%	7.10%
2720 Plumbing	↓	3.59	5.45	7.30	5.60%	6.80%	9.10%
2770 Heating, ventilating, air conditioning	S.F.	4.15	6.35	8.10	6.30%	7.90%	9.60%
2900 Electrical		4.94	7.30	9.85	7.60%	9.70%	11.60%
3100 Total: Mechanical & Electrical	↓	11.75	16.35	21.55	17%	21.60%	26.20%
590 0010 **MOTELS**	S.F.	39.75	57.65	74.10				**590**
0020 Total project costs	C.F.	3.41	4.82	7.85			
2720 Plumbing	S.F.	3.96	4.95	6	9.40%	10.50%	12.50%
2770 Heating, ventilating, air conditioning		2.09	3.60	5.25	4.90%	5.60%	8.20%
2900 Electrical		3.66	4.65	6.05	7.10%	8.10%	10.40%
3100 Total: Mechanical & Electrical	↓	8.70	11.45	15.80	18.50%	23.10%	26.10%
5000							
9000 Per rental unit, total cost	Unit	19,900	29,900	38,700			
9500 Total: Mechanical & Electrical	"	4,025	5,700	6,150			
600 0010 **NURSING HOMES**	S.F.	59.30	80.05	95.85				**600**
0020 Total project costs	C.F.	4.91	6.40	8.40			
1800 Equipment	S.F.	1.97	2.53	3.93	2.30%	3.70%	6%
2720 Plumbing		5.35	6.55	9.60	9.30%	10.30%	13.30%
2770 Heating, ventilating, air conditioning		5.50	7.65	9.80	9.20%	11.40%	11.80%
2900 Electrical		6.10	7.55	9.95	9.70%	11%	13%
3100 Total: Mechanical & Electrical	↓	14.25	18.65	28.40	22.30%	28.30%	33.20%
3200							
9000 Per bed or person, total cost	Bed	24,200	31,100	38,600			
610 0010 **OFFICES** Low Rise (1 to 4 story)	S.F.	49.60	63.55	83.55				**610**
0020 Total project costs	C.F.	3.63	5.10	6.85			
0100 Sitework	S.F.	3.59	6.25	9.75	5.20%	9.40%	13.70%
0500 Masonry		1.67	3.95	7.45	2.90%	5.70%	8.60%

Figure 7.8

A rough budget cost for the proposed building based on national averages is $71.87 per square foot.

There are two stages of project development when square foot cost estimates are most useful. The first is during the conceptual stage when few, if any details are available. At this time, square foot costs are useful for ballpark budget purposes. As soon as details become available in the project design, the square foot approach should be discontinued and the project priced more accurately. The second is after the estimate is completed. Square foot costs can be used for verification and as a check against gross errors.

When using the figures in Division 17, it is recommended that the median cost column be consulted for preliminary figures if no additional information is available. When costs have been modified to account for project size and have been converted for location (see City Cost Indexes), the median numbers (as shown in Figure 7.8) should provide a fairly accurate base figure. This figure

Square Foot Base Size							
Building Type	Median Cost per S.F.	Typical Size Gross S.F.	Typical Range Gross S.F.	Building Type	Median Cost per S.F.	Typical Size Gross S.F.	Typical Range Gross S.F.
Apartments, Low Rise	$ 46.60	21,000	9700 - 37,200	Jails	$137.00	13,700	7,500 - 28,000
Apartments, Mid Rise	58.35	50,000	32,000 - 100,000	Libraries	83.40	12,000	7,000 - 31,000
Apartments, High Rise	67.80	310,000	100,000 - 650,000	Medical Clinics	80.30	7,200	4,200 - 15,700
Auditoriums	79.15	25,000	7,600 - 39,000	Medical Offices	76.10	6,000	4,000 - 15,000
Auto Sales	48.40	20,000	10,800 - 28,600	Motels	57.65	27,000	15,800 - 51,000
Banks	106.00	4,200	2,500 - 7,500	Nursing Homes	80.05	23,000	15,000 - 37,000
Churches	70.80	9,000	5,300 - 13,200	Offices, Low Rise	63.55	8,600	4,700 - 19,000
Clubs, Country	70.45	6,500	4,500 - 15,000	Offices, Mid Rise	67.80	52,000	31,300 - 83,100
Clubs, Social	68.50	10,000	6,000 - 13,500	Offices, High Rise	83.50	260,000	151,000 - 468,000
Clubs, YMCA	72.85	28,300	12,800 - 39,400	Police Stations	106.00	10,500	4,000 - 19,000
Colleges (Class)	94.55	50,000	23,500 - 98,500	Post Offices	80.05	12,400	6,800 - 30,000
Colleges (Science Lab)	119.00	45,600	16,600 - 80,000	Power Plants	596.00	7,500	1,000 - 20,000
College (Student Union)	102.00	33,400	16,000 - 85,000	Religious Education	59.70	9,000	6,000 - 12,000
Community Center	74.40	9,400	5,300 - 16,700	Research	108.00	19,000	6,300 - 45,000
Court Houses	99.00	32,400	17,800 - 106,000	Restaurants	94.55	4,400	2,800 - 6,000
Dept. Stores	43.05	90,000	44,000 - 122,000	Retail Stores	45.55	7,200	4,000 - 17,600
Dormitories, Low Rise	70.55	24,500	13,400 - 40,000	Schools, Elementary	68.15	41,000	24,500 - 55,000
Dormitories, Mid Rise	90.95	55,600	36,100 - 90,000	Schools, Jr. High	68.05	92,000	52,000 - 119,000
Factories	42.20	26,400	12,900 - 50,000	Schools, Sr. High	69.45	101,000	50,500 - 175,000
Fire Stations	76.35	5,800	4,000 - 8,700	Schools, Vocational	66.90	37,000	20,500 - 82,000
Fraternity Houses	67.50	12,500	8,200 - 14,800	Sports Arenas	54.15	15,000	5,000 - 40,000
Funeral Homes	67.95	7,800	4,500 - 11,000	Supermarkets	46.50	20,000	12,000 - 30,000
Garages, Commercial	51.55	9,300	5,000 - 13,600	Swimming Pools	85.90	13,000	7,800 - 22,000
Garages, Municipal	61.80	8,300	4,500 - 12,600	Telephone Exchange	127.00	4,500	1,200 - 10,600
Garages, Parking	24.25	163,000	76,400 - 225,300	Terminals, Bus	60.30	11,400	6,300 - 16,500
Gymnasiums	65.90	19,200	11,600 - 41,000	Theaters	69.40	10,500	8,800 - 17,500
Hospitals	127.00	55,000	27,200 - 125,000	Town Halls	76.10	10,800	4,800 - 23,400
House (Elderly)	65.05	37,000	21,000 - 66,000	Warehouses	30.70	25,000	8,000 - 72,000
Housing (Public)	57.45	36,000	14,400 - 74,400	Warehouse & Office	35.20	25,000	8,000 - 72,000
Ice Rinks	54.00	29,000	27,200 - 33,600				

Figure 7.9

should then be adjusted according to the estimator's experience, local economic conditions, code requirements and the owner's particular requirements. There is no need to factor the percentage figures, as these should remain relatively constant from city to city.

Building Unit Prices and Assemblies for Your Own Work

(See "Systems or Assemblies Estimates" in Chapter One.) Using the preceding information about bare costs, overhead and profit, it should be possible to start to build your own database of unit costs, based on actual takeoff quantities and subcontractor prices. Your own experience as a general contractor or subcontractor should be recorded job by job, taking note of man-hours, crew size and material costs in the most accurate manner possible. Noting the jobs' logistics, building height and quality of finishes, build up your own unit costs particular to your region and type of contracting. This data should be organized so that it is easily manipulated for material, labor and units (such as LF, SF, CY, SY, EA), and can be changed or updated.

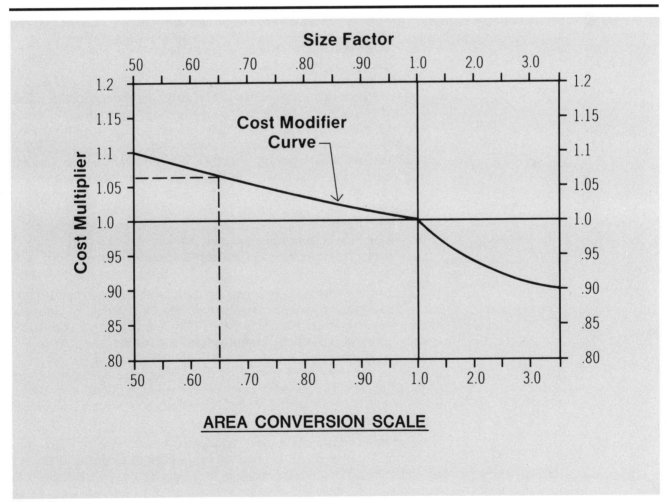

Figure 7.10

Repair & Remodeling

Cost figures in *Means Building Construction Cost Data* are based on new construction utilizing the most cost-effective combination of labor, equipment and material. The work is scheduled in the proper sequence to allow the various trades to accomplish their tasks in an efficient manner.

There are many factors unique to repair and remodeling that can affect project costs. The economy of scale associated with new construction often has no influence on the cost of repair and remodeling. Small quantities of components may have to be custom fabricated at great expense. Work schedule coordination between trades frequently becomes difficult; work area restrictions can lead to subcontractor quotations with start-up and shutdown costs in excess of the cost of the actual work involved. Some of the more prominent factors affecting repair and remodeling projects are listed below.

1. A large amount of cutting and patching may be required to match the existing construction. It is often more economical to remove entire walls rather than create many new door and window openings. This sort of trade-off has to be carefully analyzed. Matching "existing conditions" may be impossible because certain materials may no longer be manufactured, and substitutions can be expensive. Piping and ductwork runs may not be as simple as they are in the case of new construction. Wiring may have to be snaked through existing walls and floors.

2. Dust and noise protection of adjoining non-construction areas can involve a substantial number of special precautions and may alter normal construction methods.

3. The use of certain equipment may be curtailed as a result of the physical limitations of the project; workmen may be forced to use small equipment or hand tools.

4. Material handling becomes more costly due to the confines of an enclosed building. For multi-story construction, low capacity elevators and stairwells may be the only access to the upper floors.

5. Both existing and completed finish work will need to be protected in order to prevent damage during ensuing work.

6. Work may have to be done on other than normal shifts — around an existing production facility that has to stay in operation throughout the repair and remodeling. Costs for overtime work may be incurred as a result.

7. There may be an increased requirement for shoring and bracing to support the building while structural changes are being made, or to allow for the temporary storage of construction materials on above-grade floors.

These factors and their consequences, can significantly increase the costs for repair and remodeling work as compared with new construction. R.S. Means has developed a method to quantify these factors by adding percentages to the costs of work that is affected. These suggested percentages are shown in Figure 7.11 as minimums and maximums. The estimator must use sound judgment and experience when applying these factors. The effects of each of these factors should be considered in the planning, bidding, and construction phases in order to minimize the potential increased costs associated with repair and remodeling projects.

There are other considerations to be anticipated in estimating for repair and remodeling. Weather protection may be required for existing structures, and during the installation of new windows or heating systems. Pedestrian protection is often required in urban areas. On small projects and because of local conditions, it may be necessary to pay a tradesman for a minimum of four hours for a task that actually requires less time. Unit prices should be used with caution in situations when these kinds of minimum charges may be incurred.

All of the above factors can be anticipated and the basic costs developed before a repair and remodeling project begins. It is the hidden problems, the unknowns, that pose the greatest challenge to the estimator and cause the most anxiety. These problems are often discovered during demolition and may be impossible to anticipate. Projects may be delayed due to these unexpected conditions, and these delays ultimately increase construction costs. Other parts of the project, and thus their cost, are also affected. Only experience, good judgment and a thorough knowledge of the existing structure can help to reduce the number of unknowns and their potential effects.

City Cost Indexes

The unit prices in *Means Building Construction Cost Data* are national averages. When they are to be applied to a particular location, these prices must be adjusted to local conditions. R.S. Means has developed the City Cost Indexes for just that purpose. Following the crews table in the back of the *Means Building Construction Cost Data* are tables of indexes for 162 U.S. and Canadian cities based on a 30 major city average of 100. The figures are broken down into material and installation for the 16 MasterFormat divisions, as shown in Figure 7.12. Please note that for each city there is a weighted average for the material, installation and total indexes. This average is based on the relative contribution of each division to the construction process as a whole. The information in Figure 7.13 does not represent any one building type but instead, all building types as a whole. The figures may be used as a general guide to determine how much time should be spent on each portion of an estimate. When doing an estimate, more time should be spent on the divisions that have a higher percent contribution to the project. Caution should be exercised when using set percentages for projects that have unusually high or low division contributions.

In addition to adjusting costs in *Means Building Construction Cost Data* for particular locations, the City Cost Index can also be used to adjust costs from one city to another. For example, the price of a particular building type is known for City A. In order to budget the costs of the same building type in City B, the following calculation can be made:

$$\frac{\text{City B Index x City A Cost}}{\text{City A Index}} = \text{City B Cost}$$

While City Cost Indexes provide a means to adjust prices for location, the Historical Cost Index, as shown in Figure 7.14, provides a means to adjust for time. Using the same principle as above, a time adjustment factor can be calculated:

$$\frac{\text{Index for Year X}}{\text{Index for Year}} = \text{Time Adjustment Factor}$$

This time adjustment factor can be used to determine what the budget costs would be for a particular building type in Year X, based on costs for a similar building type known from Year Y. Used in conjunction, the two indexes allow for cost adjustments from one city during a given year to another city in another year (the present or otherwise). For example, an office building built in San Francisco in 1974 originally cost $1,000,000. How much will a similar building cost in Phoenix in 1993? Adjustment factors are developed as shown previously using data from Figures 7.12 and 7.14:

$$\frac{\text{Phoenix index}}{\text{San Francisco index}} \quad = \quad \frac{89.8}{124.4} \quad = \quad 0.72$$

$$\frac{\text{1993 index}}{\text{1974 index}} \quad = \quad \frac{230.1}{94.7} \quad = \quad 2.43$$

Original cost x location adjustment x time adjustment = Proposed new cost

$1,000,000   x   0.72   x   2.43   = $1,749,600

Reference Tables

Throughout the Unit Price pages of *Means Building Construction Cost Data*, certain line items contain reference numbers (see Figure 7.15) which refer the reader to expanded data and information in the back of the book. The Reference Table section contains over ninety pages of tables, charts, definitions and costs, all of which corroborate the unit price data. The development of many unit costs is explained and detailed in this section. This information can be very helpful to the estimator, particularly when more information is needed about materials and considerations that have gone into a unit price line item. Figure 7.16 is an example of the development of cost (see Figure 7.15 for the line item that references R033-100).

010 | Overhead and Miscellaneous Data

| | | 010 000 | Overhead | CREW | DAILY OUTPUT | MAN-HOURS | UNIT | 1993 BARE COSTS | | | | TOTAL INCL O&P | |
								MAT.	LABOR	EQUIP.	TOTAL		
032	0010	FACTORS To be added to construction costs for particular job	R011 -010										032
	0200												
	0500	Cut & patch to match existing construction, add, minimum					Costs	2%	3%				
	0550	Maximum						5%	9%				
	0800	Dust protection, add, minimum						1%	2%				
	0850	Maximum						4%	11%				
	1100	Equipment usage curtailment, add, minimum						1%	1%				
	1150	Maximum						3%	10%				
	1400	Material handling & storage limitation, add, minimum						1%	1%				
	1450	Maximum						6%	7%				
	1700	Protection of existing work, add, minimum						2%	2%				
	1750	Maximum						5%	7%				
	2000	Shift work requirements, add, minimum							5%				
	2050	Maximum							30%				
	2300	Temporary shoring and bracing, add, minimum						2%	5%				
	2350	Maximum						5%	12%				

Figure 7.11

CITY COST INDEXES

DIVISION		ALABAMA											ALASKA			ARIZONA		
		BIRMINGHAM			HUNTSVILLE			MOBILE			MONTGOMERY			ANCHORAGE			PHOENIX		
		MAT.	INST.	TOTAL	MAT.	INST.	TOTAL	MAT.	INST.	TOTAL	MAT.	INST.	TOTAL	MAT.	INST.	TOTAL	MAT.	INST.	TOTAL
2	SITE WORK	99.9	87.5	94.3	119.6	89.4	106.0	122.6	84.4	105.4	91.6	83.8	88.1	158.9	123.5	143.0	92.4	91.0	91.8
3.1	FORMWORK	96.8	66.3	73.3	104.0	63.6	72.8	107.0	67.9	76.9	113.2	60.7	72.7	124.7	129.0	128.0	108.9	81.6	87.9
3.2	REINFORCING	94.5	70.4	84.3	95.7	66.4	83.4	82.9	64.7	75.2	82.9	70.4	77.6	117.7	120.8	119.1	110.4	84.9	99.6
3.3	CAST IN PLACE CONC.	89.1	90.0	89.6	101.8	90.6	94.9	99.9	91.2	94.5	101.1	87.8	92.9	225.7	108.9	153.6	105.3	90.3	96.0
3	CONCRETE	91.9	78.9	83.6	100.9	77.8	86.1	97.6	79.7	86.1	99.6	75.6	84.2	180.8	117.9	140.5	107.2	86.4	93.9
4	MASONRY	81.6	68.7	71.7	88.3	59.0	65.7	93.7	71.4	76.5	86.5	48.1	56.9	149.8	126.1	131.6	93.2	75.4	79.5
5	METALS	95.6	76.7	88.7	100.0	75.2	90.9	93.4	73.8	86.3	95.7	76.6	88.8	116.2	115.7	116.0	99.0	86.2	94.3
6	WOOD & PLASTICS	92.0	67.5	78.7	107.6	63.9	83.9	91.9	70.1	80.0	101.7	64.2	81.4	117.9	125.9	122.2	99.3	81.2	89.5
7	MOISTURE PROTECTION	84.5	56.2	75.4	92.1	55.9	80.4	87.4	57.7	77.8	88.7	54.7	77.7	102.6	134.4	112.9	92.8	80.3	88.7
8	DOORS, WINDOWS, GLASS	90.6	67.8	78.8	100.8	61.6	80.5	98.7	67.6	82.6	97.6	64.5	80.5	128.6	119.3	123.8	102.8	79.2	90.5
9.2	LATH & PLASTER	95.9	65.2	72.6	91.1	63.6	70.2	91.8	74.7	78.8	108.3	64.0	74.7	120.3	129.5	127.3	93.2	82.2	84.9
9.2	DRYWALL	100.1	66.9	84.7	108.4	62.1	86.9	92.0	70.5	82.0	100.3	64.4	83.6	122.0	127.7	124.7	90.6	80.7	86.0
9.5	ACOUSTICAL WORK	97.7	66.7	80.8	100.1	63.0	80.0	93.1	69.1	80.0	93.1	63.0	76.8	123.9	126.8	125.5	103.4	80.1	90.8
9.6	FLOORING	112.0	67.3	99.9	97.5	59.2	87.1	114.1	72.3	102.8	101.2	42.5	85.3	117.3	126.0	119.6	93.2	86.1	91.3
9.9	PAINTING	104.2	63.8	72.2	110.6	62.5	72.5	121.4	72.4	82.6	119.6	71.1	81.2	123.1	132.1	130.2	96.3	75.9	80.2
9	FINISHES	102.8	65.7	83.1	105.2	62.2	82.4	99.9	71.4	84.8	102.1	65.0	82.4	121.2	129.1	125.4	92.8	79.5	85.7
10-14	TOTAL DIV. 10-14	100.0	76.5	93.0	100.0	75.7	92.8	100.0	79.0	93.8	100.0	75.1	92.6	100.0	127.8	108.2	100.0	87.5	96.3
15	MECHANICAL	96.4	64.8	80.7	99.3	65.1	82.3	97.2	67.2	82.3	98.9	62.8	80.9	107.1	115.0	111.0	98.4	85.4	91.9
16	ELECTRICAL	94.9	66.1	74.9	92.7	74.0	79.7	90.7	69.4	76.0	91.7	56.2	67.1	107.4	125.6	120.0	105.2	72.5	82.5
1-16	WEIGHTED AVERAGE	94.9	70.7	81.9	100.2	69.3	83.6	97.8	72.5	84.2	96.9	64.8	79.6	125.1	121.9	123.4	99.1	81.8	89.8

DIVISION		ARIZONA			ARKANSAS						CALIFORNIA								
		TUCSON			FORT SMITH			LITTLE ROCK			ANAHEIM			BAKERSFIELD			FRESNO		
		MAT.	INST.	TOTAL	MAT.	INST.	TOTAL	MAT.	INST.	TOTAL	MAT.	INST.	TOTAL	MAT.	INST.	TOTAL	MAT.	INST.	TOTAL
2	SITE WORK	110.2	92.9	102.5	99.9	87.7	94.4	106.9	90.2	99.4	104.5	111.7	107.7	96.8	110.5	103.0	94.5	122.1	106.9
3.1	FORMWORK	109.5	81.5	87.9	111.8	60.1	72.0	103.3	66.1	74.7	105.0	124.7	120.2	125.3	124.7	124.9	110.8	119.1	117.2
3.2	REINFORCING	95.0	84.9	90.7	124.4	70.9	101.8	117.7	54.7	91.1	99.3	124.4	109.9	96.0	124.4	108.0	106.4	124.4	114.0
3.3	CAST IN PLACE CONC.	105.5	94.9	98.9	90.4	88.6	89.3	98.4	89.0	92.6	109.3	109.0	109.1	103.1	109.1	106.8	92.8	108.5	102.5
3	CONCRETE	104.0	88.7	94.2	102.4	75.8	85.3	103.7	76.9	86.5	106.2	116.6	112.8	106.2	116.6	112.9	99.6	114.1	108.9
4	MASONRY	92.2	75.4	79.3	95.2	66.5	73.1	88.9	67.0	72.0	108.7	131.4	126.2	100.8	107.2	105.7	119.5	111.3	113.2
5	METALS	90.8	87.8	89.7	96.5	76.9	89.4	106.2	67.0	91.9	99.0	118.4	106.1	99.3	118.7	106.4	94.9	121.1	104.5
6	WOOD & PLASTICS	106.4	80.8	92.5	107.3	61.4	82.4	94.9	69.4	81.1	96.1	121.0	109.6	95.2	121.0	109.2	96.6	113.9	106.0
7	MOISTURE PROTECTION	105.5	70.4	94.2	84.9	58.6	76.4	84.4	59.8	76.5	107.7	126.5	113.8	85.0	111.5	93.5	107.4	114.2	109.6
8	DOORS, WINDOWS, GLASS	88.0	79.2	83.4	92.9	57.0	74.3	95.2	58.6	76.2	93.4	123.3	108.9	99.8	116.7	108.6	101.1	114.6	108.1
9.2	LATH & PLASTER	109.0	82.5	88.9	92.8	67.5	73.7	98.3	70.6	77.3	97.1	128.2	120.7	92.2	95.4	94.6	101.8	118.3	114.3
9.2	DRYWALL	82.2	80.7	81.5	95.4	60.3	79.1	114.7	68.5	93.3	99.7	122.6	109.3	98.2	112.2	104.7	98.5	114.8	106.1
9.5	ACOUSTICAL WORK	113.6	80.1	95.5	83.7	60.1	70.9	83.7	68.4	75.4	81.3	121.7	103.2	93.2	121.7	108.7	96.7	114.4	106.3
9.6	FLOORING	110.1	77.7	101.3	89.6	66.8	83.4	88.9	68.4	83.3	116.8	132.7	121.1	111.7	96.4	107.5	88.9	93.6	90.1
9.9	PAINTING	98.5	74.6	79.6	111.0	46.9	60.3	104.6	59.2	68.7	108.2	112.7	111.7	120.1	120.3	120.3	107.8	102.6	103.7
9	FINISHES	93.0	78.5	85.3	94.7	56.6	74.5	105.2	65.5	84.1	101.6	120.2	111.5	102.9	113.6	108.6	97.3	109.3	103.6
10-14	TOTAL DIV. 10-14	100.0	86.8	96.1	100.0	73.3	92.1	100.0	73.9	92.3	100.0	125.3	107.4	100.0	122.8	106.7	100.0	144.3	113.0
15	MECHANICAL	98.8	82.1	90.5	97.4	58.4	78.0	97.0	65.5	81.3	97.1	120.6	108.8	95.3	95.1	95.2	93.2	120.5	106.8
16	ELECTRICAL	103.1	76.8	84.9	100.1	64.7	75.6	94.3	67.8	75.9	99.5	115.9	110.8	107.0	101.8	103.4	110.4	104.9	106.6
1-16	WEIGHTED AVERAGE	99.0	82.0	89.8	97.4	66.7	80.8	98.9	69.5	83.1	101.0	120.7	111.6	99.2	109.2	104.6	99.6	115.4	108.1

DIVISION		CALIFORNIA																	
		LOS ANGELES			OXNARD			RIVERSIDE			SACRAMENTO			SAN DIEGO			SAN FRANCISCO		
		MAT.	INST.	TOTAL	MAT.	INST.	TOTAL	MAT.	INST.	TOTAL	MAT.	INST.	TOTAL	MAT.	INST.	TOTAL	MAT.	INST.	TOTAL
2	SITE WORK	97.9	115.2	105.7	101.7	104.0	102.8	98.5	110.3	103.8	86.2	106.2	95.2	95.4	107.0	100.6	102.3	116.6	108.8
3.1	FORMWORK	112.0	125.1	122.1	98.5	125.2	119.1	114.9	124.7	122.5	109.8	120.8	118.2	105.4	118.2	115.3	103.2	132.7	125.9
3.2	REINFORCING	86.7	124.4	102.6	99.3	124.4	109.9	124.4	124.4	124.4	99.3	124.4	109.9	117.4	124.4	120.4	123.1	124.4	123.7
3.3	CAST IN PLACE CONC.	96.6	112.1	106.2	102.2	109.7	106.8	102.2	109.3	106.6	115.8	107.1	110.4	100.5	104.0	102.7	101.2	116.8	110.8
3	CONCRETE	97.6	118.3	110.9	100.8	117.1	111.3	109.8	116.8	114.3	110.9	114.0	112.9	105.2	111.5	109.2	106.4	123.7	117.5
4	MASONRY	108.9	131.4	126.2	100.8	117.5	113.7	105.1	109.3	108.3	103.3	116.1	113.2	110.2	106.7	107.5	125.9	148.8	143.6
5	METALS	101.6	119.4	108.1	105.2	118.7	110.1	99.1	118.5	106.2	111.0	121.0	114.7	99.0	117.5	105.8	103.9	124.0	111.2
6	WOOD & PLASTICS	99.5	122.0	111.7	92.6	121.9	108.5	94.6	121.0	108.9	78.2	117.1	99.3	95.9	112.9	105.1	92.9	131.5	113.8
7	MOISTURE PROTECTION	103.9	129.5	112.1	90.3	127.8	102.4	90.8	123.5	101.3	85.3	123.2	97.5	94.7	109.9	99.6	100.2	134.4	111.2
8	DOORS, WINDOWS, GLASS	102.1	123.3	113.1	102.6	123.3	113.3	103.1	123.3	113.6	92.0	117.1	105.0	107.3	118.7	113.2	113.3	130.1	122.0
9.2	LATH & PLASTER	96.3	128.3	120.5	97.4	124.7	118.1	97.4	128.4	120.9	98.8	122.4	116.7	101.8	106.5	105.3	101.5	139.4	130.2
9.2	DRYWALL	90.9	122.6	105.6	99.0	119.4	108.4	94.8	122.6	107.7	96.9	117.6	106.5	100.0	113.2	106.1	81.3	133.0	105.2
9.5	ACOUSTICAL WORK	99.1	121.7	111.3	87.5	121.7	106.0	87.5	121.7	106.0	85.6	117.7	103.0	101.0	113.5	107.8	101.0	132.9	118.3
9.6	FLOORING	96.1	132.7	106.0	96.1	132.7	106.0	96.1	132.7	106.0	86.0	119.5	95.1	98.0	118.1	103.5	106.9	134.2	114.3
9.9	PAINTING	83.9	123.0	114.8	92.1	114.7	110.0	100.7	112.7	110.2	112.2	116.2	115.4	91.4	124.1	117.3	102.1	140.0	132.1
9	FINISHES	92.1	123.7	108.9	96.7	119.3	108.7	95.2	120.2	108.5	95.3	117.6	107.1	98.8	116.9	108.4	91.0	135.9	114.8
10-14	TOTAL DIV. 10-14	100.0	125.6	107.5	100.0	125.2	107.4	100.0	125.1	107.4	100.0	146.0	113.5	100.0	123.2	106.8	100.0	151.9	115.2
15	MECHANICAL	97.6	124.6	111.0	98.7	122.4	110.5	96.9	123.2	110.0	97.9	119.8	108.8	102.9	119.8	111.3	100.8	167.8	134.2
16	ELECTRICAL	101.8	128.7	120.4	99.5	117.6	112.0	99.0	111.6	107.7	110.4	98.1	101.9	105.6	92.9	96.8	107.8	155.6	141.0
1-16	WEIGHTED AVERAGE	99.3	124.1	112.7	99.4	119.1	110.0	99.7	117.4	109.2	99.7	115.7	108.3	101.7	111.5	107.0	103.2	142.5	124.4

Figure 7.12

Component Contribution of Divisions and Subdivisions

NO.	DIVISION	%	NO.	DIVISION	%	NO.	DIVISION	%
016	CONTRACTOR EQUIPMENT*	6.5%	051	Structural Metal Framing	2.2%	092	Lath, Plaster & Gypsum Board	5.1%
022	Earthwork	1.8	052,053	Metal Joists & Decking	1.5	093,094	Tile & Terrazzo	1.0
023	Tunneling, Piles & Caissons	0.7	055	Metal Fabrications	2.6	095	Acoustical Treat. & Wood Flooring	0.8
025	Paving & Surfacing	0.8	5	METALS	6.3	096	Flooring & Carpet	1.3
026,027	Utilities, Sewerage & Drainage	0.6	061	Rough Carpentry	1.7	099	Painting & Wall Coverings	2.2
028	Site Improvements	0.1	062	Finish Carpentry	0.1	9	FINISHES	10.4
029	Landscaping	1.1	6	WOOD & PLASTICS	1.8	10-14	DIVISIONS 10-14	8.7
2	SITE WORK	4.9	071	Waterproofing & Dampproofing	0.7	151-153	Plumbing: Piping & Fixtures	5.4
031	Concrete Formwork	5.8	072	Insulation & Fireproofing	0.6	164	Fire Protection	2.7
032	Concrete Reinforcing	2.4	073	Shingles	0.3	155	Heating	7.2
033	Cast in Place Concrete	9.5	074,075	Roofing & Siding	3.0	156,157	Air Conditioning & Ventilation	4.4
034	Precast Concrete	0.3	076	Flashing & Sheet Metal	0.2	15	MECHANICAL	19.7
035	Cementitious Decks	0.1	7	THERMAL & MOISTURE PROT.	4.8	16	ELECTRICAL	9.6
3	CONCRETE	18.1	081-083	Doors & Frames	1.5		TOTAL (Div. 1-16)	100.0%
041	Mortar & Masonry Accessories	0.3	085	Windows	2.5			
042	Unit Masonry	9.2	088,089	Glazing & Glazed Curtain Walls	1.8	* Percentage for contractor equipment is		
044	Stone	0.4	8	DOORS & WINDOWS	5.8	spread among divisions and included		
4	MASONRY	9.9				above for information only		

Figure 7.13

Historical and City Cost Indexes

Historical Cost Indexes

The table below lists both the Means City Cost Index based on Jan. 1, 1975 = 100 as well as the computed value of an index based on Jan. 1, 1993 costs. Since the Jan. 1, 1993 figure is estimated, space is left to write in the actual index figures as they become available through either the quarterly "Means Construction Cost Indexes" or as printed in the "Engineering News-Record." To compute the actual index based on Jan. 1, 1993 = 100, divide the Quarterly City Cost Index for a particular year by the actual Jan. 1, 1993 Quarterly City Cost Index. Space has been left to advance the index figures as the year progresses.

Year	Quarterly City Cost Index Jan. 1, 1975 = 100		Current Index Based on Jan. 1, 1993 = 100		Year	Quarterly City Cost Index Jan. 1, 1975 = 100	Current Index Based on Jan. 1, 1993 = 100		Year	Quarterly City Cost Index Jan. 1, 1975 = 100	Current Index Based on Jan. 1, 1993 = 100	
	Est.	Actual	Est.	Actual		Actual	Est.	Actual		Actual	Est.	Actual
Oct 1993					July 1978	122.4	53.2		July 1960	45.0	19.6	
July 1993					1977	113.3	49.2		1959	44.2	19.2	
April 1993					1976	107.3	46.6		1958	43.0	18.7	
Jan 1993	230.1		100.0	100.0	1975	102.6	44.6		1957	42.2	18.3	
July 1992		227.6	98.9		1974	94.7	41.2		1956	40.4	17.6	
1991		221.6	96.3		1973	86.3	37.5		1955	38.1	16.6	
1990		215.9	93.8		1972	79.7	34.6		1954	36.7	15.9	
1989		210.9	91.7		1971	73.5	31.9		1953	36.2	15.7	
1988		205.7	89.4		1970	65.8	28.6		1952	35.3	15.3	
1987		200.7	87.2		1969	61.6	26.8		1951	34.4	15.0	
1986		192.8	83.8		1968	56.9	24.7		1950	31.4	13.6	
1985		189.1	82.2		1967	53.9	23.4		1949	30.4	13.2	
1984		187.6	81.5		1966	51.9	22.6		1948	30.4	13.2	
1983		183.5	79.7		1965	49.7	21.6		1947	27.6	12.0	
1982		174.3	75.7		1964	48.6	21.1		1946	23.2	10.1	
1981		160.2	69.6		1963	47.3	20.6		1945	20.2	8.8	
1980		144.0	62.6		1962	46.2	20.1		1944	19.3	8.4	
▼ 1979		132.3	57.5		▼ 1961	45.4	19.7		▼ 1943	18.6	8.1	

Figure 7.14

033 | Cast-In-Place Concrete

		033 100 | **Structural Concrete**		CREW	DAILY OUTPUT	MAN-HOURS	UNIT	1993 BARE COSTS				TOTAL INCL O&P	
								MAT.	LABOR	EQUIP.	TOTAL		
118	1300	Non-metallic, 55 lb. bags, natural (grey), minimum						.34			.34	.37	118
	1310	Maximum						.58			.58	.64	
	1320	Non-metallic, colors, mininum						.38			.38	.42	
	1340	Maximum						.62			.62	.68	
	1400	Non-metallic, non-slip, 100 lb. bags, minimum						.38			.38	.42	
	1420	Maximum						.75			.75	.83	
	1500	Solution type,(300 to 400 S.F. per gallon)					Gal.	5.25			5.25	5.80	
	1510												
	1550	Release agent, for tilt slabs					Gal.	7.25			7.25	8	
	1570	For forms, average						4.75			4.75	5.20	
	1600	Sealer, hardener and dustproofer, clear, 450 S.F., minimum						7			7	7.70	
	1620	Maximum						19.25			19.25	21	
	1700	Colors (300-400 S.F. per gallon)						17			17	18.70	
	1710												
	1800	Set accelerator for below freezing, 1 to 1-1/2 gal. per C.Y.					Gal.	4.30			4.30	4.73	
	1900	Set retarder, 2 to 4 fl. oz. per bag of cement					"	13.60			13.60	14.95	
	2000	Waterproofing, integral 1 lb. per bag of cement					Lb.	.83			.83	.91	
	2100	Powdered metallic, 40 lbs. per 100 S.F., minimum						.83			.83	.91	
	2120	Maximum						1.75			1.75	1.93	
	2200	Water reducing admixture, average					Gal.	7.75			7.75	8.55	
122	0010	**CONCRETE, FIELD MIX** FOB forms 2250 psi	R033 -080				C.Y.	51			51	56	122
	0020	3000 psi					"	53.50			53.50	59	
126	0010	**CONCRETE, READY MIX** Regular weight, 2000 psi	R033 -040				C.Y.	45.50			45.50	50	126
	0100	2500 psi						47			47	51.50	
	0150	3000 psi	R033 -060					48			48	53	
	0200	3500 psi						49.50			49.50	54.50	
	0250	3750 psi	R033 -070					50			50	55	
	0300	4000 psi						50.50			50.50	55.50	
	0350	4500 psi						52			52	57	
	0400	5000 psi						53			53	58.50	
	0411	6000 psi						60.50			60.50	66.50	
	0412	8000 psi						98.50			98.50	108	
	0413	10000 psi						140			140	154	
	0414	12000 psi						169			169	186	
	1000	For high early strength cement, add						10%					
	1010	For structural lightweight with regular sand, add						25%					
	2000	For all lightweight aggregate, add						45%					
	3000	For integral colors, 2500 psi, 5 bag mix											
	3100	Red, yellow or brown, 1.8 lb. per bag, add					C.Y.	11.50			11.50	12.65	
	3200	9.4 lb. per bag, add						61			61	67	
	3400	Black, 1.8 lb. per bag, add						13.50			13.50	14.85	
	3500	7.5 lb. per bag, add						56			56	61.50	
	3700	Green, 1.8 lb. per bag, add						26.50			26.50	29	
	3800	7.5 lb. per bag, add						111			111	122	
130	0010	**CONCRETE IN PLACE** Including forms (4 uses), reinforcing	R033 -010										130
	0050	steel, including finishing unless otherwise indicated											
	0100	Average for concrete framed building,	R033 -100										
	0110	including finishing		C-17B	15.75	5.206	C.Y.	108	128	16	252	340	
	0130	Average for substructure only, simple design, incl. finishing			29.07	2.821		84	69	8.65	161.65	211	
	0150	Average for superstructure only, including finishing			13.42	6.110		119	150	18.75	287.75	390	
	0200	Base, granolithic, 1″ x 5″ high, straight	R033 -110	C-10	175	.137	L.F.	.12	2.96	.43	3.51	5.05	
	0220	Cove		"	140	.171	"	.12	3.69	.53	4.34	6.30	
	0300	Beams, 5 kip per L.F., 10′ span	R033 -120	C-17A	6.28	12.898	C.Y.	178	315	20	513	715	
	0350	25′ span			7.40	10.946		142	268	17.10	427.10	595	
	0500	Chimney foundations, industrial, minimum	R033 -130		26.70	3.034		96	74.50	4.73	175.23	228	
	0510	Maximum			19.70	4.112		110	101	6.40	217.40	287	

Figure 7.15

109

R033-100   Average C.Y. of Concrete (cont.)

Columns, Square Tied

	(Line 033-130-0820) 16″ Square				(Line 033-130-0920) 24″ Square			
	Material		Installation		Material		Installation	
4000 psi concrete	1 C.Y.	$ 50.78	1 C.Y.	$ 42.54	1 C.Y.	$ 50.78	1 C.Y.	$ 29.70
Formwork, 4 uses	81 S.F. @ .65	52.65	81 S.F. @ 3.18	257.58	54 S.F. @ .62	33.48	54 S.F. @ 3.12	168.48
Reinforcing steel, avg.	634 # @ .23	145.82	634 # @ .21	133.14	524 # @ .23	120.52	524 # @ .21	110.04
Total per C.Y.		$249.25		$433.26		$204.78		$308.22

Note: Reinforcing of 16″ and 24″ square columns can vary from 144 lb. to 972 lb. per C.Y.

Columns, Round Tied Reinforced

	(Line 033-130-1220) 16″ Diameter				(Line 033-130-1420) 24″ Diameter			
	Material		Installation		Material		Installation	
4000 psi concrete	1 C.Y.	$ 50.78	1 C.Y.	$ 38.55	1 C.Y.	$ 50.78	1 C.Y.	$ 29.70
Formwork, fiber forms	19 S.F. @ 5.53	105.07	19 S.F. @ 5.24	99.56	9 S.F. @10.50	94.50	9 S.F. @ 5.63	50.67
Reinforcing steel, avg.	606 # @ .23	139.38	606 # @ .17	103.02	600 # @ .23	138.00	600 # @ .17	102.00
Ties	70 # @ .51	35.70	70 # @ .28	19.60	18 # @ .51	9.18	18 # @ .28	5.04
Total per C.Y.		$330.93		$260.73		$292.46		$187.41

Note: Reinforcing of 16″ and 24″ diameter columns vary from 160 lb. to 1150 lb. per C.Y.

Flat Plate

	(Line 033-130-2100) 100 psf, 15′ Span				(Line 033-130-2150) 100 psf, 25′ Span			
	Material		Installation		Material		Installation	
4000 psi concrete	1 C.Y.	$ 50.78	1 C.Y.	$ 18.90	1 C.Y.	$ 50.78	1 C.Y.	$ 18.90
Formwork, 4 uses	61 S.F. @ .70	42.70	61 S.F. @ 2.02	123.22	33 S.F. @ .71	23.43	33 S.F. @ 2.02	66.66
Reinforcing steel	126 # @ .23	28.98	126 # @ .15	18.90	113 # @ .23	25.99	113 # @ .15	16.95
Total per C.Y.		$122.46		$161.02		$100.20		$102.51

Flat Slab

	(Line 033-130-1900) 100 psf, 20′ Span				(Line 033-130-1950) 100 psf, 30′ Span			
	Material		Installation		Material		Installation	
4000 psi concrete	1 C.Y.	$ 50.78	1 C.Y.	$ 18.90	1 C.Y.	$ 50.78	1 C.Y.	$18.90
Formwork, 4 uses	43 S.F. @ .73	31.39	43 S.F. @ 2.07	89.01	29 S.F. @ .73	21.17	29 S.F. @ 2.07	60.03
Reinforcing steel	119 # @ .23	27.37	119 # @ .15	17.85	131 # @ .23	30.13	131 # @ .15	19.65
Total per C.Y.		$109.54		$125.76		$102.08		$98.58

Grade Wall, 8′ High

	(Line 033-130-4200) 8″ Thick				(Line 033-130-4300) 15″ Thick			
	Material		Installation		Material		Installation	
3000 psi concrete	1 C.Y.	$ 48.25	1 C.Y.	$ 11.20	1 C.Y.	$48.25	1 C.Y.	$ 9.60
Formwork, 4 uses	81 S.F. @ .62	50.22	81 S.F. @ 2.24	181.44	41 S.F. @ .62	25.42	41 S.F. @ 2.24	91.84
Reinforcing steel	44 # @ .23	10.12	44 # @ .14	6.16	43 # @ .23	9.89	43 # @ .14	6.02
Total per C.Y.		$108.59		$198.80		$83.56		$107.46

Metal Pan Joists, 30″ One Way

	(Line 033-130-2500) 100 psf, 15′ Span				(Line 033-130-2550) 100 psf, 25′ Span			
	Material		Installation		Material		Installation	
4000 psi concrete	1 C.Y.	$ 50.78	1 C.Y.	$ 18.90	1 C.Y.	$ 50.78	1 C.Y.	$ 18.90
Formwork, 4 uses	49 S.F. @ .72	35.28	49 S.F. @ 2.02	98.98	40 S.F. @ .72	28.80	40 S.F. @ 2.02	80.80
Reinforcing steel	47 # @ .23	10.81	47 # @ .15	7.05	81 # @ .23	18.63	81 # @ .15	12.15
30″ metal pans	44 # @ .34	14.96	44 # @ .33	14.52	37 # @ .34	12.58	37 # @ .33	12.21
Total per C.Y.		$111.83		$139.45		$110.79		$124.06

Pile Caps

	(Line 033-130-5900) Under 5 C.Y.				(Line 033-130-5950) Over 10 C.Y.			
	Material		Installation		Material		Installation	
3000 psi concrete	1.05 C.Y.	$48.25	1 C.Y.	$11.20	1.05 C.Y.	$48.25	1 C.Y.	$ 4.90
Formwork, 4 uses	20 S.F. @ .49	9.80	20 S.F. @ 1.92	38.40	10 S.F. @ .49	4.90	10 S.F. @ 1.92	19.20
Reinforcing steel	52 # @ .23	11.96	52 # @ .12	6.24	48 # @ .23	11.04	48 # @ .12	5.76
Total per C.Y.		$70.01		$55.84		$64.19		$29.86

Slab on Grade

	(Line 033-130-4650) 4″ Thick				(Line 033-130-4700) 6″ Thick			
	Material		Installation		Material		Installation	
3500 psi concrete	1.05 C.Y.	$49.40	1 C.Y.	$ 9.15	1.05 C.Y.	$49.40	1 C.Y.	$ 6.10
Formwork, 4 uses	9 L.F. @ .21	1.93	9 L.F. @ .89	8.19	6 L.F. @ .21	1.26	6 L.F. @ 1.33	7.98
W.W.Fabric	81 # @ .06	4.86	81 # @ .18	14.58	54 # @ .06	3.24	54 # @ .18	9.72
Total per C.Y.		$56.19		$31.92		$53.90		$23.80

Figure 7.16

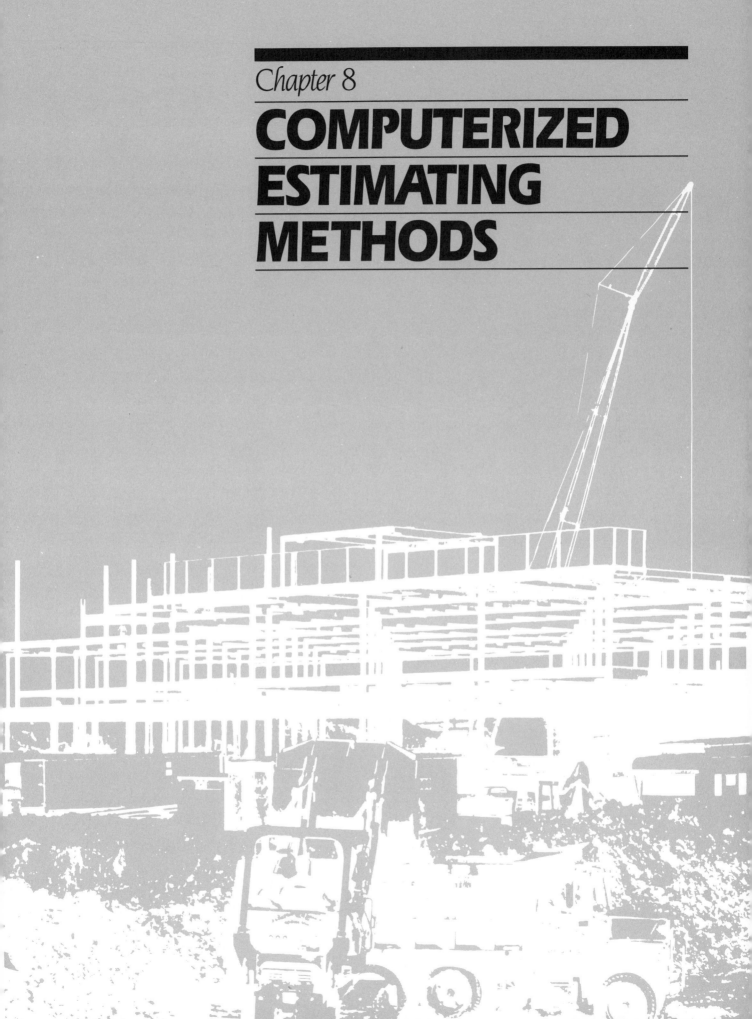

Chapter 8
COMPUTERIZED ESTIMATING METHODS

Chapter 8

COMPUTERIZED ESTIMATING METHODS

Computers have clearly added speed, power and accuracy to construction estimating. They make it possible to produce more estimates in less time, break a job down to a more detailed level for better cost control; manage change orders more easily, test "what if" scenarios with ease, and integrate estimating with other commonly used construction applications. The objective of this chapter is to provide an overview of unit price estimating through the use of computerized estimating methods. Figure 8.1 is a chart showing an overview of the various levels of estimating programs, and their features/applications.

Automating the estimating function is an evolutionary process. There are many levels of computerized estimating, which vary in functionality, sophistication, time required to learn and, most of all, price. Many estimators make the mistake of immediately transitioning their manual estimating into a fully integrated estimating software system without learning the basics of what a computer can do for the estimating process. Successful implementation of an estimating software system will not happen overnight. It usually takes many months of training and user interaction to get a system working to its full capability.

It is recommended that computerized estimating be introduced through a multi-step process. First, learn the basics of computers and estimating through the use of industry-standard spreadsheet software programs, such as *Lotus®* 123 spreadsheet add-on, *Quattro®* or *Excel*. Next, introduce spreadsheet add-on programs which will provide more versatility than a standard spreadsheet program. Finally, consider upgrading to a complete estimating software application which will utilize the computer's full power. This last step usually allows estimating software to be integrated with other related software applications, such as job cost accounting, scheduling, project management and CAD.

The basis of any computerized estimating system is its unit price cost database. No matter how sophisticated or user-friendly construction estimating software is, its overall success depends upon the completeness, functionality, and accuracy of the cost data, and the methods by which it is used. Without a fully functional database, construction estimating software is nothing more than a very expensive calculator.

One effective way to move through the different levels of computerized estimating is using industry standard data as the foundation of the system. Utilizing *MeansData*,™ for example, it is possible to seamlessly transition an

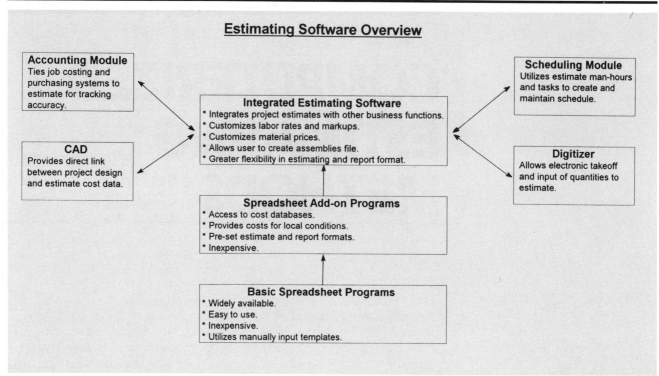

Figure 8.1

estimating system from one step to the next, easily updating the cost data and integrating it into thousands of pre-built assemblies. While it is always possible to create a customized cost database from historical job costs, *MeansData*™ will provide a foundation of costs, as well as the necessary framework to successfully estimate using a computer.

Basic Spreadsheet Programs

A computerized estimating system should perform three basic functions:

1. Calculate costs.
2. Store and manage data.
3. Generate hard copy reports.

Most industry-standard spreadsheet software programs, such as *Lotus*® 123, *Quattro*® *Pro* and *Excel*, meet these requirements. The premise of every spreadsheet program is to automate a calculation sheet. Spreadsheet programs calculate costs in vertical columns and horizontal rows using basic mathematical functions. Figure 8.2 shows a sample screen with a spreadsheet that might be used by a contractor for estimating purposes.

Everyone who has ever done construction estimating has been in the situation of rushing to finish an estimate in order to submit a bid by a certain deadline. Subcontractor quotes usually don't come in until the last minute, and it is a huge task to recalculate costs to complete the bid. Spreadsheet programs can recalculate costs in fractions of a second, which makes it fairly simple to rework the estimate prior to a bid, and allow "what if" analysis for fine tuning.

Another major capability of spreadsheet programs is managing and sorting information. A typical line item of cost data consists of some sort of a line number, description of task, material costs, labor costs and equipment costs. There is information on crews and productivities which needs to be maintained. Typical construction databases are in the thousands and tens of thousands of line items. Most spreadsheet programs allow information to be entered, managed, and sorted numerically or alphabetically.

When dealing with a client, presentation is very important. Spreadsheets make it possible to print out professional looking estimates, using different fonts, styles and formats. Some of the newer versions also have a graphics capability. Charts and graphs can be produced based on information from an estimate spreadsheet, and a company logo can be incorporated into reports.

There are some limitations in using spreadsheets. Information within a spreadsheet must be organized using the same field layout. A significant problem is likely to be difficulty locating certain line items within the database and bringing that information back into the estimate. Scrolling through a database of thousands of line items is a time consuming and cumbersome process. Keeping such a database up-to-date also requires a major investment of time. Furthermore, it is usually not possible to apply a standardized cost database to standard spreadsheets without an add-on program, discussed in the next section. Industry standard databases are important because they provide the ability to update information through database companies such as R.S. Means.

These limitations can be overcome by features offered in the next category of computerized estimating: spreadsheet add-on programs. These are systems that provide the basic features of stand-alone (integrated) estimating systems, but cost only a fraction of a full system. Spreadsheet add-on programs are inexpensive, and usually offer the opportunity to upgrade to a complete stand-alone estimating system in the future.

PROJECT: INDUSTRIAL GARAGE

DESCRIPTIONS	QUANITY	MATERIAL	LABOR	TOTALS
STRIP FOOTINGS	120 LF	$940.00	$2,640.00	$3,580.00
CAST IN PLACE WALL	120 LF	$1,206.00	$3,120.00	$4,326.00
SLAB ON GRADE	800 SF	$1,040.00	$1,620.00	$2,660.00
STEET JOIST & DECK	800 SF			$1,340.00
CONCRETE BLOCK WALL	1100 SF	$1,795.00	$4,125.00	$5,920.00
ROOF COVER	800SF			$1,070.00

TOTALS $4,981.00 $11,505.00

JOB TOTAL $18,896.00

Figure 8.2

Spreadsheet Add-on Programs

Spreadsheet add-on programs allow users to develop more power within their spreadsheet estimating systems. Estimators who require a larger database or coverage of more locations may decide to purchase an add-on program. Specialty contractors who expand into general contracting also find these systems helpful.

Means offers spreadsheet add-on programs under the product line of *MeansData™ for Spreadsheets*. The *Lotus®* version of *MeansData™* provides a macro which will standardize the estimating spreadsheet format. This format, the Construction Specifications Institute (CSI) MasterFormat numbering system, is standardized to categorize the database. Data is formatted into divisions, subdivisions and major classifications. This spreadsheet format also standardizes column breakouts for material, labor and equipment costs, using the same format as the R.S. Means cost data. See Figure 8.3 for a sample spreadsheet using a commercial database and *Lotus®* 123.

There are 15 separate trade-specific unit price databases which can be integrated into a *MeansData™ for Spreadsheets* product. These provide access to thousands of unit price cost line items which are updated on a regular basis. Additionally, the estimator's own unique data can be entered into a separate database using the same format as the R.S. Means cost data. Means cost data also comes with a City Cost Index function which will set up a certain city as the index for an estimate. As data is input to the estimate spreadsheet, it will be regionalized to the selected location. Finally, a *MeansData™ for Spreadsheet* program has a standardized report capability, which enables users to print out standard predefined reports.

Many estimators find that spreadsheet add-on programs satisfy all of their estimating needs. They can update their cost data, and create, edit, and print accurate estimates. Others may want even more functionality with a program.

Spreadsheet add-on systems such as *MeansData™ for Spreadsheets* may fall short in some areas. For example, while unit price cost data is the foundation of all estimating systems, assemblies or building systems developed from unit price cost data take greater advantage of what a computerized system can do. Assemblies make it possible to perform a substantially accurate conceptual level estimate in a fraction of the time it takes to create unit price cost estimates. It is also helpful in taking an estimate from concept to bid, or assemblies to unit price. Spreadsheet programs do not provide this relational database capability. A stand-alone system could take a prebuilt assembly, and break that system down into the unit prices that make it up, whereas spreadsheets with add-ons lack that capability.

Other features not available with spreadsheets/add-ons programs include the ability to automate the quantity takeoff process by using a digitizer or wheel pen, or extracting quantities from a computer-aided design (CAD) program. These types of technologies are only available through complete stand-alone estimating systems, such as offered by Timberline's *Precision®* or Software Shops' ACE-CSI.

Finally, some estimators are interested in integrating their estimating function into other related software applications, such as job cost accounting, scheduling, project management and CAD software. To develop these types of integrations, a complete, stand-alone estimating system is generally required.

```
=================================================================
Estimate:      Repair Garage     Date:      1993
Description:   Estimate for Unit Price Estimating
Project:       Garage            Bid Date: 7/4/93
Location:      Michigan Ave      Job #:     Unit Price 1993
Sq. footage:   4000 sf           City indx:CHICAGO, IL
=================================================================
```

Line #	Description					
	Manhours	Matl	Labor	Equipment	Sub	Total

```
=================================================================
```

0205541710   PAVEMENT REMOVAL, BITUMINOUS, 3" THICK

	Manhours	Matl	Labor	Equipment	Sub	Total
					3200.00 S.Y.	
Unit values	0.06	0.00	1.31	1.84	0.00	3.16
Totals	185.60	$0	$4,205	$5,893	$0	$10,098

0207280010   SAW CUTG, ASPHLT >1000LF PER 3" DEEP

	Manhours	Matl	Labor	Equipment	Sub	Total
					720.00 L.F.	
Unit values	0.02	0.23	0.47	0.37	0.00	1.07
Totals	15.12	$166	$341	$264	$0	$771

0222040010   BACKFILL BY HAND, NO COMPACTION, LIGHT SOIL

	Manhours	Matl	Labor	Equipment	Sub	Total
					125.00 C.Y.	
Unit values	0.57	0.00	11.42	0.00	0.00	11.42
Totals	71.38	$0	$1,427	$0	$0	$1,427

0222040600   COMPACT BACKFILL, 6" LIFTS, HAND TAMP, VIBRATORY PLATE

	Manhours	Matl	Labor	Equipment	Sub	Total
					125.00 C.Y.	
Unit values	0.13	0.00	2.66	1.06	0.00	3.72
Totals	16.63	$0	$333	$132	$0	$465

0222120100   BORROW, BANK RUN GRAVEL, HAUL 2 MI., SPREAD W/ DOZER, NO COMPACTION

	Manhours	Matl	Labor	Equipment	Sub	Total
					75.00 C.Y.	
Unit values	0.05	3.66	5.64	16.15	0.00	25.44
Totals	3.53	$274	$423	$1,211	$0	$1,908

0222381200   EXCAVTG BULK, FRONT END LOADER, TRUCK MNTD, 1.5CY 70CY/HR

	Manhours	Matl	Labor	Equipment	Sub	Total
					140.00 C.Y.	
Unit values	0.02	0.00	1.91	2.56	0.00	4.46
Totals	2.94	$0	$267	$358	$0	$625

0222540050   EXCAV TRENCH, COMMON EARTH, 1'-4' DEEP, 3/8 CY TRAC/LDR/B'HOE

	Manhours	Matl	Labor	Equipment	Sub	Total
					125.00 C.Y.	
Unit values	0.11	0.00	2.46	1.44	0.00	3.90
Totals	13.38	$0	$307	$180	$0	$487

0222580700   EXCAV UTIL TRNCH COMMON EARTH, CHAIN TRNCHR 12HP OPERWLKG 8"W 24"DP

	Manhours	Matl	Labor	Equipment	Sub	Total
					365.00 L.F.	
Unit values	0.02	0.00	0.57	0.25	0.00	0.82
Totals	8.40	$0	$208	$90	$0	$298

Figure 8.3

Complete Stand-Alone Estimating Solutions

A complete stand-alone estimating system does not require any other software in order to function. It incorporates all of the capabilities previously covered, including full integration to MeansData,™ links to electronic quantity takeoff devices, and the ability to "communicate" with other construction software applications. By integrating with the scheduling module, estimate man-hours can be used to create and maintain the project schedule. A link to the accounting module allows job cost accounting. CAD and digitizer programs can also be connected to provide electronic takeoff to estimate. Other features include the ability to customize labor rates and markups, input the company's own material prices, and build assemblies, as well as great flexibility in report formats.

Some estimating systems that fall into this category are developed by companies such as Timberline® Software, MC2, Software Shop Systems, G2, Inc. or Building Systems Design. There are hundreds of these systems, and selecting the appropriate one can be a tedious process that involves collecting printed information, seeing and using demos, and evaluating products and their costs. A product called DemoSource™ is available from Means. It is a package of demonstration diskettes and product information of industry leaders in estimating software. Each system described includes a Means database as a feature with the purchase of that system. Information can also be gathered through industry associations such as the National Association of Home Builders (NAHB). NAHB produces and sells a Software Directory and a Software Review for builders. Other associations, such as the Association of General Contractors (AGC) and the Association of Builders and Contractors (ABC), also provide information.

Figure 8.4 is an Unburdened Detailed Report in Pulsar Version 3. More detail can be included using this system and the estimate data can be automatically imported and updated either globally or selectively. Figure 8.5 is another example of a detailed estimate using Timberline Software's Precision® program. This Standard Estimate Report can be printed using a variety of options. Some of the options available are to print memos entered while performing the takeoff, combine duplicate items together on the report, or print a summary of all costs associated with each phase of the estimate. The Standard Estimate Report in a summarized format transforms large spreadsheets into more readable, less detailed reports that allow a quick review of the category totals for each division and subdivision (phase) contained in the estimate.

Summary

There are many steps in the process of automating the estimating process. A standard spreadsheet program may be adequate, an entry level estimating system may be a more appropriate level, or you may find it necessary to obtain the full capabilities of a complete stand-alone estimating system. Estimating software at the lower levels (basic spreadsheet and add-on programs) can be extremely useful, while the cost is moderate. Stand-alone systems do require a significant investment in terms of cost and learning curve, but the potential benefits in terms of accuracy, increased productivity, and control are tremendous.

==

Unit Price Estimate   UNBURDENED DETAILED REPORT   Tue Mar 16 01:20:04 Pm 1993   PAGE: 2
....

3 Concrete

3.1 Concrete Formwork

DESCRIPTION										SHEET	
LINE NO.	TAG		CREW	D/O	M/H	QUANTITY	MATERIAL	LABOR	EQUIP	TOTAL	SUB
ASMBLY#	SEARCH1	SEARCH2	PERLABOR	PERMATL	PEREQUIP		UNIT				

SUPPORTS FOR DOWELS IN FOOTINGS, WALLS, AND BEAMS

031 158 0500	000M			C1	M	500.000	0.064	600.00	0.59	1.42	0.05	2.06
01-0510	00		100.00%	100.00%	100.00%	38.40	L.F.	354.00	850.56	29.52	1234.08

FORMS IN PLACE, SPREAD FOOTING, 4 USES

031 158 5150	000M			C1	M	414.000	0.077	1200.00	0.39	1.71	0.06	2.16
01-0510	00		100.00%	100.00%	100.00%	92.75	SFCA	468.00	2054.49	71.30	2593.80

==

SUB TOTAL :   131   822   2905   101   3828   0

==

3.2 Concrete Reinforcement

DESCRIPTION										SHEET	
LINE NO.	TAG		CREW	D/O	M/H	QUANTITY	MATERIAL	LABOR	EQUIP	TOTAL	SUB
ASMBLY#	SEARCH1	SEARCH2	PERLABOR	PERMATL	PEREQUIP		UNIT				

REINFORCING IN PLACE FOOTINGS, #4 TO #7

032 107 0500	000M			RODM4M	2.100	15.238	0.60	490.00	393.90	0.00	883.90
01-0510	00		100.00%	100.00%	100.00%	9.14	Ton	294.00	236.34	0.00	530.34

==

SUB TOTAL :   9   294   236   0   530   0

==

3.3 Cast-In-Place Concrete

DESCRIPTION										SHEET	
LINE NO.	TAG		CREW	D/O	M/H	QUANTITY	MATERIAL	LABOR	EQUIP	TOTAL	SUB
ASMBLY#	SEARCH1	SEARCH2	PERLABOR	PERMATL	PEREQUIP		UNIT				

CONCRETE READY MIX, REGULAR WEIGHT, 3000 PSI

033 126 0150	000M				M	0.000	0.000	33.00	48.00	0.00	0.00	48.00
01-0510	00		100.00%	100.00%	100.00%	0.00	C.Y.	1584.00	0.00	0.00	1584.00

PLACE AND VIBRATE CONCRETE FOR SPREAD FOOTINGS OVER 5CY,DIRECT CHUTE

033 172 2600	000M			C6	M	110.000	0.436	33.00	0.00	8.57	0.59	9.16
01-0510	00		100.00%	100.00%	100.00%	14.40	C.Y.	0.00	282.72	19.44	302.16

Figure 8.4

PHASE	DESCRIPTION	PHASE QTY	LABOR AMOUNT	MATRL AMOUNT	SUB AMOUNT	EQUIP AMOUNT	TOTAL AMOUNT		
2100.00	**SITEWORK**								
2144.10	Dewater - Gravel at Slabs		1,481	3,200		445	5,126		
2144.20	Dewater - Slab Sand Fill		1,185	1,541		356	3,082		
2220.25	Excav - Footings (Mach)		72			36	108		
2220.40	Excav - Shape & Grade		120				120		
2220.45	Excav - Fine Grade		1,800				1,800		
2220.50	Backfill - Footing		951	571		570	2,091		
	SITEWORK		5,609	5,311		1,407	12,327		
				Labor hrs:	560.926	Equip hrs:		7.206	
3000.00	**CONCRETE**								
3111.00	Forms - Footings		121	262			383		
3159.00	Forms - Strip & Oil		60	18			78		
3160.01	Forms - Screeds		799	480			1,279		
3231.00	Rebar - Wiremesh Lump Sum		1,320	1,716			3,036		
3306.00	Conc - Footings		74	660			734		
3310.01	Conc - Slabs On Grade		1,111	19,580			20,691		
3375.00	Finish - Protect & Cure		600	480			1,080		
3380.01	Finish - General		6,000	6,000			12,000		
	CONCRETE		10,086	29,196			39,282		
				Labor hrs:	876.558				
7000.00	**THERMAL & MOISTURE PROT**								
7192.00	Vapor Barrier		840	958			1,798		
	THERMAL & MOISTURE P		840	958			1,798		
				Labor hrs:	84.00				

Figure 8.5

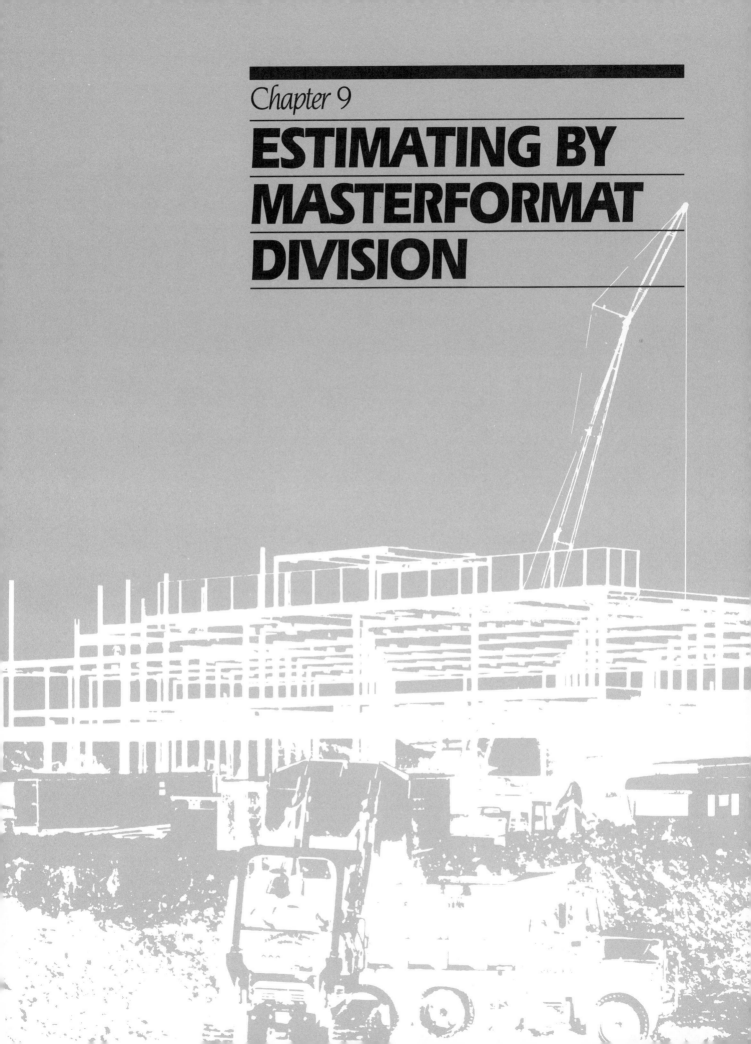

Chapter 9

ESTIMATING BY MASTERFORMAT DIVISION

Chapter 9

ESTIMATING BY MASTERFORMAT DIVISION

There are two basic approaches to performing a Unit Price estimate. One is to proceed with the estimate, the quantity takeoff and pricing in a sequence similar to the order in which a building is constructed. Using this method, concrete for footings is priced very early in the estimate, after excavation but before backfill. The concrete used for upper level floor slabs is estimated much later, after structural steel. This is the approach taken for a systems or assemblies estimate. The advantage to this method is that experienced estimators can visualize the construction process while proceeding with the estimate. As a result, omissions are less likely. The basic disadvantage of this system is that it is not easy to determine and track costs for each division (or subcontract). Costs for a particular trade may be spread throughout the estimate.

The second approach to unit price estimating is by MasterFormat division. Most architectural specifications today are written according to this format, using the sixteen MasterFormat divisions. Trades and subcontracts are generally limited to work within one division (e.g., Mechanical, or Masonry). It makes sense, therefore, that the estimate should also be organized in the MasterFormat format. Using this method, the estimator may have to be more careful to include all required work. Nevertheless, the advantages outweigh potential drawbacks. Most specifications contain references to related work for all divisions. These references serve as an aid to assure completeness, but the estimator for the general contractor still has the responsibility of making sure that subcontractors include all that is specified and required for the appropriate portions of the project. The estimator must also decide what work will be subcontracted and what will be performed by the work force of the general contractor. These decisions can have a significant effect on the final cost of a project. Traditionally, work has been done at a lower cost using the general contractor's own labor force. With the specialization of trades, however, subcontractors can often perform work faster, and thus at a lower cost.

Cost accounting and control is another area affected by the choice of estimating approach. Whichever method is chosen should be used consistently, from estimating — to field reporting — to final analysis. The first approach, estimating in the sequence of construction, brings the same challenge to cost accounting as it does to estimating — the difficulty of keeping similar items grouped together as the work of single trades.

The second method of estimating and cost accounting, by MasterFormat division, may take longer when it comes to compiling all costs for each division (e.g., until all concrete or site work is complete). However, each trade will be separated and the records will be in accordance with the specifications. Since material purchases and scheduling of manpower and subcontractors are based on the construction sequence, these items should be derived from the project schedule. This schedule is established after and formulated from the unit price estimate, and is the basis of project coordination.

Most project specifications contain a list of alternates which must be included with a submitted bid. These alternates become a series of mini-estimates within the total project estimate. Each alternate may include deductions of some items from the project, originally specified, as well as the addition of other items. Often mistakenly regarded as incidentals, alternates are often left until the project estimate is complete. In order to efficiently determine alternate costs, without performing a completely new estimate for each, the project estimate must be organized with the alternates in mind. If items are to be deducted as part of an alternate, they must be separated in the project estimate. Similarly, when measuring for quantities, pertinent dimensions and quantities for the "adds" of an alternate should be listed separately. If forethought is used, alternates can be estimated quickly and accurately.

The following discussions and the sample estimate are presented by MasterFormat division for the reasons mentioned above. Ultimately, the choice of method is not crucial as long as all items are included and all costs accounted.

Sample Estimate: Project Description

The project for the sample estimate is a three-story office building with a basement parking garage. The 2.6 acre site is located in a suburban area with good access and sufficient material storage area. The proposed building is composite steel frame with an aluminum panel and glass curtain wall system. Plans for the building are shown in Figures 9.1 to 9.15. These plans are provided for illustrative purposes only and represent the major features of the building. In actuality, such a building would require many more sheets of drawings with more plans, details, sections and elevations. Also included would be a full set of specifications. For the purposes of the example, however, these figures provide sufficient information. The quantities as given in the sample estimate represent realistic conditions. Assumptions have also been made for items not shown in Figures 9.1 to 9.15 that would normally be included in the plans and specifications of a project of this type.

Division 1: General Requirements

When estimating by MasterFormat division, the estimator must be careful to include all items which, while not attributable to one trade or to the physical construction of the building, are nevertheless required to successfully complete the project. These items are included in the General Requirements section. Often referred to as the "General Conditions" or "Project Overhead," they are usually set forth in the first part of the specifications. Some requirements may not be directly specified even though they are required to perform the work. Standardized sets of General Conditions have been developed by various segments of the construction industry, such as those by the American Institute of Architects, the Consulting Engineers Council/U.S., National

Figure 9.1

127

Figure 9.2

128

Figure 9.3

SITE PLAN

Figure 9.4

Figure 9.5a

131

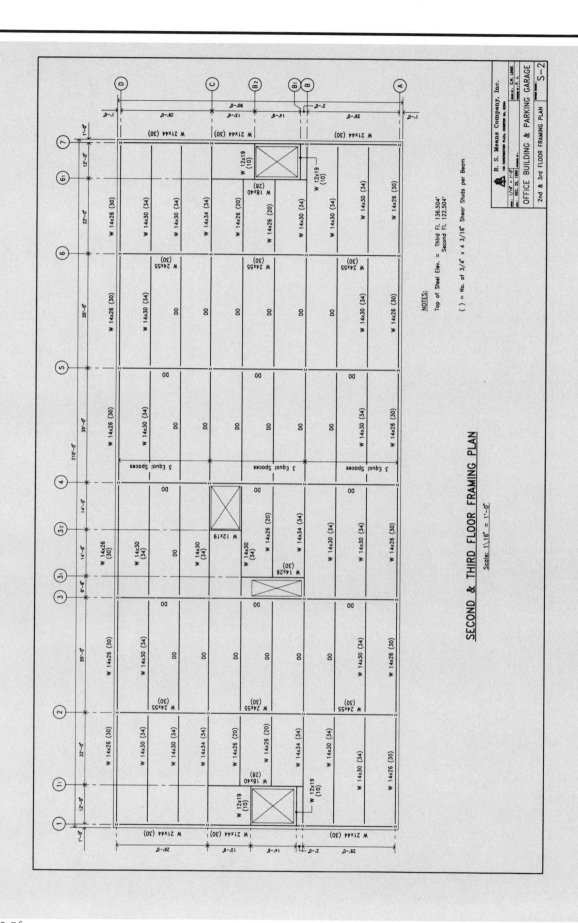

SECOND & THIRD FLOOR FRAMING PLAN

Scale: 1\16" = 1'-0"

Figure 9.5b

132

Figure 9.6

FIRST FLOOR PLAN

Figure 9.7

134

SECOND & THIRD FLOOR PLAN

Figure 9.8

PENTHOUSE FLOOR & ROOF PLAN

Figure 9.9

136

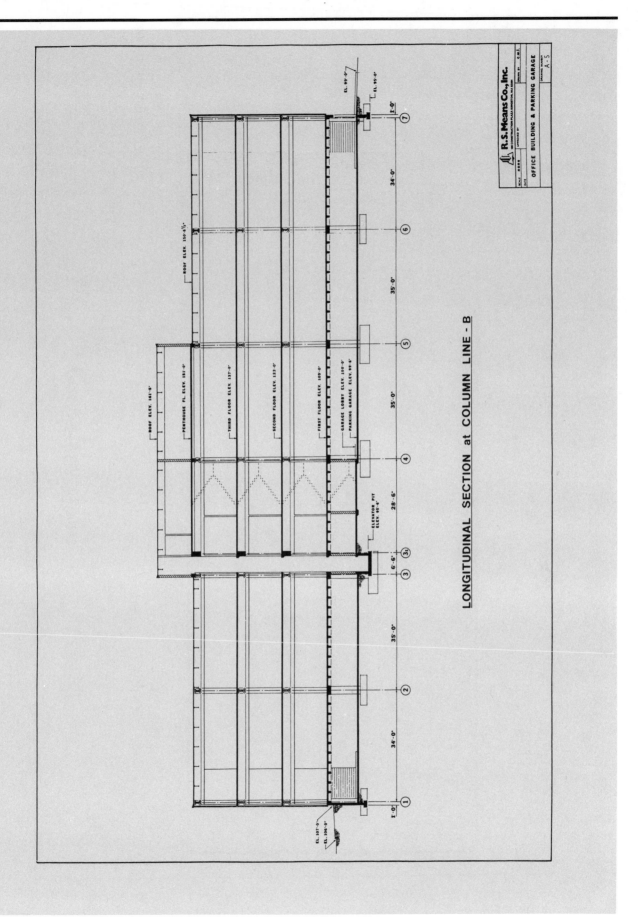

LONGITUDINAL SECTION at COLUMN LINE - B

Figure 9.10

137

ELECTRICAL LAYOUT

PARKING GARAGE PLAN

TOTAL PARKING = 26 CARS

Figure 9.11

138

Figure 9.12

SECOND & THIRD FLOOR PLAN

Figure 9.13

Figure 9.14

Figure 9.15

142

Society of Professional Engineers, and others. These standardized documents usually include:

- Definitions
- Contract document descriptions
- Contractor's rights and responsibilities
- Architect-engineer's authority and responsibilities
- Owner's rights and responsibilities
- Variation from contract provisions
- Payment requirements and restrictions
- Requirements for the performance of the work
- Insurance and bond requirements
- Job conditions and operation

Since these documents are generic, additions, deletions and modifications unique to specific projects are often included in Supplementary General Conditions.

Estimated costs for Division 1 are often recorded on a standardized form or checklist similar to the Project Overhead Summary shown in Figures 9.16 and 9.17. Such pre-printed forms or checklists are helpful to be sure that all requirements are included and priced. Many of the costs are dependent upon work in other divisions or on the total cost and/or time duration of the job. Project overhead costs should be determined throughout the estimating process and finalized when all other divisions have been estimated and a preliminary schedule established.

The following are brief discussions of various items that may be included as project overhead. The goal is to develop an approach to the estimate which will assure that all project requirements are included.

Personnel

Job site personnel may be included as either project overhead or office overhead, often depending upon the size of the project and the contractor's accounting methods. For example, if a project is large enough to require a full-time superintendent, then all costs for that person (time related) may be charged completely as project overhead. If the superintendent is responsible for a number of smaller jobs, then the expense may be either included in office overhead, or proportioned for each job. The same principles may apply to the salaries of field engineers, project managers, and time keepers.

If there is no full-time field engineer on the project, then costs may be incurred for establishing grades and setting stakes, building layout, producing as-built drawings, shop drawings or maintenance records. With regard to surveying and layout of the building and roads, it is important to determine who is the responsible party — the owner, general contractor or appropriate subcontractor. This responsibility should be established, if not done so in the contract documents, so that costs may be properly allocated.

Depending upon the size of the project, a carpenter and/or a laborer may be assigned to the job on a full-time basis for miscellaneous work. In such cases, workers are directly responsible to the job superintendent for various tasks; the costs of this work would not be attributable to any specific division and would most appropriately be included as project overhead.

Equipment

As discussed in Chapter 4, equipment costs may be recorded as project overhead or included in each appropriate division. Some equipment, however,

PROJECT
OVERHEAD SUMMARY

PROJECT:	Office Building								ESTIMATE NO:

LOCATION:		ARCHITECT:		DATE: 6/93

QUANTITIES BY:	PRICES BY:	EXTENSIONS BY:	CHECKED BY:

DESCRIPTION	QUANTITY	UNIT	MATERIAL/EQUIP.		LABOR		TOTAL COST	
			UNIT	TOTAL	UNIT	TOTAL	UNIT	TOTAL
Job Organization: Superintendent								
Project Manager								
Timekeeper & Material Clerk								
Clerical								
Safety, Watchman & First Aid								
Travel Expense: Superintendent								
Project Manager								
Engineering: Layout								
Inspection / Quantities								
Drawings								
CPM Schedule								
Testing: Soil								
Materials								
Structural								
Equipment: Cranes								
Concrete Pump, Conveyor, Etc.								
Elevators, Hoists								
Freight & Hauling								
Loading, Unloading, Erecting, Etc.								
Maintenance								
Pumping								
Scaffolding								
Small Power Equipment / Tools								
Feild Offices: Job Office Trailer								
Architect / Owner's Office								
Temporary Telephones								
Utilities								
Temporary Toilets								
Storage Areas & Sheds								
Temporary Utilities: Heat								
Light & Power								
PAGE TOTALS								

Figure 9.16

DESCRIPTION	QUANTITY	UNIT	MATERIAL/EQUIP.		LABOR		TOTAL COST	
			UNIT	TOTAL	UNIT	TOTAL	UNIT	TOTAL
Totals Brought Forward								
Winter Protection: Temp. Heat/Protection								
Snow Plowing								
Thawing Materials								
Temporary Roads								
Signs & Barricades: Site Sign								
Temporary Fences								
Temporary Stairs, Ladders & Floors								
Photographs								
Clean Up								
Dumpster								
Final Clean Up								
Continous - One Laborer								
Punch List								
Permits: Building								
Misc.								
Insurance: Builders Risk - Additional Rider								
Owner's Protective Liability								
Umbrella								
Unemployment Ins. & Social Security								
(SEE ESTIMATE SUMMARY)								
Bonds								
Performance (SEE ESTIMATE SUMMARY)								
Material & Equipment								
Main Office Expense (SEE ESTIMATE SUMMARY)								
Special Items								
Totals:								

Figure 9.17

will be used by more than one trade; examples are personnel or material hoists and cranes. The allocation of costs in these cases should be according to company practice.

Testing

Various tests may be required by the owner, local building officials or as specified in the contract documents. Depending upon the stage of design development and the role of the contractor, soil borings and/or percolation tests may be required. Usually this type of testing is the responsibility of the designer or engineer, paid for directly by the owner. Most testing during construction is required to verify conformance of the materials and methods to the requirements of the specifications. The most common testing is as follows:

Soil Compaction: Soil compaction is usually specified as a percentage of maximum density. Strict compaction methods are required under slabs on grade and at backfill of foundation walls and footings. Testing may be required every day (or possibly every lift). Soil samples may have to be lab tested for cohesiveness, permeability and/or water content. Watering may be required to achieve the specified compaction.

Concrete: Concrete tests may be required at two stages: slump tests during placement and compression tests after a specified curing time. Slump tests, indicating relative water and cement content, may be required for each truck load, after placement of a certain number of cubic yards, each day or per building section. Compression tests are performed on samples placed in cylinders usually after 7 and 28 days of curing time. The cylinders are tested by outside laboratories. If the concrete samples fail to meet design specifications, core drilling of in-place building samples for further testing may be required.

Miscellaneous Testing: Other testing may be necessary based on the type of construction and owner or architect/engineer requirements. Core samples of asphalt paving are often required to verify specified thickness. Steel connection and weld testing may be specified for critical structural points. Masonry absorption tests may be also required.

The costs of testing installed materials may be included — in different ways — as project overhead. One method is separately itemizing the costs for each individual test; or, a fixed allowance can be made based on the size and type of project. Budget costs derived from this second method are shown in Figure 9.18. A third approach is to include a percentage of total project costs.

Temporary Services

Required temporary services may or may not be included in the specifications. A typical statement in the specifications is: "Contractor shall supply all material, labor, equipment, tools, utilities and other items and services required for the proper and timely performance of the work and completion of the project." As far as the owner and designer are concerned, such a statement eliminates a great deal of ambiguity. To the estimator, this means many items that must be estimated. Temporary utilities, such as heat, light, power and water are a major consideration. The estimator must not only account for anticipated monthly (or time related) costs, but should also be sure that installation and removal costs are included, whether by the appropriate subcontractor or the general contractor.

013 | Submittals

013 800	Construction Photos	CREW	DAILY OUTPUT	MAN-HOURS	UNIT	1993 BARE COSTS				TOTAL INCL O&P	
						MAT.	LABOR	EQUIP.	TOTAL		
804	0010	PHOTOGRAPHS 8" x 10", 4 shots, 2 prints ea., std. mounting				Set	94.50			94.50	104	804
	0100	Hinged linen mounts					108			108	119	
	0200	8" x 10", 4 shots, 2 prints each, in color					190			190	209	
	0300	For I.D. slugs, add to all above					2.55			2.55	2.80	
	0500	Aerial photos, initial fly-over, 6 shots, 1 print ea., 8" x 10"					715			715	785	
	0550	11" x 14" prints					750			750	825	
	0600	16" x 20" prints					900			900	990	
	0700	For full color prints, add					40%					
	0750	Add for traffic control area					260			260	286	
	0900	For over 30 miles from airport, add per				Mile	4.60			4.60	5.05	
	1000	Vertical photography, 4 to 6 shots with										
	1010	different scales, 1 print each				Set	980			980	1,075	
	1500	Time lapse equipment, camera and projector, buy					3,675			3,675	4,050	
	1550	Rent per month					520			520	570	
	1700	Cameraman and film, including processing, B.&W.				Day	550			550	605	
	1720	Color					620			620	680	

014 | Quality Control

014 100	Testing Services	CREW	DAILY OUTPUT	MAN-HOURS	UNIT	1993 BARE COSTS				TOTAL INCL O&P	
						MAT.	LABOR	EQUIP.	TOTAL		
108	0010	TESTING For concrete building costing $1,000,000, minimum				Project					5,100	108
	0020	Maximum									50,000	
	0050	Steel building, minimum									5,100	
	0070	Maximum									11,000	
	0100	For building costing, $10,000,000, minimum									35,000	
	0150	Maximum									51,000	
	0200	Asphalt testing, compressive strength Marshall stability, set of 3				Ea.					113	
	0220	Density, set of 3									45	
	0250	Extraction, individual tests on sample									94	
	0300	Penetration									34	
	0350	Mix design, 5 specimens									705	
	0360	Additional specimen									88	
	0400	Specific gravity									41	
	0420	Swell test									69	
	0450	Water effect and cohesion, set of 6									175	
	0470	Water effect and plastic flow									69	
	0600	Concrete testing, aggregates, abrasion									78	
	0650	Absorption									39	
	0800	Petrographic analysis									510	
	0900	Specific gravity									39	
	1000	Sieve analysis, washed									74	
	1050	Unwashed									40	
	1200	Sulfate soundness									83	
	1300	Weight per cubic foot									23	
	1500	Cement, physical tests									275	
	1600	Chemical tests									235	
	1800	Compressive strength, cylinders, delivered to lab									12	
	1900	Picked up by lab, minimum									8.50	
	1950	Average									13.50	
	2000	Maximum									23	

Figure 9.18

The time of year may also have an impact on the cost of temporary services. Snow removal costs must be anticipated in climates where such conditions are likely. If construction begins during a wet season, or there is a high ground water table, then dewatering may be necessary. Usually the boring logs give the contractor a feel for the probable ground water elevation. Logs should be examined for the time of year in which the borings were taken. If high infiltration rates are expected, wellpoints may be required. The pumping allowance is usually priced from an analysis of the expected duration and volume of water. This information dictates pump size, labor to install, and power to operate the pumps. This can be an expensive item, since the pumps may have to operate 168 hours per week during certain phases of construction.

An office trailer and/or storage trailers or containers are usually required and included in the specifications. Even if these items are owned by the contractor, costs should still be allocated to the job as part of project overhead. Telephone, utility and temporary toilet facilities are other costs in this category.

Depending upon the location and local environment, some security services may be required. In addition to security personnel or guard dogs, fences, gates, special lighting and alarms may also be needed. A guard shack with heat, power and telephone, can be an expensive temporary cost.

Temporary Construction

Temporary construction may also involve many items which are not specified in the construction documents. Temporary partitions, doors, fences and barricades may be required to delineate or isolate portions of the building or site. In addition to these items, railings, catwalks or safety nets may also be necessary for the protection of workers. Depending upon the project size, an OSHA representative may visit the site to assure that all such safety precautions are being observed.

Ramps, temporary stairs and ladders are often necessary during construction for access between floors. When the permanent stairs are installed, temporary wood fillers are needed in metal pan treads until the concrete fill is placed. Workers will almost always use a new, permanent elevator for access throughout the building. While this use is almost always restricted, precautionary measures must be taken to protect the doors and cab. Invariably, some damage occurs. Protection of any and all finished surfaces throughout the course of the project must be priced and included in the estimate.

Job Cleanup

An amount should always be carried in the estimate for cleanup of the grounds and the building, both during the construction process and upon completion. The cleanup can be broken down into three basic categories, and these can be estimated separately:

- Continuous (daily or otherwise) cleaning of the building and site.
- Rubbish handling and removal.
- Final cleanup.

Costs for continuous cleaning can be included as an allowance, or estimated by required man-hours. Rubbish handling should include barrels, a trash chute if necessary, dumpster rental and disposal fees. These fees vary depending upon the project, and a permit may also be required. Costs for final cleanup should be based upon past projects and may include subcontract costs for items such as the cleaning of windows and waxing of floors. Included in the costs for final cleanup may be an allowance for repair and minor damage to finished work.

Miscellaneous General Conditions

Many other items must be taken into account when costs are being determined for project overhead. Among the major considerations are:

1. *Scaffolding or Swing Staging* — It is important to determine who is responsible for rental, erection and dismantling of scaffolding. If a subcontractor is responsible, it may be necessary to leave the scaffolding in place long enough for use by other trades. Scaffolding is priced by the section or per hundred square feet.

2. *Small Tools* — An allowance, based on past experience, should be carried for small tools. This allowance should cover hand tools as well as small power tools for use by workers on the general contractor's payroll. Small tools have a habit of "walking" and a certain amount of replacement is necessary. Special tools like magnetic drills may be required for specific tasks.

3. *Permits* — Various types of permits may be required depending upon local codes and regulations. Following are some examples:

   a. General building permit
   b. Subtrade permits (mechanical, electrical, etc.)
   c. Street use permit
   d. Sidewalk use permit
   e. Permit to allow work on Sundays
   f. Rubbish burning permit (if allowed)
   g. Blasting permit

Both the necessity of the permit and the responsibility for acquiring it must be determined. If the work is being done in an unfamiliar location, local building officials should be consulted regarding unusual or unknown requirements.

4. *Insurance* — Insurance coverage for each project and locality — above and beyond normal, required operating insurance — should be reviewed to assure that coverage is adequate. The contract documents will often specify certain required policy limits. The need for specific policies or riders should be anticipated (for example, fire or XCU — explosion collapse, underground).

Other items commonly included in project overhead are: photographs, job signs, sample panels and materials for owner/architect approval, and an allowance for replacement of broken glass. For some materials, such as imported goods or custom fabricated items, both shipping costs and off site storage fees can be expected. An allowance should be included for anticipated costs pertaining to punchlist items. These costs are likely to be based on past experience.

Some project overhead costs can be calculated at the beginning of the estimate. Others will be included as the estimating process proceeds. Still other costs are estimated last since they are dependent upon the total cost and duration of the project. Because many of the overhead items are not directly specified, the estimator must use experience and visualize the construction process to assure that all requirements are met. It is not important when or where these items are included, but that they *are* included. One contractor may list certain costs as project overhead, while another contractor would allocate the same costs (and responsibility) to a subcontractor. Either way, the costs are recorded in the estimate.

Sample Estimate: Division 1

At this initial stage of the estimating process, it is best to list as many as possible the items that are considered overhead. From a thorough review of the construction documents, especially the General and Supplementary Conditions, the estimator should be aware of both the specified requirements and those which are implied but not directly stated. Items are added to the list throughout the estimate. Pricing occurs at the end because a majority of the costs are time related or dependent upon total project cost.

The allocation of work and equipment to be included in the particular subtrades should be decided at this time. For example, the estimator must decide if the temporary fence is to be installed by the general contractor's personnel or if the work is to be subcontracted. Responsibility for establishing grades and building layout could be given to an employed field engineer, an outside engineering firm, or the appropriate subcontractors. These choices should be made at the beginning of the estimate. Figures 9.19 and 9.20 are the Project Overhead Summary for the three-story office building. All items known at this point are listed. Additions to the list and appropriate pricing will occur later in the estimate. Note that certain lump sum (LS) items have been included. Prices for these items (insurance, for example) can be determined either from historical costs or from telephone quotations.

Division 2: Site Work

Prior to quantity takeoff, pricing, or even the site visit, the estimator must read the specifications carefully and examine the plans thoroughly. By knowing — before the site visit — what to expect and what work is required, the estimator is less likely to overlook features and should be able to save time by avoiding a second site visit. In addition to being familiar with project requirements, the estimator might also find a Job Site Analysis form helpful (as in Figures 2.3 and 2.4) to assure that all items are included.

For the other divisions in new building construction, the plans and specifications include almost all of the data required for complete and proper estimating and construction. Site work, however, is similar to remodeling or renovation work. Certain existing conditions and "unknowns" may not be shown on the plans. It is the responsibility of the estimator to discover these conditions and to include appropriate costs in the estimate.

The first step in preparing the site work estimate is to determine areas and limits from the plans (to be checked in the field) for:

- Limits of the total parcel
- Limits of the work area
- Areas of tree removal and clearing
- Stripping of topsoil
- Cut and fill
- Building and utility excavation
- Roads and walks
- Paving
- Landscaping

There are three basic methods to determine area from a plan. The first is with a planimeter — a device which, when rolled along a designated perimeter, will measure area. The resulting measurement must then be converted to the

PROJECT
OVERHEAD SUMMARY

SHEET NO.

PROJECT:	Office Building

ESTIMATE NO:

LOCATION:	ARCHITECT:	DATE: 6/93

QUANTITIES BY:	PRICES BY:	EXTENSIONS BY:	CHECKED BY:

DESCRIPTION	QUANTITY	UNIT	MATERIAL/EQUIP.		LABOR		TOTAL COST	
			UNIT	TOTAL	UNIT	TOTAL	UNIT	TOTAL
Job Organization: Superintendent		WK			1070			
Project Manager								
Timekeeper & Material Clerk		WK			625			
Clerical								
Safety, Watchman & First Aid								
Travel Expense: Superintendent								
Project Manager								
Engineering: Layout		DAY			490			
Inspection / Quantities								
Drawings								
CPM Schedule								
Testing: Soil								
Materials	1	LS		7500				
Structural								
Equipment: Cranes								
Concrete Pump, Conveyor, Etc.								
Elevators, Hoists								
Freight & Hauling								
Loading, Unloading, Erecting, Etc.								
Maintenance								
Pumping								
Scaffolding								
Small Power Equipment / Tools	0.5	%						
Feild Offices: Job Office Trailer		Mo.	251					
Architect / Owner's Office								
Temporary Telephones								
Utilities		Mo.						
Temporary Toilets								
Storage Areas & Sheds		Mo.	89					
Temporary Utilities: Heat								
Light & Power	567	CSF						
PAGE TOTALS								

Figure 9.19

151

DESCRIPTION	QUANTITY	UNIT	MATERIAL/EQUIP.		LABOR		TOTAL COST	
			UNIT	TOTAL	UNIT	TOTAL	UNIT	TOTAL
Totals Brought Forward								
Winter Protection: Temp. Heat/Protection	567	CSF	18.50		22.00			
Snow Plowing								
Thawing Materials								
Temporary Roads	750	SY	2.51		1.53			
Signs & Barricades: Site Sign	1	LS	120	120				
Temporary Fences	1350	LF	1.69		2.70			
Temporary Stairs, Ladders & Floors								
Photographs								
Clean Up								
Dumpster		WK	290					
Final Clean Up	56.7	MSF	5		29			
Continous - One Laborer		WK			742			
Punch List	0.2	%						
Permits: Building	1	%						
Misc.								
Insurance: Builders Risk - Additional Rider	1	LS		35721				
Owner's Protective Liability								
Umbrella								
Unemployment Ins. & Social Security								
(SEE ESTIMATE SUMMARY)								
Bonds								
Performance (SEE ESTIMATE SUMMARY)								
Material & Equipment								
Main Office Expense (SEE ESTIMATE SUMMARY)								
Special Items								
Totals:								

Figure 9.20

scale of the drawing. Trigonometry can also be used to determine area. It is applied to the distances and bearings supplied by a survey. Sines and cosines are used to calculate coordinates, which are in turn used to calculate area. The planimeter may be used only if the drawing is to scale and the scale is known. The trigonometric method may be used on a drawing not to scale, but only if survey data is available. Both methods are accurate.

A third method, triangulation, is less accurate but can be used in either case. This method involves dividing the area into triangles, squares and rectangles and determining the area of each. Some dimensions must be scaled. An example shown in Figure 9.21. Triangulation is quick, and depending upon the shape of the site, is accurate to within a few percent.

Soil borings and analyses, if available, should be reviewed prior to the site visit. Test pit and percolation data can also be very useful. Soil type and porosity, any encountered ledge, and the height of the water table, will all have a bearing on the site work estimate.

The Site Visit

Once the estimator is familiar with the project requirements, the site visit should be used to confirm and verify information. The initial examination should cover such items as general access, the amount and kind of traffic, location of existing utilities, and site storage. These conditions cannot be quantified, but will all have an impact on site work costs. Boundary lines and stakes should be located, especially if the work area is close to property lines.

The site visit may be conducted according to the sequence in which the site work will be performed: clearing and grubbing, excavation, blasting (if necessary), utilities and drainage, backfill, roads, paving and site improvements.

Estimates for tree removal can be made by actually counting and sizing each tree to be removed. If the site is small or the number of trees few, this may be the easiest (and most accurate) method. If large quantities are involved, a random count method will suffice. The first step is to determine the total acreage to be cleared. Counts of each type and size of vegetation should be made for 16' on either side of a line, 340' long. These counts (at least 3) should be made at random. Each count will reflect relative density for one fourth of an acre. Due to rising lumber costs (especially hardwood) and the growing use of firewood, the estimator may find a company or individual to cut and remove the trees at no cost. The expense of stump and brush removal must still be included.

The estimator should determine a rough soil profile, either from test pits, soil borings, or with a shovel. The depth of loam, or topsoil is important. The specifications may state whether the topsoil is to be stripped and stockpiled for reuse on the site, or hauled away. If there is no room for topsoil storage on the site so that all is removed (and possibly sold), topsoil may have to be purchased later for the landscaping. Test pits may also be a good indicator of soil stability. Depending upon the site conditions and project requirements, shoring or sheet piling may be required at trenches and excavations.

The estimator should roughly determine the location of building utilities and other excavation areas and should visualize the excavation process. Stockpile areas should be located and a rough determination reached as to proper equipment size and type. The excavation procedure should be based on a key rule of site work — only move the material once. At this stage, the estimator may or may not have an indication as to whether fill will be required or excess hauled away. These questions will be answered during cut and fill calculations.

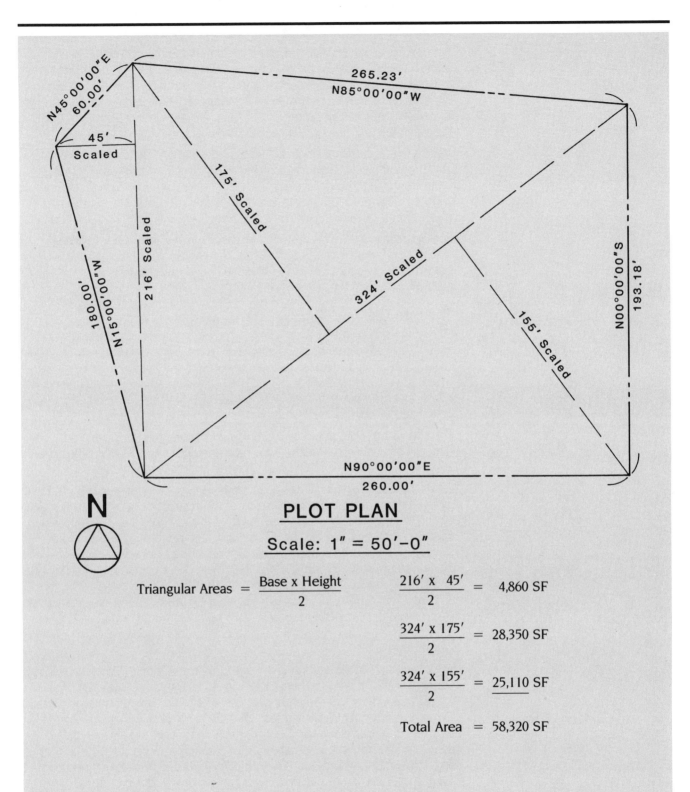

PLOT PLAN

Scale: 1" = 50'-0"

Triangular Areas = $\dfrac{\text{Base x Height}}{2}$

$\dfrac{216' \times 45'}{2} = 4{,}860 \text{ SF}$

$\dfrac{324' \times 175'}{2} = 28{,}350 \text{ SF}$

$\dfrac{324' \times 155'}{2} = 25{,}110 \text{ SF}$

Total Area = 58,320 SF

Figure 9.21

If there is excess fill, haul distance to the dumping area (whether on site or off) will have a bearing not only on cost, but on the selection of equipment. Erosion control measures may be required to prevent soil runoff from stockpiles or excavation areas. If not specified, this possibility should be determined while at the site.

If ledge is evident, either visually or from borings, the estimator should be familiar with local regulations. Where blasting is permitted, items such as mats, overtime work and special permits can be very expensive. Local regulations may require that after exposure by excavation, the ledge be covered (backfilled) before blasting. Because of the fact that subsurface conditions may be unknown, blasting is usually included in the estimate as an allowance per cubic yard. This allowance must include all possibilities.

Existing utilities, whether on-site or off, overhead or underground, should be located and noted or verified on the site plan. The estimator should roughly note locations of the proposed utilities to determine if any problems or conflicts will arise due to existing conditions. For the same reasons, existing drainage conditions should be verified and compared to the proposed drainage.

If the specifications are not clear, the estimator should determine whether or not the excavated material is suitable for backfill. If not, the unsuitable material must be removed and new material purchased and delivered.

Roads, walks, paving, site improvements and landscaping should also be visualized to anticipate any unique conditions or requirements. The quality and detail of the site visit will be reflected in the accuracy and thoroughness of the site work estimate.

Earthwork

Responsibility for layout and staking of the building, grades, utilities and other excavation should be determined prior to estimating. If not, everyone will assume that the other guy is responsible.

There are two basic methods and a third variation of determining cuts and fills for the earthwork portion of a project. The first method is most appropriate for linear excavations (roads and large trenches). It involves determining the cross-sectional area of the excavation at appropriate locations. The area of the cross-sections can be determined by using a planimeter or by the methods shown in Figure 9.22. To calculate volume, two cross-sectional areas are averaged and multiplied by the distance between the sections. The selection and frequency of cross-section locations will have an effect on the calculations. Accuracy is improved if the sections are located so that topography is relatively uniform between each pair. Separate calculations must be made for cuts and for fill.

The second method is to superimpose a grid over the site plan and to determine the existing elevation at each intersection of the grid. The elevations at the four corners of each grid square are averaged. The difference between the proposed elevation and the existing average elevation for each square is calculated (whether cut or fill). All cuts and all fills are added separately to determine excavation quantities. The difference between the two is the amount that must be borrowed or hauled away. A quicker and slightly less accurate variation of this method can also be used. Instead of determining corner elevations and averaging, the estimator can visually determine the average elevations from the relationship of the grid squares to the contours.

A number of factors must be considered when calculating excavation quantities. If all dimensions (elevations and distances) are in feet, then the final cubic

Level Cross-Section

$$\text{Trapezoid Area} = \frac{\text{sum of bases}}{2} \times \text{Height}$$

$$= \frac{20' + 50'}{2} \times 10'$$

$$= 350 \text{ square feet}$$

Three Level Cross Section

$$\text{Triangular Areas} = \text{Area 1} + \text{Area 2} + \text{Area 3} + \text{Area 4}$$

$$= \frac{W}{4}(hL) + \frac{W}{4}(hR) + \frac{C}{2}(dL) + \frac{C}{2}(dR)$$

$$= \frac{W}{4}(hL + hR) + \frac{C}{2}(dL + dR)$$

$$= \frac{20'}{4}(12.1' + 14.4') + \frac{9.4'}{2}(28.3' + 31.6')$$

$$= 414 \text{ square feet}$$

Figure 9.22

156

foot quantities must be converted to cubic yards. When finish grade elevations are taken from a plan, the estimator must be sure to account for subbases and finish materials (gravel, paving, concrete, topsoil, etc.) which will be on top of the subgrade to reach the final elevations and grades.

Another major factor to consider is the difference between bank volume (material in a natural state), loose volume (after digging), and compacted volume. The relationship of swell and shrinkage is illustrated in Figure 9.23, with conversion tables shown in Figure 9.24. As shown, the volume of materials expands when disturbed or excavated. This same material can most often be compacted to less than the natural bank volume. An example of how these conversion tables are used is shown in the sample estimate. When pricing compaction, the estimator must consider the specified depth of lifts, or layers, which must each be compacted. The specifications should also be checked for required compaction testing.

After figuring bulk excavation, the estimator should take off the quantities for the following types of excavation, paying attention for such items as steps and haunches:

- Perimeter strip footings
- Interior strip footings

Approximate Material Characteristics*

Material	Loose (lb/cu yd)	Bank (lb/cu yd)	Swell (%)	Load Factor
Clay, dry	2,100	2,650	26	0.79
Clay, wet	2,700	3,575	32	0.76
Clay and gravel, dry	2,400	2,800	17	0.85
Clay and gravel, wet	2,600	3,100	17	0.85
Earth, dry	2,215	2,850	29	0.78
Earth, moist	2,410	3,080	28	0.78
Earth, wet	2,750	3,380	23	0.81
Gravel, dry	2,780	3,140	13	0.88
Gravel, wet	3,090	3,620	17	0.85
Sand, dry	2,600	2,920	12	0.89
Sand, wet	3,100	3,520	13	0.88
Sand and gravel, dry	2,900	3,250	12	0.89
Sand and gravel, wet	3,400	3,750	10	0.91

*Exact values will vary with grain size, moisture content, compaction, etc. Test to determine exact values for specific soils.

Figure 9.23

- Spread footings
- Utility trenches, meter pits, manholes
- Special items (elevator pits, tunnels, etc.)
- Hand excavation

Caissons and Piles

Caissons, piles and pressure-injected footings are specialty items usually taken off and priced by a subcontractor. The cost of caissons and piles, although priced by the linear foot, is dependent on the number of units to be installed. This is due to the fact that mobilization for the equipment can cost thousands of dollars before the first pile is driven. Typical mobilization costs are shown in Figure 9.25. The mobilization cost will have a lesser effect per unit, as the number of units required increases. When soliciting bids, the estimator should verify that all required costs are included. Pile caps, cutting, testing, and wet conditions will all add to the total cost.

Roads

Temporary roads are an item that may easily by underestimated or overlooked. Under dry conditions, watering, oiling, or calcium chloride treatment may be necessary to prevent dust. Under wet conditions, large quantities of crushed stone and trenching for drainage may be needed. Consideration must be given to the installation of utilities; this procedure may require removal and reconstruction of the temporary road.

As with the building layout, costs must also be included for the layout and grades of roads, curbs and associated utilities. Most specifications will state the requirements for work above rough grade: gravel base, subbase, finish paving courses, etc. Bulk cuts and fills for the roadwork should be determined as part of bulk excavation. Excavation for curbs must also be included. Handwork may be necessary.

Typical Soil Volume Conversion Factors				
Soil Type	Initial Soil Condition	Bank	Converted to:	
			Loose	Compacted
Clay	Bank	1.00	1.27	0.90
	Loose	0.79	1.00	0.71
	Compacted	1.11	1.41	1.00
Common earth	Bank	1.00	1.25	0.90
	Loose	0.80	1.00	0.72
	Compacted	1.11	1.39	1.00
Rock (blasted)	Bank	1.00	1.50	1.30
	Loose	0.67	1.00	0.87
	Compacted	0.77	1.15	1.00
Sand	Bank	1.00	1.12	0.95
	Loose	0.89	1.00	0.85
	Compacted	1.05	1.18	1.00

Figure 9.24

022 | Earthwork

022 800 | Soil Treatment

		CREW	DAILY OUTPUT	MAN-HOURS	UNIT	MAT.	LABOR	EQUIP.	TOTAL	TOTAL INCL O&P	
							1993 BARE COSTS				
804	0400 Insecticides for termite control, minimum	1 Skwk	14.20	.563	Gal.	9.50	13.60		23.10	32	804
	0500 Maximum	↓	11	.727	"	16.25	17.55		33.80	45.50	

023 |Tunneling, Piles and Caissons

023 400 | Tunnel Support Systems

		CREW	DAILY OUTPUT	MAN-HOURS	UNIT	MAT.	LABOR	EQUIP.	TOTAL	TOTAL INCL O&P	
							1993 BARE COSTS				
404	0010 ROOF BOLTS for mines and tunnels 5/8" diameter, 24" long				Ea.	3.10			3.10	3.41	404
	0200 60" long					5.25			5.25	5.80	
	0400 3/4" diameter, 36" long					5.25			5.25	5.80	
	0600 96" long					11			11	12.10	
	0800 Washers for above, 1/4" thick, 4" x 4"					1.15			1.15	1.27	
	1000 6" x 6"				↓	1.25			1.25	1.38	

023 550 | Pile Driving

		CREW	DAILY OUTPUT	MAN-HOURS	UNIT	MAT.	LABOR	EQUIP.	TOTAL	TOTAL INCL O&P	
							1993 BARE COSTS				
554	0010 MOBILIZATION Set up & remove, air compressor, 600 C.F.M. R023 -620	A-5	3.30	5.455	Ea.		102	11.60	113.60	172	554
	0100 1200 C.F.M.	"	2.20	8.182			152	17.45	169.45	257	
	0200 Crane, with pile leads and pile hammer, 75 ton	B-19	.60	106			2,525	2,225	4,750	6,600	
	0300 150 ton	"	.36	177			4,225	3,700	7,925	11,000	
	0500 Drill rig, for caissons, to 36", minimum	B-43	2	24			485	785	1,270	1,625	
	0600 Up to 84"	"	1	48			970	1,575	2,545	3,225	
	0800 Auxiliary boiler, for steam small	A-5	1.66	10.843			202	23	225	340	
	0900 Large	"	.83	21.687			405	46	451	680	
	1100 Rule of thumb: complete pile driving set up, small	B-19	.45	142			3,375	2,950	6,325	8,825	
	1200 Large	"	.27	237	↓		5,625	4,925	10,550	14,700	
558	0011 PILING SPECIAL COSTS pile caps, see also division 033-130										558
	0100 Concrete pile cap for pile groups, 40 to 80 ton capacity										
	0150 2 pile cap	C-17B	15	5.467	Ea.	152	134	16.80	302.80	395	
	0200 3 pile cap		15	5.467		152	134	16.80	302.80	395	
	0250 4 pile cap		11	7.455		228	183	23	434	565	
	0300 5 pile cap		8	10.250		345	251	31.50	627.50	810	
	0350 6 pile cap		6.70	12.239		400	300	37.50	737.50	950	
	0400 7 pile cap	↓	5.30	15.472		560	380	47.50	987.50	1,275	
	0500 Cutoffs, concrete piles, plain	1 Pile	5.50	1.455			34		34	59	
	0600 With steel thin shell		38	.211			4.95		4.95	8.55	
	0700 Steel pile or "H" piles		19	.421			9.90		9.90	17.05	
	0800 Wood piles	↓	38	.211	↓		4.95		4.95	8.55	
	0900 Pre-augering up to 30' deep, average soil, 24" diameter	B-43	180	.267	L.F.		5.40	8.70	14.10	18	
	0920 36" diameter		115	.417			8.45	13.65	22.10	28	
	0960 48" diameter		70	.686			13.85	22.50	36.35	46	
	0980 60" diameter	↓	50	.960	↓		19.40	31.50	50.90	64.50	
	1000 Testing, any type piles, test load is twice the design load										
	1050 50 ton design load, 100 ton test				Ea.					10,500	
	1100 100 ton design load, 200 ton test									12,000	
	1150 150 ton design load, 300 ton test									15,700	
	1200 200 ton design load, 400 ton test									21,000	
	1250 400 ton design load, 800 ton test				↓					31,500	
	1500 Wet conditions, soft damp ground										
	1600 Requiring mats for crane, add								40%	40%	
	1700 Barge mounted driving rig, add								30%	30%	

Figure 9.25

Bituminous paving is usually taken off and priced by the square yard, but it is sold by the ton. The average weight of bituminous concrete is 145 pounds per cubic foot. By converting, 1 square yard, 1" thick weighs approximately 110 pounds. This figure can be used to determine quantities (in tons) for purchase:

Base course: 2" thick, 1,500 S.Y.

1,500 S.Y. x 2" x 110 lbs. = 330,000 lbs. = 165 tons

Finish course: 1" thick, 1,500 S.Y.

1,500 S.Y. x 1" x 110 lbs. = 165,000 lbs. = 82.5 tons

Landscaping

If the required topsoil is stockpiled on site, equipment will be needed for hauling and spreading. Likewise if the stockpile is too large or too small, trucks will have to be mobilized for transport. If large trees and shrubs are specified, equipment may be required for digging and placing.

Landscaping, including lawn sprinklers, sod, seeding, etc., is usually done by subcontractors. The estimator should make sure that the subcontract includes a certain maintenance period during which all plantings are guaranteed. The required period will be most likely stated in the specifications and should include routine maintenance and replacement of dead plantings.

Estimating Hazardous Waste Remediation/Cleanup Work

Hazardous waste cleanup/site remediation work is more difficult to estimate than standard construction. The difficulty arises because all projects are unique and the hazardous materials are very different. In addition, the estimator must consider the cost of not only complying with applicable OSHA and other government regulations, but also the reduced worker productivity associated with these regulations. The cost factors associated with compliance include the following:

- safety training for management and construction personnel
- pre-employment and conclusion of the work medical exams
- site safety meetings
- shower facility and change room
- worker and equipment decontamination
- disposal of contaminated water
- suit up/off time
- personnel protective equipment
- nonproductive support workers for crew assistance and safety related monitoring
- work breaks due to varying ambient temperature levels

Hazardous Material and Hazardous Waste, published by R.S. Means, is a good source of information on the relationship of the above factors to specific sites.

Productivity: The cost impact of these factors is dependent upon the types of hazardous waste and the remediation procedure. OSHA regulations and local authorities require different levels of personnel protective gear for different wastes. The levels of protection range from A to D. Level A protection includes a moon suite with air pack, while level D consists of standard construction clothing with the possible addition of a Tyvek suit, dust mask or safety glasses. The productivity obtained from the work force varies dramatically depending on the level of protective gear compared to normal construction productivity. In general, D level protection allows a worker to be approximately 90% productive. Therefore, published construction data can be used to estimate the work.

The productivity of a C level worker with a full face mask and Tyvek suit is cut to approximately 75%. The B level protective gear of a full suit and air supplied from an outside source drops to approximately 35% efficiency. Level A protection consisting of a full moon suit with a self-contained breathing apparatus drops worker productivity to 20%. As the level of protection increases, additional nonproductive personnel are also required at the site to monitor and assure worker safety.

Disposal: Site remediation may consist of on-site encapsulation, and off-site disposal or destruction of the hazardous material by incineration or using an exotic treatment technique. Off-site disposal requires a complete chemical analysis before the material can be moved, acceptance of the material by the proposed recipient, and EPA manifesting (proper shipping documentation). Note: It is illegal to transport hazardous materials without the proper manifest.

When estimating off-site disposal, include all transportation costs, waiting time, and disposal fees. When estimating on-site incineration, the estimate must include the cost of trial burns to ensure destruction of the hazardous material and acceptance by the EPA of the stack emissions. The cost of treatment/disposal methods should be determined in conjunction with the manufacturer of the remediation equipement. Hazardous waste disposal is generally specified on a performance basis. Therefore, the process should be prequalified to ensure compliance with the specification.

Summary: Site remediation and hazardous waste cleanup should not be undertaken without complete knowledge of all applicable federal and state regulations. Those companies in the business have compliance departments because meeting all regulations is such an overriding concern in their work. The penalties for noncompliance are severe.

Sample Estimate: Division 2

Site work quantities may be derived from several different drawings. In this case, data are taken from the topographic survey, the finish grading plan and the site plan. (Figures 9.2, 9.3 and 9.4). For smaller projects, these three plans may be combined as one. The detailed information that would normally be included in a complete set of plans and specifications is not provided for this example. For purposes of this demonstration, quantities as shown reflect realistic conditions and are based on normal construction techniques and materials.

For the site clearing portion of the estimate, areas to be cleared are measured from the topographic survey (Figure 9.2), but verification of area and determination of vegetation type must be done during the site visit. The estimate sheets for Division 2 are shown in Figures 9.26 through 9.29. Note that the units (acres and square yards) used for tree cutting and grubbing are different than those used for light clearing. The estimator should be sure to convert the required units for pricing. For the example, the whole site is to be cleared. The site dimensions are 310' x 365', or 113,150 square feet. Light clearing is priced by the acre, so the area is converted from 12,570 square yards to 2.6 acres. Prices for site clearing are taken from Figure 9.30.

Quantities for bulk excavation are derived using the alternative method as described above and as shown in Figure 9.31. In this example, a grid representing 20' x 20' squares is used. The estimator determines the average elevation change in each square and designates each as a cut ($-$) or a fill ($+$). The darkened square within the building is for excavation at the elevator pit. All cuts and fills are totalled separately and converted to cubic yards. An amount to

CONSOLIDATED ESTIMATE

PROJECT: Office Building   CLASSIFICATION: Division 2   SHEET NO. 1 of 4

LOCATION: ARCHITECT: ESTIMATE NO:

TAKE OFF BY: QUANTITIES BY: PRICES BY: EXTENSIONS BY: DATE: 6/93   CHECKED BY:

SOURCE	DESCRIPTION	QUANT.	UNIT	MATERIAL COST	MATERIAL TOTAL	LABOR COST	LABOR TOTAL	EQUIPMENT COST	EQUIPMENT TOTAL	SUBCONTRACT COST	SUBCONTRACT TOTAL	TOTAL COST	TOTAL
	Site Work - Div. 2												
	Site Clearing												
021 104 0200	Med. Trees - Cut	0.46	Acre			1350	621	1500	690				
021 104 0250	Grub & Remove Stumps	0.46	Acre			505.00	232	1500	690				
021 108 0300	Light Clearing	2.6	Acre			171.00	445	415.00	1079				
	Earthwork												
022 238 1300	Bulk Excavation	5430	CY			0.26	1412	0.73	3964				
022 238 1550	Load Trucks (Loose)	3212	CY			0.42	1349	0.51	1638				
022 266 0400	Haul (Loose)	3212	CY			0.74	2377	1.85	5942				
022 222 0300	Compact Fill	2860	CY			0.21	601	0.39	1115				
022 242 5220	Excess Excavation @ Foundation	272	CY			0.33	90	1.16	316				
022 204 1300	Backfill & Compact @ Foundation	302	CY			0.22	66	0.69	208				
0600		302	CY			2.47	746	0.98	296				
022 204 0010	Backfill & Compact @ Elev. Pit	30	CY			10.60	318	0.98	29				
0600		30	CY			2.47	74						
022 254 0060	Footing Excavation, Spread	305	CY			1.71	522	1.41	430				
2400		305	CY			0.51	156	0.42	129				
022 254 0060	Footing Excavation, Continuous	85	CY			1.71	145	1.41	120				
022 204 1900	Backfill @ Footings Incl. Spread Excess	390	CY			0.30	117	0.92	359				
	Subtotals						$9,271		$17,006				

Figure 9.26

162

CONSOLIDATED ESTIMATE

PROJECT: Office Building   CLASSIFICATION: Division 2   SHEET NO. 2 of 4

LOCATION: ARCHITECT:

TAKE OFF BY: QUANTITIES BY: PRICES BY: EXTENSIONS BY:

DESCRIPTION	SOURCE	QUANT.	UNIT	MATERIAL COST	MATERIAL TOTAL	LABOR COST	LABOR TOTAL	EQUIPMENT COST	EQUIPMENT TOTAL	SUBCONTRACT COST	SUBCONTRACT TOTAL	TOTAL
Division 2: (Cont'd) Earthwork (Cont'd)												
Utility Excavation,												
24" Drain Excavation	022 254 0300	230	CY			1.81	416	2.94	676			
Backfill & Compact	022 204 0600	287	CY			2.47	709	0.98	281			
Gas, Water, Sewer	022 258 2600	240	LF			0.28	67	0.28	67			
Compaction	022 258 3200	240	LF			0.14	34	0.14	34			
Sub Drain Gravel	022 262 1300	46	CY	8.10	373	4.29	197	0.56	26			
Floor Slab Gravel, 6" Compacted	022 262 0600	19000	SF	0.15	2850	0.11	2090	0.01	190			
Mobilization, Dozer, Loader Backhoe, Compactor	022 274 0400	4	Ea.			48.50	194	231.00	924			
Site Drainage & Utilities												
Catch Basin & Grate	027 152 1120	3	Ea.	360.00	1080	161.00	483	67.00	201			
	2100	3	Ea.	172.00	516	62.00	186	25.50	77			
Gas Service 3"	026 852 0650	80	LF	6.50	520	3.22	258	0.18	14			
Water Service 6"	026 686 1430	80	LF	11.05	884	5.60	448	1.04	83			
Gate Valve 6"	151 960 2300	1	Ea.	345.00	345	205.00	205					
Sewer, 6" PVC	027 168 2040	80	LF	1.65	132	1.44	115					
Foundation Drain	027 106 2020	620	LF	1.50	930	0.67	415					
Drain Pipe 24" Concrete	027 162 2040	310	LF	13.50	4185	6.90	2139	1.28	397			
Subtotals					$11,815		$7,957		$2,970			

Figure 9.27

CONSOLIDATED ESTIMATE

PROJECT: Office Building   CLASSIFICATION: Division 2

LOCATION: ARCHITECT:

TAKE OFF BY: QUANTITIES BY: PRICES BY: EXTENSIONS BY:

ESTIMATE NO:

DATE: 6/93

CHECKED BY:

DESCRIPTION	SOURCE			QUANT.	UNIT	MATERIAL COST	MATERIAL TOTAL	LABOR COST	LABOR TOTAL	EQUIPMENT COST	EQUIPMENT TOTAL	SUBCONTRACT COST	SUBCONTRACT TOTAL	TOTAL COST	TOTAL TOTAL
Division 2: (Cont'd)															
Roads & Walks															
Base Course 9"	022	308	0200	8530	SY	6.05	51607	0.29	2474	0.39	3327				
Paving - Bituminous															
Binder	025	104	0160	8530	SY	3.95	33694	0.36	3071	0.33	2815				
Wearing (@ $30/TON)	025	104	0340	8530	SY	2.47	21069	0.26	2218	0.24	2047				
Concrete Curb															
Precast Straight	025	254	0550	2050	LF	5.75	11788	1.60	3280	0.84	1722				
Precast Radius	025	254	0600	240	LF	7.25	1740	3.44	826	1.81	434				
Line Painting															
Stalls	025	804	0800	203	Stall	0.75	152	1.06	215	0.53	108				
Arrows	025	804	0620	150	SF	0.25	38	0.40	60	0.20	30				
Precast Bumpers	028	408	1000	203	Ea.	22.00	4466	6.30	1279						
Concrete Sidewalks	025	128	0310	1625	SF	0.92	1495	0.87	1414						
Concrete Steps from (033-130-6850)	028	416	0500	95	LF	3.77	358	8.85	841	0.30	29				
Lawns & Plantings															
Landscaping	TELEPHONE QUOTE (Includes sales tax)														
Sprinkler				15700	S.F.							0.56	8792		
Lawn, Top Soil, Fert., Seed				15.71	MSF							570.00	8952		
Trees (60) & Shrubs (200), Including Planting													15671		
Subtotals							**$126,406**		**$15,676**		**$10,511**		**$33,415**		

Figure 9.28

164

CONSOLIDATED ESTIMATE

PROJECT: Office Building
LOCATION:
TAKE OFF BY:
QUANTITIES BY:
PRICES BY:
EXTENSIONS BY:

CLASSIFICATION: Division 2
ARCHITECT:

ESTIMATE NO:
DATE: 6/93
CHECKED BY:

DESCRIPTION	SOURCE	QUANT.	UNIT	MATERIAL		LABOR		EQUIPMENT		SUBCONTRACT		TOTAL	
				COST	TOTAL	COST	TOTAL	COST	TOTAL	COST	TOTAL	COST	TOTAL
Division 2: (Cont'd)													
Sheet 1 Subtotals							9271		17006				
Sheet 2 Subtotals					11815		7957		2970				
Sheet 3 Subtotals					126406		15676		10511		33415		
Division 2 Totals					$138,220		$32,904		$30,487		$33,415		

Figure 9.29

021 100 | Site Clearing

		CREW	DAILY OUTPUT	MAN-HOURS	UNIT	1993 BARE COSTS				TOTAL INCL O&P	
						MAT.	LABOR	EQUIP.	TOTAL		
104	0010	CLEAR AND GRUB Light, trees to 6″ diam., cut & chip	B-7	1	48	Acre		950	1,050	2,000	2,625	104
	0150	Grub stumps and remove	B-30	2	12			252	750	1,002	1,200	
	0200	Medium, trees to 12″ diam., cut & chip	B-7	.70	68.571			1,350	1,500	2,850	3,775	
	0250	Grub stumps and remove	B-30	1	24	↓		505	1,500	2,005	2,425	
104	0300	Heavy, trees to 24″ diam., cut & chip	B-7	.30	160	Acre		3,175	3,475	6,650	8,775	104
	0350	Grub stumps and remove	B-30	.50	48			1,000	3,000	4,000	4,850	
	0400	If burning is allowed, reduce cut & chip				↓					40%	
108	0010	CLEARING Brush with brush saw	A-1	.25	32	Acre		595	235	830	1,200	108
	0100	By hand	"	.12	66.667			1,225	490	1,715	2,475	
	0300	With dozer, ball and chain, light clearing	B-11A	2	8			171	415	586	725	
	0400	Medium clearing	"	1.50	10.667	↓		228	555	783	960	

021 150 | Selective Clearing

		CREW	DAILY OUTPUT	MAN-HOURS	UNIT	1993 BARE COSTS				TOTAL INCL O&P	
						MAT.	LABOR	EQUIP.	TOTAL		
154	0010	SELECTIVE CLEARING										154
	1000	Stump removal on site by hydraulic backhoe, 1-1/2 C.Y.										
	1050	8″ to 12″ diameter	B-30	33	.727	Ea.		15.25	45.50	60.75	73.50	
	1100	14″ to 24″ diameter		25	.960			20	60	80	97	
	1150	26″ to 36″ diameter	↓	16	1.500	↓		31.50	94	125.50	151	
	2000	Remove selective trees, on site using chain saws and chipper,										
	2050	not incl. stumps, up to 6″ diameter	B-7	18	2.667	Ea.		53	58	111	146	
	2100	8″ to 12″ diameter		12	4			79	87	166	220	
	2150	14″ to 24″ diameter		10	4.800			95	104	199	263	
	2200	26″ to 36″ diameter	↓	8	6			119	130	249	330	
	2300	Machine load, 2 mile haul to dump, 12″ diam. tree, add				↓				40	38	

021 200 | Structure Moving

		CREW	DAILY OUTPUT	MAN-HOURS	UNIT	1993 BARE COSTS				TOTAL INCL O&P	
						MAT.	LABOR	EQUIP.	TOTAL		
204	0010	MOVING BUILDINGS One day move, up to 24′ wide										204
	0020	Reset on new foundation, patch & hook-up, average move				Total					8,500	
	0040	Wood or steel frame bldg., based on ground floor area	B-4	185	.259	S.F.		4.94	2.29	7.23	10.20	
	0060	Masonry bldg., based on ground floor area	"	137	.350			6.65	3.09	9.74	13.80	
	0200	For 24′ to 42′ wide, add				↓					15%	
	0220	For each additional day on road, add	B-4	1	48	Day		915	425	1,340	1,900	
	0240	Construct new basement, move building, 1 day										
	0300	move, patch & hook-up, based on ground floor area	B-3	155	.310	S.F.	5.25	6.25	9.95	21.45	26.50	

021 400 | Dewatering

		CREW	DAILY OUTPUT	MAN-HOURS	UNIT	1993 BARE COSTS				TOTAL INCL O&P	
						MAT.	LABOR	EQUIP.	TOTAL		
404	0010	DEWATERING Excavate drainage trench, 2′ wide, 2′ deep	B-11C	90	.178	C.Y.		3.79	2.23	6.02	8.30	404
	0100	2′ wide, 3′ deep, with backhoe loader	"	135	.119			2.53	1.49	4.02	5.55	
	0200	Excavate sump pits by hand, light soil	1 Clab	7.10	1.127			21		21	33	
	0300	Heavy soil	"	3.50	2.286	↓		42.50		42.50	66.50	
	0500	Pumping 8 hr., attended 2 hrs. per day, including 20 L.F.										
	0550	of suction hose & 100 L.F. discharge hose										
	0600	2″ diaphragm pump used for 8 hours	B-10H	4	3	Day		67	7.55	74.55	111	
	0650	4″ diaphragm pump used for 8 hours	B-10I	4	3			67	19.55	86.55	125	
	0800	8 hrs. attended, 2″ diaphragm pump	B-10H	1	12			267	30	297	445	
	0900	3″ centrifugal pump	B-10J	1	12			267	44.50	311.50	460	
	1000	4″ diaphragm pump	B-10I	1	12			267	78	345	495	
	1100	6″ centrifugal pump	B-10K	1	12	↓		267	207	474	640	
	1300	Re-lay CMP, incl. excavation 3′ deep, 12″ diameter	B-6	115	.209	L.F.	5.30	4.19	1.74	11.23	14.25	
	1400	18″ diameter		100	.240	"	7.95	4.82	2.01	14.78	18.45	
	1600	Sump hole construction, incl. excavation and gravel, pit		1,250	.019	C.F.	.37	.39	.16	.92	1.19	
	1700	With 12″ gravel collar, 12″ pipe, corrugated, 16 ga.		70	.343	L.F.	9.25	6.90	2.87	19.02	24	
	1800	15″ pipe, corrugated, 16 ga.		55	.436		11.85	8.75	3.65	24.25	30.50	
	1900	18″ pipe, corrugated, 16 ga.		50	.480		13.25	9.65	4.01	26.91	34	

Figure 9.30

166

compensate for reduction in volume is added to the total fill yardage before net calculation. This is due to the decrease in volume of earth when compacted (see Figure 9.23). The costs for bulk excavation are taken from Figure 9.32. Compaction is not included and must be added separately.

Quantities for bulk excavation are based on finish grades. Excess excavation at the foundation to be backfilled must be included as shown in Figure 9.26. Calculations for compaction at the foundation and for loading and hauling excess fill are as follows:

Compaction at foundation:

Excavation (Bank C.Y.) = 272 C.Y.

$$\frac{1.0 \text{ Bank C.Y.}}{0.9 \text{ Compacted C.Y.}} \quad x \quad 272 \text{ C.Y.} \quad = \quad 302 \text{ C.Y. required}$$

Load and haul excess fill:

Excess fill (Bank C.Y.) = 2,570 C.Y.

$$\frac{1.25 \text{ Loose C.Y.}}{1.0 \text{ Bank C.Y.}} \quad x \quad 2,570 \text{ C.Y.} \quad = \quad 3,212 \text{ Loose C.Y.}$$

The ratios of bank to loose to compacted earth were derived from Figure 9.24. If the above calculations were not made, almost 700 cubic yards of loading and hauling may not have been included in the estimate. This represents 60-70 truckloads. The calculation for foundation compaction indicates that 302 cubic yards of bank material *when compacted* are required to replace 272 cubic yards of excavated bank material. Only backfill, (and not compaction) is included for the footings, because the costs are primarily for the spreading of excess material. Compaction is included with the foundation backfill and at the floor subbase.

Costs for asphaltic concrete pavement are taken from Figure 9.33. Note on the estimate sheet that the price per ton for the sample building (Figure 9.28) is different than that in *Means Building Construction Cost Data*. By simple conversion, prices in *Means Building Construction Cost Data* can be adjusted to local conditions:

Line No.: 025-104-0851	Wearing Course
National average	$26.50
Local cost (for sample project)	$30.00

$$\frac{\$30.00}{\$26.50} \quad = \quad 1.13$$

Material cost per S.Y. x Conversion factor = Local cost per S.Y.

$2.19 per S.Y. x 1.13 = $2.47 per S.Y.

The landscaping and site improvements for the sample project are to be subcontracted. This relieves the general contractor, not only of the responsibility of pricing, but also of the problems of maintenance and potential plant replacement. The subcontract price, as received by telephone, is shown in Figure 9.34. The estimator must ask the appropriate questions to be sure that all work is included and all requirements met.

Division 3: Concrete

All cast in place for concrete concrete work involves the same basic elements: formwork, reinforcing, concrete, placement and finishing. There are two methods that can be used to estimate the concrete portion of a project. All of the above components may be grouped together to form systems or

Figure 9.31

168

022 200 | Excav, Backfill, Compact

		CREW	DAILY OUTPUT	MAN-HOURS	UNIT	1993 BARE COSTS				TOTAL INCL O&P
						MAT.	LABOR	EQUIP.	TOTAL	
238	0010	**EXCAVATING, BULK BANK MEASURE** Common earth piled R022-240									238
	0020	For loading onto trucks, add							15%	15%	
	0050	For mobilization and demobilization, see division 022-274 R022-250									
	0100	For hauling, see division 022-266									
	0200	Backhoe, hydraulic, crawler mtd., 1 C.Y. cap. = 75 C.Y./hr.	B-12A	600	.027	C.Y.		.60	.96	1.56	1.97
	0250	1-1/2 C.Y. cap. = 100 C.Y./hr.	B-12B	800	.020	↓		.45	.91	1.36	1.69
238	0260	2 C.Y. cap. = 130 C.Y./hr.	B-12C	1,040	.015	C.Y.		.35	.93	1.28	1.55	238
	0300	3 C.Y. cap. = 160 C.Y./hr.	B-12D	1,620	.010			.22	1.33	1.55	1.80
	0310	Wheel mounted, 1/2 C.Y. cap. = 30 C.Y./hr.	B-12E	240	.067			1.51	1.34	2.85	3.77
	0360	3/4 C.Y. cap. = 45 C.Y./hr.	B-12F	360	.044			1	1.26	2.26	2.92
	0500	Clamshell, 1/2 C.Y. cap. = 20 C.Y./hr.	B-12G	160	.100			2.26	2.78	5.04	6.50
	0550	1 C.Y. cap. = 35 C.Y./hr.	B-12H	280	.057			1.29	1.86	3.15	4.02
	1000	Dragline, 3/4 C.Y. cap. = 35 C.Y./hr.	B-12I	280	.057			1.29	1.63	2.92	3.76
	1050	1-1/2 C.Y. cap. = 65 C.Y./hr.	B-12P	520	.031			.70	1.42	2.12	2.62
	1200	Front end loader, track mtd., 1-1/2 C.Y. cap. = 70 C.Y./hr.	B-10N	560	.021			.48	.64	1.12	1.43
	1250	2-1/2 C.Y. cap. = 95 C.Y./hr.	B-10O	760	.016			.35	.60	.95	1.21
	1300	3 C.Y. cap. = 130 C.Y./hr.	B-10P	1,040	.012			.26	.73	.99	1.20
	1350	5 C.Y. cap. = 160 C.Y./hr.	B-10Q	1,620	.007			.16	.66	.82	.97
	1500	Wheel mounted, 3/4 C.Y. cap. = 45 C.Y./hr.	B-10R	360	.033			.74	.65	1.39	1.86
	1550	1-1/2 C.Y. cap. = 80 C.Y./hr.	B-10S	640	.019			.42	.51	.93	1.21
	1600	2-1/4 C.Y. cap. = 100 C.Y./hr.	B-10T	800	.015			.33	.63	.96	1.20
	1650	5 C.Y. cap. = 185 C.Y./hr.	B-10U	1,480	.008			.18	.64	.82	.98
	1800	Hydraulic excavator, truck mtd., 1/2 C.Y. = 30 C.Y./hr.	B-12J	240	.067			1.51	2.45	3.96	4.99
	1850	48 inch bucket, 1 C.Y. = 45 C.Y./hr.	B-12K	360	.044			1	2.25	3.25	4.01
	3700	Shovel, 1/2 C.Y. capacity = 55 C.Y./hr.	B-12L	440	.036			.82	1.01	1.83	2.37
	3750	3/4 C.Y. capacity = 85 C.Y./hr.	B-12M	680	.024			.53	.76	1.29	1.64
	3800	1 C.Y. capacity = 120 C.Y./hr.	B-12N	960	.017			.38	.61	.99	1.24
	3850	1-1/2 C.Y. capacity = 160 C.Y./hr.	B-12O	1,280	.013			.28	.65	.93	1.15
	3900	3 C.Y. cap. = 250 C.Y./hr.	B-12T	2,000	.008			.18	.54	.72	.88
	4000	For soft soil or sand, deduct								15%	15%
	4100	For heavy soil or stiff clay, add								60%	60%
	4200	For wet excavation with clamshell or dragline, add								100%	100%
	4250	All other equipment, add								50%	50%
	4400	Clamshell in sheeting or cofferdam, minimum	B-12H	160	.100			2.26	3.26	5.52	7.05
	4450	Maximum	"	60	.267	↓		6.05	8.70	14.75	18.75
	8000	For hauling excavated material, see div. 022-266									
242	0010	**EXCAVATING, BULK, DOZER** Open site									242
	2000	75 H.P., 50' haul, sand & gravel	B-10L	460	.026	C.Y.		.58	.63	1.21	1.59
	2020	Common earth		400	.030			.67	.73	1.40	1.83
	2040	Clay		250	.048			1.07	1.17	2.24	2.92
	2200	150' haul, sand & gravel		230	.052			1.16	1.27	2.43	3.18
	2220	Common earth		200	.060			1.34	1.46	2.80	3.66
	2240	Clay		125	.096			2.14	2.33	4.47	5.85
	2400	300' haul, sand & gravel		120	.100			2.23	2.43	4.66	6.10
	2420	Common earth		100	.120			2.67	2.92	5.59	7.30
	2440	Clay		65	.185			4.11	4.49	8.60	11.25
	3000	105 H.P., 50' haul, sand & gravel	B-10W	700	.017			.38	.59	.97	1.24
	3020	Common earth		610	.020			.44	.68	1.12	1.42
	3040	Clay		385	.031			.69	1.08	1.77	2.26
	3200	150' haul, sand & gravel		310	.039			.86	1.34	2.20	2.79
	3220	Common earth		270	.044			.99	1.54	2.53	3.21
	3240	Clay		170	.071			1.57	2.44	4.01	5.10
	3300	300' haul, sand & gravel		140	.086			1.91	2.96	4.87	6.20
	3320	Common earth		120	.100			2.23	3.46	5.69	7.20
	3340	Clay		100	.120			2.67	4.15	6.82	8.65
	4000	200 H.P., 50' haul, sand & gravel	B-10B	1,400	.009	↓		.19	.59	.78	.94

Figure 9.32

025 100	Walk/Rd/Parkng Paving	CREW	DAILY OUTPUT	MAN-HOURS	UNIT	1993 BARE COSTS				TOTAL INCL O&P	
						MAT.	LABOR	EQUIP.	TOTAL		
104											**104**
0010	**ASPHALTIC CONCRETE PAVEMENT** for highways	R025 -110									
0020	and large paved areas										
0080	Binder course, 1-1/2" thick	B-25	7,725	.011	S.Y.	2	.23	.21	2.44	2.79	
0120	2" thick		6,345	.014		2.67	.28	.25	3.20	3.65	
0160	3" thick		4,905	.018		3.95	.36	.33	4.64	5.25	
0200	4" thick		4,140	.021		5.30	.43	.39	6.12	6.90	
0300	Wearing course, 1" thick	B-25B	10,575	.009		1.44	.19	.17	1.80	2.06	
0340	1-1/2" thick		7,725	.012		2.19	.26	.24	2.69	3.07	
0380	2" thick		6,345	.015		2.95	.31	.29	3.55	4.04	
0420	2-1/2" thick		5,480	.018		3.63	.36	.33	4.32	4.93	
0460	3" thick		4,900	.020		4.33	.40	.37	5.10	5.80	
0800	Alternate method of figuring paving costs										
0810	Binder course, 1-1/2" thick	B-25	630	.140	Ton	26	2.83	2.54	31.37	36	
0811	2" thick		690	.128		26	2.58	2.32	30.90	35.50	
0812	3" thick		800	.110		26	2.23	2	30.23	34.50	
0813	4" thick		900	.098		26	1.98	1.78	29.76	34	
0850	Wearing course, 1" thick	B-25B	575	.167		26.50	3.43	3.17	33.10	38.50	
0851	1-1/2" thick		630	.152		26.50	3.13	2.90	32.53	37.50	
0852	2" thick		690	.139		26.50	2.86	2.64	32	37	
0853	2-1/2" thick		745	.129		26.50	2.65	2.45	31.60	36.50	
0854	3" thick		800	.120		26.50	2.47	2.28	31.25	36	
108											**108**
0010	**ASPHALTIC CONCRETE** At the plant (145 lb. per C.F.)	R025 -110			Ton	25.50			25.50	28.50	
0200	All weather patching mix					27.50			27.50	30.50	
0300	Berm mix					27.50			27.50	30.50	
112											**112**
0010	**CALCIUM CHLORIDE** Delivered, 100 lb. bags, truckload lots				Ton	300			300	330	
0200	Solution, 4 lb. flake per gallon, tank truck delivery				Gal.	.62			.62	.68	
120											**120**
0010	**CONCRETE PAVEMENT** Including joints, finishing, and curing										
0020	Fixed form, 12' pass, unreinforced, 6" thick	B-26	3,000	.029	S.Y.	13.50	.61	.60	14.71	16.45	
0100	8" thick		2,700	.033		18	.68	.66	19.34	21.50	
0200	9" thick		2,900	.030		20.50	.63	.62	21.75	24	
0300	10" thick		2,100	.042		22.50	.87	.85	24.22	27.50	
0400	12" thick		1,800	.049		27	1.02	1	29.02	32	
0500	15" thick		1,500	.059		34	1.22	1.20	36.42	40	
0510	For small irregular areas, add						100%		100%		
0700	Finishing, broom finish small areas	2 Cefi	135	.119	S.Y.		2.73		2.73	4.08	
1000	Curing, with sprayed membrane by hand	2 Clab	1,500	.011	"	.15	.20		.35	.48	
1650	For integral coloring, see div. 033-126										
122											**122**
0010	**FINE GRADE** Area to be paved with grader, small area	B-11L	800	.020	S.Y.		.43	.70	1.13	1.43	
0100	Large area	"	2,000	.008			.17	.28	.45	.57	
1100	Fine grade for slab on grade, confined area, machine	B-32C	1,500	.032			.69	1.08	1.77	2.25	
1150	Hand grading	B-18	700	.034			.66	.06	.72	1.10	
128											**128**
0010	**SIDEWALKS, DRIVEWAYS, & PATIOS** No base	R025 -110									
0020	Asphaltic concrete, 2" thick	B-37	720	.067	S.Y.	2.95	1.31	.17	4.43	5.50	
0100	2-1/2" thick	"	660	.073	"	3.63	1.43	.19	5.25	6.40	
0300	Concrete, 3000 psi, cast in place with 6 x 6 - W1.4 x W1.4 mesh,										
0310	broomed finish, no base, 4" thick	B-24	600	.040	S.F.	.92	.87		1.79	2.35	
0350	5" thick		545	.044		1.10	.95		2.05	2.68	
0400	6" thick		510	.047		1.28	1.02		2.30	2.98	
0450	For bank run gravel base, 4" thick, add	B-18	2,500	.010		.12	.18	.02	.32	.44	
0520	8" thick, add	"	1,600	.015		.24	.29	.03	.56	.74	
0550	Exposed aggregate finish, add to above, minimum	B-24	1,875	.013		.06	.28		.34	.50	
0600	Maximum	"	455	.053		.21	1.14		1.35	1.99	
1000	Crushed stone, 1" thick, white marble	2 Clab	1,700	.009		.39	.17		.56	.70	

Figure 9.33

	DATE	
PROJECT Office Building	TIME	
FIRM QUOTING Landscaping, Inc.	PHONE ( )	
ADDRESS	BY	
ITEM QUOTED Landscaping & Sprinklers	RECEIVED BY EBW	

WORK INCLUDED	AMOUNT OF QUOTATION
Automatic sprinkler system	8 7 9 2
Top soil ⎫	
Seeding ⎭	8 9 5 2
Trees ⎫	
Shrubs ⎭	1 5 6 7 1
(Area ≈ 15,700 SF or 1745 SY	
DELIVERY TIME TOTAL BID	3 3 4 1 5

DOES QUOTATION INCLUDE THE FOLLOWING: If ☐ NO is checked, determine the following:

STATE & LOCAL SALES TAXES	☒ YES	☐ NO	MATERIAL VALUE
DELIVERY TO THE JOB SITE	☒ YES	☐ NO	WEIGHT
COMPLETE INSTALLATION	☒ YES	☐ NO	QUANTITY
COMPLETE SECTION AS PER PLANS & SPECIFICATIONS	☒ YES	☐ NO	DESCRIBE BELOW

EXCLUSIONS AND QUALIFICATIONS

Maintenance: Routine   60 Days

Guarantee: Sprinkler   1 Year
            Dead Replacement 90 Days

ADDENDA ACKNOWLEDGEMENT	TOTAL ADJUSTMENTS	
	ADJUSTED TOTAL BID	

ALTERNATES

ALTERNATE NO.
ALTERNATE NO.
ALTERNATE NO.
ALTERNATE NO.
ALTERNATE NO.
ALTERNATE NO.
ALTERNATE NO.

Figure 9.34

assemblies, such as an 8″ foundation wall, 24″ x 24″ column, and a 1′ x 2′ strip footing. Prices for such systems are shown in Figure 9.35. A more accurate, but time consuming method is to quantify and price the individual components of the concrete work.

Note that the costs in Figure 9.35 are primarily shown per cubic yard of concrete. Prices may also be separated for minimum, average or maximum reinforcing. Care should be taken when using this pricing method to assure that the proposed system closely matches the priced system. For example, one foundation wall system cost cannot be developed to accurately price different size walls. An 8″ wall will require 81 square feet of formwork contact area for every cubic yard of concrete. In contrast, a 12″ wall will require 54 square feet of forms. The ratio of square feet of form contact area to concrete volume is different for the two wall thicknesses. Reinforcing quantities may also differ per cubic yard. If systems are used for concrete pricing, all variables must be considered.

In the charts below, SFCA is square feet of formwork contact area.

Wall	SFCA/S.F. Wall	SFCA/C.Y. Concrete
8″ wall	2.0	81.0
12″ wall	2.0	54.0
16″ wall	2.0	40.5

Columns	SFCA/L.F. Column	SFCA/C.Y. Concrete
12″ square	4.0	108.0
16″ square	5.3	81.0
24″ square	8.0	54.0

Unless the estimator has prices for all possible cast in place concrete system variations, the most accurate estimating method is to determine the costs for each component of the concrete work.

Cast in Place Concrete

Before beginning the quantity takeoff, the estimator should carefully review the specifications for requirements that may not be indicated on the plans. Such items may include concrete type (regular or lightweight), concrete strengths, and curing time. Specified additives — such as colors and air entrainment — must also be included in the takeoff, along with protection during curing. In addition to the specifications and plans, details and sections showing concrete work will usually be provided. Reinforcing requirements and accessories will be indicated on these drawings.

When estimating concrete work by individual component, it might be possible to apply the dimensions and quantities calculated for one component to another. It is helpful to take off quantities for all components of one type of concrete work at the same time. For example, the square feet of form contact area may also be the same area that will require finishing.

An example of this quantity takeoff method is shown in Figures 9.36 and 9.37. Footing, Column and Beam Schedules which are normally included on foundation plans, are shown in Figure 9.41. Note on Figure 9.37 that volume (to determine quantity of concrete) is not converted to cubic yards for each system until total cubic feet are determined. This eliminates the effect of rounding errors and helps to assure that such conversions are done consistently and accurately. If concrete is taken off and priced in this way, the quantities and prices of a given project can be used to develop historical costs for future projects.

033 | Cast-In-Place Concrete

033 100 | Structural Concrete

		CREW	DAILY OUTPUT	MAN-HOURS	UNIT	MAT.	LABOR	EQUIP.	TOTAL	TOTAL INCL O&P	
130	**0010**	**CONCRETE IN PLACE** Including forms (4 uses), reinforcing	R033 -010									**130**
	0050	steel, including finishing unless otherwise indicated										
	0100	Average for concrete framed building,	R033 -100									
	0110	including finishing		C-17B	15.75	5.206	C.Y.	108	128	16	252	340
	0130	Average for substructure only, simple design, incl. finishing		↓	29.07	2.821	↓	84	69	8.65	161.65	211
	0150	Average for superstructure only, including finishing		↓	13.42	6.110	↓	119	150	18.75	287.75	390
	0200	Base, granolithic, 1" x 5" high, straight	R033 -110	C-10	175	.137	L.F.	.12	2.96	.43	3.51	5.05
	0220	Cove		"	140	.171	"	.12	3.69	.53	4.34	6.30
	0300	Beams, 5 kip per L.F., 10' span	R033 -120	C-17A	6.28	12.898	C.Y.	178	315	20	513	715
	0350	25' span			7.40	10.946		142	268	17.10	427.10	595
	0500	Chimney foundations, industrial, minimum	R033 -130		26.70	3.034		96	74.50	4.73	175.23	228
	0510	Maximum			19.70	4.112		110	101	6.40	217.40	287
	0700	Columns, square, 12" x 12", minimum reinforcing	R042 -055		4.60	17.609		208	430	27.50	665.50	940
	0720	Average reinforcing		↓	4.10	19.756		298	485	31	814	1,125
	0740	Maximum reinforcing		C-17B	3.84	21.354		430	525	65.50	1,020.50	1,375
	0800	16" x 16", minimum reinforcing		C-17A	6.25	12.960		156	320	20	496	695
	0820	Average reinforcing		"	4.93	16.430		249	405	25.50	679.50	935
	0840	Maximum reinforcing		C-17B	4.34	18.894		410	465	58	933	1,250
	0900	24" x 24", minimum reinforcing		C-17A	9.08	8.921		139	219	13.90	371.90	515
	0920	Average reinforcing			6.90	11.739		205	288	18.30	511.30	700
	0940	Maximum reinforcing		↓	5.65	14.336		340	350	22.50	712.50	955
	1000	36" x 36", minimum reinforcing		C-17B	13.39	6.124		149	150	18.80	317.80	420
	1020	Average reinforcing			9.61	8.533		232	209	26	467	615
	1040	Maximum reinforcing			7.50	10.933		370	268	33.50	671.50	865
	1200	Columns, round, tied, 16" diameter, minimum reinforcing			13.02	6.298		232	154	19.35	405.35	520
	1220	Average reinforcing			8.30	9.880		330	242	30.50	602.50	780
	1240	Maximum reinforcing			6.05	13.554		530	330	41.50	901.50	1,150
	1300	20" diameter, minimum reinforcing			17.35	4.726		249	116	14.50	379.50	470
	1320	Average reinforcing			10.43	7.862		400	193	24	617	770
	1340	Maximum reinforcing			7.47	10.977		545	269	33.50	847.50	1,050
	1400	24" diameter, minimum reinforcing			22.18	3.697		196	90.50	11.35	297.85	370
	1420	Average reinforcing			11.86	6.914		293	169	21	483	610
	1440	Maximum reinforcing			8.10	10.123		450	248	31	729	920
	1500	36" diameter, minimum reinforcing			32.40	2.531		213	62	7.75	282.75	340
	1520	Average reinforcing			16.57	4.949		291	121	15.20	427.20	530
	1540	Maximum reinforcing		↓	11.15	7.354		390	180	22.50	592.50	740
	1900	Elevated slabs, flat slab, 125 psf Sup. Load, 20' span		C-17A	13.36	6.063		118	149	9.45	276.45	375
	1950	30' span		C-17B	18.25	4.493		111	110	13.80	234.80	310
	2100	Flat plate, 125 psf Sup. Load, 15' span		C-17A	10.28	7.879		123	193	12.30	328.30	455
	2150	25' span		C-17B	17.01	4.821		105	118	14.80	237.80	320
	2300	Waffle const., 30" domes, 125 psf Sup. Load, 20' span			14.10	5.816		122	143	17.85	282.85	380
	2350	30' span		↓	17.02	4.818		114	118	14.80	246.80	325
	2500	One way joists, 30" pans, 125 psf Sup. Load, 15' span		C-17A	11.07	7.317		113	179	11.40	303.40	420
	2550	25' span			11.04	7.337		114	180	11.45	305.45	420
	2700	One way beam & slab, 125 psf Sup. Load, 15' span			7.49	10.814		152	265	16.85	433.85	600
	2750	25' span			10.15	7.980		139	196	12.45	347.45	475
	2900	Two way beam & slab, 125 psf Sup. Load, 15' span		↓	8.22	9.854		137	242	15.35	394.35	550
	2950	25' span		C-17B	12.23	6.705	↓	120	164	20.50	304.50	415
	3100	Elevated slabs including finish, not										
	3110	including forms or reinforcing										
	3150	Regular concrete, 4" slab		C-8	2,685	.021	S.F.	.70	.44	.20	1.34	1.66
	3200	6" slab			2,585	.022		1.04	.45	.21	1.70	2.07
	3250	2-1/2" thick floor fill			2,685	.021		.43	.44	.20	1.07	1.36
	3300	Lightweight, 110# per C.F., 2-1/2" thick floor fill			2,585	.022		.54	.45	.21	1.20	1.52
	3400	Cellular concrete, 1-5/8" fill, under 5000 S.F.			2,000	.028	↓	.35	.59	.27	1.21	1.59
	3450	Over 10,000 S.F.		↓	2,200	.025	↓	.28	.53	.25	1.06	1.40

Figure 9.35

No matter what format estimators use to compile and list quantities' for concrete work, each of these quantities must be computed. Once the format has been established, it should be used throughout the estimate and on all future estimates, establishing consistency and minimizing errors and omissions.

Figure 9.38 graphically illustrates the relationship of the different components of concrete work based on a complete, concrete-framed structure. The way in which the components relate will vary for different and individual types of concrete work, but this pie chart suggests the relative importance of each component.

Formwork: As seen in Figure 9.38, for a complete concrete framed building, formwork can account for more than one third of all concrete costs. For some individual concrete systems using beams, columns and walls, job-built formwork can account for 50% - 60%, or more, of the costs.

Prefabricated, modular forms can help to significantly reduce formwork costs. This is because these forms can be used over and over again, in some cases, hundreds of times. The initial purchase price of prefabricated forms is higher than job-built, but the effective higher cost decreases with each reuse. These prefabricated forms are only useful and cost effective for repetitive, standard, modular concrete work. To illustrate how the cost of formwork (whether prefabricated or job-built) decreases with each use, please refer to Figure 9.39. This table shows the costs per 100 SFCA (square feet of contact area) for job-built foundation wall forms, 8' high. Costs for the first use of the forms include construction, erection, stripping and cleaning. Costs for reuse include the same erection, stripping and cleaning costs plus an allowance for 10% material replacement. The difference in cost between the first use and the reuse is the bulk of initial materials and construction labor. The effective costs of the formwork based on the number of uses are calculated below. Costs are from Figure 9.39.

$$\frac{\text{Cost of First Use} + (\text{Cost per Reuse x No. of Reuses})}{\text{No. of Uses}} = \frac{\text{Cost per Use}}{(\text{for No. of Uses})}$$

Using the costs in Figure 9.39:

Two Uses:

$$\frac{\$306.30 + (\$212.05 \times 1)}{2} = \$295.18 \text{ per use for two uses}$$

Three Uses:

$$\frac{\$306.30 + (\$212.05 \times 2)}{3} = \$243.47 \text{ per use for three uses}$$

Four Uses:

$$\frac{\$306.30 + (\$212.05 \times 3)}{4} = \$235.61 \text{ per use for four uses}$$

The estimator should figure on reuse of forms within a project as well as from one project to the next. To determine the optimum number of forms required, a preliminary schedule (as described in Chapter 5) can be extremely useful. For a building with hundreds of similar columns, only a certain percentage of that number of forms need be built. The appropriate number of forms is determined by the sequence of construction and by the curing time before the forms can be stripped and reused. (See Chapter 5 and Figures 5.4 and 5.5.) Curing time is often the limiting factor when determining the required number and reuse of forms.

FOUNDATION PLAN

SPREAD FOOTING PLAN

COLUMN & SPREAD FOOTING SECTION

Figure 9.36

MEANS QUANTITY SHEET

PROJECT **Sample Project**

ESTIMATE NO.

LOCATION	ARCHITECT	DATE

TAKE OFF BY	EXTENSIONS BY:	CHECKED BY:

DESCRIPTION	NO.	DIMENSIONS			Concrete Volume	UNIT	Form Area	UNIT	Finished Area	UNIT	MISC.	UNIT
Spread Footings						CF		SF		SF		
F-1	8	8	8	1.83	937		469		512			
F-2	12	6	6	1.33	575		383		432			
F-3	4	4.5	4.5	1	81		72		81			
Totals					1593	CF	924	SF	1025	SF		
					59	CY						
Wall Footings												
Column Line 1,4	2	38.75	2	1	155		155		155			
Column Line D,F	2	43.5	2	1	174		174		174			
Totals					329	CF	329	SF	329	SF		
					13	CY						
Walls												
Column Line 1,4	2	51.5	1	11	1133		2266		1133			
Column Line D,F	2	61.5	1	11	1353		2706		1353			
Pilasters	10	1.5	1.5	11	83		440		55			
Corners	10 x 8										80	Ea.
Brick Shelf												
Column Line 1		51.5	.33	1	(17)		52					
Column Line F		61.5	.33	1	(21)		62					
Totals					2531	CF	5526	SF	2541	SF		
					94	CY						
Set Anchor Bolts											48	Ea.
Keyway	2	39									78	
	2	44									88	
											166	LF
Columns C-1	8	2	2	12	384		768					
C-2	12	1.67	1.67	12	400		960		ALL ↓			
C-3	4	1.33	1.33	12	85		256					
Totals					869	CF	1984	SF	1984	SF		
					32	CY						

Figure 9.37

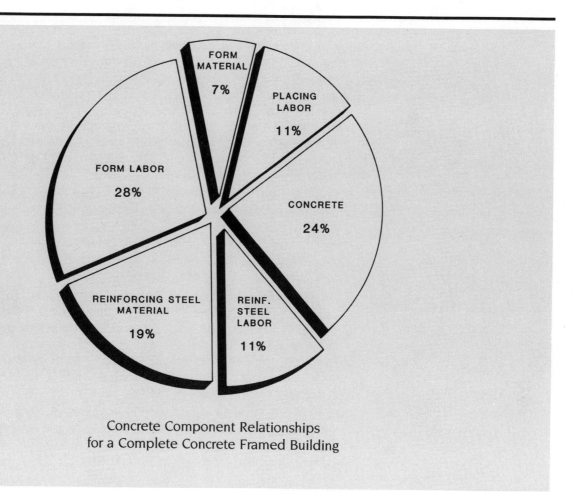

Concrete Component Relationships
for a Complete Concrete Framed Building

Figure 9.38

FOUNDATION WALL, 8′ High (Line 182-2000)			First Use			Reuse		
Item	Cost	Unit	Quantity	Material	Installation	Quantity	Material	Installation
5/8″ exterior plyform	$620.00	M.S.F.	110 S.F.	$ 68.20		11.0 S.F.	$ 6.80	
Lumber	385.00	M.B.F.	140 B.F.	53.90		14.0 B.F.	5.40	
Accessories			Allow	22.85		Allow	22.85	
Make up, crew C-2	23.56	M.H.	5.0 M.H.		$117.80	1.0 M.H.		$ 23.55
Erect and strip			6.5 M.H.		153.15	6.5 M.H.		153.15
Clean and move			1.5 M.H.		35.35	1.5 M.H.		35.35
Total per 100 S.F.C.A.			13.0 M.H.	$144.95	$306.30	9.0 M.H.	$35.05	$212.05

Figure 9.39

177

Reinforcing: The size and quantities of reinforcing steel can vary greatly with the type of structure, design load, concrete strength and type of steel. Steel material prices should always be verified by local suppliers. Labor costs will also vary depending upon the size of reinforcing. Reinforcing is priced and purchased by weight. While a smaller and lighter bar may be installed faster than a larger, heavier bar, more tonnage is installed faster with the heavier reinforcing. For example, in slabs and footings, a rodman can install a ton of heavy bars in about nine hours, while a ton of light bars requires about fifteen hours.

Specified sizes for reinforcing are shown in sections and details. Quantities are measured from the plans as linear feet for each size; this figure must then be converted to weight. Conversion factors are given in Figure 9.40. Accessories, dowels and splicing should be priced separately. If post-tensioning is specified, the estimator must be sure to include all requirements, coatings, wrappings, etc. Grouting after tensioning may also be required.

When the plans show the complete concrete design but are not sufficient to serve as placing drawings, suppliers will often provide the detailing service by preparing reinforcing steel placing drawings. This service should not be substituted for and does not take the place of structural engineering services. In conjunction with the drawings, the suppliers may produce material lists to aid the estimator. For large projects, the Concrete Reinforcing Steel Institute (CRSI) may provide these services to all prospective bidders.

Welded wire fabric for slabs should be measured allowing a 10% overlap. (Material costs for welded wire fabric, as presented in *Means Building Construction Cost Data* include a 10% overlap.) Weights, sizes and new designations of welded wire fabric are shown in Figure 9.40.

Because of the quantity and weight involved, handling costs for reinforcing must also be added. Unloading, sorting and crane placement costs can add 5% to 7% to the cost of reinforcing.

Placing Concrete: There are many ways to transport concrete from the truck to the installation locations. The most economical method is by direct chute because little labor or equipment is required from truck to forms; gravity does the work. The construction of an elaborate chute system, while an expensive initial cost, may be less costly overall than alternative methods.

The estimator should visualize the process and use experience to determine the most economical approach. The number of forms, size of the pours and size of the finishing crews will all have a direct bearing on the choice of proper placement method. If the size of the pour is large and adequate finishing workers and laborers are available, pumping concrete is the fastest, but most expensive method. If a crane is available on-site, placement with the crane and a bucket may be the most feasible. Conveyors, wheelbarrows and even hand carried buckets may be used depending upon the type of work involved. Motorized carts may also be used in conjunction with each of the above mentioned methods. Temporary ramps and runways will be required for these carts. Costs are presented in *Means Building Construction Cost Data* for each method of placing concrete for different types of structures. Only an analysis of each individual project will determine the most feasible and economical method of concrete placement.

Finishing Concrete: Requirements for concrete finishes are usually found in the specifications portion of the construction documents. For floors, walks, and other horizontal surfaces, not only must the type of finish be included (broom,

Reinforcing Bars

Bar Size Designation	Weight Pounds Per Foot	Nominal Dimensions - Round Sections		
		Diameter Inches	Cross-Sectional Area-Sq. Inches	Perimeter Inches
#3	.376	.375	.11	1.178
#4	.668	.500	.20	1.571
#5	1.043	.625	.31	1.963
#6	1.502	.750	.44	2.356
#7	2.044	.875	.60	2.749
#8	2.670	1.000	.79	3.142
#9	3.400	1.128	1.00	3.544
#10	4.303	1.270	1.27	3.990
#11	5.313	1.410	1.56	4.430
#14	7.650	1.693	2.25	5.320
#18	13.600	2.257	4.00	7.090

Common Stock Styles of Welded Wire Fabric

	New Designation	Old Designation	Steel Area Per Foot				Approximate Weight Per 100 Sq. Ft.	
	Spacing-Cross Sectional Area (IN.)-(Sq. IN. 100)	Spacing Wire Gauge (IN.)-(AS & W)	Longitudinal		Transverse			
			IN.	CM	IN.	CM	LB	KG
Rolls	6 x 6 – W1.4 x W1.4	6 x 6 - 10 x 10	0.028	0.071	0.028	0.071	21	9.53
	6 x 6 – W2.0 x W2.0	6 x 6 - 8 x 8 (1)	0.040	0.102	0.040	0.102	29	13.15
	6 x 6 – W2.9 x W2.9	6 x 6 - 6 x 6	0.058	0.147	0.053	0.147	42	19.05
	6 x 6 – W4.0 x W4.0	6 x 6 - 4 x 4	0.080	0.203	0.080	0.203	58	26.31
	4 x 4 – W1.4 x W1.4	4 x 4 - 10 x 10	0.042	0.107	0.042	0.107	31	14.06
	4 x 4 – W2.0 x W2.0	4 x 4 - 8 x 8 (1)	0.060	0.152	0.060	0.152	43	19.50
	4 x 4 – W2.9 x W2.9	4 x 4 - 6 x 6	0.087	0.221	0.087	0.221	62	28.12
	4 x 4 – W4.0 x W4.0	4 x 4 - 4 x 4	0.120	0.305	0.120	0.305	85	38.56
Sheets	6 x 6 – W2.9 x W2.9	6 x 6 - 6 x 6	0.058	0.147	0.058	0.147	42	19.05
	6 x 6 – W4.0 x W4.0	6 x 6 - 4 x 4	0.080	0.203	0.080	0.203	58	26.31
	6 x 6 – W5.5 x W5.5	6 x 6 - 2 x 2 (2)	0.110	0.279	0.110	0.279	80	36.29
	4 x 4 – W4.0 x W4.0	4 x 4 - 4 x 4	0.120	0.305	0.120	0.305	85	38.56

NOTES
1. Exact W-number size for 8 gauge is W2.1
2. Exact W-number size for 2 gauge is W5.4

Figure 9.40

trowel, etc.), but also any required surface treatments and additives. Such treatments may include hardeners, colors, and abrasives. Costs for floor finishing will also depend upon the allowable tolerances for floor leveling. Typical tolerances may allow a 1/8" variation in 10'. Closer required tolerances will require more labor and finishing costs.

Wall finishing may vary from patching voids and tie holes to creating hammered or sandblasted finishes. Architectural finishes may also be achieved using special form surface materials, such as boards or strips.

Spread Footings: Plans for a building with spread footings (as in Figure 9.36) generally include a footing schedule that lists, counts and defines each type and size of spread footing. Reinforcing data is usually included. An example footing schedule is shown in Figure 9.41; it includes information on reinforcing requirements. When the schedule is provided, it eliminates the repetition of detailing on the plans and simplifies the estimator's task. Dimensions can be transferred directly onto the Quantity Sheet (see Figure 9.37). Using this form and the footing schedule, the procedure is as follows:

- Write down the number of each size and the dimensions of each of the spread footings shown on the plans.
- Extend each of these lines to obtain the Volume, Form Area, and Finish Area.
- Total the extensions.
- Count the total number of footings on the plan to make sure none has been left out.

When working with these plans for spread footings, take off related items such as anchor bolts, templates, base plates and reinforcing steel. Reinforcing steel may be transferred to a separate sheet. These other items should be computed and totalled on the same Quantity Sheet from which they were derived in order to avoid errors and omissions.

Continuous Wall Footings and Grade Beams: Wall footings transmit loads directly to the soil. Grade Beams are self-supporting structural members that carry wall loads across unacceptable soil to spread footings, caissons or support piles. The sequence for quantity takeoff is the same as discussed above. Again, dimensions should be recorded and extended on a Quantity Sheet.

Wall footings are stepped when grade changes necessitate changes in footing elevation. Figure 9.42 illustrates a stepped footing. Notice that in plan view, the footing may easily be mistaken as continuous. Where stepped footings occur, extra formwork (2 x Area A plus Area B) and extra concrete (W x Area A) are required in addition to the quantities for the continuous footing. Accessories should also be taken off at the same time using the pertinent dimensions and derived quantities.

Pile Caps: Pile Caps are basically spread footings on piles. The shape is not always rectangular, so that the form area is determined by the perimeter x depth. Concrete volume should be not deducted for the protrusion of the piles into the cap.

Piers: Piers are used to extend the bearing of the superstructure down to the footing. They vary in length to accommodate sub-surface conditions, original site grades and frost penetration. Piers are often included on the Footing Schedule.

Walls: Walls are separated by height during takeoff. Generally this is done in 4′ increments such as under 4′, 4′ to 8′, and 8′ to 12′. Different forming and placing costs may be used for each of these heights.

- Using a quantity sheet, define each wall. If all walls have footings, the wall footing schedule can be used as a basis.
- Write in the dimensions for each of these walls.
- From these dimensions, compute the Volume and Form Area for each wall, dividing them into convenient modular categories. Brick shelves and slab seats should be listed and deducted from concrete volume.
- Total the extensions.
- Upon examination of the wall sections and details, list all associated items: beams seats, anchor bolts, base plates, chamfers, pilasters, rustications, architectural finishes, openings and reinforcing steel. Where pilasters occur, figure the wall forming straight through and then add the area of the pilasters as a separate item. Costs are different for walls and pilasters. The additional materials will be used in waste, bracing and framing.
- Building a perimeter wall with many angles and corners will take more time and more material to form than a wall with four square corners. Note the number of corners on the Quantity Sheet so that an allowance for material and labor can be made when pricing the wall forming.

Footing Schedule			
Ident.	No.	Size	Reinforcing
F-1	8	8′-0″ x 8′0″ x 1′-10″	9-#6 e.w.
F-2	12	6′-0″ x 6′0″ x 1′-4″	8-#5 e.w.
F-3	4	4′-6″ x 4′6″ x 1′-0″	5-#5 e.w.

Column Schedule			
Ident.	No.	Size	Reinforcing
C-1	8	24″ x 24″ x 12′	8-#11 ties #4 @ 22″
C-2	12	20″ x 20″ x 12′	8-#9 ties #3 @ 18″
C-3	4	16″ x 16″ x 12′	8-#9 ties #3 @ 16″

Beam Schedule			
Ident.	No.	Size	Reinforcing
B-1 Ext.	1	1′ x 2′-6″ x 60′	See Re-Bar Schedule
B-2 Ext.	2	1′ x 2′-4″ x 75′	
B-3 Int.	2	8″ x 1′-6″ x 60′	
B-4 Int.	2	6″ x 1′-6″ x 125′	

Figure 9.41

The above procedure will be identical for foundation walls and retaining walls. If retaining walls are battered, be sure to note this. Formwork erection time may be up to 20% slower as a result. For special architectural effects, the use of form liners, rustication strips, retarders, and sandblasting must be considered.

Columns: Columns are commonly listed in a schedule similar to that used for spread footings. An example is shown in Figure 9.41. Quantities are derived using the same procedure discussed above. When estimating columns, the following associated items must be considered:

- Height Measurement from floor slab below to underside of beam or slab.
- Multiple use of forms.
- Chamfer strips.
- Finishing requirements.
- Capitals.
- Reinforcing steel
- Clamps, inserts, and placing pockets.

Figure 9.42

Beams: As with footings and columns, cast in place beams are also often listed on a schedule. If not otherwise designated, interior and exterior beams should be listed separately. The following principles should be used when estimating beams:

- The depths given in schedules represent design depths. Slab thickness must be deducted when calculating volume and contact area.
- Exterior and interior beams should be listed separately. An exterior beam requires forming for the full design depth on one side. The access and bracing of this exterior form makes it more costly to erect and strip.
- Formwork or volume should not be deducted for columns.
- Beams and slabs are usually placed simultaneously. Beam quantities should be separated by floor to be included with slab placement.
- The support method should be determined — whether the formwork is hung from beams, supported with adjustable horizontal shores, or shored from the structure below. Reshoring costs must be included if required.
- Finishing requirements and design will affect the multiple use of forms.

Calculations for Formed, Cast in Place Concrete:

Spread Footings and Pile Caps:

Volume — Length (L) x Width (W) x Depth (D)

Form Area — (2L + 2W) x D

Finish Area — L x W

Continuous Footings:

Volume — Length (L) x Width (W) x Depth (D)

Form Area — 2L x D

Finish Area — L x W

Rectangular Columns:

Volume — Length (L) x Width (W) x Height (H)

Form Area — (2L + 2W) x H

Finish Area — (2L + 2W) x H

Round Columns:

Volume — 3.146 x Radius (R) x R x Height (H)

Form Area — 3.146 x Diameter (D) x H

Finish Area — 3.146 x D x H

Walls:

Volume — Length (L) x Height (H) x Thickness (T)

Form Area — L x H x 2

Finish Area — L x H (for each side)

Beams:

Exterior:

Volume — L x W x (Design depth (d) — Slab thickness (t))

Form Area — (L x W) + (L x d) + (L x (d — t))

Finish Area — Same as form area

Interior:

Volume − Length x Width x (d − t)

Form Area − (L x W) + 2(L x (d − t))

Finish Area − Same as form area

Slabs: Concrete slabs can be divided into two categories: slabs on grade including sidewalks and concrete paving, and elevated slabs. Several items must be considered when estimating slabs on grade.

- Granular Base
- Fine Grading
- Vapor Barrier
- Edge Forms and Bulkheads
- Expansion Joints
- Contraction Joints
- Screeds
- Welded Wire Fabric and Reinforcing
- Concrete Material
- Finish and Topping
- Curing and Hardeners
- Control Joints
- Concrete "Outs"
- Haunches
- Drops

Quantities for most of the items above can be derived from basic dimensions: length, width, and slab thickness. When these quantities are calculated, some basic rules can be used:

- Allow about 25% compaction for granular base.
- Allow 10% overlap for vapor barrier and welded wire fabric.
- Allow 5% extra concrete for waste.
- No deductions should be made for columns or "outs" under 10 S.F.
- If screeds are separated from forming and placing costs, figure 1 L.F. of screed per 10 S.F. of finish area.

Elevated slabs, while similar to slabs on grade, require special consideration. For all types of elevated slabs, edge forms should be estimated carefully. Stair towers, elevator shafts and utility chases all require edge forms. The appropriate quantities for each of these "outs" should be deducted from the concrete volume and finish area. Edge form materials and installation will vary depending upon the slab type and thickness. Special consideration should be given to pipe chases that require concrete placement after the pipes are in position. This is done in order to maintain the fireproofing integrity. Hand mixing and placing may be necessary.

When estimating beam supported slabs, beams should not normally be deducted from the floor form area. The extra costs for bracing and framing at the beams will account for the difference. When concrete for the beams and slab is placed at the same time, the placement costs will be the same for both.

Slab placement costs should be increased based on the beam volume. Separate costs for beam concrete placement should not be included. For hung slabs, separation of costs for beams and slab is even more difficult. These costs may be treated as one item.

Metal decking for elevated slabs is usually installed by the steel erector. When determining concrete quantities, measure the slab thickness to the middle of the corrugation.

Cast in place concrete joist and dome (or waffle) slabs are more difficult to estimate. Pans and domes are shored with either open or closed deck forming. For concrete joist systems, quantities for concrete can be calculated from Figure 9.43. Volume of beams must be added separately. Volume of waffle slabs, because of the varying sizes of solid column heads, should be estimated differently. Total volume from top of slab to bottom of pan should be calculated. The volume of the actual number of domes (voids) is then deducted. Volumes for standard domes are listed in Figure 9.44.

Stairs: When taking off cast in place stairs, a careful investigation should be made to ensure that all inserts, such as railing pockets, anchors, nosings, and reinforcing steel have been included. Also indicate on your quantity sheet any special tread finishes; these can sometimes represent a considerable cost.

Stairs cast on fill are most easily estimated and recorded by the square foot. The calculation is – slant length times width. Because of the commonly used ratios adopted by designers, this method works for high or low risers with wide or narrow treads. Shored cast in place stairs can be estimated in the same way – slant length times width.

	Concrete Quantities (CF concrete/SF floor) for Single & Multiple Span Concrete Joist Construction					
	Width					
	20" Forms			30" Forms		
Depth (Rib/Slab)	5" Rib 25" O.C.	6" Rib 26" O.C.	7" Rib 27" O.C.	5" Rib 35" O.C.	6" Rib 36" O.C.	7" Rib 37" O.C.
8"/3"	0.40	0.42	–	0.36	0.37	–
8"/4½"	0.53	0.55	–	0.48	0.50	–
10"/3"	0.45	0.47	–	0.39	0.41	–
10"/4½"	0.57	0.61	–	0.51	0.53	–
12"/3"	0.49	0.52	–	0.42	0.45	–
12"/4½"	0.62	0.65	–	0.55	0.57	–
14"/3"	0.54	0.57	–	0.45	0.48	–
14"/4½"	0.66	0.69	–	0.58	0.61	–
16"/3"	–	0.63	0.66	–	0.52	0.55
16"/4½"	–	0.75	0.79	–	0.65	0.68
20"/3"	–	0.75	0.79	–	0.61	0.64
20"/4½"	–	0.87	0.91	–	0.74	0.77

Figure 9.43

Treads and landings of prefabricated metal pan stairs should be identified on the takeoff sheet. The cost of hand placing the fill concrete should be included in Division 3.

For all cast in place, formed concrete work, the following factors can affect the number of pans to rent, the S.F. of forms to build, the number of shores to provide, etc.:

- Placement rate of concrete for crew.
- Concrete pump or crane and bucket rental cost per pour.
- Finishing rate for concrete finishers.
- Curing time before stripping and reshoring.
- Forming and stripping time.
- Number of reuses of forms.

Experience (or consultation with an experienced superintendent) will tell the estimator which combination of these six items will limit the quantity of forms to be built, or the number of pans to be rented.

Precast Concrete

Typical precast units are estimated and purchased by the square foot or linear foot. The manufacturer will most often deliver precast units. Costs for delivery are sometimes separate from the purchase price and must be included in the estimate. Most manufacturers also have the capability to erect these units, and, because of experience, are best suited to the task.

Each type and size of precast unit should be separated on the quantity or estimate sheet. Typical units are shown in Figure 9.45. The estimator should verify the availability of specified units with local suppliers. For types that are seldom used, casting beds may have to be custom built, thus increasing cost.

Connections and joint requirements will vary with the type of unit, from welding or bolting embedded steel to simple grouting. Toppings must also be included, whether lightweight or regular concrete on floors, insulating concrete for roofs. The specifications and construction details must be examined carefully.

Sample Estimate: Division 3

When performing the estimate for the sample division building project, a number of principles mentioned above, are applied. The most important is common sense, together with the ability to visualize the construction process. Most information for the quantity takeoff would normally be supplied on

	Standard Dome sizes and Volumes									
	19" Domes				30" Domes					
Depth	6"	8"	10"	12"	8"	10"	12"	14"	16"	20"
Volume (CF per Dome)	1.09	1.41	1.90	2.14	3.85	4.78	5.53	6.54	7.44	9.16

Figure 9.44

R034-030 Prestressed Precast Concrete Structural Units

See also R032-090 for post-tensioned prestressed concrete.

Type	Location	Depth	Span in Ft.		Live Load Lb. per S.F.	Cost per S.F. Incl. Subs O & P	
						Delivered	Erected
Double Tee	Floor	28" to 34"	60 to 80		50 to 80	$ 5.75 to 8.25	$ 6.85 to 9.40
	Roof	12" to 24"	30 to 50		40	$ 3.80 to 6.00	$ 4.75 to 7.05
	Wall	Width 8'	Up to 55' high		Wind	$4.15 to $ 8.25	$4.85 to $ 9.60
Multiple Tee	Roof	8" to 12"	15 to 40		40	$ 3.45	$ 4.15
	Floor	8" to 12"	15 to 30		100	$ 3.65	$ 4.20
Plank or	Roof or Floor	4" 6" 8" 10" 12"	Roof 13 22 26 33 42	Floor 12 18 25 29 32	40 for Roof 100 for Floor	$ 3.60 3.75 3.90 4.50 4.90	$ 4.55 4.65 4.70 5.15 5.50
Single Tee	Roof	28" 32" 36" 48"	40 80 100 120		40	$ 6.60* 7.80* 11.25* 11.40*	$ 6.90* 8.65* 12.05* 12.20*
AASHO Girder	Bridges	Type 4 5 6	100 110 125		Highway	$105/L.F. 140 170	$165/L.F. 165 195
Box Beam	Bridges	15" 27" 33"	40 to 100		Highway	$107/L.F. 150 174	$139/L.F. 172 195

*Costs are for 10' wide members; for 8' wide members add $.54 per S.F.

Figure 9.45

drawings, details and in the specifications. Even when all data is provided, however, the estimator must be familiar with standard materials and practices.

Concrete work is composed of many components, most of which are based on similar dimensions. It makes sense to organize all takeoff data on a Quantity Sheet as shown in Figure 9.37. A partial takeoff for Division 3 of the sample project is shown in Figure 9.46. Note that every quantity that is to be priced has been converted to the appropriate units and delineated on the sheet. As the quantities are transferred to the pricing sheets, colored pencil check marks will ensure inclusion of all items. The estimate sheets for Division 3 are shown in Figures 9.47 to 9.51.

Most quantities are derived from the plan in Figure 9.5a. Heights are determined from the building section in Figure 9.10. Dimensioned details are provided in complete plans and specifications. The spread footing quantities are easily obtained from the drawings. Care must be exercised when estimating the continuous footings. Note on Figure 9.46 that the complete perimeter is used for a gross quantity and that a deduction is included where the spread footings interrupt the continuous footing. The keyway and dowel supports, as shown in Section A-A in Figure 9.5a, continue across the spread footings. Thus, the linear dimension of the keyway and dowel supports will be greater than that of the continuous footing. (Note that the keyway and dowel supports are included in more than the perimeter footings.) The steps in the perimeter footing between column lines 5 and 6 (Figure 9.5a) are not listed separately due to their insignificant effect on the total cost. This is a judgment call of the type that should only be made based on experience.

Quantities for the perimeter wall are calculated with no deduction for the pilasters. Such a deduction should be more than compensated by extra costs for framing and bracing at the connections. Pilaster formwork should be recorded separately. Costs used for placing the pilaster concrete are the same as for the perimeter wall because placement for both will occur simultaneously.

Reinforcing quantities are taken from Reference Table R033-010 in *Means Building Construction Cost Data*. These figures are based on pounds per cubic yard of concrete. When detailed information is available, actual linear quantities and counts of splices and accessories of each size and type should be taken off and priced for greater accuracy. Note that the costs used for welded wire fabric as presented in *Means Building Construction Cost Data* (Figure 9.52) include a 10% overlap so that quantities in this case are derived from actual dimensions.

Concrete material costs for the waffle slab include a cost for high early strength. The 2nd and 3rd floor elevated slabs include percentages for high early strength and for lightweight aggregate. The appropriate percentages are obtained from Figure 9.53 and added to the unit costs before entry on the estimate sheet. Costs for concrete are readily available from local suppliers and should always be verified.

Figures 9.53 (bottom) and 9.54 show costs for complete concrete systems in place. These systems are most often priced per cubic yard of concrete. The costs are based on averages for each type and size of system as listed. These figures provide an excellent checklist to quickly compare costs of similar systems estimated by individual components for possible omissions or duplications. For the sample estimate such a comparison can be made. The

QUANTITY SHEET

PROJECT: Office Building
LOCATION:
TAKE OFF BY:

Division 3
ARCHITECT:
EXTENSIONS BY:

SHEET NO. 1 of 1
ESTIMATE NO:
DATE:
CHECKED BY:

DESCRIPTION	NO.	DIMENSIONS				Forms	UNIT	Volume	UNIT	Reinf.	UNIT	Finish	UNIT
Spread Footings	6	11.5'	11.5'	2'		552	SFCA	1587	CF				
	4	9.5'	9.5'	2'		304		722					
	18	8'	8'	2'		1152		2304					
						2008	SFCA	4613	CF				
Dowel Supports	28 Ea.							171	CY	8892	Lbs.		
										4.45	T		
Continuous Footings													
Perimeter	(1	600'	2'	1'		1200	SFCA	1200	CF				
Deduct Spr. Footings		8'	2'	1'		-288		-288)					
Ramp		166'	1.5'	0.67'		498		166					
Stoop		25'	1.5'	0.67'		75		25					
Stairs	2	40'	1.5'	0.67'		240		81					
Core		160'	1.5'	0.67'		480		161					
						2205	SFCA	1345	CF				
Dowel Supports		1031	LF					50	CY	2600	Lbs.		
Keyway		791	LF							1.30	T		
Deduct Stairs / Core													
Walls - Perimeter		600'	1'	10'		12000	SFCA	4020	CF				
Pit		42'	0.83'	4'		336		140					
Ramp & Stoop		191'	1'	~4'		1528		512					
Deduct - Doors	(2	10'	1'	10'		-400		-134)					
Openings	(6	31'	1'	~4.5'		-1674		-561)					
						11790	SFCA	3977	CF				
Box Openings		466	LF					148	CY				
Columns 28" diam.	9	30"	diam.	9"		81	LF	398	CF			636	
	1	30"	diam.	12'		12		59				94	
						93	LF	457	CF			730	SF
								17	CY				
Pilasters 3 Sides	14	2'	1.67'	9'		673	SFCA	421	CF	18988	Lbs.		
2 Sides	4	1.67'	1.67'	9'		120		100		9.49	T		
						793	SFCA	521	CF	8908	Lbs.	793	SF
								19	CY	4.45	T		
Chamfer	32	288	LF							9956	Lbs.		
										4.98	T		

Figure 9.46

189

CONSOLIDATED ESTIMATE

PROJECT: Office Building   CLASSIFICATION: Division 3

LOCATION: ARCHITECT:

TAKE OFF BY: QUANTITIES BY: PRICES BY: EXTENSIONS BY:

ESTIMATE NO:

DATE: 6/93

CHECKED BY:

DESCRIPTION	SOURCE			QUANT.	UNIT	MATERIAL		LABOR		EQUIPMENT		SUBCONTRACT		TOTAL	
						COST	TOTAL	COST	TOTAL	COST	TOTAL	COST	TOTAL	COST	TOTAL
Division 3: Concrete															
Formwork															
Spread Footings	031	158	5150	2008	SFCA	0.39	783	1.71	3434	0.06	120				
Dowel Supports	031	158	6100 6150	28	Ea.	16.95	475	38.50	1078	1.34	38				
Continuous Footings	031	158	0150	2205	SFCA	0.33	728	1.46	3219	0.05	110				
Dowel Supports	031	158	0500	1031	LF	0.59	608	1.42	1464	0.05	52				
Keyway (excl. stairs & core)	031	158	1500	791	LF	0.14	111	0.35	277						
Walls:															
Pit (10")	031	182	2000	336	SFCA	1.45	487	2.97	998	0.09	30				
Ramp & Stoops (8")	031	182	2000	1528	SFCA	1.45	2216	2.97	4538	0.09	138				
Perimeter (12" x 10')	031	182	2550	9926	SFCA	0.66	6551	2.78	27594	0.08	794				
Deduct Openings															
Garage															
Above Grade															
Box Openings	031	182	0150	466	LF	1.41	657	3.92	1827	0.12	56				
Columns - 28" Diam., 9 @ 9', 1 @ 12'	031	142	1850	93	LF	17.20	1600	5.65	525	0.20	19				
Pilasters	031	182	8600	793	SFCA	1.80	1427	4.07	3228	0.12	95				
Subtotals							$15,642		$48,182		$1,451				

Figure 9.47

CONSOLIDATED ESTIMATE

PROJECT: Office Building
LOCATION:
TAKE OFF BY:

CLASSIFICATION: Division 3
ARCHITECT:
QUANTITIES BY:
PRICES BY:
EXTENSIONS BY:

SOURCE			DESCRIPTION	QUANT.	UNIT	MATERIAL		LABOR		EQUIPMENT		SUBCONTRACT		TOTAL	
						COST	TOTAL	COST	TOTAL	COST	TOTAL	COST	TOTAL	COST	TOTAL
			Division 3: (Cont'd)												
			Formwork (Cont'd)												
031	112	2200	Chamfer 3/4"	288	LF	0.49	141	0.36	104						
031	170	3000	4" Slab Edge Form @ Pit & Openings	65	LF	0.25	16	1.18	77	0.04	3				
031	150	4500	Waffel Slab (1st Floor)	18220	SF	2.80	51016	2.71	49376	0.08	1458				
			Deduct, Stairs	18900											
			Shaft	-600											
				-80											
031	150	5000	Opening Edge Forms	273	SFCA	2.20	601	5.80	1583	0.17	46				
031	150	7100	Perimeter Edge Forms	600	SFCA	0.48	288	2.03	1218	0.07	42				
031	150	8000	Perimeter Work Deck	200	LF	6.50	1300	7.90	1580	0.27	54				
031	150	6000	Bulkhead Forms	5000	LF	1.10	5500	2.20	11000	0.07	350				
			Reinforcing Steel												
032	107	0500	Footings	5.75	T	490.00	2818	395.00	2271						
032	107	0700	Walls	9.49	T	500.00	4745	276.00	2619						
032	107	0250	Columns	9.43	T	490.00	4621	360.00	3395						
032	107	0400	Waffle Slab	23.59	T	510.00	12031	285.00	6723						
			Subtotals				$83,076		$79,946		$1,953				

Figure 9.48

CONSOLIDATED ESTIMATE

PROJECT: Office Building
LOCATION:
TAKE OFF BY:
QUANTITIES BY:
PRICES BY:
CLASSIFICATION: Division 3
ARCHITECT:
EXTENSIONS BY:
ESTIMATE NO:
DATE: 6/93
CHECKED BY:

DESCRIPTION	SOURCE	QUANT.	UNIT	MATERIAL COST	MATERIAL TOTAL	LABOR COST	LABOR TOTAL	EQUIPMENT COST	EQUIPMENT TOTAL	SUBCONTRACT COST	SUBCONTRACT TOTAL
Division 3: (Cont'd)											
Reinforcing Steel											
WWF: 6 x 6 10/10											
Elevated Slabs		37800	SF								
Garage Slab		18900									
Penthouse Floor		2100									
Deduct-Stair		-1200									
Elevator		-360									
		57240	SF								
Total WWF	032 207 0010	572.4	CSF	6.90	3950	11.80	6754				
Cast in Place Concrete											
Spread Footings											
Concrete - Incl. 5% Waste	033 126 0150	180	CY	48.00	8640						
Placing	033 172 2600	180	CY			8.55	1539	0.59	106		
Continuous Footings											
Concrete - Incl. 5% Waste	033 126 0150	52	CY	48.00	2496						
Placing	033 172 1900	52	CY			7.85	408	0.54	28		
Walls											
Concrete - Incl. 5% Waste	033 126 0300	233	CY	50.50	11767						
Placing	033 172 5100	233	CY			13.50	3146	6.40	1491		
Finishing	033 458 0010	6000	SF	0.01	60	0.34	2040				
Columns											
Concrete - Incl. 5% Waste	033 126 0300	18	CY	50.50	909						
Placing	033 172 1000	18	CY			9.15	165	4.34	78		
Finishing	033 458 0010	730	SF	0.01	7	0.34	248				
Subtotals					$27,828		$14,300		$1,704		

Figure 9.49

CONSOLIDATED ESTIMATE

PROJECT: Office Building
LOCATION:
TAKE OFF BY:
CLASSIFICATION: Division 3
ARCHITECT:
QUANTITIES BY: PRICES BY: EXTENSIONS BY:
ESTIMATE NO:
DATE: 6/93
CHECKED BY:

DESCRIPTION	SOURCE			QUANT.	UNIT	MATERIAL		LABOR		EQUIPMENT		SUBCONTRACT		TOTAL	
						COST	TOTAL	COST	TOTAL	COST	TOTAL	COST	TOTAL	COST	TOTAL
Division 3: (Cont'd)															
Cast in Place Concrete															
Pilasters															
Concrete - Incl. 5% Waste	033	126	0300	20	CY	50.50	1010								
Placing	033	172	4950	20	CY			15.10	302	7.15	143				
Finishing	033	458	0010	793	SF	0.01	8	0.34	270						
Slab on Grade															
Concrete - Incl. 5% Waste	033	126	0150	348	CY	48.00	16704								
Placing	033	172	4600	348	CY			5.70	1984	0.39	136				
Finishing	033	454	0150	18210	SF			0.27	4917	0.06	1093				
Pit Slab															
Concrete - Incl. 5% Waste	033	126	0150	3	CY	48.00	144								
Placing	033	172	4600	3	CY			5.70	17	0.39	1				
Finishing	033	454	0150	80	SF			0.27	22	0.06	5				
Waffle Slab															
Concrete - Incl. 5% Waste	033	126	0300	555	CY	50.50	28028								
	033	126	1000	555	CY	5.05	2803								
Placing	033	172	1400	555	CY			11.65	6466	5.50	3053				
Finishing	033	454	0150	18900	SF			0.27	5103	0.06	1134				
5 1/2" Elevated Slab															
4" Lt.Wt. Concrete - Incl. 5%	033	126	0300	462	CY	50.50	23331								
	033	126	1010	462	CY	12.63	5833								
Placing	033	172	1400	462	CY			11.65	5382	5.50	2541				
Finishing	033	454	0150	37800	SF			0.27	10206	0.06	2268				
Curing - 3 floors	033	134	0300	567	CSF	2.05	1162	3.12	1769						
Subtotals							$79,022		$36,437		$10,373				

Figure 9.50

193

CONSOLIDATED ESTIMATE

PROJECT: Office Building
LOCATION:
TAKE OFF BY:
CLASSIFICATION: Division 3
ARCHITECT:
QUANTITIES BY:
PRICES BY:
EXTENSIONS BY:

ESTIMATE NO:
DATE: 6/93
CHECKED BY:

DESCRIPTION	SOURCE	QUANT.	UNIT	MATERIAL COST	MATERIAL TOTAL	LABOR COST	LABOR TOTAL	EQUIPMENT COST	EQUIPMENT TOTAL	SUBCONTRACT COST	SUBCONTRACT TOTAL	COST	TOTAL
Division 3: (Cont'd)													
Cast in Place Concrete (Cont'd)													
Stair Treads & Landings	033 184 1750	1436	SF	2.60	3734	1.84	2642						
Subtotal					$3,734		$2,642						
Sheet 1 Subtotals					15642		48182		1451				
Sheet 2 Subtotals					83076		79946		1953				
Sheet 3 Subtotals					27828		14300		1704				
Sheet 4 Subtotals					79022		36437		10373				
Sheet 5 Subtotals					3734		2642						
Division 3 Total					$209,303		$181,507		$15,480				

Figure 9.51

194

032 | Concrete Reinforcement

032 200 | Welded Wire Fabric

			CREW	DAILY OUTPUT	MAN-HOURS	UNIT	1993 BARE COSTS MAT.	LABOR	EQUIP.	TOTAL	TOTAL INCL O&P	
207	0300	6 x 6 - W2.9 x W2.9 (6 x 6) 42 lb. per C.S.F. R032 -030	2 Rodm	29	.552	C.S.F.	13.10	14.25		27.35	39.50	207
	0400	6 x 6 - W4 x W4 (4 x 4) 58 lb. per C.S.F.		27	.593		17.65	15.30		32.95	46.50	
	0500	4 x 4 - W1.4 x W1.4 (10 x 10) 31 lb. per C.S.F.		31	.516		10.40	13.35		23.75	35	
	0600	4 x 4 - W2.1 x W2.1 (8 x 8) 44 lb. per C.S.F.		29	.552		12.50	14.25		26.75	39	
	0650	4 x 4 - W2.9 x W2.9 (6 x 6) 61 lb. per C.S.F.		27	.593		17.75	15.30		33.05	46.50	
	0700	4 x 4 - W4 x W4 (4 x 4) 85 lb. per C.S.F.		25	.640		26.50	16.55		43.05	58.50	
	0800	2 x 2 - #14 galv. @ 21 lb., beam & column wrap		6.50	2.462		12.70	63.50		76.20	126	
	0900	2 x 2 - #12 galv. for gunite reinforcing		6.50	2.462		16.75	63.50		80.25	130	
	0950	Material prices for above include 10% lap										
	1000	Specially fabricated heavier gauges in sheets	4 Rodm	50	.640	C.S.F.		16.55		16.55	29	
	1010	Material only, minimum				Ton	550			550	605	
	1020	Average					700			700	770	
	1030	Maximum					855			855	940	
240	0010	**FIBROUS REINFORCING**										240
	0100	Synthetic fibers				Lb.	4.50			4.50	4.95	
	0110	Synthetic fibers, 1-1/2 lb. per C.Y., add to concrete				C.Y.	6.75			6.75	7.45	
	0150	Steel fibers				Lb.	.50			.50	.55	
	0160	Steel fibers, 50 lb. per C.Y., add to concrete				C.Y.	25			25	27.50	
	0170	Steel fibers, 75 lb. per C.Y., add to concrete					37.50			37.50	41.50	
	0180	Steel fibers, 100 lb. per C.Y., add to concrete					50			50	55	

032 300 | Stressing Tendons

			CREW	DAILY OUTPUT	MAN-HOURS	UNIT	MAT.	LABOR	EQUIP.	TOTAL	TOTAL INCL O&P	
307	0010	**PRESTRESSING STEEL** Post-tensioned in field R032 -090										307
	0020											
	0100	Grouted strand, 50' span, 100 kip	C-3	1,200	.053	Lb.	1.72	1.28	.13	3.13	4.20	
	0150	300 kip		2,700	.024		1.39	.57	.06	2.02	2.55	
	0300	100' span, grouted, 100 kip		1,700	.038		1.14	.90	.09	2.13	2.87	
	0350	300 kip		3,200	.020		1.01	.48	.05	1.54	1.97	
	0500	200' span, grouted, 100 kip		2,700	.024		1.06	.57	.06	1.69	2.19	
	0550	300 kip		3,500	.018		.98	.44	.05	1.47	1.87	
	0800	Grouted bars, 50' span, 42 kip		2,600	.025		1.14	.59	.06	1.79	2.32	
	0850	143 kip		3,200	.020		1	.48	.05	1.53	1.96	
	1000	75' span, grouted, 42 kip		3,200	.020		.93	.48	.05	1.46	1.88	
	1050	143 kip		4,200	.015		.88	.36	.04	1.28	1.63	
	1200	Ungrouted strand, 50' span, 100 kip	C-4	1,275	.025		1.11	.66	.03	1.80	2.41	
	1250	200 kip		1,475	.022		1.12	.57	.02	1.71	2.26	
	1400	100' span, ungrouted, 100 kip		1,500	.021		.94	.56	.02	1.52	2.04	
	1450	200 kip		1,650	.019		.96	.51	.02	1.49	1.98	
	1600	200' span, ungrouted, 100 kip		1,500	.021		.88	.56	.02	1.46	1.98	
	1650	200 kip		1,700	.019		.89	.50	.02	1.41	1.87	
	1800	Ungrouted bars, 50' span, 42 kip		1,400	.023		1.01	.60	.03	1.64	2.20	
	1850	143 kip		1,700	.019		.94	.50	.02	1.46	1.92	
	2000	75' span, ungrouted, 42 kip		1,800	.018		.95	.47	.02	1.44	1.89	
	2050	143 kip		2,200	.015		.87	.38	.02	1.27	1.65	
	2220	Ungrouted single strand, 100' slab, 25 kip		1,200	.027		1.01	.70	.03	1.74	2.37	
	2250	35 kip		1,475	.022		.94	.57	.02	1.53	2.06	

Figure 9.52

component costs for spread footings from the estimate sheets of Division 3 are added:

Spread Footings:

	Material	Bare Costs Labor	Equipment	Total
Formwork	$ 783	$3,434	$120	$ 4,337
Reinf.	2,181	1,758		3,939
Concrete	8,640			8,640
Placing		1,539	106	1,645
Total	$ 11,604	$6,731	226	$18,561
$/CY (171 CY)	67.86	39.36	1.32	108.54

Reinforcing costs, separated for the spread footings only, are obtained from the appropriate quantities, from Figure 9.46, and the unit costs from Figure 9.49. Comparison to line 3850 in Figure 9.54, verifies that costs for the building's spread footings are good. Similar crosschecks can be made throughout the estimate to help prevent gross errors. Quantities and prices for all components of each of the concrete systems have been separately itemized. By organizing the estimate in this way, costs and quantities can be compared to historical figures and used as a comparison for future projects.

Division 4: Masonry

Masonry is generally estimated by the piece (brick, block, etc.) or by wall area (per square foot). Quantities based on square feet of surface area are a function of:

- Size of the masonry unit.
- Bond (pattern or coursing).
- Thickness of mortar joints.
- Thickness of wall.

Similar to other divisions, masonry estimates should be performed in as detailed a manner as is practical. The masonry specifications will contain pertinent information which should be noted before proceeding with the quantity takeoff. Such items as mortar types, joint reinforcing, and cleaning requirements should all be described and defined. Typical mortar types (mixtures) most commonly specified are shown in Figure 9.55. Required mortar additives (coloring, anti-hydro, bonding agents, etc.) will be specified and should be noted.

It is important that mortar specifications be followed carefully. What little money may be saved by "skimping" on the mortar is not really worth the risks involved.

When all requirements in the specifications have been noted, the plans must be carefully reviewed. Drawings and details of masonry work are usually interspersed throughout the plans. All sheets should be checked. Walls and partitions of different masonry types and sizes are estimated separately. Requirements which must be listed and estimated individually include:

- Number and type of masonry units
- Bonding patterns
- Special coursing
- Openings
- Lintels and accessories
- Joint size (mortar quantities) and finish
- Grouting (cores, pilasters, door jambs, and bond beams, incl. reinforcing)
- Joint reinforcing

033 | Cast-In-Place Concrete

<table>
<tr><th colspan="2">033 100 | Structural Concrete</th><th>CREW</th><th>DAILY OUTPUT</th><th>MAN-HOURS</th><th>UNIT</th><th>MAT.</th><th>LABOR</th><th>EQUIP.</th><th>TOTAL</th><th>TOTAL INCL O&P</th></tr>
<tr><td>118</td><td>0700</td><td colspan="9" style="text-align:right"></td></tr>
</table>

		CREW	DAILY OUTPUT	MAN-HOURS	UNIT	MAT.	LABOR	EQUIP.	TOTAL	TOTAL INCL O&P	
118 0700	Curing compound,(200 to 400 S.F. per gallon), 55 gal. lots				Gal.	6.85			6.85	7.55	**118**
0720	5 gallon lots					7.65			7.65	8.40	
0800	Premium grade,(450 S.F. per gallon), 55 gallon lots					13.25			13.25	14.60	
0820	5 gallon lots					14.10			14.10	15.50	
0900	Dustproofing compound,(200-600 S.F./gal.), 55 gallon lots					7			7	7.70	
0920	5 gallon lots					8			8	8.80	
1000	Epoxy dustproof coating, colors,(300-400 S.F. per coat),										
1010	or transparent,(400-600 S.F. per coat)				Gal.	50			50	55	
1100	Hardeners, metallic, 55 lb. bags, natural (grey)				Lb.	.41			.41	.45	
1200	Colors, average					.67			.67	.74	
1300	Non-metallic, 55 lb. bags, natural (grey), minimum					.34			.34	.37	
1310	Maximum					.58			.58	.64	
1320	Non-metallic, colors, minimum					.38			.38	.42	
1340	Maximum					.62			.62	.68	
1400	Non-metallic, non-slip, 100 lb. bags, minimum					.38			.38	.42	
1420	Maximum					.75			.75	.83	
1500	Solution type,(300 to 400 S.F. per gallon)				Gal.	5.25			5.25	5.80	
1510											
1550	Release agent, for tilt slabs				Gal.	7.25			7.25	8	
1570	For forms, average					4.75			4.75	5.20	
1600	Sealer, hardener and dustproofer, clear, 450 S.F., minimum					7			7	7.70	
1620	Maximum					19.25			19.25	21	
1700	Colors (300-400 S.F. per gallon)					17			17	18.70	
1710											
1800	Set accelerator for below freezing, 1 to 1-1/2 gal. per C.Y.				Gal.	4.30			4.30	4.73	
1900	Set retarder, 2 to 4 fl. oz. per bag of cement				"	13.60			13.60	14.95	
2000	Waterproofing, integral 1 lb. per bag of cement				Lb.	.83			.83	.91	
2100	Powdered metallic, 40 lbs. per 100 S.F., minimum					.83			.83	.91	
2120	Maximum					1.75			1.75	1.93	
2200	Water reducing admixture, average				Gal.	7.75			7.75	8.55	
122 0010	**CONCRETE, FIELD MIX** FOB forms 2250 psi R033 -080				C.Y.	51			51	56	**122**
0020	3000 psi				"	53.50			53.50	59	
126 0010	**CONCRETE, READY MIX** Regular weight, 2000 psi R033 -040				C.Y.	45.50			45.50	50	**126**
0100	2500 psi					47			47	51.50	
0150	3000 psi R033 -060					48			48	53	
0200	3500 psi					49.50			49.50	54.50	
0250	3750 psi R033 -070					50			50	55	
0300	4000 psi					50.50			50.50	55.50	
0350	4500 psi					52			52	57	
0400	5000 psi					53			53	58.50	
0411	6000 psi					60.50			60.50	66.50	
0412	8000 psi					98.50			98.50	108	
0413	10000 psi					140			140	154	
0414	12000 psi					169			169	186	
1000	For high early strength cement, add					10%					
1010	For structural lightweight with regular sand, add					25%					
2000	For all lightweight aggregate, add					45%					
3000	For integral colors, 2500 psi, 5 bag mix										
3100	Red, yellow or brown, 1.8 lb. per bag, add				C.Y.	11.50			11.50	12.65	
3200	9.4 lb. per bag, add					61			61	67	
3400	Black, 1.8 lb. per bag, add					13.50			13.50	14.85	
3500	7.5 lb. per bag, add					56			56	61.50	
3700	Green, 1.8 lb. per bag, add					26.50			26.50	29	
3800	7.5 lb. per bag, add					111			111	122	
130 0010	**CONCRETE IN PLACE** Including forms (4 uses), reinforcing R033 -010										**130**
0050	steel, including finishing unless otherwise indicated										

Figure 9.53

197

033 | Cast-In-Place Concrete

033 100 | Structural Concrete

			DAILY OUTPUT	MAN-HOURS	UNIT	1993 BARE COSTS				TOTAL INCL O&P	
		CREW				MAT.	LABOR	EQUIP.	TOTAL		
130	3800	Footings, spread under 1 C.Y.	C-17B	31.82	2.577	C.Y.	68	63	7.90	138.90	183	**130**
	3850	Over 5 C.Y.	C-17C	70.45	1.178		64	29	5.35	98.35	122	
	3900	Footings, strip, 18" x 9", plain	C-17B	34.22	2.396		59	58.50	7.35	124.85	166	
	3950	36" x 12", reinforced		49.07	1.671		63	41	5.15	109.15	140	
	4000	Foundation mat, under 10 C.Y.		32.32	2.537		107	62	7.80	176.80	225	
	4050	Over 20 C.Y.	↓	47.37	1.731		103	42.50	5.30	150.80	186	
	4200	Grade walls, 8" thick, 8' high	C-15	10.16	7.087		109	157	5.25	271.25	375	
	4250	14' high	C-20	7.30	8.767		175	176	83	434	560	
	4260	12" thick, 8' high	C-17A	13.50	6		138	147	9.35	294.35	395	
	4270	14' high	C-20	11.60	5.517		130	111	52.50	293.50	375	
	4300	15" thick, 8' high	C-17B	20.01	4.098		84	100	12.60	196.60	264	
	4350	12' high	C-20	14.80	4.324		110	87	41	238	300	
	4500	18' high	"	12	5.333	↓	130	107	50.50	287.50	365	
	4510											
	4650	Slab on grade, not including finish, 4" thick	C-17C	75.28	1.103	C.Y.	56	27	5	88	110	
	4700	6" thick	"	113.47	.731	"	54	17.95	3.33	75.28	91	
	4750	Slab on grade, incl. troweled finish, not incl. forms										
	4760	or reinforcing, over 10,000 S.F., 4" thick slab	C-8	3,520	.016	S.F.	.67	.33	.15	1.15	1.42	
	4820	6" thick slab		3,610	.016		1.04	.32	.15	1.51	1.81	
	4840	8" thick slab		3,275	.017		1.30	.36	.17	1.83	2.16	
	4900	12" thick slab		2,875	.019		1.94	.41	.19	2.54	2.97	
	4950	15" thick slab	↓	2,560	.022	↓	2.42	.46	.21	3.09	3.59	
	5000	Slab on grade, incl. textured finish, not incl. forms										
	5001	or reinforcing, 4" thick slab	C-8A	2,200	.022	S.F.	1.14	.44		1.58	1.93	
	5010	6" thick		2,000	.024		1.44	.49		1.93	2.33	
	5020	8" thick	↓	1,800	.027	↓	1.79	.54		2.33	2.81	
	5200	Lift slab in place above the foundation, incl. forms,										
	5210	reinforcing, concrete and columns, minimum	C-17E	745	.107	S.F.	2.50	2.63	.08	5.21	6.95	
	5250	Average		675	.119		4.10	2.90	.09	7.09	9.15	
	5300	Maximum	↓	430	.186	↓	4.45	4.56	.13	9.14	12.25	
	5500	Lightweight, ready mix, including screed finish only,										
	5510	not including forms or reinforcing										
	5550	1:4 for structural roof decks	C-8	80	.700	C.Y.	76	14.65	6.80	97.45	113	
	5600	1:6 for ground slab with radiant heat		90	.622		73	13	6.05	92.05	107	
	5650	1:3:2 with sand aggregate, roof deck		80	.700		77	14.65	6.80	98.45	114	
	5700	Ground slab	↓	105	.533		77	11.15	5.15	93.30	107	
	5900	Pile caps, incl. forms and reinf., sq. or rect., under 5 C.Y.	C-17C	47.26	1.756		70	43	8	121	153	
	5950	Over 10 C.Y.		76.47	1.085		64	26.50	4.94	95.44	118	
	6000	Triangular or hexagonal, under 5 C.Y.		47.95	1.731		72	42.50	7.90	122.40	155	
	6050	Over 10 C.Y.	↓	77.85	1.066		69	26	4.85	99.85	122	
	6200	Retaining walls, gravity, 4' high see division 022-708	C-17B	19.10	4.293		66	105	13.20	184.20	253	
	6250	10' high		27.10	3.026		68	74	9.30	151.30	202	
	6300	Cantilever, level backfill loading, 8' high		16.30	5.031		125	123	15.45	263.45	350	
	6350	16' high	↓	17	4.824	↓	113	118	14.80	245.80	325	
	6800	Stairs, not including safety treads, free standing	C-15	120	.600	LF Nose	5	13.30	.44	18.74	27	
	6850	Cast on ground		180	.400	"	3.77	8.85	.30	12.92	18.50	
	7000	Stair landings, free standing		285	.253	S.F.	2.10	5.60	.19	7.89	11.35	
	7050	Cast on ground	↓	685	.105	"	1.22	2.33	.08	3.63	5.10	
134	0010	**CURING** With burlap, 4 uses assumed, 7.5 oz.	2 Clab	55	.291	C.S.F.	2.70	5.40		8.10	11.40	**134**
	0100	12 oz.		55	.291		3.90	5.40		9.30	12.75	
	0200	With waterproof curing paper, 2 ply, reinforced		70	.229		5.25	4.24		9.49	12.45	
	0300	With sprayed membrane curing compound	↓	95	.168	↓	2.05	3.12		5.17	7.15	
	0400	Curing blankets, 1" to 2" thick, buy, minimum				S.F.	.80			.80	.88	
	0450	Maximum					2.50			2.50	2.75	
	0500	Electrically heated pads, 110 volts, 15 watts per S.F., buy					4.20			4.20	4.62	
	0600	20 watts per S.F., buy				↓	5.60			5.60	6.15	

Figure 9.54

198

- Wall ties
- Flashing, reglets, weepholes
- Control joints
- Cleaning (water or chemical)
- Scaffolding and equipment

Each type of specified masonry unit should be identified on a takeoff sheet, not only by the kind of unit (brick, block, etc.) but also by type of construction (wall, arch, foundation, etc.). The square feet and/or linear feet of each listing should be measured from the plans and elevations. It should be remembered that exterior measurements of a building's perimeter include an overlap of the thickness of the walls for every outside corner. This is accepted accuracy and should be included, since corners tend to require more cutting and waste.

When measuring exterior dimensions at inside corners, however, the estimator must add to the actual dimensions to account for the extra material and labor involved to construct the inside corners.

Brick Mortar Mixes*					
Type	Portland Cement	Hydrated Lime	Sand** (maximum)**	Strength	Use
M	1	1/4	3-3/4	High	General use where high strength is required, especially good compressive strength; work that is below grade and in contact with earth.
S	1	1/2	4-1/2	High	Okay for general use, especially good where high lateral strength is desired.
N	1	1	6	Medium	General use when masonry is exposed above grade; best to use when high compressive and lateral strengths are not required.
0	1	2	9	Low	Do not use when masonry is exposed to severe weathering; acceptable for non-loadbearing walls of solid units and interior non-loadbearing partitions of hollow units.

*The water used should be of the quality of drinking water. Use as much as is needed to bring the mix to a suitably plastic and workable state.
**The sand should be damp and loose. A general rule for sand content is that it should not be less than 2-1/4 or more than 3 times the sum of the cement and lime volumes.

Figure 9.55

Openings or "outs" should be deleted from overall quantity only if greater than 2 square feet. Lintels should be listed separately at this time by type and size (steel angle, precast, etc.). Responsibility for purchase of steel lintels should be established. Often, loose lintels are supplied by the steel fabricator and only installed by the masonry contractor.

When the overall square foot quantities of masonry work have been determined, the number of units may be calculated. Figure 9.56 lists different types of masonry units and corresponding quantities. Note that quantities per square foot as shown are based on certain joint sizes. If different joint sizes are specified, quantities should be adjusted. In Figure 9.56, quantities are listed not only by the type of unit but also by bond and coursing. Typical brick and block types and joints, bonds and coursing are shown in Figures 9.57 to 9.59. The descriptions of different bonds in Figure 9.58 include suggested waste allowance percentages which should be added to the quantities before pricing.

It is difficult to develop accurate unit price data for masonry due to fluctuation of both material prices and labor productivity. The estimator should always call suppliers to verify material costs and availability. All unit prices for brick masonry in *Means Building Construction Cost Data*, (Figure 9.60), include the material cost per thousand pieces in the line description. If local costs are different, the material unit costs should be adjusted.

Productivity is affected by the type and complexity of work and can be severely affected by weather. Assume that a crew (including masons, helpers and appropriate equipment) can install approximately 600 standard bricks per man per day. This productivity rate assumes fairly straight runs (few openings) and good weather. For complicated work (many openings and corners), assume the same crew can install 400 bricks per man per day. Even for a simple building elevation as shown in Figure 9.61, both rates would apply. The high productivity portions (HP) are those areas, between rows of windows, with no openings. Low productivity portions (LP) are those areas which include the window jambs, headers and sills.

Total wall area	1,920 S.F.
Deduct openings	−376 S.F.
Total masonry area	1,544 S.F.
Standard brick (Fig. 9.56)	x 6.75 brick/S.F.
Total bricks	10,422 bricks
5% waste (Running bond, Fig. 9.58)	+ 521
	10,943 bricks

56% of the wall area is high productivity and 44% is low productivity.

56% of 10,943 = 6,128 bricks (HP)

44% of 10,943 = 4,815 bricks (LP)

HP area: $\dfrac{6,128 \text{ bricks}}{600 \text{ bricks/days}}$ = 10 days

LP area: $\dfrac{4,815 \text{ bricks}}{400 \text{ bricks/day}}$ = 12 days

From quick, simple calculations, the estimator has the material quantity and the time required. A material cost is obtained from a supplier and the cost per day for the crew is multiplied by the time durations. Total costs for the work are obtained. Unit costs are determined by dividing the total costs – material or labor or both – by the appropriate units – square feet or per thousand brick.

Temperature and humidity variations can have a significant impact on masonry work. Not only are the general working conditions affected, but the drying time and workability of mortar have an effect on productivity. Figure 9.62 is a graphic representation of the relative effects of temperature and humidity. The numbers in the grid are factors to be multiplied by a maximum productivity. The following procedure can be used to derive this theoretical maximum (based on ideal weather conditions, 75 degrees F., 60% humidity – see Figure

Brick Quantities

	Running Bond					For Other Bonds Standard Size Add to S.F. Quantities in Table to Left		
	Number of Brick per S.F. of Wall - Single Wythe with 3/8" Joints				C.F. of Mortar per M Bricks, Waste Included			
Type Brick	Nominal Size (incl. mortar) L H W	Modular Coursing	Number of Brick per S.F.		3/8" Joint	1/2" Joint	Bond Type	Description	Factor
Standard	8 x 2-2/3 x 4	3C = 8"	6.75	10.3	12.9	Common	full header every fifth course	+20%
Economy	8 x 4 x 4	1C = 4"	4.50	11.4	14.6		full header every sixth course	+16.7%
Engineer	8 x 3-1/5 x 4	5C = 16"	5.63	10.6	13.6	English	full header every second course	+50%
Fire	9 x 2-1/2 x 4-1/2	2C = 5"	6.40	550 # Fireclay	—	Flemish	alternate headers every course	+33.3%
Jumbo	12 x 4 x 6 or 8	1C = 4"	3.00	23.8	30.8		every sixth course	+5.6%
Norman	12 x 2-2/3 x 4	3C = 8"	4.50	14.0	17.9	Header = W x H exposed		+100%
Norwegian	12 x 3-1/5 x 4	5C = 16"	3.75	14.6	18.6	Rowlock = H x W exposed		+100%
Roman	12 x 2 x 4	2C = 4"	6.00	13.4	17.0	Rowlock stretcher = L x W exposed		+33.3%
SCR	12 x 2-2/3 x 6	3C = 8"	4.50	21.8	28.0	Soldier = H x L exposed		—
Utility	12 x 4 x 4	1C = 4"	3.00	15.4	19.6	Sailor = W x L exposed		-33.3%

Concrete Block Quantities

Concrete Blocks Nominal Size (incl. 3/8" joint)	Approximate Weight per S.F.		Blocks per 100 S.F.	Mortar per M block	
	Standard	Lightweight		Partitions	Back up
2" x 8" x 16"	20 PSF	15 PSF	113	16 C.F.	36 C.F.
4"	30	20		31	51
6"	42	30		46	66
8"	55	38		62	82
10"	70	47		77	97
12"	85	55		92	112

Glass Block Quantities

	Per 100 S.F.		Per 1000 Block				
Size	No. of Block	Mortar ¼" Joint	Asphalt Emulsion	Caulk	Expansion Joint	Panel Anchors	Wall Mesh
6" x 6"	410 ea.	5.0 C.F.	.17 gal.	1.5 gal.	80 L.F.	20 ea.	500 L.F.
8" x 8"	230	3.6	.33	2.8	140	36	670
12" x 12"	102	2.3	.67	6.0	312	80	1000
Approximate quantity per 100 S.F.			.07 gal.	0.6 gal.	32 L.F.	9 ea.	51, 68, 102 L.F.

Figure 9.56

Surfaces of a Brick

Cull
Bed
Side
Face
Bed
End

Shapes of Cut Brick

Half or Bat
Three-Quarter
Quarter Closer
King Closer
Queen Closer
Split

Standard Common Brick

8"
3-¾"
2-¼"

Brick Positions and Courses

Header Course — Header
Stretcher Course — Stretcher
Rolok Course — Bull Header
Shiner Course — Bull Stretcher
Soldier Course — Soldier
Sailor Course — Sailor
Quoins

Masonry Joints

Stretchers
Wythe
Course
Bed Joints
Head Joints

Joints Which Shed Water

Weather Struck
Rounded
Vee-shaped

Joints Which do not Shed Water

Trowel Struck
Raked
Stripped

Common Mortar Joints

Beaded
Flush
Squeezed

Figure 9.57

Running or Stretcher Bond	The face brick are all stretchers and are tied to the backing by metal or reinforcing. Waste – 5%.
Common or American Bond	Every sixth course of stretcher bond is usually a header course. Waste – 4%.
Flemish Bond	Each course has alternate headers and stretchers with the alternate headers centered over the stretcher. Waste – 3 to 5%.
English Bond	Consists of alternate headers and stretchers with the vertical joints in the header and stretcher aligning or breaking over each other. Waste – 8 to 15%.
Stack Bond	Has no overlapping of units since all vertical joints are aligned. Usually this pattern is bonded to the backing with rigid steel ties. Waste – 3%.
English Cross or Dutch Bond	Built up of interlocking crosses. This wall consists of two headers and a stretcher forming a cross. Waste – 8%.

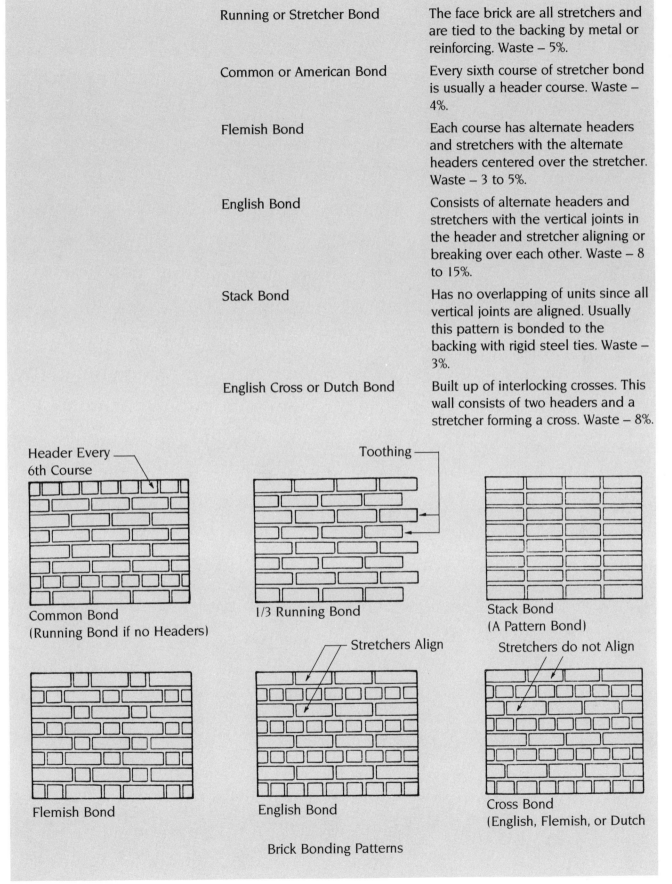

Brick Bonding Patterns

Figure 9.58

4" Concrete Block

12" Concrete Block

8" Concrete Box

Jamb Block

Pilaster Block Flush Wall Type

8" Glazed Block

Lintel Block

Concrete Block Types

2-Core Double Corner

3-Core Stretcher

Figure 9.59

204

042 500 | Ceramic Veneer

			CREW	DAILY OUTPUT	MAN-HOURS	UNIT	1993 BARE COSTS				TOTAL INCL O&P	
							MAT.	LABOR	EQUIP.	TOTAL		
510	0200	Split type, glazed, 9" wide	D-1	90	.178	L.F.	4.72	3.81		8.53	11.10	510
	0250	13" wide	↓	80	.200	↓	7.75	4.29		12.04	15.20	
	0500	Partition or back-up blocks, scored, in C.L. lots										
	0700	Non-load bearing 12" x 12", 3" thick, Special Order Only	D-8	550	.073	S.F.	4	1.60		5.60	6.85	
	0750	4" thick, standard		500	.080		3.24	1.76		5	6.30	
	0800	6" thick, standard		450	.089		3.25	1.95		5.20	6.60	
	0850	8" thick, standard		400	.100		4.10	2.20		6.30	7.90	
	1000	Load bearing, 12" x 12", 4" thick, in walls		500	.080		3.34	1.76		5.10	6.40	
	1050	In floors		750	.053		3.35	1.17		4.52	5.50	
	1200	6" thick, in walls		450	.089		3.35	1.95		5.30	6.70	
	1250	In floors		675	.059		3.35	1.30		4.65	5.70	
	1400	8" thick, in walls		400	.100		4.22	2.20		6.42	8.05	
	1450	In floors		575	.070		4.22	1.53		5.75	7	
	1600	10" thick, in walls, special order		350	.114		4.89	2.51		7.40	9.30	
	1650	In floors, special order		500	.080		4.90	1.76		6.66	8.10	
	1800	12" thick, in walls, special order		300	.133		5.85	2.93		8.78	10.95	
	1850	In floors, special order	↓	450	.089		5.85	1.95		7.80	9.45	
	2000	For reinforcing with steel rods, add to above					15%	5%				
	2100	For smooth tile instead of scored, add					.08			.08	.09	
	2200	For L.C.L. quantities, add				↓	10%	10%				
512	0010	TERRA COTTA TILE On walls, dry set, 1/2" thick										512
	0100	Square, hexagonal or lattice shapes, unglazed	1 Tilf	135	.059	S.F.	3.90	1.39		5.29	6.35	
	0300	Glazed, plain colors		130	.062		5.20	1.45		6.65	7.90	
	0400	Intense colors	↓	125	.064	↓	8.05	1.50		9.55	11.05	

042 550 | Masonry Veneer

			CREW	DAILY OUTPUT	MAN-HOURS	UNIT	1993 BARE COSTS				TOTAL INCL O&P	
							MAT.	LABOR	EQUIP.	TOTAL		
554	0010	BRICK VENEER Scaffolding not included, truck load lots										554
	0015	MATERIAL COSTS INCLUDE A 3% BRICK WASTE ALLOWANCE										
	0020	4" thk., sel. common, 8" x 2-2/3" x 4" @ $265 per M (6.75/S.F.)	D-8	1.50	26.667	M	300	585		885	1,225	
	0050	Standard 8" x 2-2/3" x 4", running bond, red face, $295 per M		1.50	26.667		335	585		920	1,275	
	0100	Full header every 6th course (7.88/S.F.) [R042 -120]		1.45	27.586		335	605		940	1,300	
	0150	English, full header every 2nd course (10.13/S.F.)		1.40	28.571		335	630		965	1,325	
	0200	Flemish, alternate header every course (9.00/S.F.) [R042 -180]		1.40	28.571		335	630		965	1,325	
	0250	Flemish, alt. header every 6th course (7.13/S.F.)		1.45	27.586		335	605		940	1,300	
	0300	Full headers throughout (13.50/S.F.) [R042 -500]		1.40	28.571		335	630		965	1,325	
	0350	Rowlock course (13.50/S.F.)		1.35	29.630		335	650		985	1,375	
	0400	Rowlock stretcher (4.50/S.F.) [R042 -550]		1.40	28.571		335	630		965	1,325	
	0450	Soldier course (6.75/S.F.)		1.40	28.571		335	630		965	1,325	
	0500	Sailor course (4.50/S.F.)		1.30	30.769		335	675		1,010	1,425	
	0601	Running bond, buff or gray face, (6.75/S.F.) $375 per M		1.50	26.667		415	585		1,000	1,350	
	0700	Glazed face, 8" x 2-2/3" x 4" @ $1030 per M, running bond		1.40	28.571		1,100	630		1,730	2,175	
	0750	Full header every 6th course (7.88/S.F.)		1.35	29.630		1,100	650		1,750	2,200	
	1000	Jumbo, 12" x 4" x 6" $1010/M (3.00/S.F.)		1.30	30.769		1,150	675		1,825	2,300	
	1051	Norman, 12" x 2-2/3" x 4" $570/M (4.50/S.F.)		1.45	27.586		625	605		1,230	1,625	
	1100	Norwegian, 12" x 3-1/5" x 4" at $640 per M (3.75/S.F.)		1.40	28.571		700	630		1,330	1,750	
	1150	Economy, 8" x 4" x 4" at $520 per M (4.50 per S.F.)		1.40	28.571		565	630		1,195	1,600	
	1201	Engineer, 8" x 3-1/5" x 4", $410/M (5.63/S.F.)		1.45	27.586		450	605		1,055	1,425	
	1251	Roman, 12" x 2" x 4", $590/M (6.00/S.F.)		1.50	26.667		645	585		1,230	1,625	
	1300	S.C.R. 12" x 2-2/3" x 6" $795/M (4.50/S.F.)		1.40	28.571		880	630		1,510	1,950	
	1350	Utility, 12" x 4" x 4" $850/M (3.00/S.F.)	↓	1.35	29.630		920	650		1,570	2,000	
	1360	For less than truck load lots, add					10					
	1400	For battered walls, add						30%				
	1450	For corbels, add						60%				
	1500	For curved walls, add						30%				
	1550	For pits and trenches, deduct				↓		20%				
	1999	Alternate method of figuring by square foot										

Figure 9.60

BUILDING ELEVATION

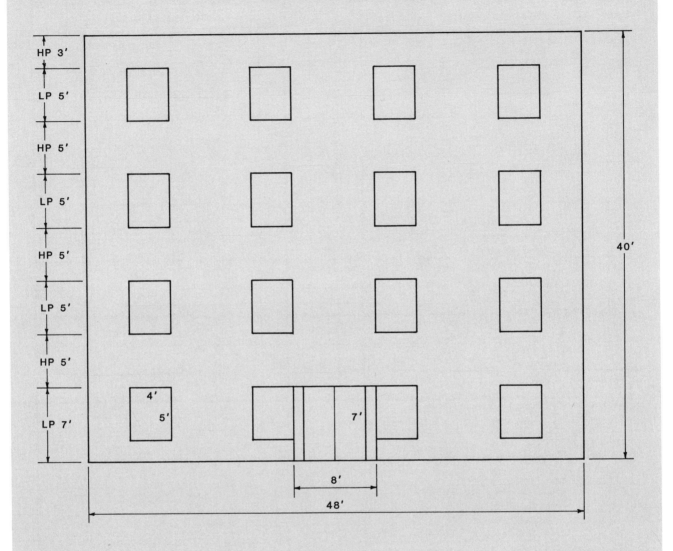

HP – HIGH PRODUCTIVITY
LP – LOW PRODUCTIVITY

Figure 9.61

206

9.62). For a given month, assume the productivity of a crew to be 500 units per day per mason. A record of the local, average temperature and humidity for that month is obtained from the National Weather Service, for example, 60 degrees F., 75% relative humidity. The factor for those conditions is 0.765, from Figure 9.62.

$$\frac{500 \text{ units/day}}{0.765} = 654 \text{ units/day (theoretical maximum)}$$

This theoretical maximum serves as a practical example for using the chart to predict productivity based on anticipated weather conditions.

Sample Estimate: Division 4

For the masonry portion sample building project, assume that good historical records are available. The following data have been developed from past jobs:

Productivity:

Regular block — 150 S.F. block/mason/day

8″ x 16″ x 8″ — 170 block/mason/day

Split face block — 125 S.F. block/mason/day

8″ x 16″ x 6″ — 142 block/mason/day

Mortar — 62 C.F./M block

(Figure 9.56) 10 C.F./mason/day

Bare Costs:

Mason	$24.05/hr., $192.40/day
Mason's helper	$18.85/hr., $150.80/day
Mortar	$2.79/C.F.
Mixer	$59.50/day
Scaffolding	$15.00/section/month
Forklift	$173.00/day
Masonry saw	$40.00/day

Even though the mixer and scaffolding are owned, costs are charged to each job. A crew of four masons and two helpers will be available and used for this job. Costs are developed as follows:

Material:

Regular block:

9,430 S.F. x 113 block/100 S.F. = 10,656 block

(10,656 + 5% waste) x $0.98 ea.

11,189 block x $0.98 = $10,965

Split face:

2,040 S.F. x 113 block/100 S.F. = 2,305 block

(2,305 + 5% waste) x $1.82 ea.

2,420 block x $2.32 = $5,614

BRICK PRODUCTIVITY TABLE

Figure 9.62

Mortar:

    62 C.F./M block x 12,961 block = 804 C.F.

    804 C.F. x $3.50 C.F. = $2,814

Reinforcing:

    6,000 L.F. x $192.64/MLF = $1,156

Lintels:

    Labor costs included below.

    Material costs included in Division 5.

Total Material Costs:

Regular Block	$10,965
Split Face Block	5,614
Mortar	2,814
Reinforcing	1,156
	$20,549

Labor

Regular block:

$$\frac{9,430 \text{ S.F.}}{150 \text{ S.F./mason/day x 4 masons}} = 16 \text{ days}$$

Split block:

$$\frac{2,040 \text{ S.F.}}{125 \text{ S.F./mason/day x 4 masons}} = 4 \text{ days}$$

4 masons x $192.40/day x 20 days = $15,392

2 helpers x $150.80/day x 20 days = $6,032

1 helper x $ 28.28/hour x 20 hours = $ 566 (overtime)

Total Labors Costs:

Masons	$15,392
Helpers	6,598
	$21,990

Equipment:

Mixer:

$59.50/day x 20 days = $1,190

Scaffolding:

24 sections for 1 month @ $195.60/month x 1 month = $196

Crane:

4 hours x $142.50/hour = $570

Forklift:

10 days x $248/day = $2,480

Masonry saw:

10 days x $40/day = $400

Total Equipment Costs:

Mixer	$1,190
Scaffolding	196
Crane	570
Forklift	2,480
Masonry saw	400
	$4,836

The costs are entered as shown in Figure 9.63. Unit costs for materials should be obtained from or verified by local suppliers. The most accurate prices are those developed from recent data. A thorough and detailed cost control and accounting system is important for the development of such costs. Overtime costs for one helper are for mixing mortar before the start of the workday.

Division 5: Metals

The metals portion of a building project, and the corresponding estimate should be broken down into basic components: structural metals, metal joists, metal decks, miscellaneous metals, ornamental metals, expansion control and fasteners. The items in a building project are shown on many different sheets of the drawings and may or may not be thoroughly listed in the specifications. This is especially true of the miscellaneous metals that are listed under Division 5. A complete and detailed review of the construction documents is therefore necessary, noting all items and requirements. Most structural steel work is subcontracted to specialty fabricators and erectors. However, the estimator for the general contractor may perform a takeoff to assure that all specific work is included. Pricing based on total weight (tonnage) can be used to verify subcontractor prices.

Structural Metals

The various structural members should be identified and separately listed by type and size. For example:

	Size	Length	Quantity
Columns:	W8 x 67	12'-6"	16
	W12 x 58	12'-6"	8
Beams:	W14 x 30	30'-0"	10
	W14 x 30	28'-0"	6
	W14 x 26	30'-0"	16
	W24 x 55	30'-0"	12

The quantities may be converted to weight (tonnage) for pricing. This figure is based on weight per linear foot. Base plates, leveling plates, anchor bolts and other accessories should be taken off and listed at this time. Connections should also be noted. Costs for structural steel in *Means Building Construction Cost Data* (Figures 9.64 and 9.65) are given for both individual members and for complete projects including bolted connections. If specified, costs for high strength steel and or high strength bolts must be added separately (Figure 9.65). Welded connections should be listed by fillet size and length and priced separately. Light gauge and special framing for items such as hanging lintels, fascias, and parapets, should be taken off and priced separately. The amount of this type of metal work will vary depending upon design and project requirements.

CONSOLIDATED ESTIMATE

PROJECT: Office Building
LOCATION:
TAKE OFF BY:

CLASSIFICATION: Division 4
ARCHITECT:
QUANTITIES BY:
PRICES BY:
EXTENSIONS BY:

DESCRIPTION	SOURCE	QUANT.	UNIT	MATERIAL COST	MATERIAL TOTAL	LABOR COST	LABOR TOTAL	EQUIPMENT COST	EQUIPMENT TOTAL	SUBCONTRACT COST	SUBCONTRACT TOTAL	COST	TOTAL
Division 4: Masonry													
Regular Block 8" x 16" x 8"	R042-200	11189	Ea.	0.98	10965								
Split Face Block 8" x 16" x 6"	042 220 6150	2420	Ea.	2.32	5614								
Mortar	041 024 2100	804	CF	3.50	2814								
Reinforcing	041 512 0010	6	MLF	192.64	1156								
Labor: Masons		80	MD			192.40	15392						
Helpers - Reg		40	MD			150.80	6032						
OT		20	Hr.			28.28	566						
Equip: Mixer	016 406 1900	20	Day					59.50	1190				
Scaffolding (24 Sections)		1	Mo.					195.60	196				
Crane	061 460 2500	4	Hr.					142.50	570				
Forklift	061 420 2040	10	Day					248.00	2480				
Masonry Saw	061 420 6000	10	Day					40.00	400				
Division 4 Total					$20,549		$21,990		$4,836				

Figure 9.63

211

For development of a budget cost or verification of a subcontractor bid, the estimator can apply average allowance percentages to gross tonnage for:

Base plates	2 to 3%	
Column splices & Beam connections	8 to 10%	
Total allowance	10 to 13%	of main members

Erection costs can be determined in two ways. The first method is to base labor and equipment costs on gross tonnage, as shown in Figure 9.65. The second method is to base costs on the number of pieces. A typical crew and crane can set 35 to 60 pieces per day on the average. Based on normal sizes of beams, girders and columns, this is equivalent to approximately 25 tons per day. The installation rate (number of pieces per day) will not only vary due to crew size, speed and efficiency, but will also be affected by job conditions (relative access or mobility) and the weight of the pieces. A crew may set more smaller, lighter pieces (but less total tonnage) per day than larger or heavier pieces.

Metal Joists and Decks

The estimator will frequently find H-Series Open Web Joists used for the direct support of floor and roof decks in buildings. When long clear spans are desired, the designer will specify often the Longspan Steel Joist LH-Series; these are suitable for the direct support of floors and roof decks. Deep Longspan Steel Joists DLH-Series may be specified for the direct support of roof decks. Some plans will not indicate each joist in place, but rather the designation and spacing. The overall length of each span will be dimensioned. Required bridging may or may not be shown, as this may be defined in the specifications. The quantity takeoff sheet should indicate the joist designation, quantity, length and weight per lineal foot for total tonnage. Extensions of bottom chords, bridging (whether diagonal or horizontal) and any other related items must also be tabulated. The weight of joists per linear foot is usually not specified on the drawings, but is shown in manufacturers' catalogues.

Metal roof deck or form deck (sometimes termed centering) is often used on open web joist construction. Metal deck used on structural steel framing are manufactured in open type, cellular or composite configuration. The finish may be either galvanized painted, or black.

Metal joists are most often priced by the ton. Installation costs may be determined in the same way as for structural steel. Metal deck is taken off and priced by the square foot based on type (open, cellular, composite) gauge and finish.

Miscellaneous and Ornamental Metals

A thorough review of all drawings and specifications is necessary to ensure that all miscellaneous metal requirements are included. Listed below are typical miscellaneous and ornamental metals and the appropriate takeoff units. All items should be listed and priced separately.

		051 200 | Structural Steel	CREW	DAILY OUTPUT	MAN-HOURS	UNIT	MAT.	LABOR	EQUIP.	TOTAL	TOTAL INCL O&P	
							1993 BARE COSTS					
235	8010	and operator hardware, painted										235
	8100	26 ga., 12″ diameter	1 Sswk	4	2	Ea.	100	52		152	204	
	8150	20″ diameter		3	2.667		122	69.50		191.50	259	
	8200	24 ga., 24″ diameter		2	4		160	104		264	365	
	8250	Galvanized		2	4		145	104		249	350	
	8300	Continuous, 26 ga., 10′ long, 9″ wide	2 Sswk	4	4		185	104		289	390	
	8400	12″ wide	"	4	4		225	104		329	435	
238	0010	SPACE FRAME Steel 4′ modular, 40′ to 70′ spans, 5.5 psf, minimum	E-2	556	.101	S.F.	10.50	2.55	1.79	14.84	17.95	238
	0200	Maximum		365	.153		15.30	3.88	2.72	21.90	26.50	
	0400	5′ modular, 4.5 psf minimum		585	.096		9.50	2.42	1.70	13.62	16.55	
	0500	Maximum		405	.138		12.95	3.50	2.46	18.91	23	
	0700	Add to above for galvanizing, 4′ modular					1.75			1.75	1.93	
	0800	5′ modular					1.35			1.35	1.49	
240	0010	STEEL CUTTING Hand burning, including preparation,										240
	0020	torch cutting, and grinding, no staging										
	0100	Steel to 1/2″ thick	E-14	70	.114	L.F.	.40	3.20	1.05	4.65	7.40	
	0150	3/4″ thick		50	.160		.55	4.48	1.47	6.50	10.30	
	0200	1″ thick		45	.178		.60	4.98	1.63	7.21	11.45	
245	0010	STRESSED SKIN Roof and ceiling system, spans to 100′, minimum	E-2	1,150	.049	S.F.	3.25	1.23	.86	5.34	6.65	245
	0200	Maximum	"	760	.074	"	8	1.86	1.31	11.17	13.50	
250	0010	STRUCTURAL STEEL MEMBERS Common WF sizes, spans 10′ to 45′										250
	0020	including bolted connections and erection										
	0100	W 6 x 9 R051 -210	E-2	600	.093	L.F.	4.83	2.36	1.66	8.85	11.20	
	0300	W 8 x 10		600	.093		5.35	2.36	1.66	9.37	11.80	
	0500	x 31 R051 -240		500	.112		16.60	2.83	1.99	21.42	25.50	
	0700	W 10 x 22		660	.085		11.80	2.15	1.51	15.46	18.40	
	0900	x 49		540	.104		26.50	2.62	1.84	30.96	35.50	
	1100	W 12 x 14		880	.064		7.50	1.61	1.13	10.24	12.30	
	1300	x 22		880	.064		11.80	1.61	1.13	14.54	17.05	
	1500	x 26		880	.064		13.95	1.61	1.13	16.69	19.40	
	1700	x 72		640	.087		37	2.21	1.55	40.76	46	
	1900	W 14 x 26		990	.057		13.95	1.43	1	16.38	18.95	
	2100	x 30		900	.062		16.10	1.57	1.11	18.78	21.50	
	2300	x 34		810	.069		18.25	1.75	1.23	21.23	24.50	
	2500	x 120		720	.078		61.50	1.97	1.38	64.85	72.50	
	2700	W 16 x 26		1,000	.056		13.95	1.42	.99	16.36	18.90	
	2900	x 31		900	.062		16.60	1.57	1.11	19.28	22.50	
	3100	x 40		800	.070		21.50	1.77	1.24	24.51	28	
	3300	W 18 x 35	E-5	960	.083		18.75	2.14	1.18	22.07	25.50	
	3500	x 40		960	.083		21.50	2.14	1.18	24.82	28.50	
	3700	x 50		912	.088		25.50	2.26	1.24	29	33.50	
	3900	x 55		912	.088		28	2.26	1.24	31.50	36.50	
	4100	W 21 x 44		1,064	.075		22.50	1.93	1.07	25.50	29.50	
	4300	x 50		1,064	.075		25.50	1.93	1.07	28.50	32.50	
	4500	x 62		1,036	.077		31.50	1.99	1.09	34.58	39.50	
	4700	x 68		1,036	.077		35	1.99	1.09	38.08	43	
	4900	W 24 x 55		1,110	.072		28	1.85	1.02	30.87	35.50	
	5100	x 62		1,110	.072		31.50	1.85	1.02	34.37	39.50	
	5300	x 68		1,110	.072		35	1.85	1.02	37.87	43	
	5500	x 76		1,110	.072		39	1.85	1.02	41.87	47.50	
	5700	x 84		1,080	.074		43	1.91	1.05	45.96	52	
	5900	W 27 x 94		1,190	.067		48	1.73	.95	50.68	57	
	6100	W 30 x 99		1,200	.067		50.50	1.71	.94	53.15	59.50	
	6300	x 108		1,200	.067		55.50	1.71	.94	58.15	65	

Figure 9.64

051 | Structural Metal Framing

051 200	Structural Steel		CREW	DAILY OUTPUT	MAN-HOURS	UNIT	MAT.	LABOR	EQUIP.	TOTAL	TOTAL INCL O&P	
250	6500	x 116		E-5	1,160	.069	L.F.	58.50	1.77	.98	61.25	68	250
	6700	W 33 x 118			1,176	.068		59.50	1.75	.96	62.21	69	
	6900	x 130			1,134	.071		65.50	1.81	1	68.31	76.50	
	7100	x 141			1,134	.071		71	1.81	1	73.81	82.50	
	7300	W 36 x 135			1,170	.068		67	1.76	.97	69.73	78	
	7500	x 150			1,170	.068		74.50	1.76	.97	77.23	86	
	7700	x 194			1,125	.071		95.50	1.83	1.01	98.34	109	
	7900	x 230			1,125	.071		113	1.83	1.01	115.84	129	
	8100	x 300			1,035	.077		148	1.99	1.10	151.09	167	
255	0010	STRUCTURAL STEEL PROJECTS Bolted, unless mentioned otherwise											255
	0200	Apts., nursing homes, etc., steel bearing, 1 to 2 stories		E-5	10.30	7.767	Ton	975	200	110	1,285	1,550	
	0300	3 to 6 stories	R050 -310	"	10.10	7.921		990	204	112	1,306	1,575	
	0400	7 to 15 stories		E-6	14.20	9.014		1,025	232	90.50	1,347.50	1,625	
	0500	Over 15 stories	R050 -510	"	13.90	9.209		1,050	237	92.50	1,379.50	1,675	
	0700	Offices, hospitals, etc., steel bearing, 1 to 2 stories		E-5	10.30	7.767		975	200	110	1,285	1,550	
	0800	3 to 6 stories	R051 -210	E-6	14.40	8.889		1,000	229	89	1,318	1,600	
	0900	7 to 15 stories			14.20	9.014		1,025	232	90.50	1,347.50	1,625	
	1000	Over 15 stories	R051 -220		13.90	9.209		1,075	237	92.50	1,404.50	1,700	
	1100	For multi-story masonry wall bearing construction, add							30%				
	1300	Industrial bldgs., 1 story, beams & girders, steel bearing	R051 -230	E-5	12.90	6.202		975	160	88	1,223	1,450	
	1400	Masonry bearing		"	10	8		975	206	113	1,294	1,550	
	1500	Industrial bldgs., 1 story, under 10 tons,	R131 -310										
	1510	steel from warehouse, trucked		E-2	7.50	7.467	Ton	1,175	189	133	1,497	1,775	
	1600	1 story with roof trusses, steel bearing		E-5	10.60	7.547		1,150	194	107	1,451	1,725	
	1700	Masonry bearing		"	8.30	9.639		1,150	248	137	1,535	1,850	
	1900	Monumental structures, banks, stores, etc., minimum		E-6	13	9.846		975	254	99	1,328	1,625	
	2000	Maximum		"	9	14.222		1,700	365	143	2,208	2,675	
	2200	Churches, minimum		E-5	11.60	6.897		925	177	97.50	1,199.50	1,450	
	2300	Maximum		"	5.20	15.385		1,250	395	218	1,863	2,300	
	2800	Power stations, fossil fuels, minimum		E-6	11	11.636		975	300	117	1,392	1,725	
	2900	Maximum			5.70	22.456		1,550	580	225	2,355	2,975	
	2950	Nuclear fuels, non-safety steel, minimum			7	18.286		975	470	183	1,628	2,100	
	3000	Maximum			5.50	23.273		1,400	600	233	2,233	2,850	
	3040	Safety steel, minimum			2.50	51.200		1,500	1,325	515	3,340	4,550	
	3070	Maximum			1.50	85.333		2,000	2,200	855	5,055	7,025	
	3100	Roof trusses, minimum		E-5	13	6.154		975	158	87	1,220	1,450	
	3200	Maximum			8.30	9.639		1,675	248	137	2,060	2,425	
	3210	Schools, minimum			14.50	5.517		975	142	78	1,195	1,400	
	3220	Maximum			8.30	9.639		1,500	248	137	1,885	2,225	
	3400	Welded construction, simple commercial bldgs., 1 to 2 stories		E-7	7.60	10.526		1,025	271	150	1,446	1,775	
	3500	7 to 15 stories		E-9	8.30	15.422		1,175	395	172	1,742	2,200	
	3700	Welded rigid frame, 1 story, minimum		E-7	15.80	5.063		1,025	130	72.50	1,227.50	1,425	
	3800	Maximum		"	5.50	14.545		1,375	375	208	1,958	2,425	
	4000	High strength steels, add to A36 price, minimum						50			50	55	
	4100	Maximum						200			200	220	
	4300	Column base plates, light		2 Sswk	2,000	.008	Lb.	.49	.21		.70	.92	
	4400	Heavy plates		E-2	15,000	.004	"	.42	.09	.07	.58	.69	
	4600	Castellated beams, light sections, to 50#/L.F., minimum			10.70	5.234	Ton	1,300	132	93	1,525	1,750	
	4700	Maximum			7	8		1,625	202	142	1,969	2,300	
	4900	Heavy sections, over 50# per L.F., minimum			11.70	4.786		1,125	121	85	1,331	1,550	
	5000	Maximum			7.80	7.179		1,500	182	128	1,810	2,100	
	5200	High strength bolts in place, light reaming, 3/4" bolts, average		2 Sswk	165	.097	Ea.	1.10	2.52		3.62	5.75	
	5300	7/8" bolts, average		"	160	.100	"	1.80	2.60		4.40	6.70	
	5500	Steel domes											
	5510												

Figure 9.65

214

Item	Unit	Item	Unit
Aluminum	Lb.	Frames	S.F.
Area Walls	Ea.	Ladders	V.L.F.
Bumper Rails	L.F.	Lampposts	Ea.
Checkered Plate	Lb.	Lintels	Lb.
Castings Misc.	Lb.	Pipe Support Framing	Lb.
Chain Link Fabric	C.S.F.	Railing	L.F.
Corner Guards	L.F.	Solar Screens	S.F.
Crane Rail	Lb.	Stairs	Riser
Curb Edging	L.F.	Toilet Part. Supports	Stall
Decorative Covering	S.F.	Window Guards	S.F.
Door Frames	Ea.	Wire	L.F.
Fire Escapes	Lb.	Wire Rope	L.F.
Floor Grating	S.F.		

Expansion Control and Fasteners

This portion of Division 5 includes fasteners for wood construction (nails, timber connectors, lag screws) as well as those for metal. Expansion anchors, shear studs and expansion joint assemblies are also included. It is up to the estimator to determine how costs for these items are to be listed in the estimate. Wood fasteners may be included in Division 6; shear studs may be considered part of the structural steel or metal deck installation. As previously emphasized, it is not as important *where* items are included as long as all required items *are* included.

Sample Estimate: Division 5

The increased use of computers and the development of estimating software in the construction industry provides the estimator with tools to increase speed, improve documentation and to lessen the chance of mathematical error. In essence, estimates can be produced better and faster with the use of these tools.

Figure 9.66 is an example of a computer generated drawing that the estimator (contractor or engineer) might produce to aid in estimating the structural steel portion of the sample building project. Such a drawing would compile data from the specifications and from different plans, sections and details of the construction documents. The drawing in Figure 9.66 is of the framing for the second and third floors. Similar drawings might show column heights, base plates, roof and penthouse framing, including metal joists and bridging. These are not construction or shop drawings and are used only for takeoff. Figure 9.67 is the estimate sheet for the drawing in Figure 9.66. Note that all information, as provided in *Means Building Construction Cost Data*, is displayed for each item on the estimate sheet (in this case, burdened, or including overhead and profit).

For the sample project, the estimator is developing costs for comparison to and verification of subcontract bids. Depending on the estimating accuracy, an estimate developed as a crosscheck may be included in the project bid if no reasonable subcontract bids are submitted. This practice involves risk; but often, no other option is available. A computer generated estimate as described above would be ideal for such a purpose.

Returning to pencil and paper, the quantity sheets for the structural steel, metal joists and deck are shown in Figures 9.68 and 9.69.

Quantities are calculated and subtotalled by the pound. The total weight is not converted to tons until it is entered on the estimate sheet. In this way,

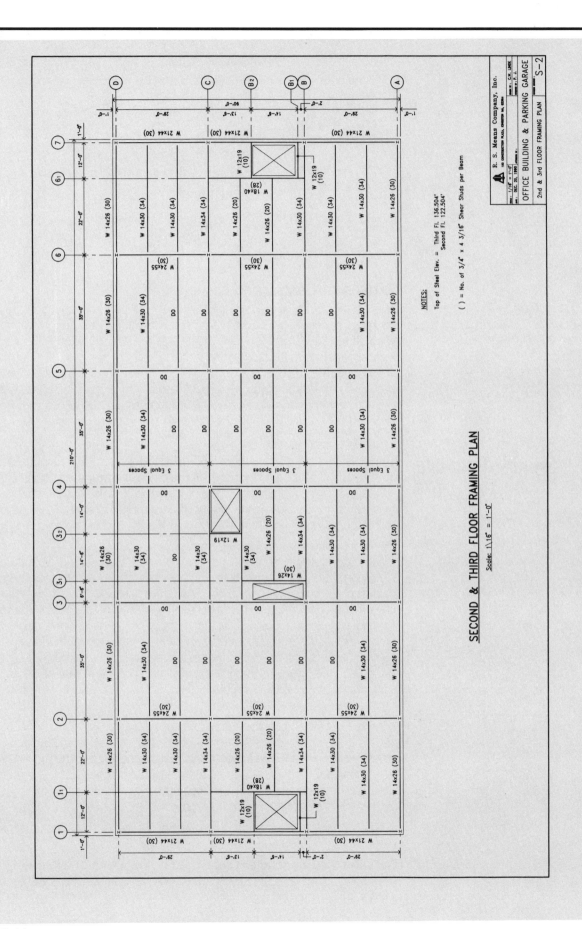

SECOND & THIRD FLOOR FRAMING PLAN

Scale: 1\16" = 1'-0"

NOTES:

Top of Steel Elev. = Third Fl. 136.504'
                     Second Fl. 122.504'

( ) = No. of 3/4" x 4 3/16" Shear Studs per Beam

R. S. Means Company, Inc.
100 CONSTRUCTION PLAZA, KINGSTON MA, 02364

OFFICE BUILDING & PARKING GARAGE

2nd & 3rd FLOOR FRAMING PLAN

S-2

Figure 9.66

216

```
================================================================================================

R.S. Means                BURDENED ITEMIZED JOB REPORT        Fri Mar 12 08:56:23 Am 1993      PAGE:   1
................................................................................................


PROJECT    : Barbara Realty Trust              LOCATION  : Kingston, Mass.
ARCH/ENGR  : Waier                             OWNER     : RSM Inc.
QUANTITIES BY: RJG                             ENTERED BY: P.W.
DESCRIPTION : Office Building                  TYPE      : K.P.F.


================================================================================================


                                        5 Metal

------------------------------------------------------------------------------------------------

 5.0 Metal
------------------------------------------------------------------------------------------------

DESCRIPTION                     CREW                                                     SHEET
LINE NO.         TAG           *      **    D/O     M/H  QUANTITY  MATERIAL   LABOR   EQUIP   TOTAL    SUB
ASMBLY#   SEARCH1    SEARCH2   PER1   PER2                 UNIT
------------------------------------------------------------------------------------------------
WELDED SHEAR CONN 3/4" X 4-3/16"
  050 560 0300 000M            E10  M 1030.000  0.0155  1450.00     0.46     0.76    0.48     1.70
                      100.00%  100.00%          22.52   Ea.       669.90  1100.53  695.92  2466.34


================================================================================================
                              SUB TOTAL :    23             670     1101     696    2466      0
================================================================================================
------------------------------------------------------------------------------------------------

 5.1 Structural Metal Framing
------------------------------------------------------------------------------------------------

DESCRIPTION                     CREW                                                     SHEET
LINE NO.         TAG           *      **    D/O     M/H  QUANTITY  MATERIAL   LABOR   EQUIP   TOTAL    SUB
ASMBLY#   SEARCH1    SEARCH2   PER1   PER2                 UNIT
------------------------------------------------------------------------------------------------
STRUCT STL, WF, 10' - 45' SPAN, W 12 X 22
  051 250 1300 000M            E2   M  880.000  0.0636    49.80    12.98     2.80    1.24    17.02
                      100.00%  100.00%           3.17   L.F.      646.40   139.36   61.90   847.66


STRUCT STL, WF, 10' - 45' SPAN, W 14 X 26
  051 250 1900 000M            E2   M  990.000  0.0566   539.10    15.35     2.49    1.10    18.94
                      100.00%  100.00%          30.49   L.F.     8272.49  1340.97  595.65 10209.11


STRUCT STL, WF, 10' - 45' SPAN, W 14 X 30
  051 250 2100 000M            E2   M  900.000  0.0622  1410.00    17.71     2.74    1.22    21.66
                      100.00%  100.00%          87.73   L.F.    24971.10  3858.00 1713.68 30542.78


STRUCT STL, WF, 10' - 45' SPAN, W 21 X 44
  051 250 4100 000M            E5   M 1064.000  0.0752   155.80    24.75     3.40    1.17    29.33
                      100.00%  100.00%          11.71   L.F.     3856.05   530.18  182.62  4568.85


STRUCT STL, WF, 10' - 45' SPAN, W 24 X 55
  051 250 4900 000M            E5   M 1110.000  0.0721   394.25    30.80     3.26    1.12    35.19
                      100.00%  100.00%          28.41   L.F.    12142.90  1286.00  442.97 13871.88


================================================================================================
                              SUB TOTAL :   178           54595     7878    3296   65770      0
================================================================================================
                            DIVISION TOTAL :   200        55265     8979    3992   68237      0
================================================================================================
                              JOB TOTAL :   200           55265     8979    3992   68237      0
================================================================================================
```

Figure 9.67

QUANTITY SHEET

PROJECT: Office Building
LOCATION:
TAKE OFF BY:

Division 5
ARCHITECT:
EXTENSIONS BY:

DESCRIPTION	NO.	DIMENSIONS L	W	Lbs.	UNIT	Lbs.	UNIT	Total Lbs.	UNIT	Acc.	UNIT
Columns											
W8 x 40	18	31.27'				22514	Lbs.				
W8 x 24	18	11.33'				4895					
W8 x 67	4	31.23'				8370					
W8 x 31	4	11.33'				1405					
W12 x 58	6	31.20'				10857					
W8 x 48	6	20.29'				5844		53885 Lbs.			
PL 1 1/2" THICK	18	1.33'	1.33'	61.2		1949	Lbs.				
2" "	4	1.75'	1.75'	81.6		1000					
2 3/8" "	6	2'	2'	96.9		2326		5275 Lbs.			
3/4" Anchor Bolts		24"								112 Ea.	
Beams - 2nd & 3rd Floors											
W14 x 26	4	34'				3536	Lbs.				
	8	35'				7280					
	4	25'				2600					
	1	27'				702					
	1	20'				520					
W14 x 30	8	34'				8160					
	30	35'				31500					
W14 x 34	5	34'				5780					
W12 x 19	5	9'				855					
W21 x 44	4	29'				5104					
	2	30'				2640					
W18 x 40	2	30'				2400					
W24 x 55	10	29'				15950					
	5	30'				8250					
Each Floor						95277	Lbs.				
Both Floors								190554 Lbs.			
3/4" Shear Studs		4 3/16"								2636 Ea.	

Figure 9.68

218

QUANTITY SHEET

PROJECT: Office Building   Division 5

LOCATION:

TAKE OFF BY:

ARCHITECT:

EXTENSIONS BY:

DESCRIPTION	NO.	DIMENSIONS L	W	Lbs.	UNIT	Lbs.	UNIT	Total Lbs.	UNIT	Acc.	UNIT
Beams - Roof											
W16 x 26	4	34'				3536	Lbs.				
	8	35'				7280					
W21 x 44	7	35'				10780					
W18 x 24	1	26'				1040					
W21 x 49	4	29'				5684					
	2	30'				2940					
W21 x 62	10	29'				17980					
	3	30'				5580					
W27 x 94	2	30'				5640					
W12 x 19	1	9'				171	Lbs.	60631	Lbs		
3/4" Shear Studs		4 3/16"								536	Ea.
Beams - Penthouse											
W21 x 49	2	30'				2940	Lbs.				
W21 x 62	1	30'				1860	Lbs.				
W16 x 26	4	35'				3640	Lbs.	8440	Lbs		
Joists - Roof & Penthouse											
2447 (R)	30	34'	11.5			11730	Lbs.				
(R)	52	35'	11.5			20930	Lbs.				
(P)	10	30'	11.5			3450	Lbs.	36110	Lbs		
Bottom Chord Ext.	32									32	Ea.
Bridging (R)	36	88'	0.8			2534	Lbs.				
(R)	24	29'	0.8			557	Lbs.				
(P)	12	30'	0.8			288	Lbs.	3379	Lbs		
Deck (22 ga.)											
3" - 2nd & 3rd Floor	2	210'	90'		39900 SF						
Incl. Penthouse		70'	30'								
1 1/2" - R & P		210'	90'		18900 SF						
Edge Form	3	210'	90' + Opening							2160	LF

Figure 9.69

errors due to rounding can be avoided. Quantities are entered and priced on the estimate sheets in Figures 9.70 to 9.72.

In Figure 9.70, the 10% addition for connections is included; it is based on the above discussion of allowances for structural steel. Base plate weights are added after the connections. Because this portion of the estimate is to be used for verification, a single price per ton for all structural steel is used (from Figure 9.65, Line 051-255-0800). Note that the price per ton includes bolting. High strength bolts are specified for the project and require more labor than standard bolts. Standard bolts, are usually used for connecting and are replaced with high strength bolts during the bolting up procedure. No deduction (from the $1,600 per ton) is used for deleting the standard bolting. The approximate quantity of high strength bolts may be determined from Figure 9.73, Reference Table R050-510.

Material costs only are included for the anchor bolts and lintels. These items will be installed by different trades.

On Sheet 3 of the estimate (Figure 9.72) the subtotals for Division 5 are separated and listed according to the major subdivisions of metals work. These costs may be used as part of the historical cost development for estimating and comparison to future projects.

Division 6: Wood and Plastics

Wood frame construction is still dominant in the residential construction industry in the United States. However, its use for large scale commercial buildings has declined. There are many reasons for this trend; among them are design criteria, cost and, in some localities, building and fire code restrictions. Nevertheless, the use of wood framing for smaller suburban office buildings is still common.

Material prices for lumber fluctuate more and with greater frequency than any other building material. For this reason, when the material list is complete it is important to obtain current, local prices for the lumber. Installation costs depend on productivity. For Division 6, accurate cost records from past jobs can be most helpful. The estimate can be tailored to the productivity of specific crews as shown in Division 4 of the Sample Estimate.

Carpentry work can be broken down into the following categories: rough carpentry, finish carpentry and millwork, and laminated framing and decking. The rough carpentry materials can be sticks of lumber or sheets of plywood — job site fabricated and installed, or may consist of trusses, and truss joists, and panelized roof systems — prefabricated, delivered and erected by a specialty subcontractor.

Rough Carpentry

Lumber is usually estimated in board feet and purchased in 1000 board foot quantities. A board foot is 1″ x 12″ x 12″ (nominal) or 3/4″ x 11-1/2″ x 12″ milled (actual). To determine board feet of a piece of framing, the nominal dimensions can be multiplied, and the result divided by 12. The final result represents the number of board feet per linear foot of that framing size.

Example: 2 x 10 joists

$$2 \times 10 = 20$$

$$\frac{20}{12} = 1.67 \qquad \frac{\text{Board feet}}{\text{Linear foot}}$$

CONSOLIDATED ESTIMATE

PROJECT: Office Building   CLASSIFICATION: Division 5   SHEET NO. 1 of 3

LOCATION: ARCHITECT: ESTIMATE NO:

TAKE OFF BY: QUANTITIES BY: PRICES BY: EXTENSIONS BY: DATE: 6/93

CHECKED BY:

SOURCE			DESCRIPTION	QUANT.	UNIT	MATERIAL		LABOR		EQUIPMENT		SUBCONTRACT		TOTAL	
						COST	TOTAL	COST	TOTAL	COST	TOTAL	COST	TOTAL	COST	TOTAL
			Division 5: Metals												
			Structural Steel												
			Columns	53,885	Lbs.										
			2nd & 3rd Fl. Beams	190,554											
			Roof	60,631											
			Penthouse	8,440											
				313,510	Lbs.										
			10 % Connections	31351											
				344,861	Lbs.										
			Base PL	5,275											
				350,136	Lbs.										
051	255	0800	Total	175	Ton							1600	280000		
051	255	5200	High Strength Bolts 20/Ton (77)	3500	Ea.							5.75	20125		
031	110	0500	Anchor Bolts (Mat. Only)	112	Ea.							2.15	241		
			Subtotals										$300,366		

Figure 9.70

CONSOLIDATED ESTIMATE

PROJECT: Office Building
LOCATION:
TAKE OFF BY:

CLASSIFICATION: Division 5
ARCHITECT:
QUANTITIES BY:
PRICES BY:
EXTENSIONS BY:

ESTIMATE NO:
DATE: 6/93
CHECKED BY:

DESCRIPTION	SOURCE			QUANT.	UNIT	MATERIAL		LABOR		EQUIPMENT		SUBCONTRACT		TOTAL
						COST	TOTAL	COST	TOTAL	COST	TOTAL	COST	TOTAL	
Division 5: (Cont'd)														
Metal Joists & Decks														
Joists				36110	Lbs.									
Bridging				3379										
				39489	Lbs.									
Total	051	255	0800	19.75	Ton							1600	31600	
Bottom Chord Extensions	052	110	1650	32	Ea.							8.80	282	
Composite Deck- 3" 22 ga.	053	104	5200	40570	SF							1.21	49090	
Roof- 1 1/2" 22 ga.	053	104	2400	18900	SF							0.92	17388	
Edge Form	053	104	7100	2160	LF							3.44	7430	
Shear Studs, 3/4" x 4 3/16"	050	560	0300	3172	Ea.							1.70	5392	
Subtotals													$111,182	

Figure 9.71

CONSOLIDATED ESTIMATE

PROJECT: Office Building   CLASSIFICATION: Division 5

LOCATION: ARCHITECT:

TAKE OFF BY: QUANTITIES BY: PRICES BY: EXTENSIONS BY:

ESTIMATE NO:

DATE: 6/93

CHECKED BY:

SOURCE	DESCRIPTION	QUANT.	UNIT	MATERIAL COST	MATERIAL TOTAL	LABOR COST	LABOR TOTAL	EQUIPMENT COST	EQUIPMENT TOTAL	SUBCONTRACT COST	SUBCONTRACT TOTAL	TOTAL COST	TOTAL TOTAL
	Division 5: (Cont'd)												
	Miscellaneous Metals												
055 104 0200	Stairs 3' - 6" w/ Rails	188	R							112.00	21056		
055 104 1500	Landings 10' - 8" x 4'	320	SF							43.00	13760		
055 203 0010	Exterior Alum. Rails	150	LF							20.50	3075		
051 232 2100	Lintels (Matl. Only)	34	Ea.							19.95	678		
	Subtotal										38569		
	Sheet 1 Subtotal										300366		
	Sheet 2 Subtotal										111182		
	Sheet 3 Subtotal										38569		
	Division 5 Total												$450,117

Figure 9.72

R050-310   Coating Structural Steel

See R051-240 for galvanizing.

For field coats use red oxide rust inhibitive paint at $18.50 a gallon or if steel remains exposed use aluminum paint at $15.80 a gallon.

On field welded jobs, shop coat is necessarily omitted. All painting must be done in the field and usually consists of two coats. Cleaning with wire brushes runs $.45 per S.F.

Sandblasting on the ground runs $.65 to $1.15; above grade $.75 to $1.40 and to sandblast previously painted steel above grade runs $1.15 to $1.50 per S.F. White metal sandblasts run an additional $.45 per S.F.

Table below shows paint coverage and daily production for field painting.

Type Construction	Surface Area per Ton	Coat	One Gallon Covers		In 8 Hrs. Man Covers		Average per Ton Spray	
			Brush	Spray	Brush	Spray	Gallons	Man-hours
Light Structural	300 S.F. to 500 S.F.	1st	500 S.F.	455 S.F.	640 S.F.	2000 S.F.	0.9 gals.	1.6 M.H.
		2nd	450	410	800	2400	1.0	1.3
		3rd	450	410	960	3200	1.0	1.0
Medium	150 S.F. to 300 S.F.	All	400	365	1600	3200	0.6	0.6
Heavy Structural	50 S.F. to 100 S.F.	1st	400	365	1920	4000	0.2	0.2
		2nd	400	365	2000	4000	0.2	0.2
		3rd	400	365	2000	4000	0.2	0.2
Weighted Average	225 S.F.	All	400	365	1350	3000	0.6	0.6

R050-510   High Strength Bolts

In factory buildings, common bolts are used in secondary connections.

Allow 20 field bolts per ton of steel for a 6 story office building, apartment house or light industrial building. For 6 to 12 stories allow

25 bolts and above 12 stories, 30 bolts. On power stations 20 to 25 bolts per ton are needed.

Cost per bolt, nut and washer combination, material only. Under 5000 lbs. A325 and A490.

Length	1-1/2"		2"		2-1/2"		3"		3-1/2"		4"		5"		6"		7"		8"	
ASTM Designation	A325	A490	A325	A490	A325	A490	A325	A490	A325	A490	A325	A490	A325	A490	A325	A490	A325	A490	A325	A490
5/8" diameter	$.52	$.56	$ .56	$ .60	$ .60	$ .65	$ .64	$ .69	$ .68	$ .75	$ .72	$ .80	$ .76	$ .84	$ .82	$ .92	$ .88	$1.00	$ .95	$1.15
3/4"	.64	.88	.72	.92	.76	.96	.80	1.04	.84	1.08	.88	1.08	.96	1.16	1.04	1.40	1.24	1.55	1.28	1.70
7/8"	–	–	1.12	1.44	1.16	1.52	1.20	1.52	1.28	1.60	1.28	1.68	1.36	1.76	1.44	1.88	1.64	2.12	1.96	2.32
1"	–	–	1.48	1.94	1.52	2.04	1.56	2.08	1.68	2.16	1.72	2.24	1.88	2.40	1.96	2.56	2.12	2.76	2.36	2.92
1-1/8"	–	–	–	–	2.68	3.16	2.72	3.48	2.76	3.60	2.84	3.64	3.00	3.92	3.12	4.20	3.36	4.40	3.60	4.64
1-1/4"	–	–	–	–	–	–	3.32	4.36	3.36	4.40	3.48	4.48	3.68	4.76	3.92	4.96	4.16	5.78	4.40	5.60

R050-520   Welded Structural Steel

Usual weight reductions with welded design run 10% to 20% compared with bolted or riveted connections. This amounts to about the same total cost compared with bolted structures since field welding is more expensive than bolts. For normal spans of 18' to 24' figure 6 to 7 connections per ton.

Trusses — For welded trusses add 4% to weight of main members for connections. Up to 15% less steel can be expected in a welded truss compared to one that is shop bolted. Cost of erection is the same whether shop bolted or welded.

General — Typical electrodes for structural steel welding are E6010, E6011, E60T and E70T. Typical buildings vary between 2# to 8# of

weld rod per ton of steel. Buildings utilizing continuous design require about three times as much welding as conventional welded structures. In estimating field erection by welding, it is best to use the average linear feet of weld per ton to arrive at the welding cost per ton. The type, size and position of the weld will have a direct bearing on the cost per linear foot. A typical field welder will deposit 1.8# to 2# of weld rod per hour manually. Using semiautomatic methods can increase production by as much as 50% to 75%. Below is the cost per hour for manual welding.

Welded Structural Steel in Field				
Item		No Operating Engr.	1/2 Operating Engr.	1 Operating Engr.
3 lb. weld rod	$.90 per lb.	$ 2.70	$ 2.70	$ 2.70
Equipment (for welding only)	$185 /40 hrs.	4.63	4.63	4.63
Operating cost @	$4.55 per hour	4.55	4.55	4.55
Welder 1 hr. @	$26.00 per hour	26.00	26.00	26.00
Operating engineer @	$23.10 per hour	–	11.55	23.10
Total per Welder Hour (Bare Costs)		$37.88	$49.43	$60.98

The welding costs per ton of structural steel will vary from $22 to $182 per ton depending on Union requirements, crew size, design and inspection required.

Figure 9.73

224

The Quantity Sheet should indicate species, grade, and any type of wood preservative or fire retardant treatment specified or required by code.

Sills, Posts, and Girders used in subfloor framing should be taken off by length and quantity. The standard lengths available vary by species and dimensions. Cut-offs are often used for blocking. Careful selection of lengths will decrease the waste factor required.

Floor Joists, shown or specified by size and spacing, should be taken off by nominal length and the quantity required. Add for double joists under partitions, headers and cripple joists at openings, overhangs, laps at bearings, and blocking or bridging.

Ceiling Joists, similar to floor joists, carry roof loads and or/ceiling finishes. Soffits and suspended ceilings should be noted and taken off separately. Ledgers may be a part of the ceiling joist system. In a flat roof system, the rafters are called joists and are usually shown as a ceiling system.

Studs required are noted on the drawings by spacing, usually 16" O.C. or 24" O.C., with the stud size given. The linear feet of partitions with the same stud size, height and spacing, and divided by the spacing will give the estimator the approximate number of studs required. Additional studs for openings, corners, double top plates, sole plates, and intersecting partitions must be taken off separately. An allowance for waste should be included (or heights should be recorded as a standard length). A rule of thumb is to allow one stud for every linear foot of wall, for 16" O.C.

Number and Size of Openings are important. Even though there are no studs in these areas, the estimator must take off headers, subsills, king studs, trimmers, cripples, and knee studs. Where bracing and fire blocking are noted, indicate the type and quantity.

Roof Rafters vary with different types of roofs. A hip and valley, because of its complexity, has a greater material waste factor than most other roof types. Although straight gable, gambrel, and mansard roofs are not as complicated, care should be taken to ensure a good material takeoff. Roof pitches, overhangs, and soffit framing all affect the quantity of material and therefore, the costs. Rafters must be measured along the slope, not the horizontal. (See Figure 9.79.)

Roof Trusses are usually furnished and delivered to the job site by the truss fabricator. The high cost of job site labor and new gang nailing technology have created a small boom in truss manufacturing. Many architects' designs of wood frame and masonry bearing wall structures now include wood trusses of both the trussed rafter type and the flat chord type (also used for floors). Depending upon the size of truss, hoisting equipment may be needed for erection. The estimator should obtain prices and weights from the fabricator and should determine whether or not erection is included in the fabricator's cost. Architecturally exposed trusses are typically more expensive to fabricate and erect.

Tongue and Groove Roof Decks of various woods, solid planks, or laminated construction are nominally 2" to 4" thick and are often used with glued laminated beams or heavy timber framing. The square foot method is used to determine quantities and consideration is given to roof pitches and non-modular areas for the amount of waste involved. The materials are purchased by board foot measurement. The conversion from square foot to board foot must allow for net sizes as opposed to board measure. In this way, loss of coverage due to the available tongue and mill lengths can be taken into account.

Sheathing on walls can be plywood of different grades and thicknesses, wallboard, or solid boards nailed directly to the studs. Insulating sheets with air infiltration barriers are often used as sheathing in colder climates. Plywood can be applied with the grain vertical, horizontal, or rarely, diagonal to the studding. Solid boards are usually nailed diagonally, but can be applied horizontally when lateral forces are not present. For solid board sheathing, add 15% to 20% more material to the takeoff when using tongue and groove, as opposed to square edge sheathing. Wallboard can be installed either horizontally or vertically, depending upon wall height and fire code restrictions. When estimating quantities of plywood or wallboard sheathing, the estimator calculates the number of sheets required by measuring the square feet of area to be covered and then dividing by sheet size. Applying these materials diagonally or on non-modular areas will create waste. This waste factor must be included in the estimate. For diagonal application of boards, plywood, or wallboard, include an additional 10% to 15% material waste factor.

Subfloors can be CDX type plywood (with the thickness dependent on the load and span), solid boards laid diagonally or perpendicular to the joists, or tongue and groove planks. The quantity takeoff for subfloors is similar to sheathing (noted above).

Stressed Skin Plywood includes prefabricated roof panels, with or without bottom skin or tie rods, and folded plate roof panels with intermediate rafters. Stressed skin panels are typically custom prefabricated. Takeoff is by the square foot or panel.

Structural Joists are prefabricated "beams" with wood flanges and plywood or tubular steel webs. This type of joist is spaced in accordance with the load and requires bridging and blocking supplied by the fabricator. Quantity takeoff should include the following: type, number required, length, spacing, end-bearing conditions, number of rows, length of bridging, and blocking.

Grounds are normally 1" x 2" wood strips used for case work or plaster; the quantities are estimated in L.F.

Furring (1" x 2" or 3") wood strips are fastened to wood masonry or concrete walls so that wall coverings may be attached thereto. Furring may also be used on the underside of ceiling joists to fasten ceiling finishes. Quantities are estimated by L.F.

Lumber and Plywood Treatments can sometimes double the costs for material. The plans and specifications should be carefully checked for required treatments – against insects, fire or decay – as well as grade, species and drying specifications.

An alternative method to pricing rough carpentry by the piece or linear foot is to determine quantities (in board feet) based on square feet of surface area. Appendix B of this book contains charts and tables that may be used for this second method. Also included are quantities of nails required for each type and spacing of rough framing. A rule of thumb for this method can be used to determine linear feet of framing members (such as studs, joists) based on square feet of surface area (wall, floor, ceiling):

Spacing of Framing Members	Board Feet per Square Foot Surface
12" O.C.	1.2 B.F./S.F.
16" O.C.	1.0 B.F./S.F.
24" O.C.	0.8 B.F./S.F.

The requirements for rough carpentry, especially those for temporary construction, may not all be directly stated in the plans and specifications. These additional items may include blocking, temporary stairs, wood inserts for metal pan stairs, and railings, along with various other requirements for different trades. Temporary construction may also be included in Division 1 of the General Requirements.

Finish Carpentry and Millwork

Finish carpentry and millwork – wood rails, paneling, shelves, casements and cabinetry – are common in buildings that have no other wood.

Upon examination of the plans and specifications, the estimator must determine which items will be built on-site, and which will be fabricated off-site by a millwork subcontractor. Shop drawings are often required for architectural woodwork and are usually included in the subcontract price.

Window and Door Trim may be taken off and priced by the "set" or by the linear foot. Check for jamb extensions at exterior walls. The common use of pre-hung doors and windows makes it convenient to take off this trim with the doors and windows. Exterior trim, other than door and window trim, should be taken off with the siding, since the details and dimensions are interrelated.

Paneling is taken off by the type, finish, and square foot (converted to full sheets). Be sure to list any millwork that would show up on the details. Panel siding and associated trim are taken off by the square foot and linear foot, respectively. Be sure to provide an allowance for waste.

Decorative Beams and Columns that are non-structural should be estimated separately. Decorative trim may be used to wrap exposed structural elements. Particular attention should be paid to the joinery. Long, precise joints are difficult to construct in the field.

Cabinets, Counters and Shelves are most often priced by the linear foot or by the unit. Job-fabricated, prefabricated, and subcontracted work should be estimated separately.

Stairs should be estimated by individual component unless accurate, complete system costs have been developed from previous projects. Typical components and units for estimating are shown in Figure 9.74. The cost development of a residential wood stair system is shown in Figure 9.75.

A general rule for budgeting millwork is that total costs will be two to three times the cost of the materials. Millwork is often ordered and purchased directly by the owner; when installation is the responsibility of the contractor, costs for handling, storage and protection should be included.

Laminated Construction

Laminated construction should be listed separately, as it is frequently supplied by a specialty subcontractor. Sometimes the beams are supplied and erected by one subcontractor, and the decking installed by the general contractor or another subcontractor. The takeoff units must be adapted to the system: square foot – floor, linear foot – members, or board foot – lumber. Since the members are factory fabricated, the plans and specifications must be submitted to a fabricator for takeoff and pricing.

Sample Estimate:
Division 6

The estimate for Division 6 – Wood and Plastics – of the sample project is minimal and straightforward. The estimate sheet is shown in Figure 9.76. The only item included for rough carpentry is fire retardant treated blocking.

064 | Architectural Woodwork

064 300 | Stairwork & Handrails

		Description	CREW	DAILY OUTPUT	MAN-HOURS	UNIT	1993 BARE COSTS MAT.	LABOR	EQUIP.	TOTAL	TOTAL INCL O&P	
306	4500	incl. railing, 9' high	2 Carp	1.50	10.667	Flight	3,200	249		3,449	3,925	306
308	0010	STAIR PARTS Balusters, turned, 30" high, pine, minimum R064-100	1 Carp	28	.286	Ea.	4.20	6.65		10.85	15.05	308
	0100	Maximum		26	.308		6.15	7.20		13.35	18.05	
	0300	30" high birch balusters, minimum		28	.286		6	6.65		12.65	17.05	
	0400	Maximum		26	.308		7.20	7.20		14.40	19.20	
	0600	42" high, pine balusters, minimum		27	.296		5.65	6.90		12.55	17.05	
	0700	Maximum		25	.320		7.20	7.45		14.65	19.65	
	0900	42" high birch balusters, minimum		27	.296		6.45	6.90		13.35	17.95	
	1000	Maximum		25	.320		9.30	7.45		16.75	22	
	1050	Baluster, stock pine, 1-1/16" x 1-1/16"		240	.033	L.F.	.75	.78		1.53	2.05	
	1100	1-5/8" x 1-5/8"		220	.036	"	1.40	.85		2.25	2.87	
	1200	Newels, 3-1/4" wide, starting, minimum		7	1.143	Ea.	36	26.50		62.50	81.50	
	1300	Maximum		6	1.333		270	31		301	345	
	1500	Landing, minimum		5	1.600		70	37.50		107.50	136	
	1600	Maximum		4	2		320	46.50		366.50	425	
	1800	Railings, oak, built-up, minimum		60	.133	L.F.	4.60	3.11		7.71	9.95	
	1900	Maximum		55	.145		11	3.40		14.40	17.45	
	2100	Add for sub rail		110	.073		3.55	1.70		5.25	6.60	
	2110											
	2300	Risers, Beech, 3/4" x 7-1/2" high	1 Carp	64	.125	L.F.	4.75	2.92		7.67	9.80	
	2400	Fir, 3/4" x 7-1/2" high		64	.125		1.35	2.92		4.27	6.05	
	2600	Oak, 3/4" x 7-1/2" high		64	.125		4.30	2.92		7.22	9.30	
	2800	Pine, 3/4" x 7-1/2" high		66	.121		1.35	2.83		4.18	5.95	
	2850	Skirt board, pine, 1" x 10"		55	.145		1.65	3.40		5.05	7.15	
	2900	1" x 12"		52	.154		2	3.59		5.59	7.85	
	3000	Treads, oak, 1-1/16" x 9-1/2" wide, 3' long		18	.444	Ea.	19	10.40		29.40	37.50	
	3100	4' long		17	.471		25.50	11		36.50	45.50	
	3300	1-1/16" x 11-1/2" wide, 3' long		18	.444		24	10.40		34.40	43	
	3400	6' long		14	.571		48.50	13.35		61.85	74	
	3600	Beech treads, add					40%					
	3800	For mitered return nosings, add				L.F.	2.60			2.60	2.86	
310	0010	RAILING Custom design, architectural grade, hardwood, minimum	1 Carp	38	.211	"	11.20	4.92		16.12	20	310
	0100	Maximum		30	.267	L.F.	38	6.25		44.25	52	
	0300	Stock interior railing with spindles 6" O.C., 4' long		40	.200		28	4.67		32.67	38.50	
	0400	8' long		48	.167		26	3.89		29.89	34.50	

064 400 | Misc. Ornamental Items

		Description	CREW	DAILY OUTPUT	MAN-HOURS	UNIT	1993 BARE COSTS MAT.	LABOR	EQUIP.	TOTAL	TOTAL INCL O&P	
402	0010	COLUMNS For base plates, see division 055-404										402
	0050	Aluminum, round colonial, 6" diameter	2 Carp	80	.200	V.L.F.	11.70	4.67		16.37	20	
	0100	8" diameter		62.25	.257		14.70	6		20.70	25.50	
	0200	10" diameter		55	.291		19.20	6.80		26	31.50	
	0250	Fir, stock units, hollow round, 6" diameter		80	.200		11.50	4.67		16.17	20	
	0300	8" diameter		80	.200		12.50	4.67		17.17	21	
	0350	10" diameter		70	.229		16.20	5.35		21.55	26	
	0400	Solid turned, to 8' high, 3-1/2" diameter		80	.200		4.50	4.67		9.17	12.30	
	0500	4-1/2" diameter		75	.213		6.80	4.98		11.78	15.30	
	0600	5-1/2" diameter		70	.229		8.70	5.35		14.05	17.95	
	0800	Square columns, built-up, 5" x 5"		65	.246		6.20	5.75		11.95	15.80	
	0900	Solid, 3-1/2" x 3-1/2"		130	.123		4.95	2.87		7.82	9.95	
	1600	Hemlock, tapered, T & G, 12" diam, 10' high		100	.160		28	3.74		31.74	37	
	1700	16' high		65	.246		43	5.75		48.75	56.50	
	1900	10' high, 14" diameter		100	.160		59	3.74		62.74	71	
	2000	18' high		65	.246		56.50	5.75		62.25	71.50	
	2200	18" diameter, 12' high		65	.246		80.50	5.75		86.25	97.50	
	2300	20' high		50	.320		72.50	7.45		79.95	92	

Figure 9.74

228

R064-100   Wood Stair, Residential

One Flight with 8'-6" Story Height, 3'-6" Wide Oak Treads Open One Side, Built in Place				
Item	Quantity	Unit Cost	Bare Costs	Costs Incl. Subs O & P
Treads 10-1/2" x 1-1/16" thick	11 Ea.	$ 23.00	$ 253.00	$ 278.30
Landing tread nosing, rabbeted	1 Ea.	8.00	8.00	8.80
Risers 3/4" thick	12 Ea.	11.60	139.00	152.90
Single end starting step (range $90 to $165)	1 Ea.	127.50	127.50	140.25
Balusters (range $3.50 to $10.00)	22 Ea.	6.75	148.50	163.35
Newels, starting & landing (range $36 to $95)	2 Ea.	65.50	131.00	144.10
Rail starter (range $29 to $90)	1 Ea.	59.50	59.50	65.45
Handrail (range $3.50 to $8.50)	26 L.F.	6.00	156.00	171.60
Cove trim	50 L.F.	.45	22.50	24.75
Rough stringers three - 2 x 12's, 14' long	84 B.F.	.50	42.00	46.20
Carpenter's installation: Bare Cost	36 Hrs.	$ 23.35	$ 840.60	
Incl. Subs O & P		$ 36.65		$1,319.40
	Total per Flight		$1,927.60	$2,515.10

Add for rail return on second floor and for varnishing or other finish. Adjoining walls or landings must be figured separately.

Figure 9.75

Blocking requirements may or may not be shown on the drawings or stated in the specifications, but in this case, previous experience dictates that an allowance be included. The only other carpentry for the project involves wall paneling at the elevator lobby of each floor, and vanities in the women's rest rooms. For custom quality finish work, it is recommended that the craftsman to perform the work be consulted. This person is able to call upon experience to best estimate the required time.

Division 7: Thermal and Moisture Protection

This division includes materials for sealing the outside of a building – for protection against moisture and air infiltration, as well as insulation and associated accessories. When reviewing the plans and specifications, the estimator should visualize the construction process, and thus determine all probable areas where these materials will be found in or on a building. The technique used for quantity takeoff depends on the specific materials and installation methods.

Waterproofing
- Dampproofing
- Vapor Barriers
- Caulking and Sealants
- Sheet and Membrane
- Integral Cement Coatings

A distinction should be made between dampproofing and waterproofing. Dampproofing is used to inhibit the migration of moisture or water vapor. In most cases, dampproofing will not stop the flow of water (even at minimal pressures). Waterproofing, on the other hand, consists of a continuous, impermeable membrane and is used to prevent or stop the flow of water.

Dampproofing usually consists of one or two bituminous coatings applied to foundation walls from about the finished grade line to the bottom of the footings. The areas involved are calculated from the total height of the dampproofing and the length of the wall. After separate areas are figured and added together to provide a total square foot area, a unit cost per square foot can be selected for the type of material, the number of coats, and the method of application specified for the building.

Waterproofing at or below grade with elastomeric sheets or membranes is estimated on the same basis as dampproofing, with two basic exceptions. First, the installed unit costs for the elastomeric sheets do not include bonding adhesive or splicing tape, which must be figured as an additional cost. Second, the membrane waterproofing under slabs must be estimated separately from the higher cost installation on walls. In all cases, unit costs are per square foot of covered surface.

For walls below grade, protection board is often specified to prevent damage to the barrier when the excavation is backfilled. Rigid foam insulation installed outside of the barrier may also serve a protective function. Metallic coating material may be applied to floors or walls, usually on the interior or dry side, after the masonry surface has been prepared (usually by chipping) for bonding to the new material. The unit cost per square foot for these materials depends on the thickness of the material, the position of the area to be covered and the preparation required. In many cases, these materials must be applied in locations where access is difficult and under the control of others. The estimator should make an allowance for delays caused by this problem.

CONSOLIDATED ESTIMATE

PROJECT: Office Building
LOCATION:
TAKE OFF BY:

CLASSIFICATION: Division 6
ARCHITECT:
QUANTITIES BY: PRICES BY: EXTENSIONS BY:

SHEET NO.   1 of 1
ESTIMATE NO:
DATE: 6/93
CHECKED BY:

DESCRIPTION	SOURCE		QUANT.	UNIT	MATERIAL		LABOR		EQUIPMENT		SUBCONTRACT		TOTAL
					COST	TOTAL	COST	TOTAL	COST	TOTAL	COST	TOTAL	
Division 6: Wood & Plastics													
Rough Carpentry													
Blocking	061	102 2740	0.1	MBF	405.00	41	1325	133					
Fire Treatment	063	102 0400	0.1	MBF	220.00	22							
Finish Carpentry													
Paneling @ Elevator Lobby	062	504 2600	1800	SF	1.60	2880	0.93	1674					
Vanities	064	140 8150	6	Ea.	340.00	2040	32.50	195					
Arch. Woodwork													
Vanity Top, with backsplash	062	408 1000	24	LF	25.00	600	6.25	150					
Cutouts	062	408 1900	9	Ea.	2.55	23	5.85	53					
Division 6 Totals						$5,605		$2,204					

Figure 9.76

231

Caulking and sealants are usually applied on the exterior of the building except for certain special conditions on the interior. In most cases, caulking and sealing is done to prevent water and/or air from entering a building. Caulking and sealing are usually specified at joints, expansion joints, control joints, door and window frames and in places where dissimilar materials meet over the surface of the building exterior. To estimate the installed cost of this type of material, two things must be determined. First, the estimator must note (from the specifications) the kind of material to be used for each caulking or sealing job. Second, the dimensions of the joints to be caulked or sealed must be measured on the plans, with attention given to any requirements for backer rods. With this information, the estimator can select the applicable cost per linear foot and multiply it by the total length in feet. The result is an estimated cost for each kind of caulking or sealing on the job. Caulking and sealing may often be overlooked as incidental items. They may, in fact, represent a significant cost, depending upon the type of construction.

The specifications may require testing of the integrity of installed waterproofing in certain cases. If required, adequate time must be allowed and costs included in the estimate.

Insulation

- Batt or Roll
- Blown-in
- Board (Rigid and Semi-rigid)
- Cavity Masonry
- Perimeter Foundation
- Poured in Place
- Reflective
- Roof
- Sprayed

Insulation is primarily used to reduce heat transfer through the exterior enclosure of the building. The type and form of this insulation will vary according to its location in the structure and the size of the space it occupies. Major insulation types include mineral granules, fibers and foams, vegetable fibers and solids, and plastic foams. These materials may be required around foundations, on or inside walls, and under roofing. Many different details of the drawings must be examined in order to determine types, methods and quantities of insulation. The cost of insulation depends on the type of material, its form (loose, granular, batt or boards), its thickness in inches, the method of installation, and the total area in square feet.

It is becoming popular to specify insulation by "R" value only. The estimator may have the choice of materials, given a required "R" value and a certain cavity space (which may dictate insulation thickness). For example, the specifications may require an "R" value of 11, and only 2" of wall cavity is available for the thickness of the insulation. From Figure 9.77 and 9.78 it is seen that only rigid urethane (Line 072-116-2560) meets the design criteria. Note that if more cavity space were available, 3-1/2" non-rigid fiberglass (Line 072-118-0420) would be a much less expensive alternative. The estimator may have to do some shopping to find the least expensive material for the specified "R" value and thickness. Installation costs may vary from one material to another. Also, wood blocking and/or nailers are often required to match the insulation thickness in some instances.

Working with the above data, the estimator can accurately select the installed cost per square foot and estimate the total cost. The estimate for insulation

072 100	Building Insulation	CREW	DAILY OUTPUT	MAN-HOURS	UNIT	1993 BARE COSTS				TOTAL INCL O&P
						MAT.	LABOR	EQUIP.	TOTAL	
116	0010	**WALL INSULATION, RIGID**										116
0040	Fiberglass, 1.5#/C.F., unfaced, 1" thick, R4.1	1 Carp	1,000	.008	S.F.	.19	.19		.38	.50
0060	1-1/2" thick, R6.2		1,000	.008		.30	.19		.49	.62
0080	2" thick, R8.3		1,000	.008		.39	.19		.58	.72
0120	3" thick, R12.4		800	.010		.60	.23		.83	1.03
0370	3#/C.F., unfaced, 1" thick, R4.3		1,000	.008		.42	.19		.61	.75
0390	1-1/2" thick, R6.5		1,000	.008		.63	.19		.82	.98
0400	2" thick, R8.7		890	.009		.84	.21		1.05	1.25
0420	2-1/2" thick, R10.9		800	.010		1.06	.23		1.29	1.54
0440	3" thick, R13		800	.010		1.26	.23		1.49	1.76
0520	Foil faced, 1" thick, R4.3		1,000	.008		.81	.19		1	1.18
0540	1-1/2" thick, R6.5		1,000	.008		1.01	.19		1.20	1.40
0560	2" thick, R8.7		890	.009		1.23	.21		1.44	1.68
0580	2-1/2" thick, R10.9		800	.010		1.45	.23		1.68	1.97
0600	3" thick, R13		800	.010		1.90	.23		2.13	2.46
0670	6#/C.F., unfaced, 1" thick, R4.3		1,000	.008		.77	.19		.96	1.14
0690	1-1/2" thick, R6.5		890	.009		1.15	.21		1.36	1.60
0700	2" thick, R8.7		800	.010		1.53	.23		1.76	2.05
0721	2-1/2" thick, R10.9		800	.010		1.90	.23		2.13	2.46
0741	3" thick, R13	↓	730	.011	↓	2.30	.26		2.56	2.93
0821	Foil faced, 1" thick, R4.3	1 Carp	1,000	.008	S.F.	1	.19		1.19	1.39
0840	1-1/2" thick, R6.5		890	.009		1.25	.21		1.46	1.71
0850	2" thick, R8.7		800	.010		1.90	.23		2.13	2.46
0880	2-1/2" thick, R10.9		800	.010		2.28	.23		2.51	2.88
0900	3" thick, R13	↓	730	.011	↓	2.65	.26		2.91	3.32
1000										
1500	Foamglass, 1-1/2" thick, R2.64	1 Carp	800	.010	S.F.	1.20	.23		1.43	1.69
1550	2" thick, R5.26	"	730	.011	"	1.75	.26		2.01	2.33
1600	Isocyanurate, 4' x 8' sheet, foil faced, both sides									
1610	1/2" thick, R3.9	1 Carp	800	.010	S.F.	.23	.23		.46	.62
1620	5/8" thick, R4.5		800	.010		.26	.23		.49	.66
1630	3/4" thick, R5.4		800	.010		.34	.23		.57	.74
1640	1" thick, R7.2		800	.010		.47	.23		.70	.89
1650	1-1/2" thick, R10.8		730	.011		.70	.26		.96	1.18
1660	2" thick, R14.4		730	.011		.94	.26		1.20	1.43
1670	3" thick, R21.6		730	.011		1.30	.26		1.56	1.83
1680	4" thick, R28.8		730	.011		1.80	.26		2.06	2.38
1700	Perlite, 1" thick, R2.77		800	.010		.40	.23		.63	.81
1750	2" thick, R5.55		730	.011		.76	.26		1.02	1.24
1900	Polystyrene, extruded blue, 2.2#/C.F., 3/4" thick, R4		800	.010		.30	.23		.53	.70
1940	1-1/2" thick, R8.1		730	.011		.48	.26		.74	.93
1960	2" thick, R10.8		730	.011		.66	.26		.92	1.13
2100	Molded bead board, white, 1" thick, R3.85		800	.010		.17	.23		.40	.56
2120	1-1/2" thick, 0.99m²·K/W		730	.011		.27	.26		.53	.70
2140	2" thick, R7.7		730	.011		.35	.26		.61	.79
2350	Sheathing, insulating foil faced fiberboard, 3/8" thick	↓	670	.012	↓	.22	.28		.50	.68
2450										
2510	Urethane, no paper backing, 1/2" thick, R2.9	1 Carp	800	.010	S.F.	.28	.23		.51	.68
2520	1" thick, R5.8		800	.010		.51	.23		.74	.93
2540	1-1/2" thick, R8.7		730	.011		.73	.26		.99	1.20
2560	2" thick, R11.7		730	.011		1	.26		1.26	1.50
2710	Fire resistant, 1/2" thick, R2.9		800	.010		.35	.23		.58	.76
2720	1" thick, R5.8		800	.010		.69	.23		.92	1.13
2740	1-1/2" thick, R8.7		730	.011		.97	.26		1.23	1.47
2760	2" thick, R11.7	↓	730	.011	↓	1.24	.26		1.50	1.76

Figure 9.77

072 100	Building Insulation	CREW	ʌILY OUTPUT	MAN-HOURS	UNIT	1993 BARE COSTS				TOTAL INCL O&P
						MAT.	LABOR	EQUIP.	TOTAL	
0010	WALL OR CEILING INSUL., NON-RIGID									
0040	Fiberglass, kraft faced, batts or blankets									
0060	3-1/2" thick, R11, 11" wide	1 Carp	1,150	.007	S.F.	.22	.16		.38	.49
0080	15" wide		1,600	.005		.22	.12		.34	.42
0100	23" wide		1,600	.005		.24	.12		.36	.44
0140	6" thick, R19, 11" wide		1,000	.008		.34	.19		.53	.67
0160	15" wide		1,350	.006		.34	.14		.48	.60
0180	23" wide		1,600	.005		.34	.12		.46	.56
0200	9" thick, R30, 15" wide		1,150	.007		.53	.16		.69	.83
0220	23" wide		1,350	.006		.53	.14		.67	.80
0240	12" thick, R38, 15" wide		1,000	.008		.69	.19		.88	1.05
0260	23" wide	▼	1,350	.006	▼	.69	.14		.83	.98
0350										
0400	Fiberglass, foil faced, batts or blankets									
0420	3-1/2" thick, R11, 15" wide	1 Carp	1,600	.005	S.F.	.24	.12		.36	.44
0440	23" wide		1,600	.005		.24	.12		.36	.44
0460	6" thick, R19, 15" wide		1,350	.006		.33	.14		.47	.59
0480	23" wide		1,600	.005		.33	.12		.45	.55
0500	9" thick, R30, 15" wide		1,150	.007		.49	.16		.65	.79
0550	23" wide	▼	1,350	.006	▼	.49	.14		.63	.76
0700										
0800	Fiberglass, unfaced, batts or blankets									
0820	3-1/2" thick, R11, 15" wide	1 Carp	1,350	.006	S.F.	.18	.14		.32	.42
0830	23" wide		1,600	.005		.18	.12		.30	.38
0860	6" thick, R19, 15" wide		1,150	.007		.32	.16		.48	.60
0880	23" wide		1,350	.006		.32	.14		.46	.57
0900	9" thick, R30, 15" wide		1,000	.008		.48	.19		.67	.81
0920	23" wide		1,150	.007		.48	.16		.64	.77
0940	12" thick, R38, 15" wide		1,000	.008		.70	.19		.89	1.05
0960	23" wide	▼	1,150	.007	▼	.70	.16		.86	1.01
1300	Mineral fiber batts, kraft faced									
1320	3-1/2" thick, R13	1 Carp	1,600	.005	S.F.	.30	.12		.42	.51
1340	6" thick, R19		1,600	.005		.44	.12		.56	.66
1380	10" thick, R30	▼	1,350	.006	▼	.74	.14		.88	1.03
1900	For foil backing, add				▼	.04			.04	.04

118

Figure 9.78

should also include associated costs, such as cutting and patching for difficult installation, or requirements for air vents and other accessories.

Insulation is not only used for controlling heat transfer. It is also specified for use in internal walls and ceilings for controlling *sound* transfer. Although the noise reduction coefficient of batt insulation is not as great as specialized sound attenuation blankets, the costs are considerably less.

Shingles

Most residences and many smaller types of commercial buildings have sloping roofs covered with some form of shingle or watershed material. The materials used in shingles vary from the more common granular-covered asphalt and fiberglass units to wood, metal, clay, concrete, or slate.

The first step in estimating the cost of a shingle roof is to determine the material specified, shingle size and weight, and installation method. With this information, the estimator can select the accurate installed cost of the roofing material.

In a sloping roof deck, the ridge and eave lengths, as well as the ridge to eaves dimension, must be known or measured before the actual roof area can be calculated. When the plan dimensions of the roof are known and the sloping dimensions are not known, the actual roof area can still be estimated, providing the slope of the roof is known. Figure 9.79 is a table of multipliers that can be used for this purpose. The roof slope is given in both the inches of rise per foot of horizontal run, and in the degree of slope, which allows direct conversion of the horizontal plan dimension into the dimension on the slope.

After the roof area has been estimated in square feet, it must be divided by 100 to convert it into roofing squares (the conventional "unit" for roofing – one square equals 100 square feet). To determine the quantity of shingles required for hips or ridges, add one square for each 100 linear feet of hips and/or ridges.

When the total squares of roofing have been calculated, the estimator should make an allowance for waste based on the design of the roof. A minimum allowance of 3% to 5% is needed if the roof has two straight sides with two gable ends and no breaks. At the other extreme any roof with several valleys, hips, and ridges may need a waste allowance of 15% or more to cover the excess cutting required.

Accessories that are part of a shingle roof include drip edges, flashings at chimneys, dormers, skylights, vents, valleys, and walls. These are necessary to complete the roof and should be included in the estimate for the shingles.

Roofing and Siding

In addition to shingles, many types of roofing and siding are used on commercial and industrial buildings. These are made of several kinds of material and come in many forms for both roofing and siding – panels, sheets, membranes and boards.

The materials used in roofing and siding panels include: aluminum, mineral fiber-cement epoxy, fibrous glass, steel, vinyl, many types of synthetic sheets and membranes, coal tar, asphalt felt, tar felt and asphalt asbestos felt. Most of the latter materials are used in job-fabricated, built-up roofs and as backing for other materials, such as shingles.

The basic data required for estimating either roofing or siding includes the specification of the material the supporting structure, the method of installation, and the area to be covered. When selecting the current unit price for these materials, the estimator must remember that basic installed unit costs are per square foot for siding and per square for roofing. The major exceptions to this general rule are prefabricated roofing panels and single-ply roofing, which are priced per square foot.

Single-ply Roofs

- Chlorinated Polyethylene (CPE)
- Chlorosulfonated Polyethylene
- Ethylene Propylene Diene Monomer (EPDM)
- Polychloroprene (Neoprene)
- Polyisobutylene (PIB)
- Polyvinyl Chloride (PVC)
- Modified Bitumen

Since the early 1970s the use of single-ply roofing membranes in the construction industry has been on the rise. Market surveys have recently shown that of all the single-ply systems being installed, about one in three is on new construction. Materially, these roofs are more expensive than other, more conventional roofs; however, labor costs are much lower because of a faster installation. Re-roofing represents the largest market for single-ply roof systems today. Single-ply roof systems are normally installed in one of the following ways:

Factors for Converting Inclined to Horizontal					
Roof Slope	Approx. Angle	Factor	Roof Slope	Approx. Angle	Factor
Flat	0	1.000	12 in 12	45.0	1.414
1 in 12	4.8	1.003	13 in 12	47.3	1.474
2 in 12	9.5	1.014	14 in 12	49.4	1.537
3 in 12	14.0	1.031	15 in 12	51.3	1.601
4 in 12	18.4	1.054	16 in 12	53.1	1.667
5 in 12	22.6	1.083	17 in 12	54.8	1.734
6 in 12	26.6	1.118	18 in 12	56.3	1.803
7 in 12	30.3	1.158	19 in 12	57.7	1.873
8 in 12	33.7	1.202	20 in 12	59.0	1.943
9 in 12	36.9	1.250	21 in 12	60.3	2.015
10 in 12	39.8	1.302	22 in 12	61.4	2.088
11 in 12	42.5	1.357	23 in 12	62.4	2.162

Example:

[20' (1.302) 90'] 2 = 4,687.2 S.F. = 46.9 Sq.

OR

[40' (1.302) 90'] = 4,687.2 S.F. = 46.9 Sq.

Figure 9.79

Loose-laid and ballasted: Generally this is the easiest type of single-ply roof to install. Some special consideration must be given, however, when flashing is attached to the roof. The membrane is typically fused together at the seams stretched out flat and ballasted with stone (1-1/2″ @12 PSF) to prevent wind blow-off. This extra load must be considered during design stages. It is particularly important if re-roofing over an existing built-up roof that already weighs 10-15 PSF. A slip-sheet or vapor barrier is sometimes required to separate the new roof from the old.

Partially-adhered: This method of installation uses a series of bar or point attachments which adhere the membrane to a substrate. The membrane manufacturer typically specifies the method to be used based on the material and substrate. Partially-adhered systems do not use ballast material. A slip-sheet may be required.

Fully-adhered: This is generally the most time-consuming of the single-plies to install, because these roofs employ a contact cement, cold adhesive, or hot bitumen to adhere the membrane uniformly to the substrate. Only manufacturer-approved insulation board or substrate should be used to receive the membrane. No ballast is required.

The materials available can be broken down into three categories:

- Thermo-Setting: EDPM, Neoprene, and PIB
- Thermo-Plastic: Hypalon, PVC and CPE
- Composites: Modified Bitumen

Each has its own requirements and performance characteristics. Most are available in all three installation methods. See Figure 9.80.

Single-ply roof systems are available from many sources. Most if not all manufacturers, however, sell their materials only to franchised installers. As a result, there may be only one source for a price in any given area. Read the specifications carefully. Estimate the system required, exactly as specified; substitutes are usually not allowed.

Sheet Metal

- Copper and Stainless Steel
- Gutters and Downspouts
- Edge Cleats and Gravel Stops
- Flashings
- Trim
- Miscellaneous

Sheet metal work included in this division is limited to that used on roofs or sidewalls of buildings, usually on the exterior exposed to the weather. Many of the items covered are wholly or partially prefabricated with labor added for installation. Several are materials that require labor added for on-site fabrication; this cost must be estimated separately.

Pricing shop-made items such as downspouts, drip edges, expansion joints, gravel stops, gutters, reglets, and termite shields requires that the estimator determine the material, size, and shape of the fabricated section, and the linear feet of the item. From this data, an accurate unit can be selected and multiplied by the linear footage in order to obtain a total cost.

The cost of items like copper roofing and metal flashing is estimated in a similar manner, except that unit costs are per square foot. Some roofing systems, particularly single-ply, require flashing materials that are unique to that roofing system.

Roofing materials like monel, stainless steel, and zinc copper alloy are also estimated by the same method, except that the unit costs are per square (100 square feet). Prefabricated items like strainers and louvers are priced on a cost-per-unit basis. Adhesives are priced by the gallon. The installed cost of roofing adhesives depends on the cost per gallon and the coverage per gallon. With trowel grade adhesive, the coverage will vary from a light coating at 25 S.F. per gallon to a heavy coating at 10 S.F. per gallon. With most flashing work, the asphalt adhesive will cover an average of 15 S.F. for each layer or course. In many specifications the coverage of special materials like adhesives will be stated and should be used as the basis for the estimate.

Roof Accessories

- Hatches
- Skylights
- Vents
- Snow Guards

Single-Ply Roofing Membrane Installation Guide

Class	Generic Materials (Classification)	Slip-Sheet Req'd.	Concrete	Exist. Asphalt Memb.	Insulation Board	Plywood	Spray Urethane Foam	Adhesive	Fully Adhered	Loose Laid/Ballast	Partially-Adhered	Adhesive	Hot Air Gun	Self-Sealing	Solvent	Torch Heating
		Compatible Substrates						Attachment Method				Sealing Method				
Thermo Setting	EPDM (Ethylene, propylene diene monomer)	X	X	X	X	X	X	X	X		X	X	X		X	X
	Neoprene (synthetic rubber)	X	X		X	X		X	X	X		X				
	PIB (Polyisobutylene)	X	X	X	X	X	X	X		X		X	X		X	
Thermo Plastic	CSPE (Chlorosulfenated polyethyene)	X	X		X	X	X	X	X	X	X	X	X			
	CPE (Chlorinated polyethylene)	X	X		X	X			X	X	X	X				
	PVC (Ployvinyl chloride)	X	X		X	X	X			X	X	X			X	
Composites	Glass reinforced EPDM/neoprene	X	X		X	X	X			X		X				
	Modified bitumen/polyester	X		X	X	X			X			X	X			X
	Modified bitumen/polyethylene & aluminum	X	X		X	X		X	X	X		X				X
	Modified bitumen/polyethylene sheet	X	X		X	X							X			X
	Modified CPE				X	X			X	.		X				
	Non-woven glass reinforced PVC							X	X	X		X				
	Nylon reinforced PVC		X		X	X				X			X		X	
	Nylon reinforced/butyl or neoprene	X							X				X		X	
	Polyester reinforce CPE	X	X	X	X	X	X			X	X	X	X			
	Polyester reinforced PVC	X	X		X	X	X			X	X	X	X		X	
	Rubber asphalt/plastic sheet	X	X	X	X	X			X					X		

Figure 9.80

Roof accessories must be considered as part of the complete weatherproofing system. Standard size accessories, such as ceiling, roof and smoke vents or hatches, and snow guards, are priced per installed unit. Accessories that must be fabricated to meet project specifications may be priced per square foot, per linear foot or per unit. Skylight costs, for example, are listed by the square foot with unit costs decreasing in steps as the nominal size of individual units increases.

Skyroofs are priced on the same basis, but due to the many variations in the shape and construction of these units, costs are per square foot of surface area. These costs will vary with the size and type of unit, and in many cases, maximum and minimum costs give the estimator a range of prices for various design variations. Because there are many types and styles, the estimator must determine the exact specifications for the skyroof being priced. The accuracy of the total cost figure will depend entirely on the selection of the proper unit cost and calculation of the skyroof area. Skyroofs are becoming widely used in the industry and the work is growing more and more specialized. Often a particular manufacturer is specified. Specialty installing subcontractors are often factory authorized and required to perform the installation to maintain warranties and waterproof integrity.

Accessories such as roof drains, plumbing vents and duct penetrations are usually installed by other appropriate subcontractors. However, costs for flashing and sealing these items are often included by the roofing subcontractor.

When estimating Division 7, associated costs must be included for items that may not be directly stated in the specifications. Placement of materials, for example, may require the use of a crane or conveyors. Pitch pockets, sleepers, pads and walkways may be required for rooftop equipment. Blocking and cant strips and items associated with different trades must also be coordinated. Once again, the estimator must visualize the construction process.

Sample Estimate: Division 7

The thermal and moisture protection portion of the sample building project is to be done partially by crews of the general contractor and partially by a subcontractor. The estimate sheets are shown in Figures 9.81 and 9.82. It is important to verify that the "units" used for takeoff are the same as those used for pricing. Note in Figure 9.83, the polyethylene vapor barrier is priced by the square (sq.). It could be an easy mistake to enter 20,800 (18,900 square feet of floor area plus 10% overlap) on the estimate sheet (Figure 9.81). Even, if one person performs the takeoff and another the pricing, such an error could possibly occur in haste. Ideally time should be allowed for someone to always cross-check the work and calculations of another.

Smoke hatches are specified to be installed at the tops of the stair towers. Costs for smoke hatches in *Means Building Construction Cost Data* are given only as percentages to be added to the *bare costs* of roof hatches. See Figures 9.84 and 9.85. Calculations to add the percentages are shown in Figure 9.86. The bare costs are increased before overhead and profit are added. 10% is added to the bare material cost for handling. In Figure 9.84, the installing crew for the roof hatches is G-3 (see Figure 9.87). The crews consists of sheet metal workers and laborers. The percentage added to the labor costs, for overhead and profit, is the average of the percentages for the two trades from Figure 9.88 — 55.2% and 57%.

The development and application of these percentages for overhead and profit are discussed in Chapter 4 and Chapter 7 of this book.

CONSOLIDATED ESTIMATE

PROJECT: Office Building CLASSIFICATION: Division 7

LOCATION: ARCHITECT:

TAKE OFF BY: QUANTITIES BY: PRICES BY: EXTENSIONS BY:

DESCRIPTION	SOURCE	QUANT.	UNIT	MATERIAL COST	MATERIAL TOTAL	LABOR COST	LABOR TOTAL	EQUIPMENT COST	EQUIPMENT TOTAL	SUBCONTRACT COST	SUBCONTRACT TOTAL	TOTAL COST	TOTAL
Division 7: Moisture & Thermal Protection													
Waterproofing													
Asphalt Coating	071 602 0600	3000	SF	0.12	360	0.34	1020						
Protective Board 1/4"	071 602 4000	3000	SF	0.35	1050	0.38	1140						
Vapor Barrier - 6 mil poly	071 922 0900	208	Sq.	2.62	545	5.05	1050						
Insulation													
3 1/2" Fiberglass Ext.	072 118 0420	17600	SF	0.24	4224	0.12	2112						
3 1/2" Fiberglass Int.	072 118 0820	7620	SF	0.18	1372	0.14	1067						
Roof Deck (Incl. Penthouse) 2 5/8" Urethane/Fiberglass	072 203 1300	18900	SF		SUBCONTRACTED →					1.47	27783		
Roofing													
4 - ply Built-up	075 102 0500	189	Sq.							145.00	27405		
4 x 4 Cant	075 103 0010	800	LF							1.48	1184		
Subtotals					$7,551		$6,389				$56,372		

Figure 9.81

CONSOLIDATED ESTIMATE

PROJECT: Office Building
LOCATION:
TAKE OFF BY:
CLASSIFICATION: Division 7
ARCHITECT:
QUANTITIES BY:
PRICES BY:
EXTENSIONS BY:

DESCRIPTION	SOURCE	QUANT.	UNIT	MATERIAL COST	MATERIAL TOTAL	LABOR COST	LABOR TOTAL	EQUIPMENT COST	EQUIPMENT TOTAL	SUBCONTRACT COST	SUBCONTRACT TOTAL	TOTAL COST	TOTAL
Division 7: (Cont'd)													
Sheet Metal													
Gravel Stop	077 105 0350	800	LF			SUBCONTRACTED →				5.85	4680		
Alum. Flashing	076 204 0100	200	SF							3.06	612		
Accessories													
Smoke Hatches (Stairs)	077 206 1200	3	Ea.							1179	3537		
Smoke Vent (Elevator)	077 208 0200	1	Ea.							1200	1200		
Subtotals											$10,029		
Sheet 1 Subtotals					$7,551		$6,389				$56,372		
Sheet 2 Subtotals											$10,029		
Division 7 Totals					$7,551		$6,389				$66,401		

Figure 9.82

071 | Waterproofing and Dampproofing

071 100 | Sheet Waterproofing

			CREW	DAILY OUTPUT	MAN-HOURS	UNIT	1993 BARE COSTS				TOTAL INCL O&P	
							MAT.	LABOR	EQUIP.	TOTAL		
104	1300	Fluid elastomeric copolymer compound, 32 mils thick	2 Rofc	4,400	.004	S.F.	2.25	.08		2.33	2.61	104

071 300 | Bentonite Waterproofing

			CREW	DAILY OUTPUT	MAN-HOURS	UNIT	MAT.	LABOR	EQUIP.	TOTAL	TOTAL INCL O&P	
301	0010	BENTONITE Panels, 4' x 4', for walls, 3/16" thick	1 Rofc	625	.013	S.F.	.75	.27		1.02	1.29	301
	0100	Under slabs, 5/8" thick	"	900	.009	"	.95	.19		1.14	1.37	
	0300	Granular bentonite, 50 lb. bags (.625 C.F.)				Bag	11			11	12.10	
	0400	3/8" thick, troweled on	1 Rofc	475	.017	S.F.	.75	.36		1.11	1.44	
	0500	Drain board, expanded polystyrene, binder encapsulated, 1" thick	1 Rohe	1,600	.005		.40	.08		.48	.57	
	0510	2" thick		1,600	.005		.71	.08		.79	.91	
	0520	3" thick		1,600	.005		1	.08		1.08	1.23	
	0530	4" thick	↓	1,600	.005		1.30	.08		1.38	1.56	
	0600	Filter fabric, minimum					.26			.26	.29	
	0610	Maximum				↓	.32			.32	.35	
	0700	Vapor retarder, see polyethelene, 071-922								.06	.07	

071 450 | Cement. Waterproofing

			CREW	DAILY OUTPUT	MAN-HOURS	UNIT	MAT.	LABOR	EQUIP.	TOTAL	TOTAL INCL O&P	
452	0010	CEMENTITIOUS WATERPROOFING One coat cement base										452
	0020	1/8" application, sprayed on	G-2	1,000	.024	S.F.	1.10	.48	.24	1.82	2.23	

071 600 | Bitum. Dampproofing

			CREW	DAILY OUTPUT	MAN-HOURS	UNIT	MAT.	LABOR	EQUIP.	TOTAL	TOTAL INCL O&P	
602	0010	BITUMINOUS ASPHALT COATING For foundation										602
	0020											
	0030	Brushed on, below grade, 1 coat	1 Rofc	665	.012	S.F.	.05	.26		.31	.50	
	0100	2 coat		500	.016		.10	.34		.44	.69	
	0300	Sprayed on, below grade, 1 coat, 25.6 S.F./gal.		830	.010		.15	.20		.35	.52	
	0400	2 coat, 20.5 S.F./gal.	↓	500	.016	↓	.19	.34		.53	.79	
	0500	Asphalt coating, with fibers				Gal.	4.10			4.10	4.51	
	0600	Troweled on, asphalt with fibers, 1/16" thick	1 Rofc	500	.016	S.F.	.12	.34		.46	.71	
	0700	1/8" thick		400	.020		.22	.43		.65	.96	
	1000	1/2" thick	↓	350	.023	↓	.94	.49		1.43	1.86	
	3470											
	4000	Protective board, asphalt coated, in mastic, 1/4" thick	1 Rofc	450	.018	S.F.	.35	.38		.73	1.03	

071 750 | Water Repellent Coat

			CREW	DAILY OUTPUT	MAN-HOURS	UNIT	MAT.	LABOR	EQUIP.	TOTAL	TOTAL INCL O&P	
754	0010	RUBBER COATING Water base liquid, roller applied	2 Rofc	7,000	.002	S.F.	.55	.05		.60	.69	754
	0200	Silicone or stearate, sprayed on masonry, 1 coat	1 Rofc	4,000	.002		.22	.04		.26	.31	
	0300	2 coats	"	2,000	.004	↓	.33	.08		.41	.50	

071 800 | Cementitious Dampprfng

				CREW	DAILY OUTPUT	MAN-HOURS	UNIT	MAT.	LABOR	EQUIP.	TOTAL	TOTAL INCL O&P	
802	0010	CEMENT PARGING 2 coats, 1/2" thick, regular P.C.	R071 -010	D-1	250	.064	S.F.	.14	1.37		1.51	2.27	802
	0100	Waterproofed portland cement		"	250	.064	"	.15	1.37		1.52	2.29	

071 920 | Vapor Retarders

			CREW	DAILY OUTPUT	MAN-HOURS	UNIT	MAT.	LABOR	EQUIP.	TOTAL	TOTAL INCL O&P	
922	0010	BUILDING PAPER Aluminum and kraft laminated, foil 1 side	1 Carp	19	.421	Sq.	4	9.85		13.85	19.85	922
	0100	Foil 2 sides		19	.421		7.20	9.85		17.05	23.50	
	0300	Asphalt, two ply, 30#, for subfloors		37	.216		5.75	5.05		10.80	14.25	
	0400	Asphalt felt sheathing paper, 15#	↓	37	.216	↓	2.75	5.05		7.80	10.95	
	0450	Housewrap, exterior, spun bonded polypropylene										
	0470	Small roll, 3' wide x 165'	1 Carp	3,800	.002	S.F.	.10	.05		.15	.19	
	0480	Large roll, 9' wide x 195'	"	4,000	.002	"	.09	.05		.14	.17	
	0500	Material only, 3' wide roll				Ea.	49.50			49.50	54.50	
	0520	9' wide roll				"	158			158	174	
	0600	Polyethylene vapor barrier, standard, .002" thick	1 Carp	37	.216	Sq.	.90	5.05		5.95	8.90	

Figure 9.83

242

077 | Roof Specialties and Accessories

077 100 | Prefab Roof Specialties

			CREW	DAILY OUTPUT	MAN-HOURS	UNIT	1993 BARE COSTS				TOTAL INCL O&P	
							MAT.	LABOR	EQUIP.	TOTAL		
103	1950	Polyethylene bellows, with galv. steel flat flanges	1 Rofc	100	.080	L.F.	3.10	1.70		4.80	6.30	103
	1960	With galvanized angle flanges	"	100	.080		3.40	1.70		5.10	6.65	
	2000	Roof joint with extruded aluminum cover, 2"	1 Shee	115	.070	↓	21.50	1.85		23.35	26.50	
	2050											
	2100	Roof joint, plastic curbs, foam center, standard	1 Rofc	100	.080	L.F.	7.85	1.70		9.55	11.55	
	2200	Large		100	.080	"	10.50	1.70		12.20	14.45	
	2300	Transitions, regular, minimum		10	.800	Ea.	64.50	17		81.50	100	
	2350	Maximum		4	2		86.50	42.50		129	168	
	2400	Large, minimum		9	.889	↓	98	18.90		116.90	140	
	2450	Maximum	↓	3	2.667		103	56.50		159.50	210	
	2500	Roof to wall joint with extruded aluminum cover	1 Shee	115	.070	L.F.	17.95	1.85		19.80	22.50	
	2600	See also divisions 031-132 & 058-104										
	2700	Wall joint, closed cell foam on PVC cover, 9" wide	1 Rofc	125	.064	L.F.	2.75	1.36		4.11	5.35	
	2800	12" wide	"	115	.070	"	3.15	1.48		4.63	6	
104	0010	FASCIA Aluminum, reverse board and batten,										104
	0100	.032" thick, colored, no furring included	1 Shee	145	.055	S.F.	1.70	1.47		3.17	4.15	
	0300	Steel, galv. and enameled, stock, no furring, long panels		145	.055		1.90	1.47		3.37	4.37	
	0600	Short panels		115	.070	↓	2.95	1.85		4.80	6.15	
105	0010	GRAVEL STOP Aluminum, .050" thick, 4" height, mill finish		145	.055	L.F.	2	1.47		3.47	4.48	105
	0080	Duranodic finish		145	.055		2.85	1.47		4.32	5.40	
	0100	Painted		145	.055		2.65	1.47		4.12	5.20	
	0300	6" face height, .050" thick, mill finish		135	.059		2.20	1.58		3.78	4.87	
	0350	Duranodic finish		135	.059		3.10	1.58		4.68	5.85	
	0400	Painted		135	.059		3	1.58		4.58	5.75	
	0600	8" face height, .050" thick, mill finish		125	.064		2.70	1.71		4.41	5.60	
	0650	Duranodic finish		125	.064		3.90	1.71		5.61	6.95	
	0700	Painted		125	.064		3.75	1.71		5.46	6.80	
	0900	12" face height, 2 piece, mill finish		100	.080		4.90	2.13		7.03	8.70	
	0950	Duranodic finish		100	.080		6	2.13		8.13	9.90	
	1000	Painted		100	.080		5.80	2.13		7.93	9.70	
	1350	Galv. steel, 24 ga., 4" leg, plain, with continuous cleat, 4" face		145	.055		2	1.47		3.47	4.48	
	1360	6" face height		145	.055		2.25	1.47		3.72	4.76	
	1500	Polyvinyl chloride, 6" face height		135	.059		2.65	1.58		4.23	5.35	
	1600	9" face height		125	.064		3.15	1.71		4.86	6.10	
	1800	Stainless steel, 24 ga., 6" face height		135	.059		6	1.58		7.58	9.05	
	1900	12" face height		100	.080		11.50	2.13		13.63	15.95	
	2100	20 ga., 6" face height		135	.059		6.80	1.58		8.38	9.95	
	2200	12" face height	↓	100	.080	↓	13.60	2.13		15.73	18.25	

077 200 | Roof Accessories

			CREW	DAILY OUTPUT	MAN-HOURS	UNIT	MAT.	LABOR	EQUIP.	TOTAL	INCL O&P	
204	0010	CEILING HATCHES 2'-6" x 2'-6", single leaf, steel frame & cover	G-3	11	2.909	Ea.	305	66	2.24	373.24	440	204
	0100	Aluminum cover		11	2.909		320	66	2.24	388.24	455	
	0300	2'-6" x 3'-0", single leaf, steel frame & steel cover		11	2.909		325	66	2.24	393.24	465	
	0400	Aluminum cover	↓	11	2.909	↓	350	66	2.24	418.24	490	
205	0010	ROOF DRAINS See division 151-125										205
206	0010	ROOF HATCHES With curb, 1" fiberglass insulation, 2'-6" x 3'-0"										206
	0500	Aluminum curb and cover	G-3	10	3.200	Ea.	305	72.50	2.46	379.96	455	
	0520	Galvanized steel		10	3.200		269	72.50	2.46	343.96	410	
	0540	Plain steel, primed		10	3.200		238	72.50	2.46	312.96	380	
	0600	2'-6" x 4'-6", aluminum curb & cover		9	3.556		420	80.50	2.74	503.24	590	
	0800	Galvanized steel		9	3.556		400	80.50	2.74	483.24	570	
	0900	Plain steel, primed		9	3.556		365	80.50	2.74	448.24	530	
	1200	2'-6" x 8'-0", aluminum curb and cover		6.60	4.848		820	110	3.73	933.73	1,075	
	1400	Galvanized steel		6.60	4.848		745	110	3.73	858.73	995	
	1500	Plain steel, primed	↓	6.60	4.848	↓	685	110	3.73	798.73	930	

Figure 9.84

		077 200	Roof Accessories	CREW	DAILY OUTPUT	MAN-HOURS	UNIT	1993 BARE COSTS MAT.	LABOR	EQUIP.	TOTAL	TOTAL INCL O&P	
206	1800	For plexiglass panels, add to above					Ea.	185			185	204	206
	2000	For galv. curb and alum. cover, deduct from aluminum					↓	15			15	16.50	
207	0010	SMOKE HATCHES Unlabeled, not including hand winch operator											207
	0100												
	0200	For 3'-0" long, add to roof hatches from division 077-206					Ea.	25%	5%				
	0300	For 8'-0" long, add to roof hatches from division 077-206					'	10%	5%				
208	0010	SMOKE VENTS Metal cover, heavy duty, low profile, 4' x 4'											208
	0100	Aluminum	G-3	13	2.462	Ea.	1,100	55.50	1.90	1,157.40	1,300	
	0200	Galvanized steel	'	13	2.462	'	1,000	55.50	1.90	1,057.40	1,200	
	0250												
	0300	4' x 8' aluminum	G-3	8	4	Ea.	1,500	90.50	3.08	1,593.58	1,800	
	0400	Galvanized steel	'	8	4		1,300	90.50	3.08	1,393.58	1,575	
	0500	Sloped cover style, add				↓	20%					
210	0010	ROOF VENTS Mushroom for built-up roofs, aluminum	1 Rofc	30	.267	Ea.	20	5.65		25.65	31.50	210
	0100	PVC, 6" high		30	.267	'	25	5.65		30.65	37	
212	0010	VENTS, ONE-WAY For insul. decks, 1 per M.S.F., plastic, min.		40	.200	Ea.	3.95	4.25		8.20	11.60	212
	0100	Maximum		20	.400		24.50	8.50		33	41.50	
	0300	Aluminum	↓	30	.267		10.75	5.65		16.40	21.50	
	0800	Fiber board baffles, 12" wide for 16" O.C. rafter spacing	1 Carp	90	.089		.42	2.08		2.50	3.72	
	0900	For 24" O.C. rafter spacing	'	110	.073	↓	.69	1.70		2.39	3.43	
214	0010	VENTILATORS See division 157-490										214

		078 100	Plastic Skylights	CREW	DAILY OUTPUT	MAN-HOURS	UNIT	1993 BARE COSTS MAT.	LABOR	EQUIP.	TOTAL	TOTAL INCL O&P	
101	0010	SKYLIGHT Plastic roof domes, flush or curb mounted, ten or										101
	0100	more units, curb not included, "L" frames										
	0300	Nominal size under 10 S.F., double	G-3	130	.246	S.F.	20	5.55	.19	25.74	31	
	0400	Single		160	.200		15.50	4.52	.15	20.17	24.50	
	0600	10 S.F. to 20 S.F., double		315	.102		15.20	2.30	.08	17.58	20.50	
	0700	Single		395	.081		12.35	1.83	.06	14.24	16.50	
	0900	20 S.F. to 30 S.F., double		395	.081		14.30	1.83	.06	16.19	18.65	
	1000	Single		465	.069		11	1.56	.05	12.61	14.60	
	1200	30 S.F. to 65 S.F., double		465	.069		13.40	1.56	.05	15.01	17.25	
	1300	Single	↓	610	.052		11	1.19	04	12.23	14	
	1500	For insulated 4" curbs, double, add					25%					
	1600	Single, add					30%					
	1800	For integral insulated 9" curbs, double, add					30%					
	1900	Single, add					40%					
	2100	Ceiling plastic domes compared with single roof domes				↓	85%	100%				
	2110											
	2120	Ventilating insulated plexiglass dome with										
	2130	curb mounting, 36" x 36"	G-3	12	2.667	Ea.	300	60.50	2.05	362.55	425	
	2150	52" x 52"		12	2.667		450	60.50	2.05	512.55	590	
	2160	28" x 52"		10	3.200		350	72.50	2.46	424.96	500	
	2170	36" x 52"	↓	10	3.200		380	72.50	2.46	454.96	535	
	2180	For electric opening system, add				↓	225			225	248	

Figure 9.85

Division 8: Doors and Windows

Any one door assembly (door, frame, hardware) can be one of hundreds of combinations of many variable features:

Door:	Frame:	Hardware:
Size	Size	Lockset
Thickness	Throat	Passage set
Wood-type	Wood-type	Panic bar
Metal-gauge	Metal-gauge	Closer
Laminate	Casing	Hinges
Hollow-core type	Stops	Stops
Solid-core material	Fire rating	Bolts
Fire rating	Knock down	Finish
Finish	Welded	Plates

Most architectural plans and specifications include door, window, and hardware schedules to tabulate these combinations. The estimator should use these schedules, and details in conjunction with the plans, to avoid duplication or omission of units when determining the quantities. The schedules should identify the location, size, and type of each unit. Schedules should also include information regarding the frame, fire rating, hardware, and special notes. If no such schedules are included, the estimator should prepare them in order to provide an accurate quantity takeoff. Figure 9.89 is an example of a form that may be used to prepare such a schedule. Most suppliers will prepare separate schedules for approval by the architect or owner.

Metal Doors and Frames

A proper door schedule on the architectural drawings identifies each opening in detail. Define each opening in accordance with the items in the schedule and any other pertinent data. Installation information should be carefully reviewed in the specifications.

For the quantity survey, combine all similar doors and frames, checking each off as you go to ensure none has been left out. An easy and obvious check is to count the total number of openings, making certain that two doors and only one frame have been included where double doors are used. Important details to check for both door and frame are:

- Material
- Gauge
- Size
- Core Material
- Fire Rating Label
- Finish
- Style

Line Number	Bare Costs			Total Including O & P
	Material	Labor	Equipment	
077-206-1200	$820	$110	$3.73	
077-207-0300	(10%) 82	(5%) 6	—	
	902	116	3.73	
Overhead & Profit	(10%) 90	(57.4%) 67	(60%) .37	
	$992	$183	$4.10	$1,179

Figure 9.86

CREWS

Crew E-13

	Bare Costs Hr.	Bare Costs Daily	Incl. Subs O & P Hr.	Incl. Subs O & P Daily	Cost Per Man-Hour Bare Costs	Cost Per Man-Hour Incl. O&P
1 Welder Foreman	$28.00	$224.00	$50.65	$405.20	$26.37	$45.52
.5 Equip. Oper. (light)	23.10	92.40	35.25	141.00		
1 Gas Welding Machine		73.40		80.75	6.12	6.73
12 M.H., Daily Totals		$389.80		$626.95	$32.49	$52.15

Crew E-14

	Bare Costs Hr.	Bare Costs Daily	Incl. Subs O & P Hr.	Incl. Subs O & P Daily	Cost Per Man-Hour Bare Costs	Cost Per Man-Hour Incl. O&P
1 Welder Foreman	$28.00	$224.00	$50.65	$405.20	$28.00	$50.65
1 Gas Welding Machine		73.40		80.75	9.18	10.09
8 M.H., Daily Totals		$297.40		$485.95	$37.18	$60.74

Crew E-15

	Bare Costs Hr.	Bare Costs Daily	Incl. Subs O & P Hr.	Incl. Subs O & P Daily	Cost Per Man-Hour Bare Costs	Cost Per Man-Hour Incl. O&P
2 Painters, Struc. Steel	$22.55	$360.80	$42.80	$684.80	$22.55	$42.80
1 Paint Sprayer, 17 C.F.M.		27.40		30.15	1.71	1.88
16 M.H., Daily Totals		$388.20		$714.95	$24.26	$44.68

Crew E-16

	Bare Costs Hr.	Bare Costs Daily	Incl. Subs O & P Hr.	Incl. Subs O & P Daily	Cost Per Man-Hour Bare Costs	Cost Per Man-Hour Incl. O&P
1 Welder Foreman	$28.00	$224.00	$50.65	$405.20	$27.00	$48.85
1 Welder	26.00	208.00	47.05	376.40		
1 Gas Welding Machine		73.40		80.75	4.59	5.05
16 M.H., Daily Totals		$505.40		$862.35	$31.59	$53.90

Crew F-1

	Bare Costs Hr.	Bare Costs Daily	Incl. Subs O & P Hr.	Incl. Subs O & P Daily	Cost Per Man-Hour Bare Costs	Cost Per Man-Hour Incl. O&P
1 Carpenter	$23.35	$186.80	$36.65	$293.20	$23.35	$36.65
1 Power Tools		8.20		9.00	1.03	1.13
8 M.H., Daily Totals		$195.00		$302.20	$24.38	$37.78

Crew F-2

	Bare Costs Hr.	Bare Costs Daily	Incl. Subs O & P Hr.	Incl. Subs O & P Daily	Cost Per Man-Hour Bare Costs	Cost Per Man-Hour Incl. O&P
2 Carpenters	$23.35	$373.60	$36.65	$586.40	$23.35	$36.65
2 Power Tools		16.40		18.05	1.03	1.13
16 M.H., Daily Totals		$390.00		$604.45	$24.38	$37.78

Crew F-3

	Bare Costs Hr.	Bare Costs Daily	Incl. Subs O & P Hr.	Incl. Subs O & P Daily	Cost Per Man-Hour Bare Costs	Cost Per Man-Hour Incl. O&P
4 Carpenters	$23.35	$747.20	$36.65	$1172.80	$23.67	$36.93
1 Equip. Oper. (crane)	24.95	199.60	38.05	304.40		
1 Hyd. Crane, 12 Ton		375.40		412.95		
2 Power Tools		16.40		18.05	9.80	10.77
40 M.H., Daily Totals		$1338.60		$1908.20	$33.47	$47.70

Crew F-4

	Bare Costs Hr.	Bare Costs Daily	Incl. Subs O & P Hr.	Incl. Subs O & P Daily	Cost Per Man-Hour Bare Costs	Cost Per Man-Hour Incl. O&P
4 Carpenters	$23.35	$747.20	$36.65	$1172.80	$23.10	$35.92
1 Equip. Oper. (crane)	24.95	199.60	38.05	304.40		
1 Equip. Oper. Oiler	20.25	162.00	30.90	247.20		
1 Hyd. Crane, 55 Ton		710.00		781.00		
2 Power Tools		16.40		18.05	15.13	16.65
48 M.H., Daily Totals		$1835.20		$2523.45	$38.23	$52.57

Crew F-5

	Bare Costs Hr.	Bare Costs Daily	Incl. Subs O & P Hr.	Incl. Subs O & P Daily	Cost Per Man-Hour Bare Costs	Cost Per Man-Hour Incl. O&P
1 Carpenter Foreman	$25.35	$202.80	$39.80	$318.40	$23.85	$37.44
3 Carpenters	23.35	560.40	36.65	879.60		
2 Power Tools		16.40		18.05	.51	.56
32 M.H., Daily Totals		$779.60		$1216.05	$24.36	$38.00

Crew F-7

	Bare Costs Hr.	Bare Costs Daily	Incl. Subs O & P Hr.	Incl. Subs O & P Daily	Cost Per Man-Hour Bare Costs	Cost Per Man-Hour Incl. O&P
2 Carpenters	$23.35	$373.60	$36.65	$586.40	$20.95	$32.88
2 Building Laborers	18.55	296.80	29.10	465.60		
2 Power Tools		16.40		18.05	.51	.56
32 M.H., Daily Totals		$686.80		$1070.05	$21.46	$33.44

Crew G-1

	Bare Costs Hr.	Bare Costs Daily	Incl. Subs O & P Hr.	Incl. Subs O & P Daily	Cost Per Man-Hour Bare Costs	Cost Per Man-Hour Incl. O&P
1 Roofer Foreman	$23.25	$186.00	$39.60	$316.80	$19.82	$33.77
4 Roofers, Composition	21.25	680.00	36.20	1158.40		
2 Roofer Helpers	15.25	244.00	26.00	416.00		
1 Application Equipment		148.40		163.25	2.65	2.92
56 M.H., Daily Totals		$1258.40		$2054.45	$22.47	$36.69

Crew G-2

	Bare Costs Hr.	Bare Costs Daily	Incl. Subs O & P Hr.	Incl. Subs O & P Daily	Cost Per Man-Hour Bare Costs	Cost Per Man-Hour Incl. O&P
1 Plasterer	$22.80	$182.40	$35.00	$280.00	$20.13	$31.10
1 Plasterer Helper	19.05	152.40	29.20	233.60		
1 Building Laborer	18.55	148.40	29.10	232.80		
1 Grouting Equipment		242.80		267.10	10.12	11.13
24 M.H., Daily Totals		$726.00		$1013.50	$30.25	$42.23

Crew G-3

	Bare Costs Hr.	Bare Costs Daily	Incl. Subs O & P Hr.	Incl. Subs O & P Daily	Cost Per Man-Hour Bare Costs	Cost Per Man-Hour Incl. O&P
2 Sheet Metal Workers	$26.65	$426.40	$41.35	$661.60	$22.60	$35.22
2 Building Laborers	18.55	296.80	29.10	465.60		
3 Power Tools		24.60		27.05	.77	.85
32 M.H., Daily Totals		$747.80		$1154.25	$23.37	$36.07

Crew G-4

	Bare Costs Hr.	Bare Costs Daily	Incl. Subs O & P Hr.	Incl. Subs O & P Daily	Cost Per Man-Hour Bare Costs	Cost Per Man-Hour Incl. O&P
1 Labor Foreman (outside)	$20.55	$164.40	$32.25	$258.00	$19.22	$30.15
2 Building Laborers	18.55	296.80	29.10	465.60		
1 Light Truck, 1.5 Ton		153.40		168.75		
1 Air Compr., 160 C.F.M.		90.20		99.20	10.15	11.17
24 M.H., Daily Totals		$704.80		$991.55	$29.37	$41.32

Crew G-5

	Bare Costs Hr.	Bare Costs Daily	Incl. Subs O & P Hr.	Incl. Subs O & P Daily	Cost Per Man-Hour Bare Costs	Cost Per Man-Hour Incl. O&P
1 Roofer Foreman	$23.25	$186.00	$39.60	$316.80	$19.25	$32.80
2 Roofers, Composition	21.25	340.00	36.20	579.20		
2 Roofer Helpers	15.25	244.00	26.00	416.00		
1 Application Equipment		148.40		163.25	3.71	4.08
40 M.H., Daily Totals		$918.40		$1475.25	$22.96	$36.88

Crew H-1

	Bare Costs Hr.	Bare Costs Daily	Incl. Subs O & P Hr.	Incl. Subs O & P Daily	Cost Per Man-Hour Bare Costs	Cost Per Man-Hour Incl. O&P
2 Glaziers	$23.50	$376.00	$35.65	$570.40	$24.75	$41.35
2 Struc. Steel Workers	26.00	416.00	47.05	752.80		
32 M.H., Daily Totals		$792.00		$1323.20	$24.75	$41.35

Crew H-2

	Bare Costs Hr.	Bare Costs Daily	Incl. Subs O & P Hr.	Incl. Subs O & P Daily	Cost Per Man-Hour Bare Costs	Cost Per Man-Hour Incl. O&P
2 Glaziers	$23.50	$376.00	$35.65	$570.40	$21.85	$33.47
1 Building Laborer	18.55	148.40	29.10	232.80		
24 M.H., Daily Totals		$524.40		$803.20	$21.85	$33.47

Crew H-3

	Bare Costs Hr.	Bare Costs Daily	Incl. Subs O & P Hr.	Incl. Subs O & P Daily	Cost Per Man-Hour Bare Costs	Cost Per Man-Hour Incl. O&P
1 Glazier	$23.50	$188.00	$35.65	$285.20	$20.80	$32.00
1 Helper	18.10	144.80	28.35	226.80		
16 M.H., Daily Totals		$332.80		$512.00	$20.80	$32.00

Figure 9.87

Installing Contractor's Overhead & Profit

Below are the **average** installing contractor's percentage mark-ups applied to base labor rates to arrive at typical billing rates.

Column A: Labor rates are based on union wages averaged for 30 major U.S. cities. Base rates including fringe benefits are listed hourly and daily. These figures are the sum of the wage rate and employer-paid fringe benefits such as vacation pay, employer-paid health and welfare costs, pension costs, plus appropriate training and industry advancement funds costs.

Column B: Workers' Compensation rates are the national average of state rates established for each trade.

Column C: Column C lists average fixed overhead figures for all trades. Included are Federal and State Unemployment costs set at 7.3%; Social Security Taxes (FICA) set at 7.65%; Builder's Risk Insurance costs set at 0.34%; and Public Liability costs set at 1.55%. All the percentages except those for Social Security Taxes vary from state to state as well as from company to company.

Columns D and E: Percentages in Columns D and E are based on the presumption that the installing contractor has annual billing of $500,000 and up. Overhead percentages may increase with smaller annual billing. The overhead percentages for any given contractor may vary greatly and depend on a number of factors, such as the contractor's annual volume, engineering and logistical support costs, and staff requirements. The figures for overhead and profit will also vary depending on the type of job, the job location, and the prevailing economic conditions. All factors should be examined very carefully for each job.

Column F: Column F lists the total of Columns B, C, D, and E.

Column G: Column G is Column A (hourly base labor rate) multiplied by the percentage in Column F (O&P percentage).

Column H: Column H is the total of Column A (hourly base labor rate) plus Column G (Total O&P).

Column I: Column I is Column H multiplied by eight hours.

		A		B	C	D	E	F		G	H		I
		Base Rate Incl. Fringes		Workers' Comp. Ins.	Average Fixed Overhead	Over-head	Profit	Total Overhead & Profit			Rate with O & P		
Abbr.	Trade	Hourly	Daily					%	Amount		Hourly		Daily
Skwk	Skilled Workers Average (35 trades)	$24.10	$192.80	17.6%	16.8%	13.0%	10.0%	57.4%	$13.85		$37.95		$303.60
	Helpers Average (5 trades)	18.10	144.80	18.8		11.0		56.6	10.25		28.35		226.80
	Foreman Average, Inside ($.50 over trade)	24.60	196.80	17.6		13.0		57.4	14.10		38.70		309.60
	Foreman Average, Outside ($2.00 over trade)	26.10	208.80	17.6		13.0		57.4	15.00		41.10		328.80
Clab	Common Building Laborers	18.55	148.40	19.2		11.0		57.0	10.55		29.10		232.80
Asbe	Asbestos Workers	26.15	209.20	16.7		16.0		59.5	15.55		41.70		333.60
Boil	Boilermakers	26.80	214.40	10.5		16.0		53.3	14.30		41.10		328.80
Bric	Bricklayers	24.05	192.40	16.8		11.0		54.6	13.15		37.20		297.60
Brhe	Bricklayer Helpers	18.85	150.80	16.8		11.0		54.6	10.30		29.15		233.20
Carp	Carpenters	23.35	186.80	19.2		11.0		57.0	13.30		36.65		293.20
Cefi	Cement Finishers	23.05	184.40	11.4		11.0		49.2	11.35		34.40		275.20
Elec	Electricians	26.70	213.60	7.3		16.0		50.1	13.40		40.10		320.80
Elev	Elevator Constructors	27.25	218.00	8.1		16.0		50.9	13.85		41.10		328.80
Eqhv	Equipment Operators, Crane or Shovel	24.95	199.60	11.7		14.0		52.5	13.10		38.05		304.40
Eqmd	Equipment Operators, Medium Equipment	24.10	192.80	11.7		14.0		52.5	12.65		36.75		294.00
Eqlt	Equipment Operators, Light Equipment	23.10	184.80	11.7		14.0		52.5	12.15		35.25		282.00
Eqol	Equipment Operators, Oilers	20.25	162.00	11.7		14.0		52.5	10.65		30.90		247.20
Eqmm	Equipment Operators, Master Mechanics	25.55	204.40	11.7		14.0		52.5	13.40		38.95		311.60
Glaz	Glaziers	23.50	188.00	13.9		11.0		51.7	12.15		35.65		285.20
Lath	Lathers	23.20	185.60	12.6		11.0		50.4	11.70		34.90		279.20
Marb	Marble Setters	24.15	193.20	16.8		11.0		54.6	13.20		37.35		298.80
Mill	Millwrights	24.35	194.80	11.6		11.0		49.4	12.05		36.40		291.20
Mstz	Mosaic and Terrazzo Workers	23.70	189.60	9.9		11.0		47.7	11.30		35.00		280.00
Pord	Painters, Ordinary	21.75	174.00	15.0		11.0		52.8	11.50		33.25		266.00
Psst	Painters, Structural Steel	22.55	180.40	52.0		11.0		89.8	20.25		42.80		342.40
Pape	Paper Hangers	21.95	175.60	11.8		11.0		52.8	11.60		33.55		268.40
Pile	Pile Drivers	23.50	188.00	29.5		16.0		72.3	17.00		40.50		324.00
Plas	Plasterers	22.80	182.40	15.6		11.0		53.4	12.20		35.00		280.00
Plah	Plasterer Helpers	19.05	152.40	15.6		11.0		53.4	10.15		29.20		233.60
Plum	Plumbers	27.40	219.20	8.7		16.0		51.5	14.10		41.50		332.00
Rodm	Rodmen (Reinforcing)	25.85	206.80	34.4		14.0		75.2	19.45		45.30		362.40
Rofc	Roofers, Composition	21.25	170.00	32.6		11.0		70.4	14.95		36.20		289.60
Rots	Roofers, Tile and Slate	21.30	170.40	32.6		11.0		70.4	15.00		36.30		290.40
Rohe	Roofer Helpers (Composition)	15.25	122.00	32.6		11.0		70.4	10.75		26.00		208.00
Shee	Sheet Metal Workers	26.65	213.20	12.4		16.0		55.2	14.70		41.35		330.80
Spri	Sprinkler Installers	29.00	232.00	9.4		16.0		52.2	15.15		44.15		353.20
Stpi	Steamfitters or Pipefitters	27.45	219.60	8.7		16.0		51.5	14.15		41.60		332.80
Ston	Stone Masons	24.15	193.20	16.8		11.0		54.6	13.20		37.35		298.80
Sswk	Structural Steel Workers	26.00	208.00	40.1		14.0		80.9	21.05		47.05		376.40
Tilf	Tile Layers (Floor)	23.50	188.00	9.9		11.0		47.7	11.20		34.70		277.60
Tilh	Tile Layer Helpers	18.70	149.60	9.9		11.0		47.7	8.90		27.60		220.80
Trlt	Truck Drivers, Light	19.15	153.20	15.2		11.0		53.0	10.15		29.30		234.40
Trhv	Truck Drivers, Heavy	19.45	155.60	15.2		11.0		53.0	10.30		29.75		238.00
Sswl	Welders, Structural Steel	26.00	208.00	40.1		14.0		80.9	21.05		47.05		376.40
Wrck	*Wrecking	18.55	148.40	40.6 ▼		11.0 ▼		78.4	14.55		33.10		264.80

*Not included in Averages.

Figure 9.88

MEANS
DOOR AND FRAME SCHEDULE

PROJECT _____ ARCHITECT _____ PAGE _____ OF _____

LOCATION _____ OWNER _____ DATE _____

BY _____

DOOR NO.	DOOR						FRAME						FIRE RATING		HARDWARE		REMARKS
	SIZE			MAT.	TYPE	GLASS	LOUVER	MAT.	TYPE	DETAILS			LAB	CON	SET NO.	KEYSIDE ROOM NO.	
	W	H	T							JAMB	HEAD	SILL					

Figure 9.89

248

Wood and Plastic Doors

The quantity survey for wood and plastic laminated doors is identical to that of metal doors. Where local work rules permit, pre-hung doors and windows are becoming prevalent in the industry. For these, locksets and interior casings are usually extra. As these may be standard for a number of doors in any particular building, they need only be counted. Remember that exterior pre-hung doors need casings on the interior.

Leave a space in the tabulation on the Quantity Sheet for casings, stops, grounds, and hardware. This can be done either on the same sheet or on separate sheets.

Special Doors

There are many types of specialty doors that may be included – for example, sliding glass doors, overhead garage doors and bulkhead doors. These items should be taken off individually. The estimator should thoroughly examine the plans and specifications to be sure to include all hardware, operating mechanisms, fire ratings, finishes, and any special installation requirements.

Fire Doors

The estimator must pay particular attention to fire doors when performing the quantity takeoff. It is important to determine the exact type of door required. Figure 9.90 is a table describing various types of fire doors. Please note that a ''B'' label door can be one of four types. If the plans or door schedule do not specify exactly which temperature rise is required, the estimator should consult the architect or local building inspector. Many building and fire codes also require that frames and hardware at fire doors be fire-rated and labelled as such. When determining quantities, the estimator must also include any glass (usually wired) or special inserts to be installed in fire doors (or in any doors).

Entrances and Storefronts

Entrances and storefronts are almost all special designs and combinations of unit items to fit a unique situation. The estimator should submit the plans and specifications to a specialty installer for takeoff and pricing.

The general procedure for the installer's takeoff is:

For stationary units:

- Determine height and width of each like unit.
- Determine linear feet of intermediate, horizontal, and vertical members, rounded to next higher foot.
- Determine number of joints.

For entrance units:

- Determine number of joints.
- Determine special frame hardware per unit.
- Determine special door hardware per unit.
- Determine thresholds and closers.

Windows

As with doors, a window schedule should be included in the architectural drawings. Items that merit special attention are:

- Material
- Gauge/Thickness
- Screens

Fire Door				
Classification	Time Rating (as shown on Label)		Temperature Rise (as shown on Label)	Maximum Glass Area
3 Hour fire doors (A) are for use in openings in walls separating buildings or dividing a single building into the areas.	3 Hr.	(A)	30 min. 250°F Max	None
	3 Hr.	(A)	30 Min. 450°F Max	
	3 Hr.	(A)	30 Min. 650°F Max	
	3 Hr.	(A)	*	
1-1/2 Hour fire doors (B) and (D) are for use in openings in 2 Hour enclosures of vertical communication through buildings (stairs, elevators, etc.) or in exterior walls which are subject to severe fire exposure from outside of the building. 1 Hour fire doors (B) are for use in openings in 1 Hour enclosures of vertical communication through buildings (stairs, elevators, etc.)	1-1/2 Hr.	(B)	30 Min. 250°F Max	100 square inches per door
	1-1/2 Hr.	(B)	30 Min. 450°F Max	
	1-1/2 Hr.	(B)	30 Min. 650°F Max	
	1-1/2 Hr.	(B)	*	
	1 Hr.		30 Min. 250°F Max	
	1-1/2 Hr.	(D)	30 Min. 250°F Max	None
	1-1/2 Hr.	(D)	30 Min. 450°F Max	
	1-1/2 Hr.	(D)	30 Min. 650°F Max	
	1-1/2 Hr.	(D)	*	
3/4 Hour fire doors (C) and (E) are for use in openings in corridor and room partitions or in exterior walls which are subject to moderate fire exposure from outside of the building.	3/4 Hr.	(C)	**	1296 square
	3/4 Hr.	(E)	**	720 square inches per light
1/2 Hour fire doors and 1/3 Hour fire doors are for use where smoke control is a primary consideration and are for the protection of openings in partitions between a habitable room and a corridor when the wall has a fire-resistance rating of not more than one hour.	1/2 Hr.		**	No limit
	1/3 Hr.		**	

*The labels do not record any temperature rise limits. This means that the temperature rise on the unexposed face of the door at the end of 30 minutes of test is in excess of 650°F.

**Temperature rise is not recorded.

Figure 9.90

- Glazing (type of glass and setting specifications)
- Trim
- Hardware
- Special installation requirements

When using pre-hung units, be sure to add interior trim and stools.

Finish Hardware and Specialties

The estimator should list the hardware separately or on the door and window schedule. Remember that most pre-hung doors and windows do not include locksets. Some casement, awning, and jalousie windows include cranks and locks.

Be sure to check the specifications for:

- Base Metal
- Finish
- Service (Heavy, Light, Medium)
- Any other special detail

Also check the specifications and code for both handicap and exit requirements. Metal thresholds and astragals are also included in this division. Weatherstripping may or may not be included with pre-hung doors and windows.

Glass and Glazing

Glazing quantities are a function of the material, method, and length to be glazed. Therefore, quantities are measured in united inches or united feet (length + width). Many installers, however, figure all glass and glazing by the square foot. Be sure to read the specifications carefully, as there are many different grades, thicknesses, and other variables in glass.

The types of glass include tempered, plate, safety, insulated, tinted, and various combinations of the above.

Sample Estimate: Division 8

There are two basic ways that doors may be shown on a schedule. The first is to list each type of door (usually accompanied by elevations) that have common characteristics. An example of this method is shown for the sample project in Figure 9.91. Quantities of each type are not shown. The second method is to list each door individually by door number. An example of this method (for another project) is shown in Figure 9.92. In both cases, the information on the schedules provides parameters for takeoff. The specifications will provide much more detailed information that will be required before pricing.

The estimate sheets for Division 8 are shown in Figures 9.93 to 9.95. Note on Sheet 2 of the estimate (Figure 9.94) that costs for hinges are for material only. Labor costs for hinges are usually included in the installation costs for doors. To a carpenter, hanging a door and installing the hinges is one operation. The costs in *Means Building Construction Cost Data* are listed accordingly.

In Figure 9.96 a percentage is to be added to the aluminum entrances for black anodized finish. This percentage is applied to *bare* material cost. Subsequently, 10% for handling is added:

Bare Material Cost: $11.25/S.F.

084-105-1000

For black finish: add 36% $4.05

084-105-1600

O & P (material handling): add 10%   .41

Total incl. O & P for black finish $4.46

Window/curtain walls are almost always custom fabricated for each project. Relatively few manufacturers supply and install these highly specialized systems, so architects will often design curtain walls based on the specifications of a particular system. These reasons dictate that a firm subcontractor quotation is required for estimating curtain walls. For budget purposes, historical costs or those in *Means Building Construction Cost Data* may be used. The telephone quotation (which would be followed by a detailed written quotation) for the sample project is shown in Figure 9.97

Division 9: Finishes

Some buildings today are built "on spec," or speculatively, before they are partially or fully tenanted. In this case, interior work (primarily finishes, and electrical and mechanical distribution) is not usually completed until a tenant is secured. "Interior contractors" are becoming more prevalent in the industry. This type of firm may perform or subcontract all work in Division 9, and may or

Door and Frame Schedule								
	Door			Frame			Hardware Set	Remarks
	Size	Type	Rating	Type	Throat	Rating		
A	6° x 7°	Alum.	—	Alum.	—	—	—	Double Door w/2° x 6° Transom
B	3° x 7°	H.M. 18 ga.	—	H.M. 16 ga.	8"	—	4-1	Insulated
C	3° x 7°	H.M. 18 ga.	"B" 1-1/2 hr.	H.M. 16 ga.	8"	"B" 1-1/2 hr.	4-1	10" x 10" Lites
D	3° x 7°	Oak Veneer	"B" 1-1/2 hr.	H.M. 16 ga.	4-3/4"	"B" 1-1/2 hr.	4-2	10" x 10" Lites
E	3° x 7°	Oak Veneer	"B" 1 hr.	H.M. 16 ga.	4-3/4"	"B" 1 hr.	4-3	
F	3° x 7°	Oak Veneer	"B" 1 hr.	H.M. 16 ga.	4-3/4"	"B" 1 hr.	4-4	
G	3° x 7°	H.M. 18 ga.	"B" 1 hr.	H.M. 16 ga.	8"	"B" 1 hr.	4-5	
H	6° x 7°	H.M. 18 ga.	"B" 1 hr.	H.M. 16 ga.	8"	"B" 1 hr.	4-6	Double Door

Figure 9.91

Door Schedule								
Door	Size	Type	Rating	Frame	Depth	Rating	Hardware Set	Remarks
B01	3^0 x 6^8	Flush Steel 18 ga.	"B" 1-1/2 Hr.	Existing	—	—	HW-1	10" x 10" Vision Lite Shop-Primed
B02	3^0 x 6^8	Flush Steel 18 ga.	"B" 1 Hr.	HMKD 16 ga.	4-7/8"	"B" 1 Hr.	HW-2	Shop-Primed
B03	3^0 x 6^8	Flush Steel 18 ga.	"B" 1 Hr.	H.M. Welded 16 ga.	8"	"B" 1 Hr.	HW-3	w/Masonry Anchors Shop-Primed
B04	3^0 x 6^8	Flush Steel 18 ga.	"B" 1-1/2 Hr.	H.M. Welded 16 ga.	8"	"B" 1-1/2 Hr.	HW-3	w/Masonry Anchors Shop-Primed
B05	3^0 x 6^8	Flush Steel 18 ga.	"B" 1-1/2 Hr.	H.M. Welded 16 ga.	8"	"B" 1-1/2 Hr.	HW-3	w/Masonry Anchors Shop-Primed
B06	3^0 x 6^8	Flush Steel 18 ga.	"B" 1 Hr.	HMKD 16 ga.	4-7/8"	"B" 1 Hr.	HW-2	Shop-Primed
101	3^0 x 6^8	Flush Steel 18 ga.	—	HMKD 16 ga.	4-7/8" —	—	HW-4	Transom Frame Above w/Masonry Anchors
102	3^0 x 6^8	Flush Steel 18 ga.	"B" 1-1/2 Hr.	Existing	—	—	HW-1	Shop-Primed
103	3^0 x 6^8	Flush Oak Face	"B" 1 Hr.	HMKD 16 ga.	4-7/8"	"B" 1 Hr.	HW-5	
104	2^0 x 6^8	Flush Oak Face SC	—	HMKD 16 ga.	4-5/8"	—	HW-6	
105 .	3^0 x 6^8	Flush Oak Face	"B" 1 Hr.	HMKD 16 ga.	4-7/8"	"B" 1 Hr.	HW-5	

Figure 9.92

CONSOLIDATED ESTIMATE

PROJECT: Office Building
LOCATION:
TAKE OFF BY:
CLASSIFICATION: Division 8
ARCHITECT:
QUANTITIES BY:
PRICES BY:
EXTENSIONS BY:
ESTIMATE NO:
DATE: 6/93
CHECKED BY:

DESCRIPTION	SOURCE	QUANT.	UNIT	MATERIAL COST	MATERIAL TOTAL	LABOR COST	LABOR TOTAL	EQUIPMENT COST	EQUIPMENT TOTAL	SUBCONTRACT COST	SUBCONTRACT TOTAL	TOTAL COST	TOTAL TOTAL
Division 8: Doors, Windows & Glass													
H.M.													
Frames 16 ga. 3' x 7'													
8"	081 118 4400	2	Ea.	106.00	212	25.00	50						
8" "B" Label	081 118 6200	10	Ea.	123.00	1230	25.00	250						
4 3/4" "B" Label	081 118 5400	21	Ea.	93.00	1953	25.00	525						
6' x 7'													
8" "B" Label	081 118 6240	1	Ea.	156.00	156	31.00	31						
Metal Doors 18 ga.													
3' x 7'	081 103 1160	2	Ea.	181.00	362	22.00	44						
3' x 7' "B" Label	081 110 0180	12	Ea.	219.00	2628	23.50	282						
10" x 10" lites	081 110 0240	12	Ea.	45.50	546								
Wood Doors - Flush Oak													
3' x 7' "B" 1 1/2 Hr.	082 070 0890	9	Ea.	165.00	1485	31.00	279						
3' x 7' "B" 1 Hr.	082 070 0190	12	Ea.	155.00	1860	31.00	372						
Hardware													
Locksets	087 120 1400	8	Ea.	137.00	1096	18.70	150						
Panic Hardware	087 127 0020	17	Ea.	305.00	5185	37.50	638						
Closers	087 206 2400	35	Ea.	108.00	3780	31.00	1085						
Subtotals					$20,493		$3,705						

Figure 9.93

CONSOLIDATED ESTIMATE

PROJECT: Office Building   CLASSIFICATION: Division 8
LOCATION: ARCHITECT:
TAKE OFF BY: QUANTITIES BY: PRICES BY: EXTENSIONS BY:

ESTIMATE NO:
DATE: 6/93
CHECKED BY:

SOURCE			DESCRIPTION	QUANT.	UNIT	MATERIAL		LABOR		EQUIPMENT		SUBCONTRACT		TOTAL
						COST	TOTAL	COST	TOTAL	COST	TOTAL	COST	TOTAL	
			Division 8: (Cont'd)											
			Hardware (Cont'd)											
087	129	0010	Push / Pull	9	Ea.	49.50	446	15.55	140					
087	118	0010	Kickplates	9	Ea.	16.80	151	12.45	112					
087	116	1400	Hinges	52.5	Ea.	54.00	2835							
			Special Doors											
083	402	0010	Roll Up Grills	200	SF			SUBCONTRACTED				24.50	4900	
083	402	1100	Motorized	2	Ea.							975.00	1950	
			Entrances and Storefronts											
084	105	1000	Front Entrances (2)	240	SF							16.65	3996	
084	105	1600	Add for Black (36% Mat.)	240	SF							4.46	1070	
084	105	1000	Basement Entrance	54	SF							16.65	899	
084	105	1600	Add for Black (36% Mat.)	54	SF							4.46	241	
			Glazing											
088	144	0200	Bathroom Mirrors	135	SF							9.55	1289	
			3 - 3' x 8'											
			3 - 3' x 7'											
			Subtotals				3,432		252				14,346	

Figure 9.94

CONSOLIDATED ESTIMATE

PROJECT: Office Building   CLASSIFICATION: Division 8

LOCATION: ARCHITECT:

ESTIMATE NO:

DATE: 6/93

TAKE OFF BY:		QUANTITIES BY:		PRICES BY:		EXTENSIONS BY:								CHECKED BY:			
DESCRIPTION	SOURCE	QUANT.	UNIT	MATERIAL		LABOR		EQUIPMENT		SUBCONTRACT			
				COST	TOTAL	COST	TOTAL	COST	TOTAL	COST	TOTAL	COST	TOTAL
Division 8: (Cont'd)													
Window/Curtain Wall	TELEPHONE QUOTE (Including Sales Tax)												
	089 206 0050	25060	SF								863818		
Sheet 1 subtotals					$20,493		$3,705						
Sheet 2 subtotals					$3,432		$252				$14,346		
Sheet 3 subtotals											$863,818		
Division 8 Totals					$23,925		$3,957				$878,164		

Figure 9.95

083 | Special Doors

		083 900	Screen & Storm Doors	CREW	DAILY OUTPUT	MAN-HOURS	UNIT	MAT.	LABOR	EQUIP.	TOTAL	TOTAL INCL O&P	
904	1040		3'-0" wide	F-2	14	1.143	Ea.	200	26.50	1.18	227.68	263	904
	1100		For 7'-0" door, add					5%					
	1500		White painted, 6'-8" x 2'-6" wide	F-2	15	1.067		210	25	1.10	236.10	271	
	1520		2'-8" wide	↓	14	1.143		210	26.50	1.18	237.68	274	
	1540		3'-0" wide	↓	14	1.143		220	26.50	1.18	247.68	285	
	1600		For 7'-0" door, add				↓	5%					
	2000		Wood door & screen, see division 082-078										
	2020												

084 | Entrances and Storefronts

		084 100	Aluminum	CREW	DAILY OUTPUT	MAN-HOURS	UNIT	MAT.	LABOR	EQUIP.	TOTAL	TOTAL INCL O&P	
103	0010	BALANCED DOORS Hdwre & frame, alum. & glass, 3' x 7', econ.		2 Sswk	.90	17.778	Ea.	3,000	460		3,460	4,125	103
	0150		Premium	"	.70	22.857	"	4,150	595		4,745	5,650	
105	0010	STOREFRONT SYSTEMS Aluminum frame, clear 3/8" plate glass,											105
	0020		incl. 3' x 7' door with hardware (400 sq. ft. max. wall)										
	0500		Wall height to 12' high, commercial grade	2 Glaz	150	.107	S.F.	11	2.51		13.51	15.90	
	0600		Institutional grade		130	.123		14.30	2.89		17.19	20	
	0700		Monumental grade	↓	115	.139	↓	20.50	3.27		23.77	27.50	
	0900												
	1000		6' x 7' door with hardware, commercial grade	2 Glaz	135	.119	S.F.	11.25	2.79		14.04	16.65	
	1100		Institutional grade		115	.139		15.25	3.27		18.52	21.50	
	1200		Monumental grade	↓	100	.160		21.50	3.76		25.26	29	
	1500		For bronze anodized finish, add					18%					
	1600		For black anodized finish, add					36%					
	1700		For stainless steel framing, add to monumental				↓	75%					
	2000		For individual doors see division 081										
107	0010	SWING DOORS Alum. entrance, 6' x 7', incl. hdwre & oper.		2 Sswk	.70	22.857	Opng.	4,000	595		4,595	5,475	107
	0020		For anodized finish, add				"	200			200	220	

		084 300	Stainless Steel										
301	0010	STAINLESS STEEL AND GLASS Entrance unit, narrow stiles											301
	0020		3' x 7' opening, including hardware, minimum	2 Sswk	1.60	10	Opng.	2,000	260		2,260	2,675	
	0050		Average		1.40	11.429		3,300	297		3,597	4,175	
	0100		Maximum	↓	1.20	13.333		3,800	345		4,145	4,800	
	1000		For solid bronze entrance units, statuary finish, add				↓	60%					
	1100		Without statuary finish, add					45%					
	2000		Balanced doors, 3' x 7', economy	2 Sswk	.90	17.778	Ea.	5,025	460		5,485	6,350	
	2100		Premium	"	.70	22.857	"	8,650	595		9,245	10,600	

		084 600	Automatic Doors										
602	0010	SLIDING ENTRANCE 12' x 7'-6" opng., 5' x 7' door, 2 way traf.,											602
	0020		mat activated, panic pushout, incl. operator & hardware,										
	0030		not including glass or glazing	2 Glaz	.70	22.857	Opng.	5,100	535		5,635	6,425	
604	0010	SLIDING PANEL Mall fronts, aluminum & glass, 15' x 9' high		2 Glaz	1.30	12.308		2,000	289		2,289	2,650	604
	0100		24' x 9' high	↓	.70	22.857		2,900	535		3,435	4,025	
	0200		48' x 9' high, with fixed panels	↓	.90	17.778		5,400	420		5,820	6,575	
	0500		For bronze finish, add				↓	17%					

Figure 9.96

257

MEANS
TELEPHONE QUOTATION

PROJECT **Office Building**	DATE
FIRM QUOTING	TIME
ADDRESS	PHONE ( )
ITEM QUOTED	BY
	RECEIVED BY **EBW**

WORK INCLUDED	AMOUNT OF QUOTATION
Window/Curtain Wall	8 2 6 9 80
25,060 S.F. @ 33.00	
Tax 6% (On Material)	3 6 8 38
DELIVERY TIME **18 Weeks** **TOTAL BID**	8 6 3 8 18

DOES QUOTATION INCLUDE THE FOLLOWING:			If ☐ NO is checked, determine the following:		
STATE & LOCAL SALES TAXES	☒ YES	☐ NO	MATERIAL VALUE		
DELIVERY TO THE JOB SITE	☒ YES	☐ NO	WEIGHT		
COMPLETE INSTALLATION	☒ YES	☐ NO	QUANTITY		
COMPLETE SECTION AS PER PLANS & SPECIFICATIONS	☒ YES	☐ NO	DESCRIBE BELOW		

EXCLUSIONS AND QUALIFICATIONS

ADDENDA ACKNOWLEDGEMENT	TOTAL ADJUSTMENTS	
	ADJUSTED TOTAL BID	

ALTERNATES

ALTERNATE NO. **1- Custom color**	5 8 7 00
ALTERNATE NO. **2- Grid texture**	1 0 2 3 50
ALTERNATE NO.	
ALTERNATE NO.	
ALTERNATE NO.	
ALTERNATE NO.	
ALTERNATE NO.	

Figure 9.97

may not be a builder of structures from the ground up – a conventional general contractor. Because of the skills involved and the quality required, subcontractors usually specialize in only one type of finish. Hence, most finish work is subcontracted.

In today's fireproof and fire-resistant types of construction, some finish materials may be the only combustibles used in a building project. Most building codes (and specifications) require strict adherence to maximum fire, flame spread, and smoke generation characteristics. The estimator must be sure that all materials meet the specified requirements. Materials may have to be treated for fire retardancy at an additional cost.

Lathing and Plastering

The different types of plaster work require varied pricing strategies. Large open areas of continuous walls or ceilings will require considerably less labor per unit of area than small areas or intricate work such as archways, curved walls, cornices and at window returns. Gypsum and metal lath are most often used as sub-bases. However, plaster may be applied directly on masonry, concrete, and in some restoration work, wood. In the latter cases, a bonding agent may be specified.

The number of coats of plaster may also vary. Traditionally, a scratch coat is applied to the substrate. A brown coat is then applied two days later, and the finish, smooth coat seven days after the brown coat. Currently, the systems most often used are two-coat and one-coat (imperial plaster on "blueboard"). Textured surfaces, with and without patterns, may be required. All of these variables in plaster work make it difficult to develop "system" prices. Each project, and even areas within each project, must be examined individually.

The quantity takeoff should proceed in the normal construction sequence – furring (or studs), lath, plaster and accessories. Studs, furring and or ceiling suspension systems, whether wood or steel, should be taken off separately. Responsibility for the installation of these items should be made clear. Depending upon local work practices, lathers may or may not install studs or furring. These materials are usually estimated by the piece or linear foot, and sometimes by the square foot. Lath is traditionally estimated by the square yard for both gypsum and metal lath and is done more recently by the square foot. Usually, a 5% allowance for waste is included. Casing bead, corner bead, and other accessories are measured by the linear foot. An extra foot of surface area should be allowed for each linear foot of corner or stop. Although wood plaster grounds are usually installed by carpenters, they should be measured when taking off the plaster requirements. Plastering is also traditionally measured by the square yard. Deductions for openings vary by preference – from zero deduction to 50% of all openings over 2 feet in width. Some estimators deduct a percentage of the total yardage for openings. The estimator should allow one extra square foot of wall area for each linear foot of inside or outside corner located below the ceiling level. Also, double the areas of small radius work. Quantities are determined by measuring surface areas (walls, ceilings). The estimator must consider both the complexity and the intricacy of the work, and in pricing plaster work, should also consider quality. Basically, there are two quality categories:

1. Ordinary – for commercial purposes, and with waves 1/8" to 3/16" in 10 feet, angles and corners fairly true.

2. First Quality – with variations less than 1/16″ in 10 feet. Labor costs for first quality work are approximately 20% more than that for ordinary plastering.

Drywall

With the advent of light gauge metal framing, tin snips are as important to the carpenter as the circular saw. Metal studs and framing are usually installed and included by the drywall subcontractor. The estimator should make sure that studs (and other framing – whether metal or wood) are not included twice by different subcontractors. In some drywall systems, such as shaftwall, the framing is integral and installed simultaneously with the drywall panels.

Metal studs are manufactured in various widths (1-5/8″, 2-1/2″, 3-5/8″, 4″ and 6″) and in various gauges, or metal thicknesses. They may be used for both load-bearing and non-load-bearing partitions, depending on design criteria and code requirements. Metal framing is particularly useful due to the prohibitive use of structural wood (combustible) materials in new building construction. Metal studs, track and accessories are purchased by the linear foot, and usually stocked in 8′ to 16′ lengths, by 2′ increments. For large orders, metal studs can be purchased in any length up to 20′.

For estimating, light gauge metal framing is taken off by the linear foot or by the square foot of wall area of each type. Different wall types – with different stud widths, stud spacing, or drywall requirements – should each be taken off separately, especially if estimating by the square foot.

Metal studs can be installed very quickly. Depending upon the specification, metal studs may have to be fastened to the track with self-tapping screws, tack welds or clips, or may not have to be prefastened. Each condition will affect the labor costs. Fasteners, such as screws, clips and powder-actuated studs are very expensive, though labor-saving. These costs must be included.

Drywall may be purchased in various thicknesses – 1/4″ to 1″ – and in various sizes – 2′ x 8′ to 4′ x 20′. Different types include standard, fire-resistant, water-resistant, blueboard, coreboard and pre-finished. There are many variables and possible combinations of sizes and types. While the installation cost of 5/8″ standard drywall may be the same as that of 5/8″ fire-resistant drywall, the two types (and all other types) should be taken off separately. The takeoff will be used for purchasing, and material costs will vary.

Because drywall is used in such large quantities, current, local prices should always be checked. A variation of a few cents per square foot can become many thousands of dollars over a whole project.

Fire-resistant drywall provides an excellent design advantage in creating relatively lightweight, easy to install firewalls (as opposed to masonry walls). As with any type of drywall partition, the variations are numerous. The estimator must be very careful to take off the appropriate firewalls exactly as specified. (Even more important, the contractor must *build* the firewalls exactly as specified. Liabilities can be great.) For example, a metal stud partition with two layers of 1/2″ fire-resistant drywall on each side may constitute a two-hour partition (when all other requirements such as staggered joints, taping, sealing openings, etc. are met). If a one-hour partition is called for, the estimator cannot assume that one layer of 1/2″ fire-resistant drywall on each side of a metal stud partition will suffice. Alone, it does not. When left to choose the appropriate assembly (given the rating required), the estimator must be sure that the system has been tested and *approved* for use — by Underwriters Laboratory as well as local building and fire codes and responsible authorities.

In all cases, the drywall (and studs) for firewalls must extend completely from the deck below to the underside of the deck above, covering the area above and around any and all obstructions. All penetrations must be protected.

In the past, structural members – such as beams or columns – to be fireproofed had to be "wrapped" with a specified number of layers of fire-resistant drywall – a very labor-intensive and expensive task. With the advent of spray-on fireproofing, structural members can be much more easily protected. This type of work is usually performed by a specialty subcontractor. Takeoff and pricing are done by square foot of surface area.

When walls are specified for minimal sound transfer, the same continuous, unbroken construction is required. Sound-proofing specifications may include additional accessories and related work. Resilient channels attached to studs, mineral fiber batts and staggered studs may all be used. In order to develop high noise reduction coefficients, double stud walls may be required with sheet lead between double or triple layers of drywall. (Sheet lead may also be required at X-ray installations.) Caulking is required at all joints and seams. All openings must be specially framed with double, "broken" door and window jambs.

Shaftwall, developed for a distinct design advantage, is another drywall assembly which should be estimated separately. Firewalls require protection from both sides of the partition, and hence drywall installation from both sides. Shaftwall, used at vertical openings (elevators, utility chases), can be installed completely from one side. Special track, studs (C-H or double E type) and drywall (usually 1" thick and 2' wide coreboard) are used and should be priced separately from other drywall partition components.

Because of the size and weight of drywall, costs for material handling and loading should be included. Using larger sheets (manufactured up to 4' x 20') may require less taping and finishing, but these sheets may each weigh well in excess of 100 pounds and are awkward to handle. The weight of drywall must also be considered (and distributed) when loading a job on elevated slabs, so that allowable floor loads are not exceeded. All material handling involves costs that must be included.

As with plaster work, open spans of drywall should be priced differently from small, intricate areas that require much cutting and piecing. Similarly, areas with many corners or curves will require higher finishing costs than open walls or ceilings. Corners, both inside and outside, should be estimated by the linear foot, in addition to the square feet of surface area.

Although difficult because of variations, the estimator may be able to develop historical systems or assemblies prices for metal studs, drywall, taping and finishing. When using systems, whether complete or partial, the estimator must be sure that the system, as specified, is exactly the same as the system for which the costs are developed. For example, a cost is developed for 5/8" fire-resistant drywall, taped and finished. The project specifications require a firewall with two layers of the 5/8" drywall on each side of the studs. It could be easy to use the "system" cost for each layer, when only one of the two layers is to be taped and finished. The more detailed the breakdown and delineation, the less chance for error.

Tile and Terrazzo

Tile, terrazo and other hard surface floor and wall finishes are most often estimated by the square foot. Linear features such as bullnose and cove base are taken off in linear feet. Small areas and individually laid tile patterns should be separately estimated, apart from large, open expanses, and installations of pre-attached tile sheets which are taken off by the square foot.

In addition to the considerable variation in material prices, the installation method of tile will also have a significant impact on the total cost. Two basic methods are used — "thin" set, with an epoxy-type adhesive, and "mud" set, using a fine-grained mortar. Mud set is approximately 30% more expensive than thin set, but provides a harder and more durable treatment. Hard, cement-like backer board can be used as a base for thin set tile. The more commonly used types of ceramic wall tile are now manufactured in pre-grouted sheets which require less labor expense.

Currently, most terrazo installed is in the form of manufactured tiles. However, the traditional method of pouring, grinding and rubbing the terrazzo over a concrete base slab is still used. In such cases, an experienced subcontractor should estimate this very labor-intensive work. Accessories, such as embedded decorative strips and grounds, must be included.

In all tile work, surface preparation may be the responsibility of the installer. Especially in renovation, this preparation may be very involved and costly.

Acoustical Treatment

Acoustical treatments may involve sound-absorbing panels on walls, sheet lead within walls or floors, suspended or "dropped" ceilings, or sound attenuation blankets in wall cavities. While sound deadening is primary, it does not have to be the only function.

Most applications of acoustical treatments are for ceilings, whether suspended or attached to the structure above, or concealed spline or lay-in. In most cases, acoustical ceilings are estimated by the square foot. Suspension systems or furring can be estimated by linear feet of pieces or by square feet of surface area. The installation and leveling of suspension grids can be very labor-intensive. The estimator must be sure that adequate points of support are available, spaced often enough to meet specified requirements. If not, attachments for support, such as anchors, toggle bolts, and carrier channels, will be required and the costs included. Invariably, a duct or other obstruction runs just above a main support "T", or runner. Design modification of the grid (or duct) system may be necessary, and the architect should be notified.

In small areas and rooms, leveling a suspension grid may be relatively easy. In large open areas, a laser may be necessary for leveling. Especially for large open areas, the cost of installing a ceiling (whether acoustical or drywall) will depend on how clear and clean the floor space is. Most ceilings are installed from rolling platforms. If the workers are only able to work in certain areas, or if the platform must be hand-lifted over material and debris, installation costs will increase significantly. When developing the preliminary schedule, good planning will help to ensure minimum installation costs for ceilings. Costs for equipment, such as lasers and rolling scaffolding, should be listed separately. For very high installations, scissors or telescoping lifts may be required.

Tile for acoustical ceilings may consist of mineral fiber, wood fiber, fiberglass or metal, and might be cloth-covered, colored, textured and/or patterned. There is little waste when installing grid systems (usually less than 5%), because pieces can be butted and joined. Waste for tile, however, can be as low as 5% for large open areas, to as high as 30%-40% for small areas and rooms. Waste for tile may depend on grid layout as well as room dimensions. Figure 9.98 demonstrates that for the same size room, the layout of a typical 2' x 4' grid has a significant effect on generated waste of ceiling tile. Since most textures and patterns on ceiling tile are aligned in one direction, pieces cannot be turned 90 degrees (to the specified alignment) to try to reduce waste.

Certain tile types, such as tegular (recessed), require extra labor for cutting and fabrication at edge moldings. Soffits, facias and "boxouts" should be estimated separately due to extra labor, material waste and special attachment techniques. Costs should also be added for unusually high numbers of tiles to be specially cut for items such as sprinkler heads, diffusers or telepoles.

While the weight of ceiling tile is not the primary consideration that it is with drywall, some material handling and storage costs will still be incurred and must be included. Acoustical tile is very bulky and cumbersome, as well as fragile, and must be protected from damage before installation.

Flooring

Finish floor coverings include carpet, resilient sheet goods and tile, rubber and vinyl stair treads and risers, and wood finish flooring. When estimating all types of finish flooring, the condition and required preparation of the subfloor must be considered.

Resilient Flooring: Resilient materials are vinyl, rubber and linoleum products in the form of tiles, sheet goods and base. The most commonly used is vinyl composition tile – mistakenly referred to as vinyl asbestos tile. Resilient flooring is taken off and priced by the square foot. Most resilient flooring is directionally patterned. The construction documents will most likely specify a particular laying pattern. Because of the size of resilient tiles (12″ x 12″ or 9″ x 9″), waste is not necessarily dependent upon room configuration. However, depending upon seam requirements, sheet goods may involve a great deal of waste. Each application should be viewed individually. Cove base and straight base are measured by the linear foot. If the specifications are not clear, the estimator must determine whether the base is to be wrapped around corners, or if premolded corners are required.

Due to the thinness and flexibility of resilient goods, defects in the subfloor easily "telegraph" through the material. Consequently, the subfloor material and the quality of surface preparation are very important. Subcontractors will often make contracts conditional on a smooth, level subfloor. Surface preparation, which can involve chipping and patching, grinding or washing, is often an "extra." Costs should be included to account for some surface preparation which will invariably be required. This is especially true in renovation where, in extreme cases, the floor may have to be leveled with a complete application of special lightweight leveling concrete.

Carpet: There are hundreds of carpeting manufacturers, each with hundreds of products. The specifications for a project will usually include a generic description of the carpeting and a recommended manufacturer. The description will include items such as pile type and weight, backing requirements, and smoke and flame characteristics. Usually this description is so generically specific that even if an approved equal is allowed, no such equal exists. It is best to estimate the carpeting exactly as specified.

Carpeting and padding is manufactured most commonly in 12′ widths (sometimes 9′ or 15′), and is taken off by the square yard. Costs for installation will vary depending upon the specified method – direct cement (without pad) or stretched (with pad and perimeter tack strips).

The specifications may also require and define the location of seams. Often, butt seams – roll end to roll end – are not allowed. Where seams do occur, costs

Reflected Ceiling Plans

Room Area = 219 S.F.

	Tiles Required	Waste
A	30	10%
B	35	28%
C	31	13%
D	36	32%

Figure 9.98

for sewing (by hand) and gluing will differ. When a carpeting subcontractor estimates a job, the whole job is drawn on a floor plan based upon the seaming requirements to determine the quantity of carpet to be purchased. Depending upon the requirements and the configuration of the installation, waste can be high.

Where carpet base is specified, costs must be included for binding, priced by the linear foot. Carpet base may or may not be the same material used on the floor. The specifications should be carefully checked. Carpet tile systems have been developed for ease of repairing damaged areas and for use with under-carpet power and telecommunication systems. Tiles are available in various sizes from 18″ to 36″ square and are normally taken off and priced by the square foot.

All resilient materials and direct cement carpeting are installed with adhesive. If adhesive materials are estimated separately, costs are per gallon. Coverage depends upon the flooring material and the type of adhesive. Prices developed or quoted for direct glue-down flooring usually include the adhesive.

Wood Flooring: Everyone loves to see a wood floor specified and installed, except for the estimator who has not included all requirements. Wood flooring can be deceptively expensive.

Wood flooring is available in strip, parquet, or block configuration. All types are estimated by the square foot. There are three basic grades of wood flooring: first, second, and third, plus combination grades of "second and better" and "third and better". There are also color grades and special grade labels for different kinds of lumber, such as oak, maple, walnut, pecan, or beech. The estimator should be acquainted with these classifications and the associated price differences. The laying pattern will influence both labor costs and material waste.

Strip wood floors may be used for applications from residences to gymnasiums and large sports complexes. While the wood may be the same, installation methods vary considerably. For residential work, the strips are nailed to wood joist/subfloor systems. For commercial applications, installation is usually over concrete. The strips may be nailed to wood sleepers or attached to steel channels with steel clips. In most cases, resilient materials, pads and/or sheets are used between wood and concrete in addition to a continuous vapor barrier. Wood expands and contracts considerably with variations in temperature and humidity. Precautions must, therefore, be taken. Since expansion joints are not aesthetically pleasing within wood floors, gaps are used at the perimeter. Costs for hiding this gap, with a wood base or metal angles, must be included. Since large, commercial wood floors are usually installed by a specialty subcontractor, the estimator must be sure that all associated work is taken into account.

Parquet floors are currently made of prefinished, manufactured tiles, installed with adhesive. Durable synthetic finishes make this type of wood flooring suitable for commercial uses and public spaces.

Wood end grain block flooring is still commonly used for industrial applications. Set in, and filled with epoxy or asphalt, this type of flooring is installed by specialty subcontractors using specialized equipment. The estimator must check with all such subcontractors who are familiar with methods and materials to ensure that all requirements are met, and the costs included. For all types of finish flooring, surface treatments may be required after installation. For wood flooring (unless prefinished), sanding and finishing will be necessary. If the wood is prefinished, as with most resilient goods, waxing and buffing is an additional expense that must be included. Carpeting should be installed after *all* other work is completed. This is rarely the case, however, and invariably, the brand new carpet gets dirty quickly. A minimum of vacuuming and spot cleaning should be anticipated. In extreme cases, steam cleaning of the entire carpet may be necessary. Stretched carpet may require restretching after steam cleaning. The estimator must try to anticipate such items, all of which involve extra cost.

In many projects, and most often with flooring, the architect or designer may not select the final finish material until the project is underway. In such cases, a specified allowance is usually carried in the estimate. The allowance is most often for material *only*, and is specified per unit (square foot for resilient and wood flooring, square yard for carpet), but must be carried in the estimate as a lump sum. The estimator must still determine quantities of materials and installation costs.

Painting: As with most finishes, architects and designers will be particularly insistent about adherence to specifications and specified colors for painting. This is not an area in which to cut corners – in estimating, or performance of the work. The specifications usually will clearly define acceptable materials, manufacturers, preparation and application methods for *each* different type of surface to be painted. Samples may be required for approval by the architect or owner. Quarts of various paint colors may be required before the final color decision is made.

When estimating painting, the materials and methods are included in the specifications. Areas to be painted are usually defined on a Room Finish Schedule and taken off from the plans and elevations in square feet of surface area. Odd-shaped and special items can be converted to an equivalent wall area. The following table includes suggested conversion factors for various types of surfaces:

Balustrades:		1 Side x 4
Blinds:	Plain	Actual area x 2
	Slotted	Actual area x 4
Cabinets:	Including interior	Front area x 5
Downspouts and Gutters:		Actual area x 2
Drop Siding:		Actual area x 1.1
Cornices:	1 Story	Actual area x 2
	2 Story	Actual area x 3
	1 Story Ornamental	Actual area x 4
	2 Story Ornamental	Actual area x 6
Doors:	Flush	Actual area x 1.5
	Two Panel	Actual area x 1.75
	Four Panel	Actual area x 2.0
	Six Panel	Actual area x 2.25
Door Trim:		LF x 0.5
Fences:	Chain Link	1 side x 3 for both sides
	Picket	1 side x 4 for both sides
Gratings:		1 side x 0.66
Grilles:	Plain	1 side x 2.0
	Lattice	Actual area x 2.0
Moldings:	Under 12" Wide	1 SF per LF
Open Trusses:		Length x Depth x 2.5
Pipes:	Up to 4"	1 SF per LF
	4" to 8"	2 SF per LF
	8" to 12"	3 SF per LF

		12" to 16"	4 SF per LF
Pipes (cont.):			Hangers Extra
Radiators:			Face area x 7
Sanding and Puttying:		Quality Work	Actual area x 2
		Average Work	Actual area x 0.5
		Industrial	Actual area x 0.25
Shingle Siding:			Actual area x 1.5
Stairs:			No. of risers x 8 widths
Tie Rods:			2 SF per LF
Wainscoting, Paneled:			Actual area x 2
Walls and Ceilings:			Length x Width, no deducts for less than 100 SF
Window Sash:			1 LF of part = 1 SF

While the above factors are used to determine quantities of equivalent wall surface areas, the appropriate, specified application method must be used for pricing.

The choice of application method will have a significant effect on the final cost. Spraying is very fast, but the costs of masking the areas to be protected may offset the savings. Oversized rollers may be used to increase production. Brushwork, on the other hand, is labor-intensive. The specifications often include (or restrict) certain application methods. Typical coverage and man-hour rates are shown in Figure 9.99 for different application methods.

R099-220   Painting

Item	Coat	One Gallon Covers			In 8 Hours Man Covers			Man-Hours per 100 S.F.		
		Brush	Roller	Spray	Brush	Roller	Spray	Brush	Roller	Spray
Paint wood siding	prime	275 S.F.	250 S.F.	325 S.F.	1150 S.F.	1400 S.F.	4000 S.F.	.695	.571	.200
	others	300	275	325	1600	2200	4000	.500	.364	.200
Paint exterior trim	prime	450	–	–	650	–	–	1.230	–	–
	1st	525	–	–	700	–	–	1.143	–	–
	2nd	575	–	–	750	–	–	1.067	–	–
Paint shingle siding	prime	300	285	335	1050	1700	2800	.763	.470	.286
	others	400	375	425	1200	2000	3200	.667	.400	.250
Stain shingle siding	1st	200	190	220	1200	1400	3200	.667	.571	.250
	2nd	300	275	325	1300	1700	4000	.615	.471	.200
Paint brick masonry	prime	200	150	175	850	1700	4000	.941	.471	.200
	1st	300	250	320	1200	2200	4400	.364	.364	.182
	2nd	375	340	400	1300	2400	4400	.615	.333	.182
Paint interior plaster or drywall	prime	450	425	550	1600	2500	4000	.500	.320	.200
	others	500	475	550	1400	3000	4000	.571	.267	.200
Paint interior doors and windows	prime	450	–	–	1300	–	–	.333	–	–
	1st	475	–	–	1150	–	–	.696	–	–
	2nd	500	–	–	1000	–	–	.800	–	–

Figure 9.99

Depending upon local work rules, some unions require that painters be paid higher rates for spraying, and even for roller work. In some cases, paint is applied to walls and surfaces with a brush and then rolled for the desired finish. Higher rates also tend to apply for structural steel painting, for high work, and for the application of fire-retardant paints. The estimator should determine which restrictions may be encountered.

The surface preparation of walls, as in the case of floor finishes, may represent a significant cost. Invariably, the painter claims that the walls were not finished properly, and the general contractor contends that a certain amount of wall prep is included in the painting subcontract. This conflict should be resolved at the estimate stage. Also, caulking at door frames and windows – the responsibility similarly argued – must be included.

Wall Covering

Wall coverings are usually estimated by the number of rolls. Single rolls contain approximately 36 S.F.; this figure forms the basis for determining the number of rolls required. Wall coverings are, however, usually sold in double or triple roll bolts.

The area to be covered is measured, length times height of wall above baseboards, in order to get the square footage of each wall. This figure is divided by 30 to obtain the number of single rolls, allowing 6 S.F. of waste per roll. Deduct one roll for every two door openings. Two pounds of dry paste makes about three gallons of ready-to-use adhesive and hangs about 36 single rolls of light to medium weight paper, or 14 rolls of heavy weight paper. Application labor costs vary with the quality, pattern, and type of joint required.

With vinyls and grass cloths requiring no pattern match, a waste allowance of 10% is normal – approximately 3.5 S.F. per roll. Wall coverings that require a pattern match may have about 25% – 30% waste, or 9 – 11 S.F. per roll. Waste can run as high as 50% – 60% on wall coverings with a large, bold, or intricate pattern repeat.

Commercial wall coverings are available in widths from 21" to 54", and in lengths from 5-1/3 yards (single roll) to 100 yard bolts. To determine quantities, independent of width, measure the linear (perimeter) footage of walls to be covered. Divide the linear footage by the width of the goods to determine the number of "strips" or drops. Then determine the number of strips per bolt or package by dividing the length per bolt by the ceiling height.

$$\frac{\text{Linear Footage of Walls}}{\text{Width of Goods}} = \text{No. of Strips}$$

$$\frac{\text{Length of Bolt Roll}}{\text{Ceiling Height}} = \frac{\text{No. of Strips (whole no.)}}{\text{Bolt (roll)}}$$

Finally, divide the quantity of strips required by the number of strips per bolt (roll) in order to determine the required amount of material. Use the same waste allowance as above.

Surface preparation costs for wall covering must also be included. If the wall covering is to be installed over new surfaces, the walls must be treated with a wall sizing, shellac or primer coat for proper adhesion. For existing surfaces, scraping, patching and sanding may be necessary. Requirements will be included in the specifications.

Sample Estimate: Division 9

Most of the finishes for the sample project involve large quantities in wide open areas. For an interior space broken up into many rooms or suites, the estimate would be much more involved, and a detailed Room Finish Schedule should be provided. The estimate sheets for the sample project are shown in Figures 9.100 to 9.103. On all the estimate sheets for the project, items are entered on every other line. Many more sheets are used this way, but paper is cheap. Invariably, omitted items must be inserted at the last minute and sheet subtotals and division totals will be recalculated as a result. If the sheets are concise, neat and organized, recalculation can be easy, and will involve less chance of error.

Particularly when estimating drywall, the same dimensions can be used to calculate the quantities of different items – in this case, drywall, metal studs, and accessories. When an opening (to be finished with drywall) is deducted from the drywall surface area, perimeter dimensions are used to calculate corner bead. Similarly, at joints with items such as windows, the same dimensions are used for J-bead. The quantity sheet for drywall and associated items is shown in Figure 9.104. Types, sizes and different applications of drywall and studs are listed (and priced) separately. The square foot quantities of studs and drywall can be used for comparison to check for possible errors. When such a method is used, the estimator must be aware of those partitions which receive drywall only on one side, as opposed to both sides, and those with more than one layer. A comparison for the sample project is performed as follows:

Framing	Stud Area	No. of Sides	No. of Layers	Drywall Area
6"	300 S.F.	2	1	600 S.F.
3-5/8"	3,560 S.F.	2	1	7,120 S.F.
3-5/8"	10,104 S.F.	1	1	10,104 S.F.
1-5/8"	5,640 S.F.	1	2	11,280 S.F.
1-5/8"	1,704 S.F.	1	1	1,704 S.F.
Furring	4,200 S.F.	1	1	4,200 S.F.
	25,508 S.F.			35,008 S.F.

$$25,508 \text{ S.F.} = 35,008 - (300 + 3560 + 5640) = 25,508 \text{ S.F.}$$

Note that furring is included in the above cross-check calculations as square feet. The estimator must always be aware of units during *any* calculations. When deductions are made from the drywall totals for two-side application and double layers, the drywall and stud quantities should equate.

For the ceiling grid, because of the large, open areas, no allowance for waste is included. Note, however, that the dimensions used are for the exterior of the building (210' x 90' x 3 floors). This includes a small overage. For purchasing purposes, all ceiling perimeter dimensions would be measured separately for edge moldings. A 5% allowance is added to the ceiling tile. The large quantity of light fixtures must be considered and is deducted from the total. Deductions for light fixtures should be based on experience. Carpeting quantities are also derived from the building perimeter measurements, with appropriate deductions for the building core.

Division 10: Specialties

Division 10 includes prefinished, manufactured items that are usually installed at the end of a project when other finish work is complete. Following is a partial list of items that may be included in Division 10:

- Bathroom accessories
- Bulletin and chalkboards
- Flagpoles

CONSOLIDATED ESTIMATE

PROJECT: Office Building
LOCATION:
TAKE OFF BY:

CLASSIFICATION: Division 9
ARCHITECT:
QUANTITIES BY:
PRICES BY:
EXTENSIONS BY:

DESCRIPTION	SOURCE	QUANT.	UNIT	MATERIAL		LABOR		EQUIPMENT		SUBCONTRACT		TOTAL	
				COST	TOTAL	COST	TOTAL	COST	TOTAL	COST	TOTAL	COST	TOTAL
Division 9: Finishes													
Framing: Metal Studs													
6" - 25 ga.	092 612 2500	300	SF	0.45	135	0.46	138						
3 5/8" - 25 ga.	092 612 2300	13664	SF	0.30	4099	0.43	5876						
1 5/8" - 25 ga.	092 612 2000	7344	SF	0.23	1689	0.42	3084						
Accessories													
7/8" Furring	092 804 0900	31.5	CLF	15.50	488	70.00	2205						
J - Bead	092 804 1120	34.1	CLF	14.50	494	63.50	2165						
Corner Bead	092 804 0300	58.4	CLF	8.25	482	46.50	2716						
Drywall													
5/8" F.R. @ Columns	092 608 4050	5640	SF	0.54	3046	1.25	7050						
5/8" F.R. @ Core	092 608 2150	7720	SF	0.26	2007	0.39	3011						
5/8" Standard	092 608 2050	16008	SF	0.24	3842	0.39	6243						
Shaftwall: @ Elevator	092 624 0300	2040	SF	1.55	3162	2.08	4243						
Subtotals					$19,445		$36,731						

Figure 9.100

CONSOLIDATED ESTIMATE

PROJECT: Office Building   CLASSIFICATION: Division 9   SHEET NO. 2 of 4

LOCATION: ARCHITECT: ESTIMATE NO:

TAKE OFF BY: QUANTITIES BY: PRICES BY: EXTENSIONS BY: DATE: 6/93   CHECKED BY:

DESCRIPTION	SOURCE	QUANT.	UNIT	MATERIAL COST	MATERIAL TOTAL	LABOR COST	LABOR TOTAL	EQUIPMENT COST	EQUIPMENT TOTAL	SUBCONTRACT COST	SUBCONTRACT TOTAL	COST	TOTAL
Division 9: (Cont'd)													
Fireproofing: @ Beams	072 554 0400	40500	SF							1.05	42525		
Total Fireproofing											(42525)		
Ceramic Tile:													
Walls	093 102 5400	1584	SF							4.80	7603		
Bull Nose	093 102 2500	396	LF							6.70	2653		
Cove Base	093 102 0700	396	LF							6.65	2633		
Floors	093 102 3300	960	SF							6.50	6240		
Total Ceramic Tile											(19130)		
Acoustical Ceilings:													
Grid	091 304 0050	56700	SF	0.35	19845	0.23	13041						
Tile	095 104 3740	53735	SF	1.20	64482	0.32	17195						
Total Ceiling					(84327)		(30236)						

Figure 9.101

271

CONSOLIDATED ESTIMATE

PROJECT: Office Building
LOCATION:
TAKE OFF BY:
CLASSIFICATION: Division 9
ARCHITECT:
QUANTITIES BY:
PRICES BY:
EXTENSIONS BY:

ESTIMATE NO:
DATE: 6/93
CHECKED BY:

DESCRIPTION	SOURCE			QUANT.	UNIT	MATERIAL		LABOR		EQUIPMENT		SUBCONTRACT		TOTAL	
						COST	TOTAL	COST	TOTAL	COST	TOTAL	COST	TOTAL	COST	TOTAL
Division 9: (Cont'd)															
Flooring:															
Carpet	096	852	3200	5850	SY							27.50	160875		
Cove Base	096	601	1150	2530	LF							1.45	3669		
Parquet @ Lobby & Elevators	095	604	6500	1800	SF							5.95	10710		
Total Flooring													175254		
Painting:															
Walls (Drywall)	099	224	0840	27784	SF							0.33	9169		
Wood Doors	099	216	1800	21	Ea.							33.00	693		
Metal Doors (Primed)	099	216	1000	14	Ea.							18.00	252		
Block Walls	099	224	2880	9846	SF							0.35	3446		
Total Painting													13560		

Figure 9.102

CONSOLIDATED ESTIMATE

PROJECT: Office Building   CLASSIFICATION: Division 9

LOCATION: ARCHITECT:

TAKE OFF BY: QUANTITIES BY: PRICES BY: EXTENSIONS BY:

ESTIMATE NO:

DATE: 6/93

CHECKED BY:

DESCRIPTION	SOURCE	QUANT.	UNIT	MATERIAL		LABOR		EQUIPMENT		SUBCONTRACT		TOTAL	
				COST	TOTAL	COST	TOTAL	COST	TOTAL	COST	TOTAL	COST	TOTAL
Division 9: (Cont'd)													
Drywall & Framing	Sheet 1				$19,445		$36,731						
Fireproofing	Sheet 2										$42,525		
Ceramic Tile	Sheet 2										$19,130		
Acoustical Ceiling	Sheet 2				$84,327		$30,236						
Flooring	Sheet 3										$175,254		
Painting	Sheet 3										$13,560		
Division 9 Totals					$103,772		$66,967				$250,468		

Figure 9.103

QUANTITY SHEET

PROJECT: Office Building
LOCATION:
TAKE OFF BY:

Division 9
ARCHITECT:
EXTENSIONS BY:

ESTIMATE NO:
DATE:
CHECKED BY:

DESCRIPTION	NO.	DIMENSIONS L	W	H	Studs	UNIT	5/8" Std. Drywall	UNIT	5/8" F.R. Drywall	UNIT	Acc.	UNIT
Partitions - 25 ga.												
Bath Chase 6"	3	10'		10'	300	SF			600	SF		
Interior 3 5/8"												
Lobby ,	1	86'		10'	860	SF			1720	SF		
Core	3	90'		10'	2700	SF			5400	SF		
Corner Bead	27										270	LF
Furring 16" O.C.	3	140'		10'			4200	SF			3151	LF
Exterior 3 5/8"	3	560'		10'	10104	SF	10104	SF				
Deduct Windows	(	496'		4'-5'	} 10104	SF						
Corner Bead	6 / 96	496' / 4.5'									3408	LF
J - Bead	6 / 96	496' / 4.5'									3408	LF
Window Returns		3408'	0.5'		1704	SF	1704	SF				
1 5/8" Studs	3	188'		10'	5640	SF						
Columns 1 5/8"												
Unfinished									5640	SF		
Taped									5640	SF		
Corner Bead	3	72'		10'							2160	LF
Quantity Summary												
Studs: 6"					300	SF						
3 5/8"					13664	SF						
1 5/8"					7344	SF	16008	SF				
Drywall: 5/8" F.R.									13360	SF		
Unfinished: 5/8" F.R.									5640	SF		
5/8" Std.												
Corner Bead											5838	LF
J - Bead											3408	LF
Furring											3151	LF

Figure 9.104

274

- Lockers
- Mailboxes
- Partitions
  - Toilet
  - Office
  - Accordion
  - Woven Wire

Items as listed in *Means Building Construction Cost Data* provide a good checklist to help ensure that all appropriate work is included. The prices shown in *Means Building Construction Cost Data* are national averages and do not reflect any particular manufacturer's product or prices.

A thorough review of the drawings and specifications is necessary to be sure that all items are accounted for. The estimator should list each type of item and the recommended manufacturers. Often, no substitutes are allowed. Each type of item is then counted. Takeoff units will vary with different items.

Quotations and bids should be solicited from local suppliers and specialty subcontractors. The estimator must include all appropriate shipping and handling costs. If no historical costs for installation are available, then costs for labor may be taken from cost data books, such as *Means Building Construction Cost Data*, or estimated from scratch. When a specialty item is particularly large, job-site equipment may be needed for placement or installation.

The estimator should pay particular attention to the construction requirements which are necessary to Division 10 work but are included in other divisions. Almost all items in Division 10 require some form of base or backing for proper installation. These requirements may or may not be included in the construction documents, but are usually listed in the manufacturers' recommendations for installation. It is often stated in the General Conditions of the specifications that "the contractor shall install all products according to manufacturers' recommendations" – another catch-all phrase that places responsibility on the contractor (and estimator).

Examples of such items are concrete bases for lockers and supports for ceiling-hung toilet partitions. Concrete bases for lockers cannot be installed until partitions are erected, or at least accurately laid out. The specific locker must be approved by the architect before the exact size of the base is determined. Installation of the concrete often requires a small truckload (hence an extra charge for a minimum order) and hand placement with wheelbarrow and shovel. Similarly, supports for toilet partitions cannot be installed until precise locations are determined. Such supports can be small steel beams, or large angles that must be welded in place. For a room-dividing accordion, folding or telescoping partitions, supports must be strong enough so that no deflection is allowed.

Preparation costs prior to the installation of specialty items may, in some cases, exceed the costs of the items themselves. The estimator must visualize the installation in order to anticipate all of the work and costs.

Sample Estimate: Division 10

The estimate sheet for Division 10 is shown in Figure 9.105. The takeoff and pricing involve a simple counting process. If not included on a schedule, these items should be counted a few times to ensure that all items are included, and in the proper quantities. When estimating for Division 10, it is important to be sure that all backing, supports and blocking are included, usually elsewhere in the estimate. Accessories attached only to drywall with toggles or plastic anchors will work loose very quickly. Installing backing after a wall is finished is very expensive.

There are a few specific manufacturers that are usually specified for bathroom accessories and toilet partitions. A good estimator will find that there are many less expensive but "equal" products (almost exact copies) on the market, and these may be approved by the architects. Smart shopping for such costly items can help to lower the bid.

Division 11: Equipment

Equipment includes permanent fixtures that cause the space to function as designed – i.e., book stacks for libraries, vaults for banks, etc. Often leaving this division until the end of the estimate, the estimator can use the average costs shown in *Means Building Construction Cost Data* for budget pricing purposes. *Means Building Construction Cost Data* can also serve as a checklist to ensure that items have not been omitted.

The construction documents may specify that the owner will purchase equipment directly, and that the contractor will install it. In such cases, the daily output shown in the cost book can be used to complete the labor portion of the estimate. If equipment is furnished by the owner, it is common practice to add about 10% of the materials cost into the estimate. This procedure protects the contractor from the risks, and covers handling costs associated with the materials. Often the contractor is responsible for receipt, storage and protection of these owner-purchased items until they are installed.

As with specialties in Division 10, equipment must also be evaluated to determine what is required from other divisions for its successful installation. Some possibilities are:

- Concrete
- Miscellaneous Metals
- Rough Carpentry
- Mechanical Coordination
- Electrical Requirements

Division 11 includes equipment that can be packaged and delivered complete or partially assembled by the factory. Also, some items can or must be purchased and installed by an authorized factory representative. The estimator must investigate these variables in order to include adequate costs.

Division 12: Furnishings

Division 12, Furnishings, is best defined as furniture designed for specific uses, such as for dormitories, hospitals, hotels, offices and restaurants. Window treatments are also included in Division 12. These important furnishings may be listed in the budget estimate to help determine the total financial investment, though they are usually not a part of the actual construction contract. If the furnishings are built-in, then additional man-hours for unpacking, installing, and clean-up are necessary and must be calculated. In most cases, architects will separately specify and arrange for the purchase and installation of furnishings.

Division 13: Special Construction

The items in this division are specialized subsystems that are usually manufactured or constructed, and installed by specialty subcontractors. The costs shown in *Means Building Construction Cost Data* are for budget purposes only. Final cost figures should be furnished by the appropriate subcontractor after the exact requirements of the project have been specified.

CONSOLIDATED ESTIMATE

PROJECT: Office Building   CLASSIFICATION: Division 10

LOCATION: ARCHITECT:

TAKE OFF BY: ESTIMATE NO:

QUANTITIES BY: DATE: 6/93

PRICES BY: CHECKED BY:

EXTENSIONS BY:

DESCRIPTION	SOURCE			QUANT.	UNIT	MATERIAL		LABOR		EQUIPMENT		SUBCONTRACT		TOTAL	
						COST	TOTAL	COST	TOTAL	COST	TOTAL	COST	TOTAL	COST	TOTAL
Division 10: Specialties															
Bathroom Accessories:															
Towel / Waste	108	204	0610	9	Ea.	305.00	2745	18.70	168						
Grab Bar	108	204	1100	6	Ea.	42.00	252	9.35	56						
Napkin Dispenser	108	204	4200	6	Ea.	360.00	2160	12.45	75						
Mirrors (Handicapped)	108	204	3000	3	Ea.	45.00	135	9.35	28						
Soap Dispenser	108	204	4600	15	Ea.	38.50	578	9.35	140						
S. S. Shelves	108	204	5700	6	Ea.	65.50	393	11.70	70						
T. P. Holder	108	204	6100	18	Ea.	9.60	173	6.25	113						
Ash Trays	108	204	7800	12	Ea.	98.00	1176	10.40	125						
Toilet Partitions:															
Floor Mounted, Headrail	101	602	2500	15	Ea.	365.00	5475	62.50	938						
Urinal Screens	101	602	4700	3	Ea.	155.00	465	46.50	140						
Division 10 Totals							$13,551		$1,852						

Figure 9.105

It is a good idea to review this portion of the project with the subcontractor to determine both the exact scope of the work and those items that are not covered by the quotation. If the subcontractor requires services such as excavation, unloading, or other temporary work, then these otherwise excluded items must be included elsewhere in the estimate.

The specialty subcontractor will have more detailed information at hand concerning the system. The more detailed the estimator's knowledge of a system, the easier it will be to subdivide that system into cost components. Each component can be further subdivided into material, labor, and equipment costs that will fully identify the direct cost of the specialty item for future purposes.

Division 14: Conveying Systems

The following systems may be included in this division:

- Correspondence Lifts
- Dumbwaiters
- Elevators
- Escalators and Moving Ramps
- Material Handling Systems
- Pneumatic Tube Systems
- Handicapped Lifts

Because of the specialized construction of the above units, it is almost impossible for the general estimator to price most of this equipment, except in a preliminary, budgetary capacity. Sometimes the plans specify package units that carry standard prices. For general budget pricing, refer to *Means Building Construction Cost Data*. When quotations on specific equipment are received, they should be checked against the specifications to verify that all requirements are met. All required inspections, tests and permits, as well as the responsibility for their costs, should be included in the installed price of each system.

Many of the costs associated with conveying systems are not included in the subcontract bid. When drilling for hydraulic pistons, for example, the preliminary project schedule must be adjusted so that the work can be performed prior to the erection of the superstructure. Drill tailings must also be disposed of, and if ledge or boulders are encountered, drilling costs will increase substantially. Contracts for elevator installations often have more exclusions than inclusions. The estimator must be sure that all associated costs are taken into account.

One of the most commonly underestimated or unanticipated costs is that for the installation of elevator door frames and sills. Typically, frames and sills are supplied by the elevator subcontractor and installed by the general contractor when constructing the elevator shaft walls. At this stage, shop drawings for the elevator usually have not yet been approved. The resulting late installation often involves the cutting and patching of other completed work (concrete floors and block walls). Even if shop drawings are approved, the materials often arrive late. Good planning and proper estimating can help to alleviate or lessen these problems.

Even when determining budget costs for elevators, many variables must be considered. Reference Table R142-200 from *Means Building Construction Cost Data*, shown in Figures 9.106 and 9.107, indicates the complexity of estimating for elevators.

Sample Estimate: Division 14

The architect's design criteria is apt to be based on the standard elevator "packages" of certain manufacturers. In such cases, firm subcontract bids would be received. For the sample estimate, a budget price is developed and shown in Figure 9.108. The costs would be based on project specifications and are derived from Figures 9.106 and 9.107. If a budget price for elevators is carried in an estimate for bidding, a qualification should be included that the bid may change upon receipt of subcontract prices. Budget prices should be carried only if no specifications are available or obtainable.

Division 15: Mechanical

Unit price estimates for the mechanical and electrical portions of a project should always be performed by the installing subcontractors. Each field requires specialized experience and expertise. Nevertheless, the estimator for the general contractor often requires costs to compare to subcontract bids. In most cases, adjusted square foot costs based on previous, similar projects will suffice. A Systems Estimate may be used if more accuracy is needed. It is essential to understand both the work and the estimating process in order to properly interpret and analyze subcontract costs, and to ensure that all requirements are met. Following are brief discussions of the estimating process for mechanical and electrical work.

When a complete set of mechanical plans and specifications is available, the first step in preparing an estimate is to review all information, making notes on any special or unique requirements. Also, while it is not unusual to see an item on the plans that is not reflected in the specifications, or vice versa, the estimator should make careful note of any contradictions. Such inconsistencies will require resolution before a meaningful estimate can be put together. A review of the other drawings is also advised to determine how the building structure, site layout and other work will affect the mechanical installation. The scales of architectural and engineering drawings should be compared. Plumbing, sprinkler and HVAC designs are frequently prepared by consulting engineers who are not associated with the architects. In these cases, inconsistencies in scale, location, and terminology may result.

One basic feature of almost all mechanical designs is the fact that their different elements can be separated into systems, such as hot water, cold water, fire protection, and heating and/or cooling. Some of these systems may be interconnected or have some common parts, but they are nevertheless distinct. Most systems can be broken down into the following categories: source, conductor or connector, and a terminal unit; for example, water meter – copper tubing – sink faucet. Note that while the sink with faucet or a water closet may be terminal units for the cold water system, they are a source for the drain-waste-vent (DWV) system.

Pre-printed forms are especially useful for preparing the mechanical portion of the estimate. While careful measurements and a count of components are important, they will not compensate for omissions such as forgetting to include pipe insulation. A well-designed form acts as a checklist, a guide for standardization, and a permanent record.

Plumbing

The first step in preparing a plumbing estimate is to visualize the scope of the job by scanning all of the drawings and specifications. The next step is to make a list of the types of materials on a takeoff sheet. This process will help the estimator to remember the various components as they are located on the drawings. For major items, pieces of equipment and fixtures, the quantity sheet can serve as a checklist. The estimator must be sure to include

R142-200 Elevator Selective Costs
See R142-400 for cost development.

	Passenger		Freight		Hospital	
A. Base Unit	Hydraulic	Electric	Hydraulic	Electric	Hydraulic	Electric
Capacity	1,500 Lb.	2,000 Lb.	2,000 Lb.	4,000 Lb.	4,000 lb.	4,000 lb.
Speed	100 F.P.M.	200 F.P.M.	50 F.P.M.	200 F.P.M.	100 F.P.M.	200 F.P.M.
#Stops/Travel Ft.	2/12	4/40	2/20	4/40	2/20	4/40
Push Button Oper.	Yes	Yes	Yes	Yes	Yes	Yes
Telephone Box & Wire	"	"	"	"	"	"
Emergency Lighting	"	"	No	No	"	"
Cab	Plastic Lam. Walls	Plastic Lam. Walls	Painted Steel	Painted Steel	Plastic Lam. Walls	Plastic Lam. Walls
Cove Lighting	Yes	Yes	No	No	Yes	Yes
Floor	V.C.T.	V.C.T.	Wood w/Safety Treads	Wood w/Safety Treads	V.C.T.	V.C.T.
Doors, & Speedside Slide	Yes	Yes	Yes	Yes	Yes	Yes
Gates, Manual	No	No	No	No	No	No
Signals, Lighted Buttons	Car and Hall	Car and Hall	Car and Hall	Car and Hall	Car and Hall	Car and Hall
O.H. Geared Machine	N.A.	Yes	Yes	Yes	N.A.	Yes
Variable Voltage Contr.	"	"	N.A.	"	"	"
Emergency Alarm	Yes	"	Yes	"	Yes	"
Class "A" Loading	N.A.	N.A.	"	"	N.A.	N.A.
Base Cost	$35,000	$64,500	$33,600	$60,000	$42,000	$76,800
B. Capacity Adjustment						
2,000 Lb.	$ 500					
2,500	1,050	$ 2,680	$ 2,550			
3,000	2,550	3,100	2,980			
3,500	4,575	4,250	4,550			
4,000	5,600	5,150	5,600		$ 4,600	
4,500	6,150	6,150	6,200		5,200	$ 4,100
5,000	8,200	7,400	7,580	$ 2,750	7,600	5,300
6,000			9,200	4,300		
7,000			11,300	4,300		
8,000			13,350	13,150		
10,000			15,600	15,600		
12,000			19,300	19,300		
16,000			22,650	22,650		
20,000			26,600	22,700		
C. Travel Over Base	$ 300 V.L.F.	$ 185 V.L.F.	$ 300 V.L.F.	$ 185 V.L.F.	$ 300 V.L.F.	$ 185 V.L.F.
D. Additional Stops	$ 3,300 Ea.	$ 5,025 Ea.	$ 3,000 Ea.	$ 4,500 Ea.	$ 5,400 Ea.	$ 5,200 Ea.
E. Speed Adjustment						
100 F.P.M.			$ 550			
125	$ 760		775		$ 775	
150	1,050		1,100		1,250	
175	3,100		3,200		3,150	
200	4,600				4,600	
Geared 250		$ 1,980		$ 8,300		$ 1,980
4 Flrs. 300		3,600		10,350		3,600
Min. 350		4,700		11,800		4,700
400		6,600		12,900		6,600
Gearless 500		25,900		16,500		26,800
4 Flrs. 600		29,980		18,200		29,980
Min. 700		31,150		21,200		31,150
800		38,600		23,600		38,650
1,000		Spec. Applic.		Spec. Applic.		Spec. Applic.
1,200		"		"		"
F. Other Than Class "A" Loading						
"B"			$ 1,500	$ 1,500		
"C-1"			3,600	3,600		
"C-2"			4,300	4,300		
"C-3"			5,900	5,900		

Figure 9.106

R142-200   Elevator Selective Costs (cont.)

	Passenger	Freight	Hospital
G. Options			
1. Controls			
Automatic, 2 car group	$3,100		$3,100
3 car group	4,600		4,600
4 car group	7,150		7,150
5 car group	9,300		9,300
6 car group	13,200		13,200
Emergency, fireman service	Yes		Yes
Intercom service	750		750
Selective collective, single car	–		–
Duplex car	3,100		3,100
2. Doors			
Center opening, 1 speed	$1,550		$1,550
2 speed	1,890		1,890
Rear opening-opposite front	3,600		3,600
Side opening, 2 speed	5,600		5,600
Freight, bi-parting	–	$ 3,100	–
Power operated door and gate	–	19,200	–
3. Emergency power switching, automatic	$2,250		$2,250
Manual	210		210
4. Finishes based on 3500# cab			
Ceilings, acrylic panel	$235		
Aluminum egg crate	310		$360
Doors, stainless steel	585 Ea.		585 Ea.
Floors, carpet, class "A" – (Finish flooring by others)	105		–
Epoxy	220		235
Quarry tile	180		235
Slate	205		–
Steel plate	–	$ 590	
Textured rubber	95		70
Walls, plastic laminate	Std.		Std.
Stainless steel	1,550		1,850
Return at door	440		440
Steel plate, 1/4" x 4' high, 14 ga. above	–	$ 1,360	–
Entrance, doors, baked enamel	Std.		Std.
Stainless steel	585 Ea.		585 Ea.
Frames, baked enamel	Std.		Std.
Stainless steel	720 Ea.		720 Ea.
5. Maintenance contract - 12 months	$2,400	$ 1,800	$3,600
6. Signal devices			
Hall lantern, each	$380	$ 380	$380
Position indicator, car or lobby	280	280	280
Add for over three each, per floor	85	85	85
7. Specialties			
High speed, heavy duty door opener	$625		$625
Variable voltage, O.H. gearless machine	27,000-60,000		27,000-60,000
Basement installed geared machine	$11,150	$11,150	$11,150

Figure 9.107

CONSOLIDATED ESTIMATE

PROJECT: Office Building
LOCATION:
TAKE OFF BY:

CLASSIFICATION: Division 14
ARCHITECT:
QUANTITIES BY:
PRICES BY:
EXTENSIONS BY:

ESTIMATE NO:
DATE:　6/93
CHECKED BY:

DESCRIPTION	SOURCE	QUANT.	UNIT	MATERIAL COST	MATERIAL TOTAL	LABOR COST	LABOR TOTAL	EQUIPMENT COST	EQUIPMENT TOTAL	SUBCONTRACT COST	SUBCONTRACT TOTAL
Division 14: Conveying Systems											
Ref. No. R142-200											
Pass. Hydraulic - Base	35000										
2500 Lbs. Capacity	500										
Travel 37'	10500										
Stops (plus 2)	6600										
Speed - 100 fpm											
S. S. Doors	585										
Carpet	105										
P. L. Walls											
S. S. Entrance - Doors	585										
- Frame	720										
Each Elevator	54595	2	Ea.								109190
Automatic Controls		1	Ea.							3100	3100
Fire Service		1	Ea.								
Hall Lanterns		8	Ea.							380.00	3040
Position Indicators		4	Ea.							365.00	1460
Maintenance		2	Ea.							2400	4800
Division 14 Total											**$121,590**

Figure 9.108

the required labor-only items, such as cleaning, adjusting, purifying, testing, and balancing, since these will not show up on the drawings and have little, if any, material costs.

The easiest way to do a material takeoff is by system, as most of the pipe components of a system will tend to be related as a group – of the same material, class, weight, and grade. For example, a waste system could consist of pipe varying from 3″ to 8″ in diameter, but would probably be all service weight cast iron, DWV copper, or PVC up to a specified size, and then cast iron for the larger sizes.

Fixtures: Fixture takeoff is usually nothing more than counting the various types, sizes and styles, and then entering them on a fixture form. It is important, however, that each fixture be fully identified. A common error occurs when parts that must be purchased separately are overlooked; examples are trim, carriers, and flush valves. Equipment like pumps, water heaters, water softeners, and all items not previously counted are also listed at this time. The order in which the takeoff proceeds is not as important as the development of a consistent method. With consistency, the estimator can speed up the process while minimizing the chances of overlooking any item or class of items. Taking off fixtures and equipment before the piping is best for several reasons. Done in this order, the fixture and equipment lists can be given to suppliers for pricing while the estimator is performing the more arduous and time-consuming piping takeoff. Taking off the fixtures and equipment first also gives the estimator a good perspective on the building and its systems. The next step is transferring these figures to the estimate sheet. Figure 9.109 shows relative installation times for different types of fixtures.

Piping: Fixture costs in *Means Building Construction Cost Data* (Figure 9.110) are based on the cost per fixture set in place. The rough-in piping cost, which must be added for each fixture, includes a carrier, if required, some supply, waste and vent pipe, connecting fittings and stops. The lengths of rough-in pipe

Plumbing Fixture Installation Time

Item	Rough-In	Set	Total Hrs.	Item	Rough-In	Set	Total Hrs.
Bathtub	5	5	10	Shower head only	2	1	3
Bathtub and shower, cast iron	6	6	12	Shower drain	3	1	4
Fire hose reel and cabinet	4	2	6	Shower stall, slate		15	15
Floor drain to 4″ diameter	3	1	4	Slop sink	5	3	8
Grease trap, single, cast iron	5	3	8	Test 6 fixtures			14
Kitchen gas range		4	4	Urinal, wall	6	2	8
Kitchen sink, single	4	4	8	Urinal, pedestal or floor	6	4	10
Kitchen sink, double	6	6	12	Water closet and tank	4	3	7
Laundry tubs	4	2	6	Water closet and tank, wall hung	5	3	8
Lavatory wall hung	5	3	8	Water heater, 45 gals. gas, automatic	5	2	7
Lavatory pedestal	5	3	8	Water heaters, 65 gals. gas, automatic	5	2	7
Shower and stall	6	4	10	Water heaters, electric, plumbing only	4	2	6

Figure 9.109

are nominal runs which would connect to the larger runs and stacks (to within 10′). The supply runs and DWV runs and stacks must be accounted for in separate entries.

Pipe runs for any type of system consist of straight sections and fittings of various shapes and styles, for various purposes. Depending on the required detail, pipe and fittings can be itemized or included as a percentage of the fixtures. If detail is required, the estimator should measure and record the lengths of each size of pipe. When a fitting is crossed, a list of all fitting types and sizes can be used for counting. Colored pencils can be used to mark runs that have been completed, and to note termination points on the main line where measurements are stopped so that a branch may be taken off. Care must be taken to note changes in pipe material. Since different materials can only meet at a joint, it should become an automatic habit to see that the piping material going into a joint is the same as that leaving the joint.

When summarizing quantities of piping for estimate or purchase, it is good practice to round the totals of each size up to the lengths normally available from the supply house or mill. This method is even more appropriate in larger projects where rounding might be done to the nearest hundred or thousand feet. With this approach, a built-in percentage for scrap or waste is allowed. Rigid copper tubing and rigid plastic pipe are normally supplied in 20′ lengths, cast iron soil pipe in either 5′ or 10′ sections. Steel pipe of 2″ diameter or less is furnished in 21′ lengths, and pipe of a larger diameter is available in single random lengths ranging from 16′ to 22′.

Apart from counting and pricing every pipe and fitting, there are other ways to determine budget costs for plumbing. *Means Building Construction Cost Data* provides costs for fixtures, as well as the associated costs for rough-in of the supply, waste and vent piping as shown in Figure 9.110. The rough-in costs include piping within 10′ of the fixture. If these prices are used, further costs must be added for the stacks and mains. Another method involves adding percentages to the cost of the fixtures. Recommended percentages are shown in Figure 9.111. Using information such as that provided in Figures 9.110 and 9.111, the estimator can develop "systems" to be used for budget pricing.

In addition to the cost of pipe installation, the estimator must also consider any associated costs. In many cases, mechanical and electrical subcontractors must dig, by hand, their own underslab trenches. Site utility excavation (and backfill) may also be included, if required. Underground piping may require special wrapping. For interior piping, the estimator must visualize the installation in order to determine how – and to what – the pipe hangers are attached. Overhead installations will require rolling scaffolding. For installations higher than an average of 15′, labor costs may be increased by the following suggested percentages:

Ceiling Height	Labor Increase
15′ to 20′	10%
20′ to 25′	20%
25′ to 30′	30%
30′ to 35′	40%
35′ to 40′	50%
Over 40′	60%

Fire Protection

The takeoff of fire protection systems (sprinklers and standpipes) is very much like that of other plumbing – the estimator should measure the pipe

152 | Plumbing Fixtures

152 100 | Fixtures

		Description	CREW	DAILY OUTPUT	MAN-HOURS	UNIT	MAT.	LABOR	EQUIP.	TOTAL	TOTAL INCL O&P	
148	3000	Fiberglass, one piece, with 3 walls, 32″ x 32″ square	Q-1	2.40	6.667	Ea.	390	164		554	680	148
	3100	36″ x 36″ square		2.40	6.667		440	164		604	735	
	3250	64″ x 65-3/4″ x 81-1/2″ fold. seat, whlchr.		1.80	8.889		2,825	219		3,044	3,425	
	4000	Polypropylene, with molded-stone floor, 30″ x 30″		2	8		320	197		517	650	
	4960	Rough-in, supply, waste and vent for above showers	↓	2.05	7.805		66.50	192		258.50	365	
	5000	Built-in, head, arm, 4 GPM valve	1 Plum	4	2		62.50	55		117.50	152	
	5200	Head, arm, by-pass, integral stops, handles	'	3.60	2.222	↓	189	61		250	300	
	6000	Group, w/valve, rough-in and rigging not included										
	6800	Column, 6 heads, no receptors, less partitions	Q-1	3	5.333	Ea.	2,100	131		2,231	2,525	
	6900	With stainless steel partitions		1	16		5,550	395		5,945	6,700	
	7600	5 heads, no receptors, less partitions		3	5.333		1,675	131		1,806	2,050	
	7700	With stainless steel partitions		1	16		4,650	395		5,045	5,725	
	8000	Corner, 2 heads, no receptors, less partitions		4	4		795	98.50		893.50	1,025	
	8100	With stainless steel partitions	↓	2	8	↓	1,775	197		1,972	2,250	
152	0010	SINKS With faucets and drain R151 -420										152
	2000	Kitchen, counter top, P.E. on C.I., 24″ x 21″ single bowl	Q-1	5.60	2.857	Ea.	194	70.50		264.50	320	
	2100	30″ x 21″ single bowl		5.60	2.857		220	70.50		290.50	350	
	2200	32″ x 21″ double bowl		4.80	3.333		252	82		334	400	
	2300	42″ x 21″ double bowl		4.80	3.333		395	82		477	560	
	3000	Stainless steel, self rimming, 19″ x 18″ single bowl		5.60	2.857		241	70.50		311.50	370	
	3100	25″ x 22″ single bowl		5.60	2.857		270	70.50		340.50	405	
	4000	Steel, enameled, with ledge, 24″ x 21″ single bowl		5.60	2.857		108	70.50		178.50	226	
	4100	32″ x 21″ double bowl	↓	4.80	3.333		130	82		212	268	
	4960	For color sinks except stainless steel, add					10%					
	4980	For rough-in, supply, waste and vent, counter top sinks	Q-1	2.14	7.477	↓	75	184		259	360	
	5000	Kitchen, raised deck, P.E. on C.I.										
	5100	32″ x 21″, dual level, double bowl	Q-1	2.60	6.154	Ea.	285	152		437	545	
	5700	For color, add					20%					
	5790	For rough-in, supply, waste & vent, sinks	Q-1	1.85	8.649		75	213		288	410	
	6650	Service, floor, corner, P.E. on C.I., 28″ x 28″		4.40	3.636		465	89.50		554.50	645	
	6790	For rough-in, supply, waste & vent, floor service sinks		1.64	9.756		150	240		390	530	
	7000	Service, wall, P.E. on C.I., roll rim, 22″ x 18″		4	4		335	98.50		433.50	520	
	7100	24″ x 20″		4	4		365	98.50		463.50	555	
	8600	Vitreous china, 22″ x 20″	↓	4	4		380	98.50		478.50	570	
	8960	For stainless steel rim guard, front or side, add					26			26	28.50	
	8980	For rough-in, supply, waste & vent, wall service sinks	Q-1	1.30	12.308	↓	199	305		504	680	
168	0010	URINALS										168
	0020											
	3000	Wall hung, vitreous china, with hanger & self-closing valve	Q-1	3	5.333	Ea.	365	131		496	600	
	3300	Rough-in, supply, waste & vent		2.83	5.654		72.50	139		211.50	291	
	5000	Stall type, vitreous china, includes valve		2.50	6.400		450	158		608	735	
	5100	3″ seam cover, add		12	1.333		118	33		151	180	
	5200	6″ seam cover, add		12	1.333		164	33		197	230	
	6980	Rough-in, supply, waste and vent	↓	1.99	8.040	↓	101	198		299	410	
176	0010	WASH FOUNTAINS Rigging not included										176
	1900	Group, foot control										
	2000	Precast terrazzo, circular, 36″ diam., 5 or 6 persons	Q-2	3	8	Ea.	1,450	205		1,655	1,900	
	2100	54″ diameter for 8 or 10 persons		2.50	9.600		1,825	245		2,070	2,375	
	2400	Semi-circular, 36″ diam. for 3 persons		3	8		1,350	205		1,555	1,775	
	2500	54″ diam. for 4 or 5 persons		2.50	9.600		1,625	245		1,870	2,175	
	2700	Quarter circle (corner), 54″ for 3 persons	↓	3.50	6.857	↓	1,575	175		1,750	2,000	
	2850											
	3000	Stainless steel, circular, 36″ diameter	Q-2	3.50	6.857	Ea.	1,625	175		1,800	2,075	
	3100	54″ diameter		2.80	8.571		2,125	219		2,344	2,675	
	3400	Semi-circular, 36″ diameter		3.50	6.857		1,425	175		1,600	1,850	
	3500	54″ diameter	↓	2.80	8.571		1,825	219		2,044	2,325	

Figure 9.110

loops and count fittings, valves, sprinkler heads, alarms, and other components. The estimator then makes note of special requirements, as well as any conditions that would affect job performance and cost.

There are many different types of sprinkler systems; examples are wet pipe, dry pipe, pre-action, and chemical. Each of these types involves a different set of requirements and costs. Figure 9.112, from *Means Mechanical Cost Data*, provides descriptions of various sprinkler systems.

Most sprinkler systems must be approved by Factory Mutual for insurance purposes *before* installation. This requirement means that shop drawings must be produced and submitted for approval. The shop drawings take time and the approval process takes more time. This process can cause serious delays and added expense if it is not anticipated and given adequate consideration at the estimating and scheduling phase.

Square foot historical costs for fire protection systems may be developed for budget purposes. These costs may be based on the relative hazard of occupancy – light, ordinary and extra. A comparison of some requirements of the different hazards is shown in Figure 9.113. Consideration must also be given to special or unusual requirements. For example, many architects specify that sprinkler heads must be located in the center of ceiling tiles. Each head may require extra elbows and nipples for precise location. Recessed heads are more expensive. Special dry pendant heads are required in areas subject to freezing. When installing a sprinkler system in an existing structure, a completely new water service may be required in addition to the existing domestic water service. These are just a few examples of requirements which may necessitate an adjustment of square foot costs.

Heating, Ventilation, and Air Conditioning
As with plumbing, equipment for HVAC should be taken off first so that the estimator is familiarized with the various systems and layouts. While actual pieces

---

Plumbing Approximations for Quick Estimating

Water Control:
Water Meter; Backflow Preventer, Shock Absorbers; Vacuum Breakers; Mixer. . . . . 10 to 15% of Fixtures

Pipe and Fittings: . . . . 30 to 60% of Fixtures

Note: Lower percentage for compact buildings or larger buildings with plumbing in one area.
Larger percentage for large buildings with plumbing spread out.
In extreme cases pipe may be more than 100% of fixtures.
Percentages **do not** include special purpose or process piping.

Plumbing Labor:
1 & 2 Story Residential . . . . .Rough-in Labor = 80% of Materials
Apartment Buildings . . . . Rough-in Labor = 90 to 100% of Materials
Labor for handling and placing fixtures is approximately 25 to 30% of fixtures.

Quality/Complexity Multiplier (For all installations)
Economy installation, add . . . . .0 to 5%
Good quality, medium complexity, add . . . . .5 to 15%
Above average quality and complexity, add . . . . .15 to 25%

Figure 9.111

R154-110   Sprinkler Systems (Automatic)

Sprinkler systems may be classified by type as follows:

1. **Wet Pipe System.** A system employing automatic sprinklers attached to a piping system containing water and connected to a water supply so that water discharges immediately from sprinklers opened by a fire.

2. **Dry Pipe System.** A system employing automatic sprinklers attached to a piping system containing air under pressure, the release of which as from the opening of sprinklers permits the water pressure to open a valve known as a "dry pipe valve". The water then flows into the piping system and out the opened sprinklers.

3. **Pre-Action System.** A system employing automatic sprinklers attached to a piping system containing air that may or may not be under pressure, with a supplemental heat responsive system of generally more sensitive characteristics than the automatic sprinklers themselves, installed in the same areas as the sprinklers; actuation of the heat responsive system, as from a fire, opens a valve which permits water to flow into the sprinkler piping system and to be discharged from any sprinklers which may be open.

4. **Deluge System.** A system employing open sprinklers attached to a piping system connected to a water supply through a valve which is opened by the operation of a heat responsive system installed in the same areas as the sprinklers. When this valve opens, water flows into the piping system and discharges from all sprinklers attached thereto.

5. **Combined Dry Pipe and Pre-Action Sprinkler System.** A system employing automatic sprinklers attached to a piping system containing air under pressure with a supplemental heat responsive system of generally more sensitive characteristics than the automatic sprinklers themselves, installed in the same areas as the sprinklers; operation of the heat responsive system, as from a fire, actuates tripping devices which open dry pipe valves simultaneously and without loss of air pressure in the system. Operation of the heat responsive system also opens approved air exhaust valves at the end of the feed main which facilitates the filling of the system with water which usually procedes the opening of sprinklers. The heat responsive system also serves as an automatic fire alarm system.

6. **Limited Water Supply System.** A system employing automatic sprinklers and conforming to these standards but supplied by a pressure tank of limited capacity.

7. **Chemical Systems.** Systems using halon, carbon dioxide, dry chemical or high expansion foam as selected for special requirements. Agent may extinguish flames by chemically inhibiting flame propagation, suffocate flames by excluding oxygen, interrupting chemical action of oxygen uniting with fuel or sealing and cooling the combustion center.

8. **Firecycle System.** Firecycle is a fixed fire protection sprinkler system utilizing water as its extinguishing agent. It is a time delayed, recycling, preaction type which automatically shuts the water off when heat is reduced below the detector operating temperature and turns the water back on when that temperature is exceeded. The system senses a fire condition through a closed circuit electrical detector system which controls water flow to the fire automatically. Batteries supply up to 90 hour emergency power supply for system operation. The piping system is dry (until water is required) and is monitored with pressurized air. Should any leak in the system piping occur, an alarm will sound, but water will not enter the system until heat is sensed by a Firecycle detector.

Area coverage sprinkler systems may be laid out and fed from the supply in any one of several patterns as shown below. It is desirable, if possible, to utilize a central feed and achieve a shorter flow path from the riser to the furthest sprinkler. This permits use of the smallest sizes of pipe possible with resulting savings.

Central End
Feed

Side End
Feed

Side Central
Feed

Center Central
Feed

Figure 9.112

287

of equipment must be counted at this time, it is also necessary to note sizes, capacities, controls, special characteristics and features. The weight and size of equipment may be important if the unit is especially large or is going into comparatively close quarters. If hoisting or rigging is not included in the subcontract price, then costs for placing the equipment must be figured and listed. From the equipment totals, other important items, such as motor starters, valves, strainers, gauges, thermometers, traps, and air vents can also be counted.

Sheet metal ductwork for heating, ventilation and air conditioning is usually estimated by weight. The lengths of the various sizes are measured and recorded on a worksheet. The weight per foot of length is then determined. Figure 9.114 is a conversion chart for determining the weight of ductwork based on size and material. A count must also be made of all duct-associated accessories, such as fire dampers, diffusers, and registers. This count may be done during the duct takeoff. It is usually less confusing, however, to make a separate count. For budget purposes, ductwork, insulation, diffusers and registers may be estimated using the information in Figure 9.115.

The takeoff of heating, ventilation and air conditioning pipe and fittings is accomplished in a manner similar to that of plumbing. In addition to the general, miscellaneous items noted during the review of plans and specifications, the heating, ventilation and air conditioning estimate usually includes the work of subcontractors. All material suppliers and appropriate subcontractors should be notified as soon as possible to verify material availability and pricing and to ensure timely submission of bids. Typical subcontract work includes:

- Balancing
- Controls
- Insulation
- Water Treatment
- Sheet Metal
- Core Drilling

Sprinkler Quantities for Various Size and Types of Pipe

Sprinkler Quantities: The table below lists the usual maximum number of sprinkler heads for each size of copper and steel pipe for both wet and dry systems. These quantities may be adjusted to meet individual structural needs or local code requirements. Maximum area on any one floor for one system is: light hazard and ordinary hazard 52,000 S.F., extra hazardous 25,000 S.F.

Pipe Size	Light Hazard Occupancy		Ordinary Hazard Occupancy		Extra Hazard Occupancy	
Diameter	Steel Pipe	Copper Pipe	Steel Pipe	Copper Pipe	Steel Pipe	Copper Pipe
1"	2 sprinklers	2 sprinklers	2 sprinklers	2 sprinklers	1 sprinklers	1 sprinklers
1-1/4"	3	3	3	3	2	2
1-1/2"	5	5	5	5	5	5
2"	10	12	10	12	8	8
2-1/2"	30	40	20	25	15	20
3"	60	65	40	45	27	30
3-1/2"	100	115	65	75	40	45
4"			100	115	55	65
5"			160	180	90	100
6"			275	300	150	170

Figure 9.113

If similar systems are used repeatedly, it is easy to develop historical square foot costs for budget and comparison purposes. However, with variation in the types and size of HVAC systems, the estimator must use caution when using square foot prices. A way to adjust such relative prices can be to adjust costs based on the quality or complexity of the installation:

Quality/Complexity	Adjustment
Economy/Low	0 to 5%
Good/Medium	5 to 15%
Above Average/High	15 to 25%

Sample Estimate: Division 15

For bidding purposes, firm subcontract prices should always be solicited for all phases of mechanical work. However, the estimator should still be familiar with the project requirements and the basics of mechanical estimating. Only with an understanding of what is involved will the estimator be able to judge the validity of a subcontract quote.

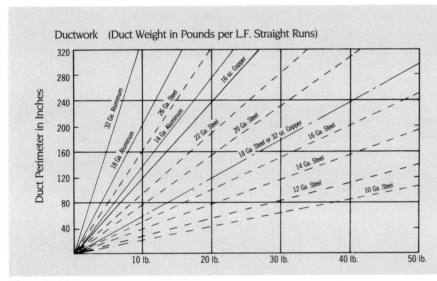

Add to the above for fittings: 90° elbow is 3 L.F.; 45° elbow is 2.5 L.F.; offset is 4 L.F.; transition offset is 6 L.F.; square-to-round transition is 4 L.F.; 90° reducing elbow is 5 L.F. For bracing and waste, add 20% to aluminum and copper, 15% to steel.

Figure 9.114

Ductwork Packages (per ton of cooling)

System	Sheet Metal	Insulation	Diffusers	Return Register
Roof Top Unit Single Zone	120 Lbs.	52 S.F.	1	1
Roof Top Unit Multizone	240 Lbs.	104 S.F.	2	1
Self-contained Air or Water Cooled	108 Lbs.	—	2	—
Split System Air Cooled	102 Lbs.	—	2	—

Figure 9.115

For the purposes of this sample estimate, Figures 9.116 through 9.121 are included to show how a subcontractor might prepare a bid for the HVAC work. Unit prices are from *Means Mechanical Cost Data*. Different types of ductwork installations are separated on the quantity sheet in Figure 9.116. The weight (pounds per linear foot) for each size of duct is derived from the table in Figure 9.122 from *Means Mechanical Cost Data*. The detail of the HVAC estimate reflects the precision required for proper mechanical estimating.

Overhead and profit are added to the bare cost totals using the methods described in Chapters 4 and 7. Ten percent is added to each – material, equipment and subcontracts – for handling and supervision. To labor, an average 57.4% is added. This includes employer-paid taxes and insurance, office overhead, and profit.

While usually only one subcontractor will handle the complete mechanical portion of the project, different subcontractors may separately bid and perform the plumbing, fire protection and HVAC portions of the estimate. When soliciting quotes, the estimator for the general contractor should try to obtain detailed breakdowns of each. The estimator will be able to use these breakdowns for comparing bids if the quote is not as expected, and can thereby discover which areas are "out of line." While subcontractors are often reluctant to provide detailed information, it is to their own benefit if possible errors or omissions which exist in their prices are discovered.

A summary of the subcontract prices is shown in Figure 9.123. Separation and breakdowns as shown can be used to help develop historical costs for future projects, whether they are done by system or square foot.

Division 16: Electrical

A good estimator must be able to visualize the proposed electrical installation from source (service) to end use (fixtures or devices). This process helps to identify each component needed to make the system work. Before starting the takeoff, the estimator should follow some basic steps:

- Read the electrical specifications thoroughly.
- Scan the electrical plans. Check other sections of the plans and specifications for their potential effect on electrical work (special attention should be given to mechanical and site work).
- Check the architectural and structural plans for unique or atypical requirements.
- Check and become familiar with the fixture and power symbols.
- Clarify with the architect or engineer any unclear areas, making sure that the scope of work is understood. Addenda may be necessary to clarify certain items of work so that the responsibility for the performance of all work is defined.
- Immediately contact suppliers, manufacturers, and subsystem specialty contractors in order to get their quotations, sub-bids, and drawings.

Certain information should be taken from complete plans and specifications in order to properly estimate the electrical portion of the work. In addition to floor plans, other sources of information are:

- Power riser diagram
- Panelboard schedule
- Fixture schedule
- Electrical symbol legend
- Reflected ceiling plans
- Branch circuit plans

QUANTITY SHEET

PROJECT: Office Building   Division 15

LOCATION: ARCHITECT:

TAKE OFF BY: EXTENSIONS BY:

DESCRIPTION	NO.	DIMENSIONS		Insulated Supply	UNIT	Supply not Insulated	UNIT	Return	UNIT	Toilet Exhaust	UNIT
Ductwork											
Supply (Insul.)	3rd										
45 x 14	80	14.8	22	1184	Lbs.						
25 x 14	92	8.4	24	773							
22 x 14	144	7.8	"	1123							
18 x 14	192	6.9	"	1325							
14 x 14	96	6.0	"	576							
12 x 9	96	4.5	"	432							
15 x 14	96	6.2	"	595							
13 x 12	64	5.4	"	346							
12 x 8	96	4.3	"	413							
				(6767) Lbs.							
Supply (not Insul.)	1st & 2nd										
6767 x 2						(13534) Lbs.					
Return											
50 x 14	144	16.0	22					2304	Lbs.		
33 x 14	132	11.8	22					1558			
18 x 14	132	6.9	24					911			
								(4773) Lbs.			
Toilet Exhaust											
18 x 12	18	6.5	24							117	Lbs.
16 x 12	14	6.0	"							84	
12 x 12	14	5.2	"							73	
6 x 6	18	2.6	"							47	
										(321)	Lbs.

Figure 9.116

CONSOLIDATED ESTIMATE

PROJECT: Office Building
LOCATION:
TAKE OFF BY:
CLASSIFICATION: Division 15
ARCHITECT:
QUANTITIES BY:
PRICES BY:
ESTIMATE NO:
DATE: 6/93
CHECKED BY:

EXTENSIONS BY:

DESCRIPTION	SOURCE	QUANT.	UNIT	MATERIAL COST	MATERIAL TOTAL	LABOR COST	LABOR TOTAL	EQUIPMENT COST	EQUIPMENT TOTAL	SUBCONTRACT COST	SUBCONTRACT TOTAL	COST	TOTAL
HVAC Sheet Metal Duct Work													
Supply Duct 3rd Floor (Insul)		6800	Lb.										
Supply Duct (Not Insulated)		14000	Lb.										
Return Duct (Not Insulated)		4800	Lb.										
Toilet Exhaust Duct Work	157 250 0580	325	Lb.										
Total Duct Work		25925	Lb.	0.37	9592	2.09	54183						
9" x 9" Supply Diffusers	157 450 2020	3	Ea.	57.50	173	15.25	46						
15" x 15" Supply Diffusers	157 450 2060	132	Ea.	96.00	12672	19.40	2561						
24" x 24" Framed Eggcrate	157 460 4040	19	Ea.	48.50	922	14.20	270						
Splitter Damper, 1 Foot Rod	157 480 7000	12	Ea.	13.00	156	8.90	107						
6" Flexible Toilet Exhaust Duct	157 250 1560	200	LF	1.01	202	1.37	274						
4" Flexible Toilet Exhaust Duct	157 250 1520	90	LF	0.73	66	1.07	96						
8" x 6" Exhaust Register	157 470 5040	3	Ea.	13.75	41	8.90	27						
8" x 4" Exhaust Register	157 470 5020	1	Ea.	13.75	14	8.20	8						
Roof Exhaust Fan 4600 CFM	157 290 7240	1	Ea.	1125	1125	123.00	123						
24" Double Wall Galv. Chimney	155 680 0340	12	LF	112.00	1344	18.65	224						
24" Roof Flashing Collar	155 680 1170	1	Ea.	188.00	188	49.50	50						
24" Double Wall Tee	155 680 1330	1	Ea.	555.00	555	49.50	50						
24" Tee Cap	155 680 1590	1	Ea.	36.50	37	28.50	29						
24" Rain Cap & Screen	155 680 1880	1	Ea.	515.00	515	30.00	30						
Subtotals					$27,600		$58,076						

Figure 9.117

CONSOLIDATED ESTIMATE

PROJECT: Office Building   CLASSIFICATION: Division 15

LOCATION: ARCHITECT:

TAKE OFF BY: QUANTITIES BY: PRICES BY:

ESTIMATE NO:

DATE: 6/93

CHECKED BY:

EXTENSIONS BY:

SOURCE	DESCRIPTION	QUANT.	UNIT	MATERIAL COST	MATERIAL TOTAL	LABOR COST	LABOR TOTAL	EQUIPMENT COST	EQUIPMENT TOTAL	SUBCONTRACT COST	SUBCONTRACT TOTAL	TOTAL
	Division 15: (Cont'd)											
	Air - Conditioning											
157 190 1600	Chiller, 175 Tons	1	Ea.	76500	76500	14000	14000					
157 150 0260	30 Ton Fan Coil Unit	6	Ea.	5325	31950	1025	6150					
157 240 1900	175 Ton Tower	175	Ton	76.50	13388	4.88	854					
157 420 4500	6" Thermometer 30° - 140° F	4	Ea.	24.00	96	6.85	27					
157 420 2300	3 1/2" Dial Pressure Gague	6	Ea.	12.00	72	6.85	41					
152 410 4420	7 1/2 HP Condenser Water Pump	1	Ea.	1500	1500	247.00	247					
152 410 4410	5 HP Chill Water Pump	2	Ea.	1625	3250	247.00	494					
151 701 2110	4" Steel Pipe, Bevel End	180	LF	8.20	1476	10.65	1917					
151 701 0610	2" Steel Pipe, Thread & Coupled	340	LF	3.57	1214	6.15	2091					
151 720 3440	4" Weld Tee	15	Ea.	31.00	465	131.00	1965					
151 720 3130	4" Weld Elbow	20	Ea.	16.80	336	79.00	1580					
151 720 6500	4" Weld Neck Flange	14	Ea.	13.00	182	39.50	553					
151 720 0670	4" Sets, Nuts, Bolts & Gaskets	30	Ea.	8.85	266	27.50	825					
151 716 0580	2" Cast Iron Tee	12	Ea.	8.35	100	36.00	432					
151 716 0140	2" Cast Iron Elbow	24	Ea.	5.95	143	22.00	528					
151 960 3680	4" OS & Y Gate Valve 1B	8	Ea.	209.00	1672	131.00	1048					
151 960 6670	4" Wafer, Check Valve	3	Ea.	175.00	525	79.00	237					
151 955 3480	2" Bronze Gate Valve	6	Ea.	45.50	273	19.95	120					
151 990 7030	4" Balancing Valve, Flanged	3	Ea.	305.00	915	131.00	393					
151 990 1080	2" Stop and Balance Valve	6	Ea.	120.00	720	27.50	165					
156 612 1060	4" Flanged Y Strainer	3	Ea.	206.00	618	132.00	396					
155 671 3020	ASME 31 Gal. Expan. Tank	1	Ea.	1125	1125	49.50	50					
	Subtotals				$136,785		$34,113					

Figure 9.118

CONSOLIDATED ESTIMATE

PROJECT: Office Building
LOCATION:
TAKE OFF BY:
CLASSIFICATION: Division 15
ARCHITECT:
QUANTITIES BY:
PRICES BY:
EXTENSIONS BY:

DESCRIPTION	SOURCE		QUANT.	UNIT	MATERIAL		LABOR		EQUIPMENT		SUBCONTRACT		TOTAL
					COST	TOTAL	COST	TOTAL	COST	TOTAL	COST	TOTAL	
Division 15: (Cont'd)													
Heating													
3500 MBH, Gas, CI Water Heater	155 115	3400	1	Ea.	20800	20800	3225	3225					
Electric Duct Heater	155 408	0160	1	Ea.	890.00	890	37.50	38					
79 Gal. ASME Expansion Tank	155 671	3060	1	Ea.	1700	1700	79.00	79					
3" Steel Pipe, Bevel End	151 701	2090	120	LF	5.70	684	9.15	1098					
1 1/2" Stl Pipe, Thread & Coupled	151 701	0600	320	LF	2.70	864	4.93	1578					
3" Weld Tee	151 720	3430	15	Ea.	22.50	338	98.50	1478					
3" Weld Elbow	151 720	3120	12	Ea.	10.20	122	56.50	678					
3" Weld Neck Flange	151 720	6480	8	Ea.	17.85	143	28.00	224					
3" Sets, Bolts, Nuts & Gaskets	151 720	0650	16	Ea.	4.40	70	19.95	319					
1 1/2" Cast Iron Tee	151 716	0570	12	Ea.	6.10	73	30.50	366					
1 1/2" Cast Iron Elbow	151 716	0140	24	Ea.	5.95	143	22.00	528					
3" OS & Y Iron Boot Gate Valve	151 960	3660	4	Ea.	146.00	584	87.50	350					
3" Wafer Check Valve	151 960	6660	2	Ea.	144.00	288	49.50	99					
1 1/2" Bronze Gate Valve	151 955	3470	6	Ea.	32.00	192	16.85	101					
1 1/2" Balancing Valve, Flanged	151 990	7020	2	Ea.	255.00	510	87.50	175					
1 1/2" Stop & Balance Valve	151 990	1070	6	Ea.	85.00	510	19.95	120					
3" Iron Body, Flanged Strainer	156 612	1040	2	Ea.	105.00	210	88.00	176					
3" Air Control Fitting	156 205	0100	1	Ea.	700.00	700	99.00	99					
6" Thermometer, 40° to 240° F	157 420	4500	2	Ea.	24.00	48	6.85	14					
3 1/2" Dial Pressure Gauge	157 420	2300	4	Ea.	12.00	48	6.85	27					
5 HP Hot Water Pump	152 410	4300	2	Ea.	1075	2150	219.00	438					
Subtotals						$31,067		$11,209					

Figure 9.119

294

CONSOLIDATED ESTIMATE

PROJECT: Office Building	
LOCATION:	
TAKE OFF BY:	
CLASSIFICATION: Division 15	ESTIMATE NO:
ARCHITECT:	DATE: 6/93
QUANTITIES BY:	CHECKED BY:
PRICES BY:	
EXTENSIONS BY:	

DESCRIPTION	SOURCE	QUANT.	UNIT	MATERIAL COST	MATERIAL TOTAL	LABOR COST	LABOR TOTAL	EQUIPMENT COST	EQUIPMENT TOTAL	SUBCONTRACT COST	SUBCONTRACT TOTAL
HVAC: Miscellaneous											
Record Drawings		8	Hr.								
Operating Instructions		8	Hr.								
Maintenance Manuals		4	Hr.								
Cleaning Systems		16	Hr.								
	Total	36	Hr.			27.45	988				
Subcontracts											
Insulation											19653
Balancing											7987
Controls											38168
Crane									1341		
Subtotals					0		$988		$1,341		$65,808

Figure 9.120

CONSOLIDATED ESTIMATE

PROJECT: Office Building	CLASSIFICATION: Division 15		ESTIMATE NO:
LOCATION:	ARCHITECT:		DATE: 6/93
TAKE OFF BY:	QUANTITIES BY:	PRICES BY:	CHECKED BY:
		EXTENSIONS BY:	

DESCRIPTION	SOURCE	QUANT.	UNIT	MATERIAL		LABOR		EQUIPMENT		SUBCONTRACT		TOTAL	
				COST	TOTAL	COST	TOTAL	COST	TOTAL	COST	TOTAL	COST	TOTAL
Division 15: (Cont'd)													
HVAC: Summary													
Ductwork	Sheet 1				$27,600		$58,076		$0		$0		
Air Conditioning	Sheet 2				$136,785		$34,113		$0		$0		
Heating	Sheet 3				$31,067		$11,209		$0		$0		
Miscellaneous	Sheet 4				$0		$988		$0		$0		
Subcontracts	Sheet 4				$0		$0		$1,341		$65,808		
Material Subtotal					$195,452								
Sales Tax				6%	$11,727								
Bare Cost Totals					$207,179		$104,386		$1,341		$65,808		
Overhead & Profit				10%	$20,718	55.2	$57,621	10%	$134	10%	$6,581		
Totals					$227,897		$162,006		$1,475		$72,389		$463,768
Total Bid to GC													$463,768

Figure 9.121

R157-100 Sheet Metal Calculator (Weight in Lb./Ft. of Length)

Gauge	26	24	22	20	18	16	Gauge	26	24	22	20	18	16
Wt.-Lb./S.F.	.906	1.156	1.406	1.656	2.156	2.656	Wt.-Lb./S.F.	.906	1.156	1.406	1.656	2.156	2.656
SMACNA Max. Dimension - Long Side		30"	54"	84"	85" Up		SMACNA Max. Dimension - Long Side		30"	54"	84"	85" Up	
Sum-2 Sides							Sum-2 Sides						
2	.3	.40	.50	.60	.80	.90	56	9.3	12.0	14.0	16.2	21.3	25.2
3	.5	.65	.80	.90	1.1	1.4	57	9.5	12.3	14.3	16.5	21.7	25.7
4	.7	.85	1.0	1.2	1.5	1.8	58	9.7	12.5	14.5	16.8	22.0	26.1
5	.8	1.1	1.3	1.5	1.9	2.3	59	9.8	12.7	14.8	17.1	22.4	26.6
6	1.0	1.3	1.5	1.7	2.3	2.7	60	10.0	12.9	15.0	17.4	22.8	27.0
7	1.2	1.5	1.8	2.0	2.7	3.2	61	10.2	13.1	15.3	17.7	23.2	27.5
8	1.3	1.7	2.0	2.3	3.0	3.6	62	10.3	13.3	15.5	18.0	23.6	27.9
9	1.5	1.9	2.3	2.6	3.4	4.1	63	10.5	13.5	15.8	18.3	24.0	28.4
10	1.7	2.2	2.5	2.9	3.8	4.5	64	10.7	13.7	16.0	18.6	24.3	28.8
11	1.8	2.4	2.8	3.2	4.2	5.0	65	10.8	13.9	16.3	18.9	24.7	29.3
12	2.0	2.6	3.0	3.5	4.6	5.4	66	11.0	14.1	16.5	19.1	25.1	29.7
13	2.2	2.8	3.3	3.8	4.9	5.9	67	11.2	14.3	16.8	19.4	25.5	30.2
14	2.3	3.0	3.5	4.1	5.3	6.3	68	11.3	14.6	17.0	19.7	25.8	30.6
15	2.5	3.2	3.8	4.4	5.7	6.8	69	11.5	14.8	17.3	20.0	26.2	31.1
16	2.7	3.4	4.0	4.6	6.1	7.2	70	11.7	15.0	17.5	20.3	26.6	31.5
17	2.8	3.7	4.3	4.9	6.5	7.7	71	11.8	15.2	17.8	20.6	27.0	32.0
18	3.0	3.9	4.5	5.2	6.8	8.1	72	12.0	15.4	18.0	20.9	27.4	32.4
19	3.2	4.1	4.8	5.5	7.2	8.6	73	12.2	15.6	18.3	21.2	27.7	32.9
20	3.3	4.3	5.0	5.8	7.6	9.0	74	12.3	15.8	18.5	21.5	28.1	33.3
21	3.5	4.5	5.3	6.1	8.0	9.5	75	12.5	16.1	18.8	21.8	28.5	33.8
22	3.7	4.7	5.5	6.4	8.4	9.9	76	12.7	16.3	19.0	22.0	28.9	34.2
23	3.8	5.0	5.8	6.7	8.7	10.4	77	12.8	16.5	19.3	22.3	29.3	34.7
24	4.0	5.2	6.0	7.0	9.1	10.8	78	13.0	16.7	19.5	22.6	29.6	35.1
25	4.2	5.4	6.3	7.3	9.5	11.3	79	13.2	16.9	19.8	22.9	30.0	35.6
26	4.3	5.6	6.5	7.5	9.9	11.7	80	13.3	17.1	20.0	23.2	30.4	36.0
27	4.5	5.8	6.8	7.8	10.3	12.2	81	13.5	17.3	20.3	23.5	30.8	36.5
28	4.7	6.0	7.0	8.1	10.6	12.6	82	13.7	17.5	20.5	23.8	31.2	36.9
29	4.8	6.2	7.3	8.4	11.0	13.1	83	13.8	17.8	20.8	24.1	31.5	37.4
30	5.0	6.5	7.5	8.7	11.4	13.5	84	14.0	18.0	21.0	24.4	31.9	37.8
31	5.2	6.7	7.8	9.0	11.8	14.0	85	14.2	18.2	21.3	24.7	32.3	38.3
32	5.3	6.9	8.0	9.3	12.2	14.4	86	14.3	18.4	21.5	24.9	32.7	38.7
33	5.5	7.1	8.3	9.6	12.5	14.9	87	14.5	18.6	21.8	25.2	33.1	39.2
34	5.7	7.3	8.5	9.9	12.9	15.3	88	14.7	18.8	22.0	25.5	33.4	39.6
35	5.8	7.5	8.8	10.2	13.3	15.8	89	14.8	19.0	22.3	25.8	33.8	40.1
36	6.0	7.8	9.0	10.4	13.7	16.2	90	15.0	19.3	22.5	26.1	34.2	40.5
37	6.2	8.0	9.3	10.7	14.1	16.7	91	15.2	19.5	22.8	26.4	34.6	41.0
38	6.3	8.2	9.5	11.0	14.4	17.1	92	15.3	19.7	23.0	26.7	35.0	41.4
39	6.5	8.4	9.8	11.3	14.8	17.6	93	15.5	19.9	23.3	27.0	35.3	41.9
40	6.7	8.6	10.0	11.6	15.2	18.0	94	15.7	20.1	23.5	27.3	35.7	42.3
41	6.8	8.8	10.3	11.9	15.6	18.5	95	15.8	20.3	23.8	27.6	36.1	42.8
42	7.0	9.0	10.5	12.2	16.0	18.9	96	16.0	20.5	24.0	27.8	36.5	43.2
43	7.2	9.2	10.8	12.5	16.3	19.4	97	16.2	20.8	24.3	28.1	36.9	43.7
44	7.3	9.5	11.0	12.8	16.7	19.8	98	16.3	21.0	24.5	28.4	37.2	44.1
45	7.5	9.7	11.3	13.1	17.1	20.3	99	16.5	21.2	24.8	28.7	37.6	44.6
46	7.7	9.9	11.5	13.3	17.5	20.7	100	16.7	21.4	25.0	29.0	38.0	45.0
47	7.8	10.1	11.8	13.6	17.9	21.2	101	16.8	21.6	25.3	29.3	38.4	45.5
48	8.0	10.3	12.0	13.9	18.2	21.6	102	17.0	21.8	25.5	29.6	38.8	45.9
49	8.2	10.5	12.3	14.2	18.6	22.1	103	17.2	22.0	25.8	29.9	39.1	46.4
50	8.3	10.7	12.5	14.5	19.0	22.5	104	17.3	22.3	26.0	30.2	39.5	46.8
51	8.5	11.0	12.8	14.8	19.4	23.0	105	17.5	22.5	26.3	30.5	39.9	47.3
52	8.7	11.2	13.0	15.1	19.8	23.4	106	17.7	22.7	26.5	30.7	40.3	47.7
53	8.8	11.4	13.3	15.4	20.1	23.9	107	17.8	22.9	26.8	31.0	40.7	48.2
54	9.0	11.6	13.5	15.7	20.5	24.3	108	18.0	23.1	27.0	31.3	41.0	48.6
55	9.2	11.8	13.8	16.0	20.9	24.8	109	18.2	23.3	27.3	31.6	41.4	49.1
							110	18.3	23.5	27.5	31.9	41.8	49.5

Example: If duct is 34" x 20" x 15' long, 34" is greater than 30" maximum, for 24 ga. so must be 22 ga. 34" + 20" = 54" going across from 54" find 13.5 lb. per foot. 13.5 x 15' = 202.5 lbs. For

S.F. of surface area 202.5 ÷ 1.406 = 144 S.F.
Note: figures include an allowance for scrap.

Figure 9.122

CONSOLIDATED ESTIMATE

| PROJECT: | Office Building | CLASSIFICATION: | Division 15 | | SHEET NO. | 1 of 1 |

LOCATION:
ARCHITECT:
ESTIMATE NO:
DATE: 6/93
CHECKED BY:

TAKE OFF BY:
QUANTITIES BY:
PRICES BY:
EXTENSIONS BY:

| DESCRIPTION | SOURCE | QUANT. | UNIT | MATERIAL | | LABOR | | EQUIPMENT | | SUBCONTRACT | | TOTAL |
				COST	TOTAL	COST	TOTAL	COST	TOTAL	COST	TOTAL	COST	TOTAL
Division 15: Mechanical													
				SUBCONTRACTOR QUOTATIONS (INCLUDING SALES TAX)									
Plumbing:													
Base Price											126678		
Pipe Insulation (HW only)											3801		
Total Plumbing											130478		
Fire Protection:													
Standpipes											37326		
Sprinklers											60269		
Total Fire Protection											97595		
HVAC: (Includes the following)													
Base Price													
Insulation													
Balancing													
Controls													
Crane													
Total HVAC											463768		
Division 15 Totals											$691,841		

Figure 9.123

298

- Fire alarm and telephone riser diagrams
- Special systems

Performing a fixture and device takeoff can be a good way to become familiar with the proposed electrical installation. Take off one bay, section, or floor at a time. Mark each fixture and device with colored pencils and list them as you proceed. Check the site plans for exterior fixtures.

Fixtures should be taken off using the fixture schedule in conjunction with the reflected ceiling plan. Fixture counts should have outlet boxes, plaster rings, or Greenfield with connectors and fixture wire if needed. Include fixture supports as needed.

Separate quantity sheets should be used for each of the major categories of electrical work. By keeping each system on different sheets, the estimator will find it easy to isolate various costs. This format becomes a reference for purchasing and cost control. It also provides a breakdown of items that can be submitted to the general contractor when billing.

While making takeoffs of each category, identify all other required components of the systems. Determine the materials that will be part of a quotation or sub-bid from a supplier, including additional items to complete the vendor's package.

Switchgear

Material costs for large equipment such as switchgear, motor control centers and associated items should be obtained from suppliers or manufacturers. When determining the installation cost for large equipment (for any division) the estimator must consider a number of factors to be sure that all work is included:

- Access and placement
- Uncrating
- Rigging and setting
- Pads and anchors
- Leveling and shimming
- Assembly of components
- Connections
- Temporary protection requirements

While pads and anchors for large equipment may be well designated on the plans, supports for smaller equipment, such as panels and transformers, may not be well defined. For example, floor to ceiling steel supports may be required. The same consideration must be given to large cable troughs and conduits. Special support requirements may be necessary. If so, they must be included, whether they are the responsibility of the electrical or general contractor. For elevated installation of equipment, labor costs should be adjusted. Suggested adjustments follow:

Ceiling Height	Labor Adjustment
10' – 15'	+ 15%
15' – 25'	+ 30%
Over 25'	+ 35%

Ducts and Cable Trays

Bus ducts and cable trays should be estimated by component:

- Type and size of duct or tray
- Material (aluminum or galvanized)
- Hangers
- Fittings

The installation of under floor ducts systems (and conduit) must be scheduled after placement of any reinforcing at the bottom of slabs, but before installation of the upper steel. Without proper coordination, delays can occur. The estimate and preliminary schedule should reflect associated costs. Because of the high cost of tray and duct systems, the takeoff should be as accurate as possible. Fittings should not be deducted from straight lengths. In this way, an adequate allowance for waste should be provided. For high ceiling installations, labor costs for bus duct and cable trays should be adjusted accordingly. Suggested adjustments are:

Ceiling Height	Labor Adjustment
15' — 20'	+ 10%
20' — 25'	+ 20%
25' — 30'	+ 25%
30' — 35'	+ 30%
35' — 40'	+ 35%
Over 40'	+ 40%

Feeders

Feeder conduit and wire should be carefully taken off using a scale or printed dimensions. This is a more accurate method than the use of a rotometer. Large conduit and wire are expensive and require a considerable amount of labor. Accurate quantities are important. Switchboard locations should be marked on each floor before measuring horizontal runs. The distance between floors should be marked on riser plans and added to the horizontal for a complete feeder run. Conduits should be measured at right angles to the structure unless it has been determined that they can be routed directly. Elbows, terminations, bends, or expansion joints should also be taken off at this time. Under-slab and high ceiling installations should be treated the same as in the case of ducts and trays. The estimator should also consider the weight of material for high ceiling installations. Extra workers may be required for heavier components. Typical weights are shown in Figure 9.124. If standard feeder takeoff sheets are used, the wire column should reflect longer lengths than the conduit. This is because of added amounts of wire used in the panels and switchboard to make connections. If the added length is not shown on the plans, it can be determined by checking a manufacturer's catalog. Conduit, cable supports, and accessories should all be totalled at this time.

Branch Circuits

Branch circuits may be taken off using a rotometer. The estimator should take care to start and stop accurately at boxes. Start with two wire circuits and mark with colored pencil as items are taken off. Add about 5% to conduit quantities for normal waste. On wire, add 10% to 12% overage to make connections. Add conduit fittings, such as locknuts, bushings, couplings, expansion joints, and fasteners. Two conduit terminations per box are average. Figure 9.125 shows prices for conduit as presented in *Means Building Construction Cost Data*. Note that a minimum amount of fittings are included in the costs.

Conduit Weight Comparisons (Lbs. per 100 ft.)

Type	1/2"	3/4"	1"	1-1/4"	1-1/2"	2"	2-1/2"	3"	3-1/2"	4"	5"	6"
Rigid Aluminum	28	37	55	72	89	119	188	246	296	350	479	630
Rigid Steel	79	105	153	201	249	332	527	683	831	972	1314	1745
Intermediate Steel (IMC)	60	82	116	150	182	242	401	493	573	638		
Electrical Metallic Tubing (EMT)	29	45	65	96	111	141	215	260	365	390		
Polyvinyl Chloride, Schedule 40	16	22	32	43	52	69	109	142	170	202	271	350
Polyvinyl Chloride Encased Burial						38		67	88	105	149	202
Fibre Duct Encased Burial						127		164	180	206	400	511
Fibre Duct Direct Burial						150		251	300	354		
Transite Encased Burial						160		240	290	330	450	550
Transite Direct Burial						220		310		400	540	640

Weight Comparisons of Common Size Cast Boxes in Lbs.

Size NEMA 4 or 9	Cast Iron	Cast Aluminum	Size NEMA 7	Cast Iron	Cast Aluminum
6" x 6" x 6"	17	7	6" x 6" x 6"	40	15
8" x 6" x 6"	21	8	8" x 6" x 6"	50	19
10" x 6" x 6"	23	9	10" x 6" x 6"	55	21
12" x 12" x 6"	52	20	12" x 6" x 6"	100	37
16" x 16" x 6"	97	36	16" x 16" x 6"	140	52
20" x 20" x 6"	133	50	20" x 20" x 6"	180	67
24" x 18" x 8"	149	56	24" x 18" x 8"	250	93
24" x 24" x 10"	238	88	24" x 24" x 10"	358	133
30" x 24" x 12"	324	120	30" x 24" x 10"	475	176
36" x 36" x 12"	500	185	30" x 24" x 12"	510	189

Size Required and Weight (Lbs./1000 L.F.) of Aluminum and Copper THW Wire by Ampere Load

Amperes	Copper Size	Aluminum Size	Copper Weight	Aluminum Weight
15	14	12	24	11
20	12	10	33	17
30	10	8	48	39
45	8	6	77	52
65	6	4	112	72
85	4	2	167	101
100	3	1	205	136
115	2	1/0	252	162
130	1	2/0	324	194
150	1/0	3/0	397	233
175	2/0	4/0	491	282
200	3/0	250	608	347
230	4/0	300	753	403
255	250	400	899	512
285	300	500	1068	620
310	350	500	1233	620
335	400	600	1396	772
380	500	750	1732	951

Weight (Lbs./L.F.) of 4 Pole Aluminum and Copper Bus Duct by Ampere Load

Amperes	Aluminum Feeder	Copper Feeder	Aluminum Plug-In	Copper Plug-In
225			7	7
400			8	13
600	10	10	11	14
800	10	19	13	18
1000	11	19	16	22
1350	14	24	20	30
1600	17	26	25	39
2000	19	30	29	46
2500	27	43	36	56
3000	30	48	42	73
4000	39	67		
5000		78		

Figure 9.124

Wiring devices should be entered with plates, boxes, and plaster rings. Calculate stub ups or drops for wiring devices. Switches should be counted and multiplied by the distance from switch to ceiling.

Receptacles are handled similarly, depending on whether they are wired from the ceiling or floor. In many cases, there are two conduits going to a receptacle box as you feed in and out to the next outlet. Some estimators let rotometers overrun outlets purposely as an adjustment for vertical runs; this practice can, however, lead to inaccuracies.

In metal stud partitions, it is often acceptable to go horizontally from receptacle to receptacle. In wood partitions, horizontal runs are also the usual practice. In suspended ceilings, the specifications should be checked to see if straight runs are allowed. If the space above the ceiling is used as a return air plenum, conduit is usually required for all wiring.

Motors, safety switches, starters, and controls, should each include power lines, junction boxes, supports, wiring troughs, and wire terminations. Short runs of Greenfield or Sealtite with appropriate connectors and wire should be added for motor wiring.

For large installations, the economy of scale may have a definite impact on the electrical costs. If large quantities of a particular item are installed in the same general area, certain deductions can be made for labor. Suggested deductions include:

	Quantity	Labor Deduction
Under floor ducts, bus ducts, conduit, cable systems:	150 to 250 LF	−10%
	250 to 350 LF	−15%
	350 to 500 LF	−20%
	Over 500 LF	−25%
Outlet boxes:	25 to 50	−15%
	50 to 75	−20%
	75 to 100	−25%
	Over 100	−30%
Wiring devices:	10 to 25	−20%
	25 to 50	−25%
	50 to 100	−30%
	Over 100	−35%
Lighting fixtures:	25 to 50	−15%
	50 to 75	−20%
	75 to 100	−25%
	Over 100	−30%

The estimator for the general contractor may require only a budget cost for the purpose of verifying subcontractor bids. As described in the section on mechanical estimating, square foot or systems costs developed from similar, past projects can also be useful for electrical estimating.

Sample Estimate: Division 16

While electrical work should be accurately estimated by a subcontractor for bidding purposes, the estimator for the general contractor should understand the work involved. Complete plans and specifications will include a number of schedules and diagrams that will help the estimator to determine quantities. Figures 9.126 and 9.127 are the lighting fixture and panelboard schedules,

		160 100	Cable Trays	CREW	DAILY OUTPUT	MAN-HOURS	UNIT	1993 BARE COSTS				TOTAL INCL O&P	
								MAT.	LABOR	EQUIP.	TOTAL		
105	3230		18" wide	1 Elec	57	.140	.L.F.	11.30	3.75		15.05	18.10	105
	3240		24" wide	↓	53	.151	↓	12.60	4.03		16.63	19.90	
	9980		Allow. for tray ftngs., 5% min.-20% max.										
150	0010	WIREWAY to 15' high											150
	0100		Screw cover, with fittings and supports, 2-1/2" x 2-1/2"	1 Elec	45	.178	L.F.	6.25	4.75		11	14.05	
	0200		4" x 4"		40	.200		7.05	5.35		12.40	15.75	
	0400		6" x 6"		30	.267		11.60	7.10		18.70	23.50	
	0600		8" x 8"	↓	20	.400	↓	16.55	10.70		27.25	34.50	
	9980		Allow. for wireway ftngs., 5% min.-20% max.										

		160 200	Conduits										
205	0010	CONDUIT To 15' high, includes 2 terminations, 2 elbows and	R160 -205										205
	0020		11 beam clamps per 100 L.F.										
	0300		Aluminum, 1/2" diameter	1 Elec	100	.080	L.F.	.90	2.14		3.04	4.20	
	0500		3/4" diameter		90	.089		1.20	2.37		3.57	4.88	
	0700		1" diameter		80	.100		1.70	2.67		4.37	5.90	
	1000		1-1/4" diameter		70	.114		2.20	3.05		5.25	7	
	1030		1-1/2" diameter		65	.123		2.70	3.29		5.99	7.90	
	1050		2" diameter		60	.133		3.75	3.56		7.31	9.50	
	1070		2-1/2" diameter		50	.160		6.05	4.27		10.32	13.05	
	1100		3" diameter		45	.178		8	4.75		12.75	15.95	
	1130		3-1/2" diameter		40	.200		9.90	5.35		15.25	18.90	
	1140		4" diameter		35	.229		11.75	6.10		17.85	22	
	1750		Rigid galvanized steel, 1/2" diameter		90	.089		1.20	2.37		3.57	4.88	
	1770		3/4" diameter		80	.100		1.50	2.67		4.17	5.65	
	1800		1" diameter		65	.123		2	3.29		5.29	7.15	
	1830		1-1/4" diameter		60	.133		2.55	3.56		6.11	8.15	
	1850		1-1/2" diameter		55	.145		3.15	3.88		7.03	9.30	
	1870		2" diameter		45	.178		4	4.75		8.75	11.55	
	1900		2-1/2" diameter		35	.229		6.70	6.10		12.80	16.50	
	1930		3" diameter		25	.320		8.60	8.55		17.15	22.50	
	1950		3-1/2" diameter		22	.364		11.25	9.70		20.95	27	
	1970		4" diameter		20	.400		13.05	10.70		23.75	30.50	
	2500		Steel, intermediate conduit (IMC), 1/2" diameter		100	.080		.97	2.14		3.11	4.28	
	2530		3/4" diameter		90	.089		1.19	2.37		3.56	4.87	
	2550		1" diameter		70	.114		1.58	3.05		4.63	6.30	
	2570		1-1/4" diameter		65	.123		2	3.29		5.29	7.15	
	2600		1-1/2" diameter		60	.133		2.55	3.56		6.11	8.15	
	2630		2" diameter		50	.160		3.15	4.27		7.42	9.85	
	2650		2-1/2" diameter		40	.200		5.25	5.35		10.60	13.80	
	2670		3" diameter		30	.267		7.05	7.10		14.15	18.45	
	2700		3-1/2" diameter		27	.296		9.75	7.90		17.65	22.50	
	2730		4" diameter		25	.320		11.45	8.55		20	25.50	
	5000		Electric metallic tubing (EMT), 1/2" diameter		170	.047		.37	1.26		1.63	2.30	
	5020		3/4" diameter		130	.062		.53	1.64		2.17	3.05	
	5040		1" diameter		115	.070		.76	1.86		2.62	3.63	
	5060		1-1/4" diameter		100	.080		1.10	2.14		3.24	4.42	
	5080		1-1/2" diameter		90	.089		1.32	2.37		3.69	5	
	5100		2" diameter		80	.100		1.75	2.67		4.42	5.95	
	5120		2-1/2" diameter		60	.133		3.80	3.56		7.36	9.55	
	5140		3" diameter		50	.160		4.75	4.27		9.02	11.60	
	5160		3-1/2" diameter		45	.178		6.45	4.75		11.20	14.25	
	5180		4" diameter	↓	40	.200	↓	7.65	5.35		13	16.40	
	9900		Add to labor for higher elevated installation										
	9910		15' to 20' high, add						10%				

Figure 9.125

respectively, for the building project. While such schedules may not always provide quantities, they can serve as a checklist to ensure that all types are counted.

Figure 9.128 is the quantity sheet for lighting. Note that associated boxes, devices and wiring are taken off at the same time as the fixtures and that the takeoff is done by floor. By performing the estimate in this way, quantities

Type	Manufacturer & Catalog #	Fixture	Type	Lamps		Watts	Mounting	Remarks
				Qty	Volts			
A	Meansco #7054	2′ x 4′ Troffer	F-40 CW	4	277	40	Recessed	Acrylic Lens
B	Meansco #7055	1′ x 4′ Troffer	F-40 CW	2	277	40	Recessed	Acrylic Lens
C	Meansco #7709	6″ x 4′	F-40 CW	1	277	40	Surface	Acrylic Wrap
D	Meansco #7710	6″ x 8′ Strip	F96T12 CW	1	277	40	Surface	
E	Meansco #7900A	6″ x 4′	F-40	1	277	40	Surface	Mirror Light
F	Kingston #100A	6″ x 4′	F-40	1	277	40	Surface	Acrylic Wrap
G	Kingston #110C	′ Strip	F-40 CW	1	277	40	Surface	
H	Kingston #3752	Wallpack	HPS	1	277	150	Bracket	W/Photo Cell
J	Kingston #201-202	Floodlight	HPS	1	277	400	Surface	2′ Below Fascia
K	Kingston #203		HPS	1	277	100	Wall Bracket	
L	Meansco #8100	Exit Light	1-13W 20W	1	120	13	Surface	
			T6-1/2	2	6½	20		
M	Meansco #9000	Battery Unit	Sealed Beam	2	12	18	Wall Mount	12 Volt Unit

Figure 9.126

Panel	Main Breaker	Main	Lugs	Amps	Circ.	Breakers		Location	Volts
						#	Type		
PP-1	No	3-P	Wire	100	20	(20)	IP-20 A	Basement	120/208
PP-2	No	3-P	4 Wire	225	42	(42)	IP-20 A	1st Floor	120/208
PP-3	No	3-P	4 Wire	225	42	(42)	IP-20 A	2nd Floor	120/208
PP-4	No	3-P	4 Wire	225	42	(42)	IP-20 A	3rd Floor	120/208
LP-1	No	3-P	4 Wire	225	42	(42)	IP-20 A	Basement	277/480
LP-2	No	3-P	4 Wire	225	42	(42)	IP-20 A	1st Floor	277/480
LP-3	No	3-P	4 Wire	225	42	(42)	IP-20 A	2nd Floor	277/480
LP-4	No	3-P	4 Wire	225	42	(42)	IP-20 A	3rd Floor	277/480

Figure 9.127

for purchase are easily determined and changes can be calculated quickly. For example, in a typical project, lighting fixtures are often changed or substituted, either because of aesthetic decisions or unavailability. If quantities and costs are isolated, adjustments are easily made.

The estimate sheets for lighting – as might be prepared by an electrical subcontractor – are shown in Figures 9.129 and 9.130. Prices are from *Means Electrical Cost Data*. By including the associated costs for boxes, devices and wiring with the lighting fixtures and the other major components, the electrical estimator is able to develop system costs for comparison to other projects, and for cross-checking. Since this is only part of the electrical work, overhead and profit are not likely to be added until the end of the electrical estimate. However, if a breakdown of costs is provided as part of the quotation, each portion of that breakdown would include overhead and profit. Such is the case in the estimate sheet for Division 16 as prepared by the general contractor, in Figure 9.131. For each system, the associated costs for devices and wiring are included, in addition to overhead and profit.

Estimate Summary

At this point in the estimating process, the estimate is complete for Divisions 2 through 16. All vendor quotations and subcontractors' bids should be in hand (ideally, but not necessarily realistic); and all costs should be determined for the work to be done "in-house." All costs known at this time should be entered on the Estimate Summary sheet as shown in Figure 9.132. Based on the subtotal of these costs, the items in Division 1 which are dependent on job costs can then be calculated.

The Project Overhead Summary is shown in Figures 9.133 and 9.134. In addition to those items related to job costs, there are also certain project overhead items that depend on job duration. A preliminary schedule is required in order to calculate these time-related costs. Using the procedure described in Chapter 5, a preliminary precedence schedule is prepared for the project as shown in Figure 9.135. Note that only those items that affect the project duration are calculated and included in the total time (247 working days). A more extensive and detailed project schedule is completed when the construction contract is awarded. The corresponding preliminary bar schedule is shown in Figure 9.136.

Throughout the estimate for all divisions, the estimator should note all items which should be included as project overhead as well as those which may affect the project schedule. The estimator must be especially aware of items which are implied but may not be directly stated in the specifications. Some of the "unspecified" costs which may be included are for the preparation of shop drawings, as-built drawings and the final project schedule. Costs for general job safety – such as railings, safety nets, fire extinguishers – must also be included if these items are required. If costs for job safety are not listed in the estimate, the items may not be installed on the job – until an OSHA fine, or worse, an accident.

Costs for shop drawings are mentioned above because the time involved in their preparation, submission and approval must also be considered when preparing the schedule. Construction delays are often blamed on the fact that shop drawings or "cuts" weren't submitted early enough, or approved in a timely fashion. The estimator must base such scheduling decisions on experience.

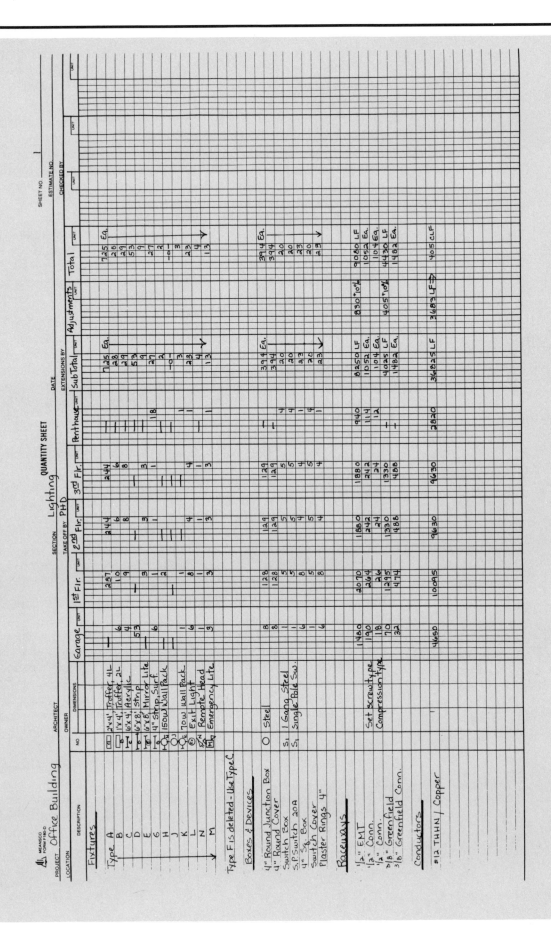

Figure 9.128

CONSOLIDATED ESTIMATE

PROJECT: Office Building   CLASSIFICATION: Division 16   ESTIMATE NO:
LOCATION: ARCHITECT: DATE: 6/93
TAKE OFF BY: QUANTITIES BY: PRICES BY: EXTENSIONS BY: CHECKED BY:

SOURCE	DESCRIPTION	QUANT.	UNIT	MATERIAL		LABOR		EQUIPMENT		SUBCONTRACT		TOTAL	
				COST	TOTAL	COST	TOTAL	COST	TOTAL	COST	TOTAL	COST	TOTAL
	Division 16: Electrical												
	Lighting												
	Fixtures:												
	Type												
166 130 0600	A 2'x4' w/4L	725	Ea.	69.00	50025	45.50	32988						
166 130 0200	B 1'x4' w/2L	28	Ea.	49.00	1372	37.50	1050						
166 130 2020	C 6"x4' w/1L	29	Ea.	45.00	1305	26.50	769						
166 130 2600	D 6"x8' w/1L	53	Ea.	46.50	2465	32.00	1696						
166 130 6900	E 6"x4' Mirror Light	9	Ea.	65.00	585	26.50	239						
166 130 2200	G 4' Surface Mount	27	Ea.	27.00	729	25.00	675						
166 115 1170	H 150 W HPS Wall Pk	2	Ea.	315.00	630	53.50	107						
166 115 1160	K 70 W HPS Wall Pk	3	Ea.	290.00	870	53.50	161						
166 110 0080	L Exit, Single Face	23	Ea.	50.00	1150	26.50	610						
166 110 0780	M Remote Head	4	Ea.	20.00	80	8.00	32						
166 110 0500	N Emergence Battery Unit	13	Ea.	250.00	3250	53.50	696						
	Raceways:												
160 205 5000	1/2" EMT	9080	LF	0.37	3360	1.26	11441						
160 205 6500	Set Screw Conn.	1052	Ea.	0.42	442	1.78	1873						
160 205 8800	Com. Pr. Conn.	104	Ea.	1.26	131	1.78	185						
160 270 0050	Greenfield	4430	LF	0.20	886	1.07	4740						
160 270 0420	Connectors	1482	Ea.	0.58	860	2.14	3171						
	Subtotals				$68,139		$60,430						

Figure 9.129

CONSOLIDATED ESTIMATE

PROJECT: Office Building   CLASSIFICATION: Division 16   ESTIMATE NO:

LOCATION: ARCHITECT: DATE: 6/93

TAKE OFF BY: QUANTITIES BY: PRICES BY: EXTENSIONS BY: CHECKED BY:

DESCRIPTION	SOURCE			QUANT.	UNIT	MATERIAL		LABOR		EQUIPMENT		SUBCONTRACT		TOTAL	
						COST	TOTAL	COST	TOTAL	COST	TOTAL	COST	TOTAL	COST	TOTAL
Division 16: (Cont'd)															
Lighting: (Cont'd)															
Conductors:															
THHN copper #12	161	165	1200	405	CLF	7.30	2957	19.40	7857						
Boxes & Devices:															
Box - 4" Octagon	162	110	0020	394	Ea.	1.15	453	10.70	4216						
4" Blank Cover	162	110	0250	394	Ea.	0.55	217	3.34	1316						
Box - 4" Square	162	110	0150	23	Ea.	1.46	34	10.70	246						
Plaster Rings	162	110	0300	23	Ea.	0.85	20	3.34	77						
Switch Box	162	110	0650	20	Ea.	1.32	26	7.90	158						
S. P. Switch 20A	162	320	0500	20	Ea.	5.25	105	7.90	158						
Switch Plate	162	320	2600	20	Ea.	1.78	36	2.67	53						
Subtotals							$3,846		$14,081						
Sheet 1 subtotals							$68,139		$60,430						
Sheet 2 subtotals							$3,846		$14,081						
Material Subtotal							$71,985								
Sales Tax						6%	$4,319								
Bare Cost Totals							$76,304		$74,511						
Overhead & Profit						10%	$7,630	50.1%	$37,330	10%		10%			
Totals							$83,934		$111,841						
Total Lighting Bid to GC														$195,776	$195,776

Figure 9.130

CONSOLIDATED ESTIMATE

SHEET NO. 1 of 1

PROJECT: Office Building
LOCATION:
TAKE OFF BY:

CLASSIFICATION: Division 16
ARCHITECT:
QUANTITIES BY: PRICES BY:
                        EXTENSIONS BY:

ESTIMATE NO:
DATE: 6/93
CHECKED BY:

DESCRIPTION	SOURCE	QUANT.	UNIT	MATERIAL		LABOR		EQUIPMENT		SUBCONTRACT		TOTAL	
				COST	TOTAL	COST	TOTAL	COST	TOTAL	COST	TOTAL	COST	TOTAL
Division 16: Electrical													
	SUBCONTRACTOR QUOTATIONS (INCLUDING SALES TAX)												
Lighting											$195,776		
Service & Distribution											$94,252		
Branch Circuits													
Incl. Under Carpet System											$100,843		
Motors											$22,223		
Fire Alarm											$32,998		
Division 16 Total											$446,092		

Figure 9.131

309

CONDENSED
ESTIMATE SUMMARY

PROJECT   Office Building   ESTIMATE NO:

LOCATION	TOTAL AREA / VOLUME	DATE:	6/93
ARCHITECT	COST PER S.F. / C.F.	NO. OF STORIES	
PRICES BY:	EXTENSIONS BY:	CHECKED BY:	

DIV.	DESCRIPTION	MAT'L.	LABOR	EQUIP.	SUB w/ TAX	SUB w/o TAX	TOTAL
1	General Requirements						
2	Site Work	$138,220	$32,904	$30,487	$33,415		
3	Concrete	$209,303	$181,507	$15,480			
4	Masonry	$20,549	$21,990	$4,836			
5	Metals					$450,117	
6	Wood & Plastics	$5,605	$2,204				
7	Thermal & Moisture Protection	$7,551	$6,389			$66,401	
8	Doors & Windows	$23,925	$3,957		$863,818	$14,346	
9	Finishes	$103,772	$66,967			$250,468	
10	Specialties	$13,551	$1,852				
11	Equipment						
12	Furnishings						
13	Special Construction						
14	Conveying Systems					$121,590	
15	Mechanical				$691,841		
16	Electrical				$446,092		
	Subtotals						
	Sales Tax 6% (3% on Sub-Contr.)						
	Overhead & Profit 10/57.4/10/10%						
	Subtotal						
	Bond ($12 /M)						
	Contingency 2%						
	Adjustments						
	TOTAL BID						

Figure 9.132

310

PROJECT OVERHEAD SUMMARY

					SHEET NO.
PROJECT: Office Building					**ESTIMATE NO:**
LOCATION:		**ARCHITECT:**			**DATE:** 6/93
QUANTITIES BY: PRICES BY:		**EXTENSIONS BY:**		**CHECKED BY:**	

DESCRIPTION	QUANTITY	UNIT	MATERIAL/EQUIP. UNIT	MATERIAL/EQUIP. TOTAL	LABOR UNIT	LABOR TOTAL	TOTAL COST UNIT	TOTAL COST TOTAL
Job Organization: Superintendent	49	WK			1070	52430		
Project Manager								
Timekeeper & Material Clerk	40	WK			625	25000		
Clerical								
Safety, Watchman & First Aid								
Travel Expense: Superintendent								
Project Manager								
Engineering: Layout	10	DAY			490	4900		
Inspection / Quantities								
Drawings								
CPM Schedule								
Testing: Soil								
Materials	1	LS		7500				
Structural								
Equipment: Cranes								
Concrete Pump, Conveyor, Etc.								
Elevators, Hoists								
Freight & Hauling								
Loading, Unloading, Erecting, Etc.								
Maintenance								
Pumping								
Scaffolding								
Small Power Equipment / Tools	0.5	%		3331				
Feild Offices: Job Office Trailer	11	Mo.	251	2761				
Architect / Owner's Office								
Temporary Telephones								
Utilities	11	Mo.	78	858				
Temporary Toilets								
Storage Areas & Sheds	11	Mo.	89	979				
Temporary Utilities: Heat								
Light & Power	567	CSF	12.15	6889				
PAGE TOTALS				$22,318		$82,330		

Figure 9.133

DESCRIPTION	QUANTITY	UNIT	MATERIAL/EQUIP.		LABOR		TOTAL COST	
			UNIT	TOTAL	UNIT	TOTAL	UNIT	TOTAL
Totals Brought Forward				$8,050		$82,330		
Winter Protection: Temp. Heat/Protection	567	CSF	18.50	10490	22.00	12474		
Snow Plowing								
Thawing Materials								
Temporary Roads	750	SY	2.51	753	1.53	752		
Signs & Barricades: Site Sign	1	LS	102	102				
Temporary Fences	1350	LF	1.69	2282	2.70	3645		
Temporary Stairs, Ladders & Floors								
Photographs								
Clean Up								
Dumpster	40	WK	290	11600				
Final Clean Up	56.7	MSF	5	286	29	1644		
Continous - One Laborer	45	WK			742	33390		
Punch List	0.2	%		7144				
Permits: Building	1	%		35721				
Misc.								
Insurance: Builders Risk - Additional Rider	1	LS		35721				
Owner's Protective Liability								
Umbrella								
Unemployment Ins. & Social Security								
(SEE ESTIMATE SUMMARY)								
Bonds								
Performance (SEE ESTIMATE SUMMARY)								
Material & Equipment								
Main Office Expense (SEE ESTIMATE SUMMARY)								
Special Items								
Totals:				$112,147		$134,235		

Figure 9.134

Figure 9.135

313

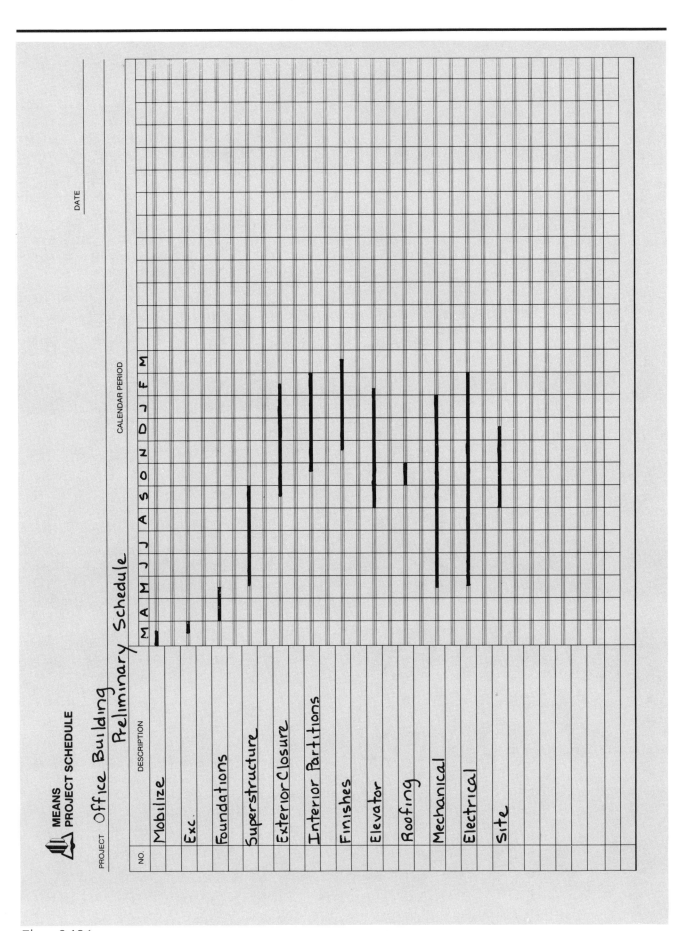

Figure 9.136

At this point, all divisions for the building project have been estimated. The preliminary schedule and project overhead summary are complete. Finally, the Estimate Summary sheet can be completed and the final number can be derived. The completed Estimate Summary sheet for the sample estimate is shown in Figure 9.137. Note that the difference between the subtotal of bare costs for all divisions and the "Total Bid" figure is roughly $846,000 – almost 20%. This amount is the sum of all the indirect costs. (See Chapters 4 and 7.)

Sales tax (in this example, 6%) is added to the total bare costs of materials. An additional 10% — for handling and supervision — is added to the material (including tax), equipment and subcontract costs. This is standard industry practice. Bare labor costs, however, are treated differently. As discussed in Chapter 7, office overhead expenses may be more directly attributable to labor. Consequently, the percentage markup for labor (57.4%) includes employer-paid taxes and insurance, office overhead and profit. This relationship is shown in Figure 9.138. (Profit may or may not be listed as a separate item.) Since all trades are included in the bare labor subtotal, the percentage used is the average for all skilled workers. The requirements for bonds are determined from the specifications and their costs are obtained from local bonding agencies. Finally, a contingency is added if the job warrants. This decision is made when the estimator's role comes to an end and the job of the bidder begins. The decision to add a contingency is often based on the relative detail of the plans and specifications, experience, knowledge of the market and competition, and most likely – a gut feeling. The estimate total, with all indirect costs included, may still not be the same number as that which is *finally* submitted as the bid.

Bid day in a contractor's office is usually a frantic, hectic time. Many subcontractors delay telephoning/faxing quotations until the last possible moment in order to prevent the possibility of bid shopping. Subs to subcontractors also withhold quotes in the same way and for the same reason. This situation, in many instances, forces the prime contractor to use a budget or even a "ballpark" figure so that the bid sheets can be tabulated to obtain a final number. The importance of the estimator's reviewing all disciplines of the estimate cannot be overstressed. The chaotic atmosphere of bid day can only be compensated by thoroughness, precision and attention to detail during the whole preceding estimating process. If an estimate is poorly prepared and put together, flaws will be amplified at these late stages.

Many general or prime contractors or construction managers use an adjustment column to arrive at a "quote" in the last hour before bid is due. Such adjustments might appear as follows:

Structural Steel	+ $10,000
Mechanical	− 35,000
Partitions	− 10,000
Electrical (Use 2nd Bidder)	+ 6,000
Total Deduct	$29,000

These deductions or additions may be obtained from last minute phone calls, faxed quotes, error corrections or discovered omissions. The final number, or bid price, is, in many cases, arrived at by a principal or senior member of the firm. Bidding strategies are discussed in Chapter 6, but the final quotation is usually determined by personal judgment, good or bad.

Factors that may affect a final decision are: the risk involved, competition from other bidders, thoroughness of the plans and specs, and above all, the

CONDENSED
ESTIMATE SUMMARY

PROJECT Office Building					ESTIMATE NO:	
LOCATION		TOTAL AREA / VOLUME			DATE: 6/93	
ARCHITECT		COST PER S.F. / C.F.			NO. OF STORIES	
PRICES BY:		EXTENSIONS BY:			CHECKED BY:	

DIV.	DESCRIPTION	MAT'L.	LABOR	EQUIP.	SUB w/ TAX	SUB w/o TAX	TOTAL
1	General Requirements	$126,813	$134,235				
2	Site Work	$138,220	$32,904	$30,487	$33,415		
3	Concrete	$209,303	$181,507	$15,480			
4	Masonry	$20,549	$21,990	$4,836			
5	Metals					$450,117	
6	Wood & Plastics	$5,605	$2,204				
7	Thermal & Moisture Protection	$7,551	$6,389			$66,401	
8	Doors & Windows	$23,925	$3,957		$863,818	$14,346	
9	Finishes	$103,772	$66,967			$250,468	
10	Specialties	$13,551	$1,852				
11	Equipment						
12	Furnishings						
13	Special Construction						
14	Conveying Systems					$121,590	
15	Mechanical				$691,841		
16	Electrical				$446,092		
	Subtotals	$649,289	$452,005	$50,803	$2,035,166	$902,922	$4,090,184
	Sales Tax 6% (3% on Sub-Contr.)	$38,957				$27,088	$66,045
	Overhead & Profit 10/57.4/10/10%	$64,929	$259,451	$5,080	$203,517	$90,292	$623,269
	Subtotal	$753,176	$711,456	$55,883	$2,238,682	$1,020,302	$4,779,498
	Bond ($12 /M)						$57,354
	Contingency 2%						$95,590
	Adjustments						$4,932,442
	TOTAL BID						$4,932,000

Figure 9.137

Installing Contractor's Overhead & Profit

Below are the **average** installing contractor's percentage mark-ups applied to base labor rates to arrive at typical billing rates.

Column A: Labor rates are based on union wages averaged for 30 major U.S. cities. Base rates including fringe benefits are listed hourly and daily. These figures are the sum of the wage rate and employer-paid fringe benefits such as vacation pay, employer-paid health and welfare costs, pension costs, plus appropriate training and industry advancement funds costs.

Column B: Workers' Compensation rates are the national average of state rates established for each trade.

Column C: Column C lists average fixed overhead figures for all trades. Included are Federal and State Unemployment costs set at 7.3%; Social Security Taxes (FICA) set at 7.65%; Builder's Risk Insurance costs set at 0.34%; and Public Liability costs set at 1.55%. All the percentages except those for Social Security Taxes vary from state to state as well as from company to company.

Columns D and E: Percentages in Columns D and E are based on the presumption that the installing contractor has annual billing of $500,000 and up. Overhead percentages may increase with smaller annual billing. The overhead percentages for any given contractor may vary greatly and depend on a number of factors, such as the contractor's annual volume, engineering and logistical support costs, and staff requirements. The figures for overhead and profit will also vary depending on the type of job, the job location, and the prevailing economic conditions. All factors should be examined very carefully for each job.

Column F: Column F lists the total of Columns B, C, D, and E.

Column G: Column G is Column A (hourly base labor rate) multiplied by the percentage in Column F (O&P percentage).

Column H: Column H is the total of Column A (hourly base labor rate) plus Column G (Total O&P).

Column I: Column I is Column H multiplied by eight hours.

		A		B	C	D	E	F	G	H	I
		Base Rate Incl. Fringes		Workers' Comp. Ins.	Average Fixed Overhead	Overhead	Profit	Total Overhead & Profit		Rate with O & P	
Abbr.	Trade	Hourly	Daily					%	Amount	Hourly	Daily
Skwk	Skilled Workers Average (35 trades)	$24.10	$192.80	17.6%	16.8%	13.0%	10.0%	57.4%	$13.85	$37.95	$303.60
	Helpers Average (5 trades)	18.10	144.80	18.8		11.0		56.6	10.25	28.35	226.80
	Foreman Average, Inside ($.50 over trade)	24.60	196.80	17.6		13.0		57.4	14.10	38.70	309.60
	Foreman Average, Outside ($2.00 over trade)	26.10	208.80	17.6		13.0		57.4	15.00	41.10	328.80
Clab	Common Building Laborers	18.55	148.40	19.2		11.0		57.0	10.55	29.10	232.80
Asbe	Asbestos Workers	26.15	209.20	16.7		16.0		59.5	15.55	41.70	333.60
Boil	Boilermakers	26.80	214.40	10.5		16.0		53.3	14.30	41.10	328.80
Bric	Bricklayers	24.05	192.40	16.8		11.0		54.6	13.15	37.20	297.60
Brhe	Bricklayer Helpers	18.85	150.80	16.8		11.0		54.6	10.30	29.15	233.20
Carp	Carpenters	23.35	186.80	19.2		11.0		57.0	13.30	36.65	293.20
Cefi	Cement Finishers	23.05	184.40	11.4		11.0		49.2	11.35	34.40	275.20
Elec	Electricians	26.70	213.60	7.3		16.0		50.1	13.40	40.10	320.80
Elev	Elevator Constructors	27.25	218.00	8.1		16.0		50.9	13.85	41.10	328.80
Eqhv	Equipment Operators, Crane or Shovel	24.95	199.60	11.7		14.0		52.5	13.10	38.05	304.40
Eqmd	Equipment Operators, Medium Equipment	24.10	192.80	11.7		14.0		52.5	12.65	36.75	294.00
Eqlt	Equipment Operators, Light Equipment	23.10	184.80	11.7		14.0		52.5	12.15	35.25	282.00
Eqol	Equipment Operators, Oilers	20.25	162.00	11.7		14.0		52.5	10.65	30.90	247.20
Eqmm	Equipment Operators, Master Mechanics	25.55	204.40	11.7		14.0		52.5	13.40	38.95	311.60
Glaz	Glaziers	23.50	188.00	13.9		11.0		51.7	12.15	35.65	285.20
Lath	Lathers	23.20	185.60	12.6		11.0		50.4	11.70	34.90	279.20
Marb	Marble Setters	24.15	193.20	16.8		11.0		54.6	13.20	37.35	298.80
Mill	Millwrights	24.35	194.80	11.6		11.0		49.4	12.05	36.40	291.20
Mstz	Mosaic and Terrazzo Workers	23.70	189.60	9.9		11.0		47.7	11.30	35.00	280.00
Pord	Painters, Ordinary	21.75	174.00	15.0		11.0		52.8	11.50	33.25	266.00
Psst	Painters, Structural Steel	22.55	180.40	52.0		11.0		89.8	20.25	42.80	342.40
Pape	Paper Hangers	21.95	175.60	15.0		11.0		52.8	11.60	33.55	268.40
Pile	Pile Drivers	23.50	188.00	29.5		16.0		72.3	17.00	40.50	324.00
Plas	Plasterers	22.80	182.40	15.6		11.0		53.4	12.20	35.00	280.00
Plah	Plasterer Helpers	19.05	152.40	15.6		11.0		53.4	10.15	29.20	233.60
Plum	Plumbers	27.40	219.20	8.7		16.0		51.5	14.10	41.50	332.00
Rodm	Rodmen (Reinforcing)	25.85	206.80	34.4		14.0		75.2	19.45	45.30	362.40
Rofc	Roofers, Composition	21.25	170.00	32.6		11.0		70.4	14.95	36.20	289.60
Rots	Roofers, Tile and Slate	21.30	170.40	32.6		11.0		70.4	15.00	36.30	290.40
Rohe	Roofer Helpers (Composition)	15.25	122.00	32.6		11.0		70.4	10.75	26.00	208.00
Shee	Sheet Metal Workers	26.65	213.20	12.4		16.0		55.2	14.70	41.35	330.80
Spri	Sprinkler Installers	29.00	232.00	9.4		16.0		52.2	15.15	44.15	353.20
Stpi	Steamfitters or Pipefitters	27.45	219.60	8.7		16.0		51.5	14.15	41.60	332.80
Ston	Stone Masons	24.15	193.20	16.8		11.0		54.6	13.20	37.35	298.80
Sswk	Structural Steel Workers	26.00	208.00	40.1		14.0		80.9	21.05	47.05	376.40
Tilf	Tile Layers (Floor)	23.50	188.00	9.9		11.0		47.7	11.20	34.70	277.60
Tilh	Tile Layer Helpers	18.70	149.60	9.9		11.0		47.7	8.90	27.60	220.80
Trlt	Truck Drivers, Light	19.15	153.20	15.2		11.0		53.0	10.15	29.30	234.40
Trhv	Truck Drivers, Heavy	19.45	155.60	15.2		11.0		53.0	10.30	29.75	238.00
Sswl	Welders, Structural Steel	26.00	208.00	40.1		14.0		80.9	21.05	47.05	376.40
Wrck	*Wrecking	18.55	148.40	40.6	▼	11.0	▼	78.4	14.55	33.10	264.80

*Not included in Averages.

Figure 9.138

years of experience – the qualification to make such a judgment. Some firms are so scientific and calculating that every quoted price includes a lucky number.

A great deal of success in bidding can be attributed to the proper choice of jobs to bid. A contracting firm can go broke estimating every available job. The company must be able to recognize which jobs are too risky and when the competition is too keen, while not overlooking those which can be profitable. Again, knowledge of the marketplace and *experience* are the keys to successful bidding.

The primary purpose of this text has not been to tell the reader how much an item will cost, but instead, how to develop a consistent and thorough approach to the estimating process. If such a pattern is developed, employing consistency, attention to detail, experience and above all, common sense, accurate costs will follow.

If an estimate is thorough, organized, neat and concise, the benefits go beyond winning contracts. The information and data that is developed will be useful throughout a project – for purchasing, change orders, cost accounting and control and development of historical costs.

APPENDIX A

APPENDIX A

The following is a multiple-page form, called Means' SPEC-AID, which was developed to aid the estimator in preparing all parts of a building project estimate. Each of the sixteen MasterFormat divisions is represented by a complete and thorough checklist. These lists are used to record project requirements and to help ensure inclusion of all items in an estimate.

R.S. Means has published two complete books of reproducible forms, checklists and aids to the estimator. The first, entitled *Means Forms for Building Construction Professionals*, includes the SPEC-AID. The second, *Means Forms for Contractors*, is a collection of forms for estimating, bidding and scheduling as well as project administrative tasks, personnel management. Both forms books show sample uses and include a full explanation of each type of form.

SPEC - AID

OUTLINE SPECIFICATION

AND

QUESTIONNAIRE

FOR

PROJECT _____

ADDRESS _____

CITY/STATE/ZIP _____

PREPARED BY _____

_____

DATE _____

Means
A Southam Company

R.S. Means Company, Inc.
100 Construction Plaza, P.O. Box 800, Kingston, MA 02364-0800, 617-585-7880

TABLE OF CONTENTS

INSTRUCTIONS FOR USE OF SPEC-AID©

A. A primary use of SPEC-AID© is to provide construction planners with a detailed checklist that will facilitate concurrent precise development of specifications with drawings. (It will ensure that all planning groups are talking about the same type and quality of building.)

B. DIVISION 1 is a General Project Description which outlines code requirements and basic building parameters. It is usually completed by the project manager, architect or engineer, having responsible knowledge of the appropriate necessary information.

C. DIVISION 2 through 16 are arranged according to the CSI MasterFormat. Section items should be completed by designers or other technical personnel as appropriate. This should be done as early in the design stage as possible.

D. When an item or product is specifically selected or the drawings are detailed around it, identify it by name, type, number, manufacturer, and reference. Use additional sheets as required.

E. The PROJECT SCHEDULE on page 324 should be one of the first items considered. It can be refined, added to, and revised as the project requirements develop. It is used to show lead time, to coordinate systems, and to visually indicate major project components by events (design, bid, begin construction, etc.), date and duration.

F. The PROJECT SKETCH on page 325 is a set of grid lines to facilitate schematic representation of project phases, column lines, etc. Use of this feature helps to define the scope of the project.

G. The SYSTEM ESTIMATE can be summarized on pages 355 and 356. The systems headings can be coordinated with the PROJECT SCHEDULE on page 324. By filling in the columns (Quantity, Unit, Unit Price, Total Cost, Cost/S.F., and % of Bldg.), each estimated aspect of the project is shown at a glance. By keeping a complete copy of SPEC-AID© for each project on file, valuable preliminary estimating quantities and costs as well as specifications will be at your fingertips for future reference.

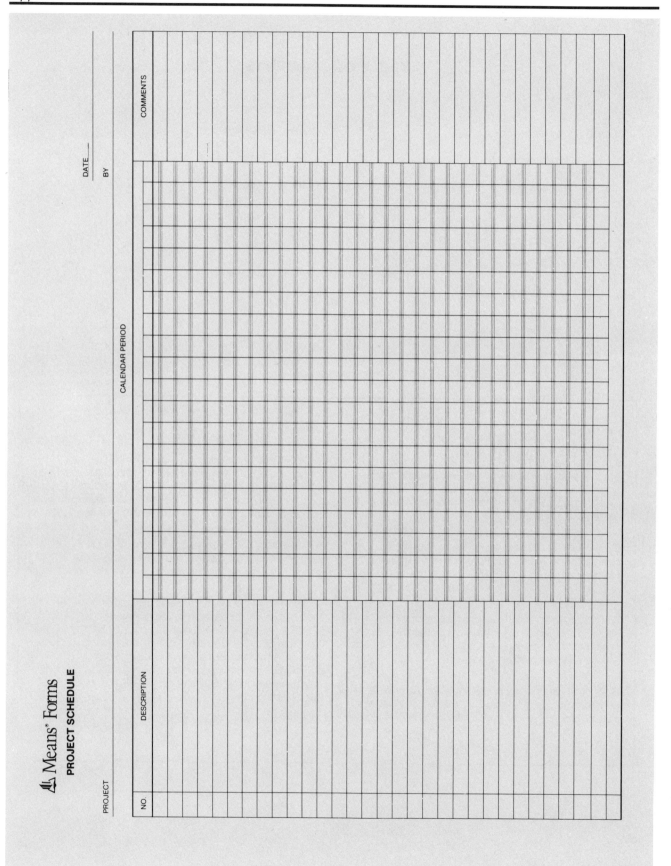

Means® Forms
PROJECT SCHEDULE

PROJECT _____

DATE ____

BY ____

NO	DESCRIPTION	CALENDAR PERIOD	COMMENTS

⚓ Means® Forms

SPEC-AID

PROJECT _____   DATE _____

ADDRESS _____

CITY/STATE/ZIP _____   PREPARED BY: _____

PROJECT SKETCH   1″ = _____ Ft.

⚓ Means® Forms

SPEC-AID

DATE _____

DIVISION 1: GENERAL

PROJECT _____ LOCATION _____

Owner _____ **Architect** _____ **Project Mgr.** _____

Engineer: Structural _____ Plumbing _____

H.V.A.C. _____ Electrical _____

Contractor: General _____ Structural _____

Mechanical _____ Electrical _____

Building Type _____

Building Capacities: _____

_____

Quality ☐ Economy ☐ Average ☐ Good ☐ Luxury Describe _____

Size

Ground Floor Area _____ S.F.

Supported Levels (No.) _____ x Area/Level _____ S.F.

Supported Levels (No.) _____ x Area/Level _____ S.F.

Below Grade Area _____ S.F.

Other Area _____ S.F.

TOTAL GROSS AREA _____ S.F.

Floor to Floor Height: Maximum _____ Minimum _____ Average _____

Floor to Ceiling Height: Maximum _____ Minimum _____ Average _____

Floor System Depth: Maximum _____ Minimum _____ Average _____

Building Codes ☐ City _____ ☐ County _____

☐ State _____ ☐ National _____

☐ Other _____ Seismic Zone _____

Zoning ☐ Residential ☐ Commercial ☐ Industrial ☐ None ☐ Other _____

Design Criteria Live Loads: Roof _____ psf. End Walls _____ psf. Window Openings _____ %

Supported Floor _____ psf. Side Walls _____ psf. Window Openings _____ %

Ground Floor _____ psf. WIND PRESSURE

Corridors _____ psf. _____ psf. from _____ to _____ ft.

Balconies _____ psf. _____ psf. from _____ to _____ ft.

Allow for Partitions _____ psf. _____ psf. from _____ to _____ ft.

Miscellaneous _____ psf. _____ psf. from _____ to _____ ft.

Comments _____

_____

Typical Bay Spacing _____

Structural Frame ☐ Concrete ☐ Steel ☐ Wood ☐ Wall Bearing ☐ Other _____

Describe _____

Fireproofing ☐ None ☐ Columns _____ Hours ☐ Girders _____ Hours ☐ Beams _____ Hours ☐ Floor _____ Hours

Estimating Budget Estimate Due _____ 19 _____ Schematic Estimate Due _____ 19 ____

Preliminary Estimate Due _____ 19 ____ Final Estimate Due _____ 19 ____ at ____ % Working Drawings

Labor Market ☐ Highly Competitive ☐ Normal ☐ Non-Competitive ☐ Unreliable ☐ Union ☐ Non-union

Describe _____

Taxes Tax exempt ☐ No ☐ Yes State ____ % County ____ % City ____ % Other ____ %

Bond ☐ Not Required ☐ Required _____

Bidding Date _____ Start Date _____ Construction Duration _____ Months

☐ Open Competitive ☐ Selected Competitive ☐ Negotiated ☐ Filed Bids _____

Contract ☐ Single ☐ Multiple Describe _____

Multiple Type assigned to General Contractor ☐ No ☐ Yes _____

Means® Forms

SPEC-AID

DATE _____

DIVISION 2: SITEWORK
_____

PROJECT _____ LOCATION _____

Demolition Site: ☐ No ☐ Yes Allowance _____ ☐ Separate Contract

Interior: ☐ No ☐ Yes ☐ Allowance _____ ☐ Separate Contract

Removal From Site: ☐ No ☐ Yes Dump Location _____ Distance _____

Topography ☐ Level ☐ Moderate Grades ☐ Steep Grades Describe _____

Subsurface Exploration ☐ Borings ☐ Test Pits ☐ USDA Maps ☐ Other _____

Performed by: ☐ Owner ☐ Engineer ☐ Contractor _____

Site Area: Total _____ Acres to Clear _____ Acres To Thin _____ Acres Open _____ Acres

Clearing and Grubbing: ☐ No ☐ Light ☐ Medium ☐ Heavy _____

Topsoil: ☐ No ☐ Strip ☐ Stockpile ☐ Dispose on Site ☐ Dispose off Site _____ Miles ☐ Furnish

Existing _____ Inches Deep Final Depth _____ Inches Describe _____

Soil Type: ☐ Gravel ☐ Sand ☐ Clay ☐ Silt ☐ Rock ☐ Peat ☐ Other _____

Rock Expected: ☐ No ☐ Ledge ☐ Boulders ☐ Hardpan ☐ Describe _____

How Paid _____

Ground Water Expected: ☐ No ☐ Yes Depth or Elevation _____

Disposal by ☐ Pumping ☐ Wells ☐ Wellpoints ☐ Other _____

Excavation: ☐ Grade and Fill on Site ☐ Dispose off Site _____ Miles ☐ Borrow Expected _____ Miles

Quantity Involved _____

Describe _____

Sheeting Required: ☐ No ☐ Yes Describe _____

Protect Existing Structures: ☐ No ☐ Yes Describe _____

Backfill: ☐ No ☐ Yes Area _____ Material _____ Inches Deep _____ % Compaction

Landscape Area ☐ No ☐ Yes Area _____ Material _____ Inches Deep _____ % Compaction

Building Area ☐ No ☐ Yes Area _____ Material _____ Inches Deep _____ % Compaction

Source of Materials _____

Water Control: ☐ Ditching ☐ Sheet Piling ☐ Pumping ☐ Wells ☐ Wellpoints ☐ Pressure Grouting

☐ Chemical Grouting ☐ Other _____

Describe _____

Termite Control: ☐ No ☐ Yes Describe _____

Special Considerations: _____

Piles: ☐ No ☐ Yes ☐ Friction ☐ End Bearing ☐ Concrete ☐ Pipe, Empty ☐ Pipe, Concrete Filled ☐ Steel

☐ Step Tapered ☐ Tapered Thin Shell ☐ Wood ☐ Capacity _____ Tons

Size _____ Length _____ Number Required _____

Caissons: ☐ No ☐ Yes ☐ Cased ☐ Uncased Capacity _____

Size _____ Length _____ Number Required _____

Pressure Injected Footings: ☐ No ☐ Yes ☐ Cased ☐ Uncased Capacity _____

Size _____ Length _____ Number Required _____

Special Considerations: _____

Storm Drains: ☐ No ☐ Yes ☐ Asbestos Cement ☐ Bituminous Fiber ☐ Concrete ☐ Corrugated Metal ☐ _____

Size and Length _____

Headwall: ☐ No ☐ Yes Type _____ Number _____

Catch Basins: ☐ No ☐ Yes ☐ Block ☐ Brick ☐ Concrete ☐ Precast Size _____ Number _____

Manholes: ☐ No ☐ Yes ☐ Block ☐ Brick ☐ Concrete ☐ Precast Size _____ Number _____

Building Sub Drains: ☐ No ☐ Yes ☐ Type _____ Length _____

French Drains: ☐ No ☐ Yes Size _____ Length _____

Trenches: Swales, etc.: ☐ No ☐ Yes Describe _____

Rip Rap: ☐ No ☐ Yes Describe _____

Special Considerations: _____

▲ Means® Forms

SPEC-AID

DIVISION 2: SITEWORK

Water Supply Existing Main: ☐ No ☐ Yes Location _____ Size _____
  Service Piping: By Utility ☐ By Others ☐ This Contract _____ Size _____
  Wells: ☐ No ☐ Yes ☐ By Others ☐ This Contract _____ Capacity _____
  Water Pumping Station: ☐ No ☐ Yes Type _____ Capacity _____
Sewers: ☐ No ☐ Yes ☐ By Others ☐ Asbestos Cement ☐ Concrete ☐ Plastic ☐ Vitrified Clay ☐ _____
  Manholes: ☐ No ☐ Yes ☐ Block ☐ Brick ☐ Concrete ☐ Precast Size _____ Number _____
  Sewage Pumping Station: ☐ No ☐ Yes Type _____ Capacity _____
Sewage Treatment: ☐ No ☐ Yes ☐ By Others ☐ This Contract ☐ Septic Tank ☐ Package Treatment Plant
  Describe _____
Special Considerations: _____
_____

Driveways: ☐ No ☐ Yes ☐ By Others ☐ Bituminous ☐ Concrete ☐ Gravel ☐ _____ Thickness _____
Parking Area: ☐ No ☐ Yes ☐ By Others ☐ Bituminous ☐ Concrete ☐ Gravel ☐ _____ Thickness _____
  Base Course: ☐ No ☐ Yes ☐ By Others ☐ Gravel ☐ Stone ☐ _____ Thickness _____
Curbs: ☐ No ☐ Yes ☐ By Others ☐ Bituminous ☐ Concrete ☐ Granite ☐ _____ Size _____
Parking Bumpers: ☐ No ☐ Yes ☐ By Others ☐ Concrete ☐ Timber _____
Painting Lines: ☐ No ☐ Yes ☐ By Others ☐ Paint ☐ Thermo Plastic ☐ Traffic Lines ☐ Stalls ☐ _____
Guard Rail: ☐ No ☐ Yes ☐ By Others ☐ Cable ☐ Steel ☐ Timber _____
Sidewalks: ☐ No ☐ Yes ☐ By Others ☐ Bituminous ☐ Brick ☐ Concrete ☐ Stone _____
  Width _____ Thickness _____
Steps: ☐ No ☐ Yes ☐ Brick ☐ Concrete ☐ Stone ☐ Timber _____
Signs: ☐ No ☐ Yes ☐ Stock ☐ Custom _____
Traffic Signals: ☐ No ☐ Yes ☐ By Others _____
Special Considerations: _____

Fencing: ☐ No ☐ Yes ☐ By Others ☐ Chain link ☐ Aluminum ☐ Steel ☐ Other _____
  Height _____ Length _____ Gates _____
Fountains: ☐ No ☐ Yes ☐ By Others _____
Planters: ☐ No ☐ Yes ☐ By Others ☐ Asbestos Cement ☐ Concrete ☐ Fiberglass ☐ _____
Playground Equipment: ☐ No ☐ Yes ☐ By Others ☐ Benches _____ ☐ Bleachers _____
  ☐ Bike Rack _____ ☐ Goal Posts _____ ☐ Posts _____
  ☐ Running Track _____
  ☐ See Saw _____ ☐ Shelters _____ ☐ Slides _____
  ☐ Swings _____ ☐ Whirlers _____ ☐ _____
Playing Fields: ☐ No ☐ Yes ☐ By Others _____
Railroad Work: ☐ No ☐ Yes ☐ By Others Weight _____ lb. per L.Y. ☐ New ☐ Relay Length _____
  Turnout: ☐ No ☐ Yes _____ ☐ Bumpers _____ ☐ Derails _____
  Wheel Stops _____ ☐ Others _____
Retaining Walls: ☐ No ☐ Yes ☐ By Others ☐ Gravity Concrete ☐ Cantilever Concrete ☐ Steel Bin ☐ Cribbing
  ☐ Timber ☐ Other _____ Height _____ Length _____
Irrigation System: ☐ No ☐ Yes ☐ By Others _____
Tennis Courts: ☐ No ☐ Yes ☐ By Others Type _____ Number _____
Trash Closures: ☐ No ☐ Yes Size _____
Lawns & Planting: ☐ No ☐ Yes ☐ By Others _____ Allowance _____
  Topsoil: ☐ No ☐ Yes ☐ By Others Depth _____ Inches Source _____
  Shrubs: ☐ No ☐ Yes ☐ By Others Describe _____ Allowance _____
  Trees: ☐ No ☐ Yes ☐ By Others Describe _____ Allowance _____
  Seeding: ☐ No ☐ Yes ☐ By Others Describe _____
  Sodding: ☐ No ☐ Yes ☐ By Others Describe _____ Thickness _____
  ☐ Ground Cover _____ ☐ Edging _____ ☐ Mulching _____
Special Considerations: _____

Means® Forms

SPEC-AID

DATE _____

DIVISION 3: CONCRETE

PROJECT _____ LOCATION _____

Foundations Bearing on: ☐ Rock ☐ Earth ☐ Piles ☐ Caissons ☐ Other _____
 Bearing Capacity _____
Footings Pile Caps: ☐ No ☐ Yes _____ psi Size _____
 Forms _____ Reinforcing _____ Waterproofing _____
 Spread Footings: ☐ No ☐ Yes ___ psi Size _____ Soil Bearing Capacity _____
 Forms _____ Reinforcing _____ Waterproofing _____
 Continuous Footings: ☐ No ☐ Yes _____ psi Size _____
 Forms _____ Reinforcing _____ Waterproofing _____
 Grade Beams: ☐ No ☐ Yes _____ psi Size _____
 Forms _____ Reinforcing _____ Waterproofing _____
Piers: ☐ No ☐ Yes _____ psi Size _____
 Forms _____ Reinforcing _____ Finish _____
Anchor Bolts: ☐ No ☐ Yes Size _____
 Grout Column Base Plates: ☐ No ☐ Yes _____
Underslab Fill: ☐ No ☐ Yes Material _____ Depth _____
Vapor Barrier: ☐ No ☐ Yes Material _____ Thickness _____
Perimeter Insulation: ☐ No ☐ Yes Material _____ Dimensions _____
Slab on Grade: ☐ No ☐ Yes _____ psi _____ Thickness _____
 Forms: ☐ Cold Keyed ☐ Expansion ☐ Other _____ Spacing _____
 Reinforcing: ☐ No ☐ Mesh ☐ Bars _____ Type _____
 Finish: ☐ Screed ☐ Darby ☐ Float ☐ Broom ☐ Trowel ☐ Granolithic _____
 Special Finish: ☐ No ☐ Hardner ☐ Colors ☐ Abrasives ☐ _____
Columns: ☐ No ☐ Round ☐ Square ☐ Rectangular ☐ Precast ☐ Steel ☐ Encased Steel ☐ Lightweight
 _____ _____ psi Size _____
 Forms: ☐ Optional ☐ Framed Plywood ☐ Plywood ☐ Fiber Tube ☐ Steel ☐ Round Fiberglass ☐ _____
 Reinforcing: ☐ No ☐ Square Tied ☐ Spirals Grade _____ Bar Sizes _____ Type Splice _____
 Finish: ☐ Break Fins ☐ Rubbed ☐ Other _____
Elevated Slab System: ☐ No ☐ Flat Plate ☐ Flat Slab ☐ Domes ☐ Pans ☐ Beam & Slab ☐ Lift Slab ☐ Composite
 ☐ Floor Fill ☐ Roof Fill ☐ Standard Weight ☐ Lightweight Concrete Strength _____
 Forms: ☐ Optional ☐ Plywood ☐ Other _____ Ceiling Height _____
 Reinforcing: ☐ Mesh ☐ Bars Grade _____ Size: _____
  Post-tension: ☐ No ☐ Simple Spans ☐ Continuous Spans _____ Depth _____
  ☐ Grouted ☐ Ungrouted Perimeter Conditions _____
 Slab Finish: ☐ Screed ☐ Darby ☐ Float ☐ Broom ☐ Trowel ☐ Granolithic ☐ _____
 Special Finish: ☐ No ☐ Hardener ☐ Colors ☐ Abrasives ☐ _____
 Ceiling Finish: ☐ No ☐ Break Fins ☐ Rubbed ☐ Other _____
Beams: ☐ No ☐ Steel ☐ Encased Steel ☐ Precast ☐ Regular Weight ☐ Lightweight ☐ Steel Composite _____
 Description: _____
 Forms: ☐ Optional ☐ Framed Plywood ☐ Plywood ☐ Steel ☐ Other _____ Ceiling Height _____
 Reinforcing: ☐ Conventional ☐ Post-tension ☐ Simple Span ☐ Continuous Spans _____ Depth _____
  ☐ Grouted ☐ Ungrouted Perimeter Conditions _____
Walls: ☐ No ☐ Precast ☐ Tilt up ☐ Regular Weight ☐ Lightweight _____ psi Thickness _____
 Forms: ☐ Optional ☐ Framed Plywood ☐ Plywood ☐ Steel ☐ Slipform ☐ _____
 Reinforcing: ☐ No ☐ Bars Grade _____ Clear Height _____
 Finish: ☐ No ☐ Break Fins ☐ Rubbed ☐ _____
Stairs: ☐ No ☐ Precast ☐ Ground Cast ☐ Form Cast ☐ Pan Fill Treads ☐ _____
 Forms: ☐ Plywood ☐ Steel ☐ Prefab Steel, Left in Place ☐ _____
 Reinforcing: ☐ Conventional Grade _____
 Finish: ☐ All Surfaces ☐ Treads ☐ Risers ☐ Abrasives ☐ Nosings _____

⚓ Means® Forms

SPEC-AID

DIVISION 3: CONCRETE

Reinforcing Splices: ☐ No ☐ Yes ☐ Lap Type ☐ Compression Only ☐ 125% Yield ☐ Full Tension
☐ Horizontal ☐ Vertical ☐ Special _____

Gunite: ☐ No ☐ Yes _____

Cast in Place Special Considerations: _____
_____
_____
_____
_____

Copings: ☐ No ☐ Yes Size _____ Finish _____

Curbs: ☐ No ☐ Yes Size _____ Finish _____

Joists: ☐ No ☐ Yes Live load _____ psf. Span _____ Size _____
Describe _____

Lift Slab: ☐ No ☐ Yes No. Slabs _____ Thickness _____ Inches Columns Spacing _____
Story Height _____ ☐ Conventional Reinforcing ☐ Post-tension _____

Lintels: ☐ No ☐ Yes ☐ Doors ☐ Windows ☐ Other _____
☐ Conventional Reinforcing ☐ Prestressed _____

Prestressed Precast Floors: ☐ No ☐ Yes ☐ Plank ☐ Multiple Tee Depth _____ Span _____ Width _____
Roofs: ☐ No ☐ Yes ☐ Plank ☐ Double Tee ☐ Single Tee Depth _____ Span _____ Width _____
Supporting Beams: ☐ No ☐ Yes ☐ Cast in Place ☐ Precast Describe _____

Columns: ☐ No ☐ Yes ☐ Steel ☐ Cast in Place ☐ Precast Size _____
Walls: ☐ No ☐ Yes ☐ Multiple Tee ☐ Other Thickness _____ Height _____ Width _____
Stairs: ☐ No ☐ Yes ☐ Treads Only ☐ Tread & Riser Units ☐ Complete Stairs ☐ Other _____
Describe _____

Tilt Up Walls: ☐ No ☐ Yes Size _____ Finish _____

Wall Panels: ☐ No ☐ Yes ☐ Insulated ☐ Regular Weight ☐ Lightweight Panel Size _____
Finish: ☐ Gray ☐ White ☐ Exposed Aggregate ☐ Other _____
Reinforcing: ☐ Conventional ☐ Prestressed ☐ Plain ☐ Galvanized _____
Erection: ☐ No. Stories _____ Maximum Lift _____ Overhangs, etc. _____

Window Section: ☐ No ☐ Yes ☐ Size _____ Finish _____

Window Sills: ☐ No ☐ Yes Size _____ Finish _____

Precast Special Considerations: _____
_____
_____
_____
_____
_____

Concrete Decks: ☐ No ☐ Yes ☐ Cast in Place ☐ Plank ☐ Topping ☐ Cement Fiber ☐ Channel Slab ☐ _____
Depth _____ Span _____ Sub Purlins _____ Roof Pitch _____

Concrete Fill: ☐ No ☐ Yes ☐ Regular Weight ☐ Lightweight Type _____ Depth _____

Formboard: ☐ No ☐ Yes ☐ Type _____ Depth _____ Spans _____
Sub Purlins: ☐ No ☐ Yes Span _____ Describe _____

Gypsum Decks Floor Plank: ☐ No ☐ Yes Depth _____ Span _____ Underlayment _____
Roofs: ☐ No ☐ Yes ☐ Cast in Place ☐ Plank Depth _____ Span _____ Pitch _____

Other Cementitious Decks: ☐ No ☐ Yes Describe _____
_____

Cementitious Decks: Special Considerations _____
_____
_____

General Notes: Concrete Section _____
_____
_____
_____

⚓ Means° Forms

SPEC-AID

DATE _____

DIVISION 4: MASONRY

PROJECT _____ LOCATION _____

Exterior Walls: ☐ No ☐ Yes ☐ Load Bearing ☐ Non Load Bearing Story Height _____
Describe _____
Interior Walls: ☐ No ☐ Yes ☐ Load Bearing ☐ Non Load Bearing Ceiling Height _____
Describe _____
Mortar: ☐ Optional ☐ Type K ☐ Type 0 ☐ Type N ☐ Type S ☐ Type M ☐ Thinset ☐ _____
☐ Colors _____ ☐ Other _____
Cement Brick: ☐ No ☐ Yes ☐ Solid ☐ Cavity ☐ Veneer ☐ _____
Describe _____
_____ Compressive Strength _____ psi. ASTM No. _____
Size _____ Bond _____ Joints _____ Reinforcing _____ Ties _____
Common Brick: ☐ No ☐ Yes ☐ Solid ☐ Cavity ☐ Veneer ☐ _____
Describe _____
_____ Compressive Strength _____ psi. ASTM No. _____
Size _____ Bond _____ Joints _____ Reinforcing _____ Ties _____
Face Brick: ☐ No ☐ Yes ☐ Solid ☐ Cavity ☐ Veneer ☐ _____
Describe _____
_____ Compressive Strength _____ psi. ASTM No. _____
Size ☐ Standard ☐ Jumbo ☐ Norman ☐ Roman ☐ Engineer ☐ Double ☐ _____
Allowance: ☐ No ☐ Yes $ _____ per M Delivered ☐ Unglazed ☐ Single Glazed ☐ Double Glazed
Bond: ☐ Running ☐ Common ☐ English ☐ Flemish ☐ Stack ☐ _____ Headers Every _____ Course.
Joints: ☐ Concave ☐ Struck ☐ Flush ☐ Raked ☐ Weathered ☐ Stripped ☐ _____
Reinforcing: ☐ No ☐ Yes Describe _____
Wall Ties: ☐ No ☐ Yes Describe _____
Anchor Bolts: ☐ No ☐ Yes Size _____
Chimneys: ☐ No ☐ Yes ☐ Regular Brick ☐ Radial Brick Size _____
Columns: ☐ No ☐ Yes Size _____
Control Joints: ☐ No ☐ Yes Spacing _____ Material _____
Copings ☐ No ☐ Yes ☐ Concrete ☐ Stone ☐ _____ Describe _____
Fire Brick: ☐ No ☐ Yes ☐ Low Duty ☐ High Duty Describe _____
Fireplaces: ☐ No ☐ Yes Describe _____
Accessories _____
Flooring: ☐ No ☐ Yes ☐ Laid Flat ☐ Laid on Edge ☐ Pattern _____
☐ Regular ☐ Acid Resisting Describe _____
Insulating Brick: ☐ No ☐ Yes Describe _____
Insulation: ☐ No ☐ Yes ☐ Board ☐ Poured ☐ Sprayed Material _____
Thickness _____ Describe _____
Lintels: ☐ No ☐ Yes ☐ Block ☐ Precast ☐ Steel Describe _____
Masonry Restoration: ☐ No ☐ Yes ☐ Cut ☐ Recaulk ☐ Repoint ☐ Stucco Finish ☐ _____
Sand Blast: ☐ No ☐ Yes Describe _____
Steam Clean: ☐ No ☐ Yes Describe _____
Piers: ☐ No ☐ Yes Size _____
Pilasters: ☐ No ☐ Yes Size _____
Refractory Work: ☐ No ☐ Yes Describe _____
Simulated Brick: ☐ No ☐ Yes Material _____ Describe _____
Steps: ☐ No ☐ Yes Describe _____
Vent Box: ☐ No ☐ Yes ☐ Aluminum ☐ Bronze Size _____
Weep Holes: ☐ No ☐ Yes Spacing _____ Describe _____
Window Sills and Stools: ☐ No ☐ Yes ☐ Brick ☐ Concrete ☐ Stone ☐ _____
Describe _____

⚞ Means· Forms

SPEC-AID

DIVISION 4: MASONRY

Concrete Block: ☐ No ☐ Yes ☐ Exterior ☐ Interior ☐ Regular Weight ☐ Lightweight ☐ Solid ☐ Hollow
☐ Load Bearing ☐ Non Load Bearing Describe _____
_____ Compressive Strength _____ psi. ASTM No. _____
Size: _____
Finish: ☐ Regular ☐ Ground ☐ Ribbed ☐ Glazed ☐ _____
Bond: ☐ Common ☐ Stack ☐ Other _____ Headers Every _____ Course.
Joints: ☐ Concave ☐ Struck ☐ Flush ☐ Raked ☐ Weathered ☐ Stripped ☐ _____
Reinforcing: ☐ No ☐ Yes _____ Strips Every _____ Course.
Wall Ties: ☐ No ☐ Yes Describe _____
Bond Beams: ☐ No ☐ Yes Size _____ Describe _____
Reinforcing _____ Grout _____
Lintels: ☐ No ☐ Yes ☐ Precast ☐ Steel ☐ Block Size _____ Describe _____
Reinforcing _____ Grout _____
Columns: ☐ No ☐ Yes Size _____
Pilasters: ☐ No ☐ Yes Size _____
Glass Block: ☐ No ☐ Yes ☐ Size _____ Type _____
Special Block _____
Describe _____
Glazed Concrete Block: ☐ No ☐ Yes ☐ Solid ☐ Hollow Type _____
☐ Non Reinforced ☐ Reinforced _____ Strips Every _____ Course.
Describe _____
Gypsum Block: ☐ No ☐ Yes ☐ Solid ☐ Hollow Thickness _____ Describe _____

Grouting: ☐ No ☐ Yes ☐ Block Cores ☐ Bond Beams ☐ Cavity Walls ☐ Door Frames ☐ Lintels ☐ _____
Describe _____
Insulation: ☐ No ☐ Yes ☐ Board ☐ Poured ☐ Sprayed Material _____
Thickness _____ Describe _____
Solar Screen: ☐ No ☐ Yes Describe _____
Special Block: ☐ No ☐ Yes Describe _____
☐ Parge Block ☐ Clean Cavity ☐ Spandrel Flashing _____
Special Considerations: _____
Ceramic Veneer: ☐ No ☐ Yes Describe _____
Structural Facing Tile: ☐ No ☐ Yes ☐ 6T Series ☐ 8W Series ☐ Other _____
Describe _____
Terra Cotta: ☐ No ☐ Yes ☐ Floors ☐ Partitions ☐ Fireproofing ☐ Load Bearing ☐ Non Load Bearing
Describe _____
Ashlar Stone: ☐ No ☐ Yes Type _____ Thickness _____
Describe _____
Rubble Stone: ☐ No ☐ Yes ☐ Coarsed ☐ Uncoarsed Type _____ Thickness _____
Describe _____
Cut Stone: ☐ No ☐ Yes ☐ Granite ☐ Limestone ☐ Marble ☐ Sand Stone ☐ Slate ☐ _____
☐ Base _____ ☐ Columns _____ ☐ Coping _____
☐ Curbs _____ ☐ Facing Panels _____
☐ Flooring _____ ☐ Showers _____
☐ Soffits _____ ☐ Stair Treads _____
☐ Stairs _____ ☐ Thresholds _____
☐ Window Sills _____ ☐ Window Stools _____
☐ _____
Simulated Stone: ☐ No ☐ Yes Material _____ Describe _____
Special Stone _____
General Notes: Masonry _____
_____
_____

⚓ Means® Forms

SPEC-AID

DATE _____

DIVISION 5: METALS _____

PROJECT _____ LOCATION _____

Design Criteria: In Division 1 _____

　Typical Bay Spacings: _____

　_____

　Floor to Ceiling Heights: _____

　Beam Depths: _____

　Roof Slope:　☐ Flat　☐ Other _____

　Eave Height: _____

Anchor Bolts:　☐ No　☐ By Others　☐ Yes　Describe _____ Number _____

Base Plates:　☐ No　☐ By Others　☐ Yes　Describe _____

　_____ Number _____

Metal Decking Floors:　☐ No　☐ By Others　☐ Cellular　☐ Non Cellular　☐ Painted　☐ Galv.　Depth _____

　☐ Acoustical　☐ Ventilating　Gauge _____ Describe _____

　Roof Deck:　☐ No　☐ By Others　☐ Cellular　☐ Non Cellular　☐ Painted　☐ Galv.　Depth _____

　☐ Acoustical　☐ Ventilating　Gauge _____ Describe _____

Structural System:　☐ Wall Bearing　☐ Free Standing　☐ Simple Spans　☐ Continuous Spans _____

　☐ Conventional Design　☐ Plastic Design　☐ Field Welded　☐ Field Bolted　☐ Composite Design

　☐ Other _____

　Type Steel _____ Grade _____

　Estimated Weights: Beams _____ Roof Frames _____ Adjustable Spandrel Angles _____

　　Girders _____ Girts _____ Hanger Pods _____ Bracing _____

　　Columns _____ Connections _____ Other _____

　Paint: Shop　☐ No　☐ Yes _____ Coats　Material _____

　　Field Paint　☐ No　☐ Yes　☐ Brush　☐ Roller　☐ Spray _____ Coats　Material _____

　Galvanizing:　☐ No　☐ Yes　Thickness _____

　Other: _____

Fireproofing:　☐ No　☐ Yes　☐ Beams　☐ Columns　☐ Decks　☐ Other _____ Rating _____ Hr.

　☐ Concrete Encasement　☐ Spray　☐ Plaster　☐ Drywall　☐ _____

　Describe _____

Open Web Joists:　☐ No　☐ Yes　☐ H Series　☐ LH Series　☐ _____

　Estimated Weights: _____

　Bridging:　☐ No　☐ Yes　☐ Bolted　☐ Welded　☐ Pod Bridging _____

　Paint: Shop　☐ Standard　☐ Special _____ Coats　Field Paint　☐ No　☐ Yes　Describe _____

Light Gauge Joists:　☐ No　☐ Yes　Describe _____

Light Gauge Framing:　☐ No　☐ Yes　Describe _____

Special Considerations: _____

_____

_____

Fasteners: Expansion Bolts _____ High Strength Bolts _____

　Machine Screws _____ Machinery Anchors _____

　Nails _____ Roof Bolts _____

　Sheet Metal Screws _____ Studs _____

　Timber Connectors _____ Toggle Bolts _____

　Welded Studs _____ Other _____

Page 9 of 30

⚓ Means® Forms

SPEC-AID

DIVISION 5: METALS

Area Walls: ☐ No ☐ Yes _____ Gratings _____ Caps _____

Bumper Rails: ☐ No ☐ Yes _____

Canopy Framing: ☐ No ☐ Yes _____

Checkered Plate: ☐ No ☐ Trench Covers ☐ Pit Covers ☐ Platforms ☐ _____

Columns: ☐ No ☐ Aluminum ☐ Steel ☐ Square ☐ Rectangular ☐ Round ☐ _____

Construction Castings: ☐ No ☐ Chimney Specialties _____ ☐ Column Bases _____

☐ Manhole Covers _____ ☐ Wheel Guards _____

☐ _____

Corner Guards: ☐ No ☐ Yes _____

Crane Rail: ☐ No ☐ Yes _____

Curb Angles: ☐ No ☐ Straight ☐ Curved _____

Decorative Covering: ☐ No ☐ Stock Sections ☐ Custom Sections _____

Doors _____ Walls _____

Door Frames: ☐ No ☐ Yes _____ ☐ Protection: ☐ No ☐ Yes _____

Expansion Joints Ceilings: ☐ No ☐ Yes _____ Cover Plates: ☐ No ☐ Yes _____

Floors: ☐ No ☐ Yes _____ Cover Plates: ☐ No ☐ Yes _____

Walls: ☐ No ☐ Yes _____ Cover Plates: ☐ No ☐ Yes _____

Fire Escape: ☐ No ☐ Yes _____ Size _____

Stairs _____ Ladders _____ Cantilever _____

Floor Grating: ☐ No ☐ Aluminum ☐ Steel ☐ Fiberglass ☐ Platforms ☐ Stairs ☐ _____

Type _____ Weight _____

Special Finish _____

Ladders: ☐ No ☐ Aluminum ☐ Steel ☐ _____

☐ With Cage ☐ No Cage _____ ☐ Inclined Type _____

Lamp Posts: ☐ No ☐ Yes _____

Lintels: ☐ No ☐ Yes ☐ Plain ☐ Built-up ☐ Painted ☐ Galvanized _____

Louvers: ☐ No ☐ Yes _____

Manhole Covers: ☐ No ☐ Yes _____

Mat Frames: ☐ No ☐ Yes _____

Overhead Supports: ☐ No ☐ Toilet ☐ Partitions ☐ _____

Pipe Bumpers: ☐ No ☐ Yes _____

Pipe Supports: ☐ No ☐ Yes _____

Railings: ☐ No ☐ Yes ☐ Aluminum ☐ Steel ☐ Pipe ☐ _____

Balconies: ☐ No ☐ Yes _____

Stairs: ☐ No ☐ Yes _____

Wall: ☐ No ☐ Yes _____

Solar Screens: ☐ No ☐ Yes _____

Stairs: ☐ No ☐ Yes ☐ Aluminum ☐ Steel ☐ Stock ☐ Custom ☐ _____

Size _____ Landings _____

Spiral: ☐ No ☐ Aluminum ☐ Steel ☐ Stock ☐ Custom ☐ _____

Pre-erected: ☐ No ☐ Yes _____

Stair Treads: ☐ No ☐ Yes _____

Trench Covers: ☐ No ☐ Yes _____

Weather Vanes: ☐ No ☐ Yes _____

Window Guards: ☐ No ☐ Bars ☐ Woven Wire ☐ _____

Wire: ☐ No ☐ Yes _____

Wire Rope: ☐ No ☐ Yes _____

Special Considerations: _____

_____

_____

🜂 Means® Forms

SPEC-AID
DIVISION 6: CARPENTRY

DATE _____

PROJECT _____ LOCATION _____

Framing: Type Wood _____ Fiber Stress _____ psi.

_____

Beams: ☐ Single ☐ Built Up _____ Grade _____

Bracing: ☐ No ☐ Let In ☐ _____

Bridging: ☐ Steel ☐ Wood _____

Canopy Framing: _____

Columns _____ Fiber Stress _____ psi.

Door Bucks: ☐ No ☐ Treated ☐ Untreated _____

Floor Planks _____ Grade _____

Furring: ☐ Metal ☐ Wood _____

Grounds: ☐ No ☐ Casework ☐ Plaster ☐ On Wood ☐ On Masonry _____

Joists: ☐ No ☐ Floor ☐ Ceiling _____ Grade _____

Ledgers: ☐ No ☐ Bolted ☐ Nailed _____

Lumber Treatment: ☐ No ☐ Creosote ☐ Salt Treated ☐ Fire Retardant _____

☐ Kiln Dry _____

Nailers: ☐ No ☐ Treated ☐ Untreated _____

Plates: _____ **Platform Framing:** _____

Plywood Treatment: ☐ No ☐ Salt Treated ☐ Fire Retardant _____

Posts & Girts: _____

Rafters: ☐ No ☐ Ordinary ☐ Hip _____

Roof Cants: ☐ No ☐ Yes _____ **Roof Curbs:** ☐ No ☐ Yes _____

Roof Decks: ☐ No ☐ Yes _____ Inches Thick

Roof Purlins: ☐ No ☐ Yes _____

Roof Trusses: ☐ No ☐ Timber Connectors ☐ Nailed ☐ Glued Spaced _____ O.C. Span _____ feet

Sheathing, Roof: ☐ No ☐ Plywood ☐ Boards ☐ Wood Fiber ☐ Gypsum _____

Wall: ☐ No ☐ Plywood ☐ Boards ☐ Wood Fiber ☐ Gypsum _____

Siding Hardboard: ☐ Plain ☐ Primed ☐ Stained _____

Particle Board: _____ Wood Fiber _____

Plywood: ☐ Cedar ☐ Fir ☐ Redwood ☐ Marine ☐ Natural ☐ Stained ☐ Plastic Faced ☐ _____

Wood: ☐ Cedar ☐ Redwood ☐ White Pine ☐ Bevel ☐ Board & Batten ☐ Channel ☐ T & C ☐ Shiplap _____

☐ Natural ☐ Stained _____

Sills: _____ **Sleepers:** _____

Soffits: ☐ No ☐ Open ☐ Vented ☐ Plywood _____

Stressed Skin Plywood Box Beams: _____ Depth _____

Floor Panels: ☐ No ☐ Yes _____ Depth _____

Roof Panels: ☐ No ☐ Straight ☐ Curved _____ Depth _____

Folded Plate: ☐ No ☐ Yes _____ Depth _____

Studs: ☐ No ☐ Yes _____ Grade _____

Subfloor: ☐ No ☐ Plywood ☐ Boards ☐ Wood Fiber ☐ _____

Suspended Ceiling Framing: ☐ No ☐ Yes _____

Underlayment: ☐ No ☐ Particle Board ☐ Plywood ☐ Wood Fiber ☐ Hardboard _____

Special Considerations: _____

_____

Laminated Framing: ☐ Beams ☐ Straight ☐ Curved _____ Span _____

☐ Bowstring Trusses ☐ Radial Arch ☐ Tudor Arch ☐ Columns _____

Span _____ Height _____

☐ Industrial Grade ☐ Premium Grade ☐ Exterior Glue ☐ Stain ☐ Varnish ☐ Treated ☐ _____

Laminated Roof Deck: ☐ No ☐ Yes _____ Thickness _____

Special Considerations: _____

⚓ Means° Forms

SPEC-AID

DIVISION 6: CARPENTRY

Base: ☐ No ☐ One Piece ☐ Built up ☐ Pine ☐ Hardwood _____

Cabinets: ☐ No ☐ Corner ☐ Kitchen ☐ Toilet Room ☐ Other _____
  ☐ Stock ☐ Custom _____
  ☐ Unfinished ☐ Prefinished _____
  Base Cabinets: ☐ Softwood ☐ Hardwood ☐ Drawer Units _____
  Wall Cabinets: ☐ Softwood ☐ Hardwood _____
  Tall Cabinets: ☐ Softwood ☐ Hardwood _____
  Special: _____

Casings: ☐ No ☐ Doors ☐ Windows ☐ Beams ☐ Others _____
  ☐ Softwood ☐ Hardwood _____

Ceiling Beams: ☐ No ☐ Cedar ☐ Pine ☐ Fir ☐ Plastic _____

Chair Rail: ☐ No ☐ Pine ☐ Other _____

Closets: ☐ No ☐ Pole ☐ Shelf ☐ Prefabricated _____

Columns: ☐ No ☐ Square ☐ Round ☐ Solid ☐ Built up ☐ Hollow ☐ Tapered _____
  Diameter _____ Height _____

Convector Covers: ☐ No ☐ Yes _____

Cornice: ☐ No ☐ 1 Piece ☐ 2 Piece ☐ 3 Piece ☐ Pine ☐ Cedar ☐ Other _____

Counter Tops: ☐ No ☐ Plastic ☐ Ceramic Tile ☐ Marble ☐ Suede Finish ☐ Other _____
  ☐ Stock ☐ Custom _____
  ☐ No Splash ☐ Square Splash ☐ Cover Splash _____
  ☐ Self Edge ☐ Stainless Edge ☐ Aluminum Edge _____
  Special _____

Cupolas: ☐ No ☐ Stock ☐ Custom ☐ Wood ☐ Fiberglass ☐ Square ☐ Octagonal Size _____
  ☐ Aluminum Roof ☐ Copper Roof ☐ Other _____

Doors and Frames: See Division 8 _____

Door Moldings: ☐ No ☐ Yes _____

Door Trim: ☐ No ☐ Yes _____

Fireplace Mantels: ☐ No ☐ Beams ☐ Moldings _____
  Size _____

Moldings: ☐ No ☐ Softwood ☐ Hardwood ☐ Metal ☐ Other _____

Paneling Hardboard: ☐ No ☐ Tempered ☐ Untempered ☐ Pegboard ☐ Plastic Faced _____
  Plywood, Unfinished: ☐ No ☐ Veneer Core ☐ Lumber Core Grade _____ Thick _____
  Plywood, Prefinished: ☐ No ☐ Stock ☐ Architectural Finish _____
  Size _____
  Wood Boards: ☐ No ☐ Softwood ☐ Hardwood _____

Railings: ☐ No ☐ Stock ☐ Custom ☐ Softwood ☐ Hardwood _____
  ☐ Stairs ☐ Balcony ☐ Porch ☐ Wall ☐ Other _____

Shelving: ☐ No ☐ Prefinished ☐ Unfinished ☐ Stock ☐ Custom ☐ Plywood ☐ Particle Board ☐ Boards _____
  ☐ Book Shelves _____ ☐ Linen Shelves _____
  ☐ Storage Shelves _____ ☐ Other _____

Stairs: ☐ No ☐ Prefabricated ☐ Built in Place ☐ Softwood ☐ Hardwood _____
  ☐ Box ☐ Open ☐ Circular _____

Thresholds: ☐ No ☐ Interior ☐ Exterior _____

Wainscot: ☐ No ☐ Boards ☐ Plywood ☐ Moldings _____

Windows and Frames: See Division 8 _____

Window Trim: ☐ No ☐ Yes _____

Special Considerations: _____

⚓ Means® Forms

SPEC-AID

DATE _____

DIVISION 7: MOISTURE PROTECTION

PROJECT _____ LOCATION _____

Bentonite: ☐ No ☐ Panels ☐ Granular _____

Bituminous Coating: ☐ No ☐ Brushed ☐ Sprayed ☐ Troweled ☐ 1 Coat ☐ 2 Coat ☐ Protective Board _____

Building Paper: ☐ No ☐ Asphalt ☐ Polyethylene ☐ Rosin ☐ Kraft ☐ Foil Backed ☐ _____
☐ Roof Deck Vapor Barrier

Caulking: ☐ No ☐ Gun Grade ☐ Knife Grade ☐ Plain ☐ Colors _____
☐ Doors ☐ Windows ☐ _____

Cementitious: ☐ No ☐ 1 Coat ☐ 2 Coat Thickness _____ Inches Mix _____

Control Joints: _____ **Expansion Joints:** _____

Elastomeric Waterproofing: ☐ No ☐ EPDM ☐ Neoprene ☐ PVC ☐ Urethane ☐ _____

Liquid Waterproofing: ☐ No ☐ Silicone ☐ Stearate ☐ _____

Membrane Waterproofing: ☐ 1 Ply ☐ 2 Ply ☐ 3 Ply ☐ Felt ☐ Fabric ☐ Elastomeric ☐ _____

Metallic Coating: ☐ No ☐ Walls _____ in. Thick ☐ Floors _____ in. Thick _____

Preformed Vapor Barrier: ☐ No ☐ Yes _____

Sealants: ☐ No ☐ Butyl ☐ Polysulfide ☐ PVC ☐ Urethane ☐ _____
☐ Doors ☐ Windows ☐ _____

Special Waterproofing _____

Building Insulation: Rigid: ☐ No ☐ Fiberglass ☐ Polystyrene ☐ Urethane ☐ _____
Non Rigid: ☐ No ☐ Fiberglass ☐ Mineral Fiber ☐ Vermiculite ☐ Perlite ☐ _____

Form Board: ☐ No ☐ Acoustical ☐ Asbestos Cement ☐ Fiberglass ☐ Gypsum ☐ Mineral Fiber ☐ Wood Fiber
☐ Other _____ ☐ Sub Purlins _____ Span _____

Masonry Insulation: ☐ No ☐ Cavity Wall ☐ Block Cores ☐ Poured ☐ Foamed Type _____

Perimeter Insulation: ☐ No ☐ Yes Type _____ Thickness _____

Roof Deck Insulation: ☐ No ☐ Fiberboard ☐ Fiberglass ☐ Foamglass ☐ Polystyrene ☐ Urethane ☐ _____
Thickness _____ ☐ **Cants** _____ Size _____

Sprayed: ☐ No ☐ Fibrous ☐ Cementitious ☐ Urethane ☐ _____

Special Insulation _____

Shingles: Aluminum: ☐ No ☐ Yes _____ Asbestos: ☐ No ☐ Yes _____
Asphalt: ☐ No ☐ Class C ☐ Class A ☐ _____ Weight _____ lb. per Sq. _____
Clay Tile: ☐ No ☐ Plain ☐ Glazed ☐ Spanish ☐ _____ Weight _____ lb. per Sq. _____
Concrete Tile: ☐ No ☐ Yes _____ Porcelain Enamel: ☐ No ☐ Yes _____
Slate: ☐ No ☐ Yes Type _____ Color _____ Exposure _____
Wood: ☐ No ☐ Roofing ☐ Siding ☐ Fire Retardant Type _____ Grade _____ Exposure _____

Shingle Underlayment: ☐ No ☐ Asbestos ☐ Asphalt ☐ _____ Weight _____

Special Shingles: _____

Aluminum: ☐ No ☐ Roofing ☐ Siding ☐ Painted ☐ Insulated ☐ Sandwich ☐ _____
Thickness _____ Type _____

Asbestos Cement: ☐ No ☐ Roofing ☐ Siding ☐ Flat ☐ Corrugated ☐ Natural ☐ Painted ☐ Sandwich
☐ Fire Rated Thickness _____ Type _____

Epoxy Panels: ☐ No ☐ Solid ☐ Plywood Back ☐ Hardboard Back ☐ Exposed Aggregate ☐ _____

Fiberglass Panels: ☐ No ☐ Roofing ☐ Siding ☐ Flat ☐ Corrugated ☐ _____ Thickness _____

Metal Facing Panels: ☐ No ☐ Field Assembled ☐ Factory Made Insulation _____
Outside Face _____ Inside Face _____

Protected Metal: ☐ No ☐ Roofing ☐ Siding Type _____ Gauge _____

Steel: ☐ No ☐ Roofing ☐ Siding ☐ Painted ☐ Galvanized ☐ Insulated ☐ Sandwich ☐ _____
Type _____ Gauge _____

Vinyl Siding: ☐ No ☐ Plain ☐ Insulated Type _____

Special Roofing & Siding: _____

▲ Means® Forms

SPEC-AID

DIVISION 7: MOISTURE PROTECTION

Built Up Roofing: ☐ No ☐ Tar & Gravel ☐ Asphalt & Gravel ☐ Felt ☐ Mineral Surface ☐ Aggregate
☐ 1 Ply ☐ 2 Ply ☐ 3 Ply ☐ 4 Ply ☐ 5 Ply ☐ Bonded _____ years Roof Pitch _____ Type Deck _____
Underlayment: ☐ No ☐ Rosin Paper ☐ Vapor Barrier ☐ _____

Elastic Sheet Roofing: ☐ No ☐ Butyl ☐ Neoprene ☐ _____ Thickness _____
Describe _____

Fluid Applied Roofing: ☐ No ☐ Hypalon Neoprene ☐ Silicone ☐ Vinyl ☐ _____ Thickness _____
Describe _____

Roll Roofing: ☐ No ☐ Smooth ☐ Granular _____ Weight _____ lbs. per Sq.
Special Membrane Roofing: _____

Downspouts: ☐ No ☐ Aluminum ☐ Copper ☐ Lead Coated Copper ☐ Galvanized Steel ☐ Stainless Steel
☐ Steel Pipe ☐ Vinyl ☐ Zinc Alloy ☐ Stock ☐ Custom ☐ _____ Size _____
Describe _____

Expansion Joints: ☐ No ☐ Roof ☐ Walls ☐ No Curbs ☐ Curbs ☐ Rubber ☐ Metallic ☐ _____
Describe _____

Fascia: ☐ No ☐ Yes Describe _____ Thickness _____

Flashing: ☐ No ☐ Aluminum ☐ Asphalt ☐ Copper ☐ Fabric ☐ Lead ☐ Lead Coated Copper ☐ PVC ☐ Rubber
☐ Stainless Steel ☐ Terne ☐ Zinc Alloy ☐ Paper Backed ☐ Mastic Backed ☐ Fabric Backed ☐ _____
Describe _____ Thickness _____

Gravel Stop: ☐ No ☐ Aluminum ☐ Copper ☐ PVC ☐ Stainless Steel ☐ _____
☐ With Fascia ☐ No Fascia ☐ Natural ☐ Painted Thickness _____ Face Height _____

Gutters: ☐ No ☐ Aluminum ☐ Copper ☐ Lead Coated Copper ☐ Galvanized Steel ☐ Stainless Steel _____
☐ Vinyl ☐ Wood ☐ Zinc Alloy ☐ _____ Thickness _____
☐ Box Type ☐ K Type ☐ Half Round ☐ Stock ☐ Custom ☐ _____ Size _____

Louvers: ☐ No ☐ Yes _____

Mansard: ☐ No ☐ Yes _____ Thickness _____

Metal Roofing: ☐ No ☐ Copper ☐ Copper Bearing Steel ☐ Lead ☐ Lead Coated Copper ☐ Stainless Steel
☐ Terne ☐ Zinc Alloy ☐ _____ Size _____ Thickness _____
☐ Standing Seam ☐ Flat Seam ☐ Batten Seam ☐ _____ Weight _____ lbs. per Sq.

Underlayment: ☐ No ☐ 15 lb. Felt ☐ 30 lb. Felt ☐ Rosin Paper ☐ _____

Reglet: ☐ No ☐ Aluminum ☐ Copper ☐ Galvanized Steel ☐ Stainless Steel ☐ Zinc Alloy ☐ _____
Thickness _____ Counter Flashing: ☐ No ☐ Yes _____ Thickness _____

Soffit: ☐ No ☐ Yes _____ Thickness _____

Special Sheet Metal Work: _____

Ceiling Hatches: ☐ No ☐ Steel ☐ Galvanized ☐ Painted ☐ Aluminum ☐ _____
Size _____

Roof Drains: ☐ No ☐ In Plumbing ☐ Yes _____

Roof Hatches: ☐ No ☐ Steel ☐ Galvanized ☐ Painted ☐ Aluminum ☐ _____
☐ Insulated ☐ Not Insulated ☐ With Curbs ☐ No Curbs ☐ _____ Size _____

Smoke Hatches: ☐ No ☐ Yes _____

Snow Guards: ☐ No ☐ Yes _____

Skylights: ☐ No ☐ Domes ☐ Vaulted ☐ Ridge Units ☐ Field Fabricated ☐ Glass ☐ Plastic ☐ Single
☐ Double ☐ Sandwich Panels ☐ With Curbs ☐ No Curbs ☐ _____ Size _____

Smoke Vents: ☐ No ☐ Yes _____

Skyroofs: ☐ No ☐ Yes _____

Ventilators: ☐ No ☐ In Ventilating ☐ Stationary ☐ Spinners ☐ Motorized _____
Special Roof Accessories _____

⚖ Means° Forms

SPEC-AID

DATE _____

DIVISION 8: DOORS, WINDOWS & GLASS

PROJECT _____ LOCATION _____

Hollow Metal Frames: ☐ No ☐ Baked Enamel ☐ Galvanized ☐ Porcelain Enamel _____

Hollow Metal Doors: ☐ No _____ ☐ Core _____ ☐ Labeled _____

Aluminum Frames: ☐ No ☐ Clear ☐ Bronze ☐ Black _____

Aluminum Doors and Frames: ☐ No ☐ Yes _____ Frames _____

Wood Frames: ☐ No ☐ Exterior ☐ Interior ☐ Custom ☐ With Sill ☐ Vinyl Covered ☐ Pine ☐ Oak

Wood Doors: ☐ No _____ Core ☐ Labeled _____ Frames _____

Interior Door Frames: ☐ No ☐ Aluminum ☐ Hollow Metal ☐ Steel ☐ Wood ☐ Prehung ☐ Stock

☐ Custom ☐ _____

Custom Doors: ☐ No ☐ Swing ☐ Bi-Passing ☐ Bi-Folding _____ Frames _____

Accordion Folding Doors: ☐ No ☐ Yes _____ Frames _____

Acoustical Doors: ☐ No ☐ Yes _____ Decibels _____ Frames _____

Cold Storage: ☐ No ☐ Manual ☐ Power ☐ Sliding ☐ Hinged _____

Counter Doors: ☐ No ☐ Aluminum ☐ Steel ☐ Wood _____ Frames _____

Dark Room Doors: ☐ N0 ☐ Revolving ☐ 2 Way ☐ 3 Way _____

Floor Opening Doors: ☐ No ☐ Aluminum ☐ Steel ☐ Single ☐ Double ☐ Commercial ☐ Industrial _____

Glass Doors: ☐ No ☐ Sliding ☐ Swing _____ Frames _____

Hangar Doors: ☐ No ☐ Bi-Fold ☐ Other ☐ Electric _____

Jalousie Doors: ☐ No ☐ Plain Glass ☐ Tempered Glass _____

Kalamein: ☐ No ☐ Yes ☐ Labeled _____ Frames _____

Kennel Doors: ☐ No ☐ 2 Way Swing _____

Overhead Doors: ☐ No ☐ Regular Duty ☐ Heavy Duty ☐ Stock ☐ Custom ☐ One Piece ☐ Sectional

☐ Manual ☐ Electric ☐ Aluminum ☐ Fiberglass ☐ Steel ☐ Wood ☐ Hardboard ☐ Commercial

☐ Residential Size _____

Rolling Doors Exterior: ☐ No ☐ Manual ☐ Electric ☐ Labeled _____

Rolling Doors Interior: ☐ No ☐ Manual ☐ Electric ☐ Labeled _____ Frames _____

Rolling Grilles: ☐ No ☐ Manual ☐ Electric ☐ Aluminum ☐ Steel _____

Service Door Frames: ☐ No ☐ Aluminum ☐ Hollow Metal ☐ Steel ☐ Wood ☐ Stock ☐ Custom _____

Service Doors: ☐ No ☐ Stock ☐ Custom _____ ☐ Transoms _____ ☐ Sidelights _____

☐ Aluminum _____ ☐ Hollow Metal _____ ☐ Core _____ ☐ Kalamein _____

☐ Steel _____ ☐ Wood _____ ☐ Core _____ ☐ Labeled _____ ☐ Special Finish _____

Shock Absorbing Doors: ☐ No ☐ Flexible ☐ Rigid _____ Frames _____

Sliding Doors: ☐ No ☐ Glazed ☐ Unglazed Aluminum ☐ Steel ☐ Wood _____

Swing Doors: ☐ No ☐ Single ☐ Double _____

Telescoping Door: ☐ No ☐ Manual ☐ Electric _____

Tinclad Doors: ☐ No ☐ Manual ☐ Electric _____

Vault Front Doors: ☐ No ☐ Stainless Steel ☐ Time Lock ☐ 1 Hr. Test ☐ 2 Hr. Test ☐ 4 Hr. Test _____

Special Exterior Doors: ☐ No ☐ Yes _____

Special Interior Doors: ☐ No ☐ Yes _____

Balanced Doors: ☐ No ☐ Economy ☐ Premium ☐ Aluminum ☐ Stainless Steel _____

Revolving Doors: ☐ No ☐ Stock ☐ Custom ☐ Manual ☐ Electric ☐ Diameter _____

Entrance Units: ☐ No ☐ Aluminum ☐ Bronze ☐ Glass ☐ Hollow Metal ☐ Stainless Steel ☐ Wood ☐ Steel

☐ Stock ☐ Custom ☐ Balanced ☐ Sidelights ☐ Transoms Special Finish _____

Entrance Frames: ☐ No ☐ Aluminum ☐ Hollow Metal ☐ Steel ☐ Wood ☐ Stainless Steel ☐ Stock

☐ Custom _____

Store Fronts: ☐ No ☐ Sliding ☐ Fixed ☐ Institutional Grade ☐ Monumental Grade ☐ Commercial Grade _____

Windows: _____ % of Exterior Walls _____

Projected: ☐ No ☐ Glazed ☐ Unglazed ☐ Aluminum ☐ Steel ☐ Wood _____

Single Hung: ☐ No ☐ Glazed ☐ Unglazed ☐ Aluminum ☐ Steel ☐ Wood _____

Sliding: ☐ No ☐ Glazed ☐ Unglazed ☐ Aluminum ☐ Steel ☐ Wood _____

Security Windows: ☐ No ☐ Yes _____

Page 15 of 30

⚓ Means® Forms

SPEC-AID

DIVISION 8: DOORS, WINDOWS & GLASS

Casement: ☐ No ☐ Fixed _____ % Vented ☐ Aluminum ☐ Steel ☐ Wood _____

Picture Window: ☐ No ☐ Glazed ☐ Unglazed ☐ Aluminum ☐ Steel ☐ Wood _____

Double Hung: ☐ No ☐ Glazed ☐ Unglazed ☐ Aluminum ☐ Steel ☐ Wood _____

Special Windows: ☐ No ☐ Yes _____

Screens: ☐ No ☐ Aluminum ☐ Steel ☐ Wood _____

Finish Hardware Allowance: ☐ No ☐ Yes _____

 Exterior Doors _____

 Interior Doors _____

Automatic Openers: ☐ No ☐ 1 Way ☐ 2 Way ☐ Double Door ☐ Activating Carpet

Automatic Operators: ☐ No ☐ Sliding ☐ Swing ☐ Controls _____

Bumper Plates: ☐ No ☐ U Channel ☐ Teardrop _____

Door Closers: ☐ No ☐ Regular ☐ Fusible Link ☐ Concealed ☐ Heavy Use _____

Door Stops: ☐ No ☐ Yes _____

Floor Checks: ☐ No ☐ Single Acting ☐ Double Acting _____

Hinges: ☐ No ☐ Butt ☐ Pivot ☐ Spring ☐ Frequency _____

Kick Plates: ☐ No ☐ Yes _____

Lock Set: ☐ No ☐ Cylindrical ☐ Mortise ☐ Heavy Duty ☐ Commercial ☐ Residential _____

Panic Device: ☐ No ☐ Yes ☐ Exit Only ☐ Exit & Entrance _____

Push-Pull Device: ☐ No ☐ Yes ☐ Bronze ☐ Aluminum ☐ Other _____

Cabinet Hardware: ☐ No ☐ Yes _____

Window Hardware: ☐ No ☐ Yes _____

Special Hardware: ☐ No ☐ Yes _____

Threshold: ☐ No ☐ Yes _____

Weather Stripping Doors: ☐ No ☐ Zinc ☐ Bronze ☐ Stainless Steel ☐ Spring Type ☐ Extruded Sections

 Windows: ☐ No ☐ Zinc ☐ Bronze _____

Acoustical Glass: ☐ No ☐ Yes _____ Thickness _____

Faceted Glass: ☐ No ☐ Yes _____ Thickness _____

Glazing: ☐ No ☐ Putty ☐ Flush ☐ Bead ☐ Gasket ☐ Butt ☐ Riglet ☐ _____

Insulated Glass: ☐ No ☐ Standard ☐ Non-Standard _____ Thickness _____

Laminated Glass: ☐ No ☐ Yes _____ Thickness _____

Mirrors: ☐ No ☐ Plate ☐ Sheet ☐ Transparent ☐ Incl. Frames ☐ No Frames ☐ _____

 Door Type _____ Wall Type _____

Obscure Glass: ☐ No ☐ Yes _____ Thickness _____

Plate Glass: ☐ No ☐ Clear ☐ Tinted ☐ Tempered _____ Thickness _____

Plexiglass: ☐ No ☐ Masked ☐ Unmasked _____ Thickness _____

Polycarbonate: ☐ No ☐ Masked ☐ Unmasked _____ Thickness _____

Reflective: ☐ No ☐ Clear ☐ Tinted _____ Thickness _____

Sand Blasted: ☐ No ☐ Yes _____ Thickness _____

Sheet or Float Glass: ☐ No ☐ Clear ☐ Gray _____ Thickness _____

Spandrel Glass: ☐ No ☐ Plain ☐ Insulated ☐ Sandwich _____ Thickness _____

Stained Glass: ☐ No ☐ Yes _____

Vinyl Glazing: ☐ No ☐ Yes _____ Thickness _____

Window Glass: ☐ No ☐ DSA ☐ DBS ☐ Tempered _____ Thickness _____

Wire Glass: ☐ No ☐ Yes _____ Thickness _____

Special Glazing: ☐ No ☐ Yes _____

Curtain Walls: ☐ No ☐ Yes _____

Window Walls: ☐ No ☐ Yes _____

⚼ Means° Forms

SPEC-AID

DATE _____

DIVISION 9: FINISHES

PROJECT _____ LOCATION _____

Furring: Ceiling: ☐ No ☐ Wired Direct ☐ Suspended _____

Partitions: ☐ No ☐ Load Bearing ☐ Non Load Bearing _____ Thickness _____

Walls: ☐ No ☐ Yes _____

Gypsum Lath: ☐ No ☐ Walls ☐ Ceilings ☐ Regular ☐ Foil Faced ☐ Fire Resistant ☐ Moisture Resistant_____

Thickness _____

Metal Lath: ☐ No ☐ Diamond ☐ Rib ☐ _____ Weight _____

☐ Painted ☐ Galvanized ☐ Paper Backed _____

☐ Walls ☐ Ceilings ☐ Suspended ☐ Partitions ☐ Load Bearing ☐ Non Load Bearing _____

Drywall Finishes: ☐ Taped & Finished ☐ Thin Coat Plaster ☐ Prime Coat ☐ Electric Heat Compound ☐ _____

Mountings: ☐ Nailed ☐ Screwed ☐ Laminated ☐ Clips ☐ _____

Beams: ☐ No _____ Layers _____ Thickness _____

Ceilings: ☐ No ☐ Standard ☐ Fire Resistant ☐ Water Resistance _____ Thickness _____

Columns: ☐ No _____ Layers _____ Thickness _____

Partitions: ☐ No ☐ Wood Studs ☐ Steel Studs _____ Layers _____ Thickness _____

Prefinished: ☐ No ☐ Standard ☐ Fire Resistance _____ Thickness _____

Soffits: ☐ No _____ Layers _____ Thickness _____

Sound Deading Board: ☐ No Type _____ Thickness _____

Walls: ☐ No _____ Layers _____ Thickness _____

Plaster Finishes: ☐ 1 Coat ☐ 2 Coat ☐ 3 Coat ☐ Gypsum ☐ Perlite ☐ Vermiculite ☐ Wood ☐ _____

Beams: ☐ No _____ Ceilings: ☐ _____

Columns: ☐ No _____ Soffits: ☐ No _____

Partitions: ☐ No ☐ Wood Studs ☐ Steel Studs ☐ Solid ☐ Hollow _____

Walls: ☐ No _____

Special Plaster: _____

Sprayed Acoustical: ☐ No ☐ Yes _____ Thickness _____

Fireproofing: ☐ No ☐ Yes _____ Thickness _____

Stucco: ☐ No ☐ On Mesh ☐ Masonry _____

Cast Stone: ☐ No ☐ Glazed ☐ Unglazed ☐ Waxed _____ Thickness _____

Ceramic Tile Base: ☐ No ☐ Cove ☐ Sanitary ☐ _____ Set _____ Height _____

Floors: ☐ No ☐ _____ Set ☐ Natural Clay ☐ Porcelain ☐ Conductive ___ Color Group _____

Walls: ☐ No ☐ _____ Set ☐ Interior ☐ Exterior ☐ Glazed ☐ Crystalline Glazed ☐ _____

☐ Unmounted ☐ Backmounted _____

Panels: ☐ No ☐ Yes _____

Glass Mosaics: ☐ No ☐ Yes _____ Color Group _____

Metal Tile: ☐ No ☐ Aluminum ☐ Copper ☐ Stainless Steel _____

Plastic Tile: ☐ No ☐ Yes _____ Thickness _____

Quarry Tile Base: ☐ No ☐ Cove ☐ Sanitary _____ Height _____

Floor ☐ No _____ Set Size _____ Color _____

Stairs: ☐ No ☐ Treads ☐ Risers _____

Wainscot: ☐ No _____ Set Size _____

Cast In Place Terrazzo Base: ☐ No ☐ Yes _____ Curb: ☐ No ☐ Yes _____

Floor: ☐ No ☐ Bonded ☐ Unbonded ☐ Gray Cement ☐ White Cement ☐ Conventional ☐ Venetian _____

☐ Conductive ☐ Monolithic ☐ Epoxy ☐ _____

Divider Strips: ☐ No ☐ Brass ☐ Zinc _____ Spacing _____

Stairs: ☐ No ☐ Yes _____ Wainscot: ☐ No ☐ Yes _____

Precast Terrazzo Base: ☐ No ☐ Yes Curb: ☐ No ☐ Yes _____

Floor Tiles: ☐ No Size _____ Thickness _____

Stairs: ☐ No ☐ Treads ☐ Risers ☐ Stringers ☐ Landings _____

Wainscot: ☐ No ☐ Yes _____ Thickness _____

Page 17 of 30

⚘ Means® Forms

SPEC-AID

DIVISION 9: FINISHES

Barriers: ☐ No ☐ Aluminum ☐ Foil ☐ Mesh ☐ Lead ☐ Leaded Vinyl _____

Acoustical Barriers: ☐ No ☐ Yes _____

Ceilings: ☐ No ☐ Boards ☐ Tile ☐ Cemented ☐ Stapled ☐ On Suspension ☐ _____
  ☐ Fiberglass ☐ Mineral Fiber ☐ Wood Fiber ☐ Metal Pan _____
  ☐ Fire Rated ☐ Ventilating ☐ _____ Ceiling Height_____
  ☐ Luminous Panels _____ ☐ Access Panels _____

Suspension System: ☐ No ☐ T Bar ☐ Z Bar ☐ Carrier Channels ☐ _____

Strip Lighting: ☐ No ☐ Yes _____ Foot Candles _____

Special Acoustical _____

Brick Flooring: ☐ No ☐ Yes _____

Carpet ☐ No ☐ Yes ☐ With Padding ☐ With Backing ☐ _____ Allowance _____
  Type: ☐ Acrylic ☐ Nylon ☐ Polypropylene ☐ Wool ☐ Tile ☐ _____ Face Weight _____
  Padding: ☐ No ☐ Yes _____ Backing: ☐ No ☐ Yes _____

Composition Flooring: ☐ No ☐ Acrylic ☐ Epoxy ☐ Mastic ☐ Neoprene ☐ Polyester ☐ _____
  ☐ Regular Duty ☐ Heavy Duty _____ Thickness _____

Concrete Floor Topping: ☐ No ☐ In Concrete ☐ Yes _____

Resilient Floors: Base: ☐ No ☐ Rubber ☐ Vinyl _____ Height _____
  Asphalt Tile: ☐ No ☐ Yes _____ Color Group _____
  Conductive Tile: ☐ No ☐ Yes _____ Thickness _____
  Cork Tile: ☐ No ☐ Yes _____ Thickness _____
  Linoleum: ☐ No ☐ Yes _____ Thickness _____
  Polyethylene: ☐ No ☐ Yes _____
  Polyurethane: ☐ No ☐ Yes _____ Thickness _____
  Rubber Tile: ☐ No ☐ Yes _____ Thickness _____
  Vinyl: ☐ Sheet ☐ Tile _____ Thickness _____
  Vinyl Asbestos Tile: ☐ No ☐ Yes _____ Color Group _____

Stair Covering: ☐ No ☐ Risers ☐ Treads ☐ Landings ☐ Nosings ☐ Rubber ☐ Vinyl _____

Steel Plates: ☐ No ☐ Cement Bed ☐ Epoxy Bed _____

Wood Floor: ☐ No ☐ Block ☐ Strip ☐ Parquetry ☐ Unfinished ☐ Prefinished ☐ Stock ☐ Custom _____
  Fir: ☐ No ☐ Flat Grain ☐ Vertical Grain _____ Size _____
  Gym: ☐ No ☐ Yes Type _____
  Maple: ☐ No ☐ Yes Grade _____ Size _____
  Oak: ☐ No ☐ Red ☐ White Grade _____ Size _____
  Other: ☐ _____ Grade _____ Size _____
  Finish Required: ☐ No ☐ Yes _____

Wood Block Floor: ☐ No ☐ Creosoted ☐ ☐ Natural _____ Thickness _____

Special Coatings: ☐ No ☐ Floor ☐ Wall _____

Painting: ☐ No ☐ Regular ☐ Fireproof ☐ Fire Retardant ☐ Brush ☐ Roller ☐ Spray _____
  Casework: ☐ No _____ Coats _____ Ceilings: ☐ No _____ Coats _____
  Doors: ☐ No _____ Coats _____ Trim: ☐ No _____ Coats _____
  Walls, Exterior: ☐ No _____ Coats _____ Interior Walls: ☐ No _____ Coats _____
  Windows: ☐ No _____ Coats _____ Piping: ☐ No _____ Coats _____
  Other: _____
  Structural Steel: ☐ No ☐ Yes _____ Miscellaneous Metals: ☐ No ☐ Yes _____

Wall Covering: ☐ No ☐ Cork Tile _____ ☐ Metal Foil _____
  ☐ Flexible Wood Veneers _____ ☐ Vinyl _____ Weight _____
  Wall Paper _____ Vinyl _____ Murals _____
  Other _____

Guards: Corner: ☐ No ☐ Rubber ☐ Steel ☐ Vinyl _____
  Wall: ☐ No ☐ Rubber ☐ Steel ☐ Vinyl _____

⚓ Means° Forms

DATE _____

DIVISION 10: SPECIALTIES

PROJECT _____ LOCATION _____

Bathroom Accessories: ☐ No ☐ Curtain Rod _____ ☐ Dispensers _____ ☐ Grab Bar _____
☐ Hand Dryer _____ ☐ Medicine Cabinet _____ ☐ Mirror _____ ☐ Robe Hook _____
☐ Soap Dispenser _____ ☐ Shelf _____ ☐ Tissue Dispenser _____ ☐ Towel Bar _____
☐ Tumbler Holder _____ ☐ Wall Urn _____ ☐ Waste Receptical _____ ☐ _____
Bulletin Board: ☐ No ☐ Cork ☐ Vinyl Cork ☐ Unbacked ☐ Backed ☐ Stock ☐ Custom
☐ Tan ☐ Framed ☐ No Frames ☐ Changeable Letter ☐ _____ _____ Thickness _____

Canopies: ☐ No ☐ Free Standing ☐ Wall Hung ☐ Stock ☐ Custom _____
Chalkboard: ☐ No ☐ Cement Asbestos ☐ Hardboard ☐ Metal _____ Ga. ☐ Slate _____ in. Thick ☐ Tempered Glass _____
☐ Treated Plastic ☐ _____ ☐ Unbacked ☐ Backed with _____
☐ No Frames ☐ Frames ☐ Chalk Tray ☐ Map Rail ☐ _____
☐ Built in Place ☐ Prefabricated _____
☐ Portable ☐ Reversible ☐ Swing Wing ☐ Sliding Panel _____

Chutes Linen: ☐ No ☐ Aluminum ☐ Aluminized Steel ☐ Stainless Steel ☐ _____ Ga. Diameter _____
☐ Bottom Collector ☐ Sprinklers _____
Mail: ☐ No ☐ Aluminum ☐ Bronze ☐ Stainless ☐ _____ Size _____ ☐ Bottom Collector
Package: ☐ No ☐ Aluminum ☐ Bronze ☐ Stainless _____
Rubbish: ☐ No ☐ Aluminum ☐ Aluminized Steel ☐ Stainless Steel _____ Ga. Diameter _____
☐ Bottom Collector ☐ Sprinklers _____
Compartments & Cubicles: ☐ No ☐ Hospital _____ ☐ Office _____
☐ Shower _____ ☐ Toilet _____ ☐ _____
Control Boards: ☐ No ☐ Yes _____
Decorative Grilles and Screens: ☐ No ☐ Yes _____
Directory Boards: ☐ No ☐ Exterior ☐ Interior ☐ Aluminum ☐ Bronze ☐ Stainless ☐ Lighted _____
Describe _____
Disappearing Stairs: ☐ No ☐ Stock ☐ Custom ☐ Manual ☐ Electric _____ Ceiling Height _____
Display Cases: ☐ No ☐ Economy ☐ Deluxe _____
Fire Extinguishers: ☐ No ☐ CO_2 ☐ Dry Chemical ☐ Foam ☐ Pressure Water ☐ Soda Acid ☐ _____
☐ Aluminum ☐ Copper ☐ Painted Steel ☐ Stainless Steel ☐ _____ Size _____
Cabinets: ☐ No ☐ Aluminum ☐ Painted Steel ☐ Stainless Steel ☐ _____
Hose Equipment: ☐ No ☐ Blanket ☐ Cabinets ☐ Hose _____ Size _____
Protection System: ☐ No ☐ Yes _____
Fireplace, Prefabricated: ☐ No ☐ Economy ☐ Deluxe ☐ Wall Hung ☐ Free Standing _____

Flagpoles: ☐ No ☐ Aluminum ☐ Bronze ☐ Fiberglass ☐ Stainless ☐ Steel ☐ Wood ☐ Tapered ☐ Sectional _____
☐ Ground Set ☐ Wall Set ☐ Counterbalanced ☐ Outriggers _____ Height _____
Bases: ☐ No ☐ Economy ☐ Deluxe _____
Foundation: ☐ No ☐ Yes _____
Folding Gates: ☐ No ☐ Scissors Type ☐ Vertical Members ☐ Stock ☐ Custom _____ Opening _____
Lockers: ☐ No ☐ No Locks ☐ Keyed ☐ Combination _____ Tier Size _____ Height _____
Athletic: ☐ No ☐ Basket ☐ Ventilating ☐ Overhead _____ Size _____
Benches: ☐ No ☐ Yes _____
Special Lockers: _____
Mail Specialties Boxes: ☐ No ☐ Front Loading ☐ Rear Loading ☐ Aluminum ☐ Stainless ☐ _____
Size _____
Letter Slot: ☐ No ☐ Yes _____ Counter Window: ☐ No ☐ Yes _____
Directory: ☐ No ☐ Yes _____ Key Keeper _____
Other: _____

🔺 Means® Forms

SPEC-AID
DIVISION 10: SPECIALTIES

Accordion Folding Partitions: ☐ No ☐ Acoustical ☐ Non Acoustical _____ Weight _____ psf.
Ceiling Height _____ Describe _____

Folding Leaf Partitions: ☐ No ☐ Acoustical ☐ Non Acoustical _____ Weight _____ psf.
Ceiling Height _____ Describe _____

Hospital Partitions: ☐ No ☐ Metal ☐ Curtain Track _____

Movable Office Partitions: ☐ No ☐ Acoustical ☐ Non Acoustical ☐ Asbestos Cement ☐ Hardboard
☐ Laminated Gypsum ☐ Plywood ☐ _____
☐ With Glass ☐ No Glass Describe _____ Partition Height _____
Special Finish: _____
Doors: ☐ No ☐ Yes Type _____ Finish _____ Size _____

Operable Partitions: ☐ No ☐ Yes Type _____

Portable Partitions: ☐ No ☐ Acoustical ☐ Non Acoustical _____ Weight _____ psf.
Partition Height _____ Describe _____

Shower Partitions: ☐ No ☐ Fiberglass ☐ Glass ☐ Marble ☐ Metal ☐ _____ Finish _____
☐ Stock ☐ Custom ☐ Economy ☐ Deluxe Size _____
Doors: ☐ No ☐ Glass ☐ Tempered Glass ☐ Plastic ☐ Curtain Only _____ Size _____
Receptors: ☐ No ☐ Concrete ☐ Metal ☐ Plastic ☐ Terrazzo _____ Size _____
Tub Enclosure: ☐ No ☐ Stock ☐ Custom ☐ Economy ☐ Deluxe _____ Size _____

Toilet Partitions: ☐ No ☐ Fiberglass ☐ Marble ☐ Metal ☐ Slate ☐ Wood ☐ _____
☐ Floor Mounted ☐ Wall Hung ☐ Ceiling Hung _____
Special Finish _____
Doors: ☐ No ☐ Yes _____
Screens: ☐ No ☐ Full Height ☐ Urinal ☐ Floor Mounted ☐ Wall Hung ☐ Ceiling Hung _____

Woven Wire Partitions: ☐ No ☐ Walls ☐ Ceilings ☐ Panel Width _____ Height _____
Doors: ☐ No ☐ Sliding ☐ Swing _____ Windows: ☐ No ☐ Yes _____
☐ Painted ☐ Galvanized _____

Other Partitions: _____

Parts Bins: ☐ No ☐ Yes _____

Scales: ☐ No ☐ Built in ☐ Portable ☐ Beam Type ☐ Dial Type _____ Capacity _____
Platform Size _____ Material _____ Foundations _____
Accessory Items _____

Shelving, Storage: ☐ No ☐ Metal ☐ Wood _____

Signs: Individual Letters: ☐ No ☐ Aluminum ☐ Bronze ☐ Plastic ☐ Stainless ☐ Steel ☐ _____
☐ Cast ☐ Fabricated Describe _____
Plaques: ☐ No ☐ Aluminum ☐ Bronze _____
Signs: ☐ No ☐ Metal ☐ Plastic ☐ Lighted _____

Sun Control Devices: ☐ No ☐ Yes _____

Telephone Enclosures: ☐ No ☐ Indoor ☐ Outdoor _____

Turnstiles: ☐ No ☐ Yes _____

Vending Machines: ☐ No ☐ Yes _____

Wardrobe Specialties: ☐ No ☐ Yes _____

Other Specialties: _____

_____
_____
_____

Page 20 of 30

344

⚓ Means® Forms

SPEC-AID

DATE _____

DIVISION 11: ARCHITECTURAL EQUIPMENT

PROJECT _____ LOCATION _____

Appliances, Residential: ☐ No ☐ Yes Allowance _____ ☐ Separate Contract
☐ Cook Tops _____ ☐ Compactors _____ ☐ Dehumidifier _____ ☐ Dishwasher _____
☐ Dryer _____ ☐ Garbage Disposer _____ ☐ Heaters, Electric _____
☐ Hood _____ ☐ Humidifier _____ ☐ Ice Maker _____ ☐ Oven _____
☐ Refrigerator _____ ☐ Sump Pump _____ ☐ Washing Machine _____ ☐ Water Heater _____
☐ Water Softener _____ ☐ _____

Automotive Equipment: ☐ No ☐ Yes Allowance _____ ☐ Separate Contract
☐ Hoists _____ ☐ Lube _____ ☐ Pumps _____ ☐ _____

Bank Equipment: ☐ No ☐ Yes Allowance _____
☐ Counters _____ ☐ Safes _____ ☐ Vaults _____ ☐ Windows _____
☐ _____

Check Room Equipment: ☐ No ☐ Yes Allowance _____ ☐ Separate Contract
Describe _____

Church Equipment: ☐ No ☐ Yes Allowance _____ ☐ Separate Contract
☐ Altar _____ ☐ Baptistries _____ ☐ Bells & Carillons _____ ☐ Confessionals _____
☐ Organ _____ ☐ Pews _____ ☐ Pulpit _____ ☐ Spires _____
☐ Wall Cross _____ ☐ _____

Commercial Equipment: ☐ No ☐ Yes Allowance _____ ☐ Separate Contract
Describe _____

Darkroom Equipment: ☐ No ☐ Yes Allowance _____ ☐ Separate Contract
Describe _____

Data Processing Equipment: ☐ No ☐ Yes Allowance _____ ☐ Separate Contract
Describe _____

Dental Equipment: ☐ No ☐ Yes Allowance _____ ☐ Separate Contract
☐ Chair _____ ☐ Drill _____ ☐ Lights _____ ☐ X-Ray _____
☐ _____

Dock Equipment: ☐ No ☐ Yes Allowance _____ ☐ Separate Contract
☐ Bumpers _____ ☐ Boards _____ ☐ Door Seal _____ ☐ Levelers _____
☐ Lights _____ ☐ Shelters _____ ☐ _____

Food Service Equipment: ☐ No ☐ Yes Allowance _____ ☐ Separate Contract
☐ Bar Units _____ ☐ Cooking Equip. _____ ☐ Dishwashing Equip. _____ ☐ Food Prep. _____
☐ Food Serving _____ ☐ Refrigerated Cases _____ ☐ Tables _____ ☐ _____

Gymnasium Equipment: ☐ No ☐ Yes Allowance _____ ☐ Separate Contract
☐ Basketball Backstops _____ ☐ Benches _____ ☐ Bleachers _____
☐ Divider Curtain _____ ☐ Gymnastic Equip. _____ ☐ Mats _____ ☐ Scoreboards _____
☐ _____

Industrial Equipment: ☐ No ☐ Yes Allowance _____ ☐ Separate Contract
Describe _____

Laboratory Equipment: ☐ No ☐ Yes Allowance _____ ☐ Separate Contract
☐ Casework _____ ☐ Counter Tops _____ ☐ Hoods _____ ☐ Sinks _____
☐ Tables _____ ☐ _____

Laundry Equipment: ☐ No ☐ Yes Allowance _____ ☐ Separate Contract
☐ Dryers _____ ☐ Washers _____ ☐ _____

Library Equipment: ☐ No ☐ Yes Allowance _____ ☐ Separate Contract
☐ Book Shelves _____ ☐ Book Stacks _____ ☐ Card Files _____ ☐ Carrels _____
☐ Charging Desks _____ ☐ Racks _____ ☐ _____

Medical Equipment: ☐ No ☐ Yes Allowance _____ ☐ Separate Contract
☐ Casework _____ ☐ Exam Room _____ ☐ Incubators _____ ☐ Patient Care _____
☐ Radiology _____ ☐ Sterilizers _____ ☐ Surgery Equip. _____ ☐ Therapy Equip. _____
☐ _____

⚓ Means® Forms

SPEC-AID

DIVISION 11: ARCHITECTURAL EQUIPMENT

Mortuary Equipment: ☐ No ☐ Yes Allowance _____ ☐ Separate Contract
Describe _____

Musical Equipment: ☐ No ☐ Yes Allowance _____ ☐ Separate Contract
Describe _____

Observatory Equipment: ☐ No ☐ Yes Allowance _____ ☐ Separate Contract
Describe _____

Parking Equipment: ☐ No ☐ Yes Allowance _____ ☐ Separate Contract
☐ Automatic Gates _____ ☐ Booths _____ ☐ Control Station _____
☐ Ticket Dispenser _____ ☐ Traffic Detectors _____
☐ _____

Playground Equipment: In Division 2 _____

Prison Equipment: ☐ No ☐ Yes Allowance _____ ☐ Separate Contract
☐ Ceiling Lining _____ ☐ Wall Lining _____ ☐ Bar Walls _____ ☐ Doors _____
☐ Bunks _____ ☐ Lavatory _____ ☐ Water Closet _____ ☐ _____

Residential Equipment: ☐ No ☐ Yes Allowance _____ ☐ Separate Contract
☐ Kitchen Cabinets (Also Div. 6) _____ ☐ Lavatory Cabinets _____ ☐ Kitchen Equipment _____
☐ Laundry Equip. _____ ☐ Unit Kitchens _____ ☐ Vacuum Cleaning _____ ☐ _____
☐ _____

Safes: ☐ No ☐ Yes Allowance _____ ☐ Separate Contract
☐ Office _____ ☐ Money _____ ☐ _____ ☐ Rating _____
Describe _____

Saunas: ☐ No ☐ Yes Allowance _____ ☐ Separate Contract
☐ Built in Place ☐ Prefabricated Size _____ Describe _____
☐ Heater _____ ☐ Seats _____ ☐ Timer _____ ☐ _____

School Equipment: ☐ No ☐ Yes Allowance _____ ☐ Separate Contract
☐ Art & Crafts _____ ☐ Audio-Visual _____ ☐ Language Labs _____ ☐ Vocational _____
☐ Wall Benches _____ ☐ Wall Tables _____ ☐ _____
☐ _____

Shop Equipment: ☐ No ☐ Yes Allowance _____ ☐ Separate Contract
Describe _____

Stage Equipment: ☐ No ☐ Yes Allowance _____ ☐ Separate Contract
Describe _____

Steam Baths: ☐ No ☐ Yes Allowance _____ ☐ Separate Contract
Describe _____

Swimming Pool Equipment: ☐ No ☐ Yes Allowance _____ ☐ Separate Contract
☐ Diving Board _____ ☐ Diving Stand _____ ☐ Life Guard Chair _____ ☐ Ladders _____
☐ Heater _____ ☐ Lights _____ ☐ Pool Cover _____ ☐ Slides _____
☐ _____

Unit Kitchens: ☐ No ☐ Yes Allowance _____ ☐ Separate Contract
Describe _____

Vacuum Cleaning, Central: ☐ No ☐ Yes Allowance _____ ☐ Separate Contract
☐ _____ Valves Describe _____

Waste Disposal Compactors: ☐ No ☐ Yes _____
Incinerators: ☐ No ☐ Electric ☐ Gas Type Waste _____ Capacity _____

Special Equipment: _____
_____
_____
_____
_____
_____

Page 22 of 30

⚓ Means® Forms

SPEC-AID   DATE _____

DIVISION 12: FURNISHINGS _____

PROJECT _____ LOCATION _____

Artwork: ☐ No   ☐ Yes   Allowance _____ ☐ Separate Contract
☐ Murals _____ ☐ Paintings _____ ☐ Photomurals _____ ☐ Sculptures _____
☐ Stained Glass _____ ☐ _____

Interior Landscaping: ☐ No   ☐ Yes Allowance _____ **Blinds, Exterior:**   ☐ No   ☐ Yes   Allowance _____ ☐ Separate Contract
☐ Solid   ☐ Louvered   ☐ Aluminum   ☐ Nylon   ☐ Vinyl   ☐ Wood   ☐ _____
Describe _____

Blinds, Interior: ☐ No   ☐ Yes   Allowance _____ ☐ Separate Contract
Folding: ☐ No   ☐ Stock   ☐ Custom   ☐ Wood   ☐ _____
Describe _____
Venetian: ☐ No   ☐ Stock   ☐ Custom   ☐ Aluminum   ☐ Plastic   ☐ Steel   ☐ Wood   ☐ _____
Describe _____
Vertical: ☐ No   ☐ Aluminum   ☐ Cloth   ☐ Vinyl   ☐ _____
Describe _____
Other: _____

Cabinets: ☐ No   ☐ Yes   Allowance _____ ☐ Separate Contract
☐ Classroom _____
☐ Dormitory _____
☐ Hospital _____
☐ _____

Carpets: In Division 9 _____

Dormitory Units: ☐ No   ☐ Yes   Allowance _____ ☐ Separate Contract
☐ Beds _____ ☐ Desks _____ ☐ Wardrobes _____ ☐ _____
☐ _____

Drapery & Curtains: ☐ No   ☐ Yes   Allowance _____ ☐ Separate Contract
Describe _____
_____

Floor Mats: ☐ No   ☐ Yes   Allowance _____ ☐ Separate Contract
☐ Recessed   ☐ Non Recessed _____
☐ Link   ☐ Solid _____

Furniture: ☐ No   ☐ Yes   Allowance _____ ☐ Separate Contract
☐ Beds _____ ☐ Chairs _____ ☐ Chests _____ ☐ Desks _____
Sofas _____ ☐ Tables _____ ☐ _____
☐ _____

Seating Auditorium: ☐ No   ☐ Yes   Allowance _____ ☐ Separate Contract
Describe _____
Classroom: ☐ No   ☐ Yes   Allowance _____ ☐ Separate Contract
Describe _____
Stadiuim: ☐ No   ☐ Yes   Allowance _____ ☐ Separate Contract
Describe _____

Shades: ☐ No   ☐ Yes   Allowance _____ ☐ Separate Contract
☐ Stock   ☐ Custom   ☐ Lightproof   ☐ Fireproof _____
☐ Cotton   ☐ Fiberglass   ☐ Vinyl   ☐ Woven Aluminum   ☐ _____
Describe _____

Wardrobes: ☐ No   ☐ Yes   Allowance _____ ☐ Separate Contract
☐ Classroom _____ ☐ Dormitory _____ ☐ Hospital _____ ☐ _____
Describe _____

Other Furnishings: _____
_____
_____

𝐿 Means® Forms

SPEC-AID

DATE _____

DIVISION 13: SPECIAL CONSTRUCTION _____

PROJECT _____ LOCATION _____

Acoustical Echo Chamber: □ No   □ Yes   Allowance _____ □ Separate Contract
Describe _____
Enclosures: □ No   □ Yes   Allowance _____ □ Separate Contract
Describe _____
Panels: □ No   □ Yes   Allowance _____ □ Separate Contract
Describe _____
Air Curtains: □ No   □ Yes   Allowance _____ □ Separate Contract
□ Heated Air   □ Unheated Air   □ Recirculating   □ Non Recirculating   □ _____
Describe _____
Air Inflated Buildings: □ No   □ Yes   Describe _____ □ Separate Contract
Anechoic Chambers: □ No   □ Yes   Allowance _____ □ Separate Contract
Describe _____
Audiometric Rooms: □ No   □ Yes   Allowance _____ □ Separate Contract
Describe _____
Bowling Alleys: □ No   □ Yes   Allowance _____ □ Separate Contract
Describe _____
Broadcasting Studio: □ No   □ Yes   Allowance _____ □ Separate Contract
Describe _____
Chimneys: □ No   □ Yes   Allowance _____ □ Separate Contract
Concrete: □ No   □ Unlined   □ Lined   □ _____ Diameter_____ Height_____
Metal: □ No   □ Insulated   □ Not Insulated   □ U.L. Listed   □ Not U.L. Listed   □ _____
Describe _____ Diameter_____ Height_____
Radial Brick: □ No   □ Unlined   □ Lined   □ _____ Diameter_____ Height_____
Foundation: □ No   □ Yes _____
Clean Rooms: □ No   □ Yes   Allowance _____ □ Separate Contract
Describe _____
Comfort Stations: □ No   □ Yes   Describe _____
Dark Rooms: □ No   □ Yes   Allowance _____ □ Separate Contract
Describe _____
Domes, Observation: □ No   □ Yes   Allowance _____ □ Separate Contract
Describe _____
Garage: □ No   □ Yes   Describe _____ Cars_____
Garden House: □ No   □ Yes   Allowance _____ □ Separate Contract
Describe _____
Grandstand: □ No   □ Yes   Describe _____ Seats_____
Greenhouse: □ No   □ Yes   Allowance _____ □ Separate Contract
Describe _____
Hangars: □ No   □ Yes   Describe _____ Planes_____
Hyperbaric Rooms: □ No   □ Yes   Allowance _____ □ Separate Contract
Describe _____
Incinerators (See also Division 10):   □ No   □ Yes   Allowance _____ □ Separate Contract
Describe _____ Capacity_____
Insulated Rooms: □ No   □ Yes   Allowance _____ □ Separate Contract
Doors: □ No   □ Cooler   □ Freezer   □ Manual   □ Electric _____
□ Galvanized   □ Stainless   Describe _____
Coolers: □ No   □ Yes   Describe _____
Freezers: □ No   □ Yes   Describe _____
Partitions: □ No   □ Yes   □ Stock   □ Custom   Describe _____
Other: _____

⚓ Means® Forms

SPEC-AID

DIVISION 13: SPECIAL CONSTRUCTION

Integrated Ceilings: ☐ No ☐ Yes Module _____ Ceiling Height _____
Lighting: ☐ No ☐ Yes Describe _____ Foot Candles _____
Heating: ☐ No ☐ Yes Describe _____
Ventilating: ☐ No ☐ Yes Describe _____
Air Conditioning: ☐ No ☐ Yes Describe _____

Music Practice Rooms: ☐ No ☐ Yes Allowance _____ ☐ Separate Contract
Describe _____

Pedestal Floors: ☐ No ☐ Yes Allowance _____ ☐ Separate Contract
☐ Aluminum ☐ Plywood ☐ Steel ☐ _____ Panel Size _____ Height _____
☐ High Density Plastic ☐ Vinyl Tile ☐ V.A. Tile ☐ _____
Describe _____

Portable Booths: ☐ No ☐ Yes Allowance _____ ☐ Separate Contract
Describe _____

Prefabricated Structures: ☐ No ☐ Yes Allowance _____ ☐ Separate Contract
Describe _____

Radiation Protection, Fluoroscopy Room: ☐ No ☐ Yes _____
Nuclear Reactor: ☐ No ☐ Yes _____
Radiological Room: ☐ No ☐ Yes _____
X-Ray Room: ☐ No ☐ Yes _____
Other: _____

Radio Frequency Shielding: ☐ No ☐ Yes Allowance _____ ☐ Separate Contract
Describe _____

Radio Tower: ☐ No ☐ Yes Allowance _____ ☐ Separate Contract
☐ Guyed ☐ Self Supporting Wind Load _____ psf. _____ Height _____
Foundations _____

Saunas and Steam Rooms: ☐ No ☐ Yes Allowance _____ ☐ Separate Contract
Describe _____

Silos: ☐ No ☐ Yes Allowance _____ ☐ Separate Contract
☐ Concrete ☐ Steel ☐ Wood ☐ _____ Diameter _____ Height _____
Foundations _____

Squash & Hand Ball Courts: ☐ No ☐ Yes Allowance _____ ☐ Separate Contract
Describe _____

Storage Vaults: ☐ No ☐ Yes Allowance _____ ☐ Separate Contract
Describe _____

Swimming Pool Enclosure: ☐ No ☐ Yes Allowance _____ ☐ Separate Contract
Describe _____

Swimming Pool Equipment: In Division 11 _____

Swimming Pools: ☐ No ☐ Yes Allowance _____ ☐ Separate Contract
☐ Aluminum ☐ Concrete ☐ Gunite ☐ Plywood ☐ Steel ☐ _____
☐ Lined ☐ Unlined _____
Deck: ☐ No ☐ Concrete ☐ Stone _____ Size _____
Bath Houses: ☐ No ☐ Yes _____ Fixtures _____

Tanks: ☐ No ☐ Yes Allowance _____ ☐ Separate Contract
☐ Concrete ☐ Fiberglass ☐ Steel ☐ Wood ☐ _____ Capacity _____
☐ Fixed Roof ☐ Floating Roof ☐ _____ Height _____
Foundations: _____

Therapeutic Pools: ☐ No ☐ Yes Describe _____

Vault Front: ☐ No ☐ Yes Allowance _____ ☐ Separate Contract
Describe _____ Hour Test _____

Zoo Structures: ☐ No ☐ Yes Describe _____

Other Special Construction: _____

◢◣ Means® Forms

SPEC-AID

DATE _____

DIVISION 14: CONVEYING SYSTEMS

PROJECT _____ LOCATION _____

Ash Hoist: ☐ No ☐ Yes Allowance _____ ☐ Separate Contract
Describe _____

Conveyers: ☐ No ☐ Yes Allowance _____ ☐ Separate Contract
Describe _____

Correspondence Lift: ☐ No ☐ Yes Allowance _____ ☐ Separate Contract
Describe _____

Dumbwaiters: ☐ No ☐ Yes Allowance _____ ☐ Separate Contract
Capacity _____ Size _____ Number _____ Floors _____
Stops _____ Speed _____ Finish _____
Describe _____

Elevators, Freight: ☐ No ☐ Yes Allowance _____ ☐ Separate Contract
☐ Hydraulic ☐ Electric ☐ Geared ☐ Gearless _____
Capacity _____ Size _____ Number _____ Floors _____
Stops _____ Speed _____ Finish _____
Machinery Location _____ Door Type _____
Signals _____ Special Requirements _____

Elevators, Passenger: ☐ No ☐ Yes Allowance _____ ☐ Separate Contract
☐ Hydraulic ☐ Electric ☐ Geared ☐ Gearless _____
Capacity _____ Size _____ Number _____ Floors _____
Stops _____ Speed _____ Finish _____
Machinery Location _____ Door Type _____
Signals _____ Special Requirements _____

Escalators: ☐ No ☐ Yes Allowance _____ ☐ Separate Contract
Capacity _____ Size _____ Number _____ Floors _____
Story Height _____ Speed _____ Finish _____
Machinery Location _____ Incline Angle _____
Special Requirements _____

Hoists & Cranes: ☐ No ☐ Yes Allowance _____ ☐ Separate Contract
Describe _____

Lists: ☐ No ☐ Yes Allowance _____ ☐ Separate Contract
Describe _____

Material Handling Systems: ☐ No ☐ Yes Allowance _____ ☐ Separate Contract
☐ Automated ☐ Non Automated ☐ _____
Describe _____

Moving Stairs & Sidewalks ☐ No ☐ Yes Allowance _____ ☐ Separate Contract
Capacity _____ Size _____ Number _____ Floors _____
Story Height _____ Speed _____ Finish _____
Machinery Location _____ Incline Angle _____
Special Requirements _____

Pneumatic Tube System: ☐ No ☐ Yes Allowance _____ ☐ Separate Contract
☐ Automatic ☐ Manual ☐ _____ Size _____ Stations _____
Length _____ Special Requirements _____

Vertical Conveyer: ☐ No ☐ Yes Allowance _____ ☐ Separate Contract
☐ Automatic ☐ Non Automatic ☐ _____
Describe _____

Other Conveying: _____

⚓ Means® Forms

SPEC-AID

DATE _____

DIVISION 15: MECHANICAL

PROJECT _____   LOCATION _____

Building Drainage: Design Rainfall _____ □ Roof Drains _____ □ Court Drains _____
   □ Floor Drains _____ □ Yard Drains _____ □ Lawn Drains _____ □ Balcony Drains _____
   □ Area Drains _____ □ Sump Drains _____ Shower Drains _____ □ _____
   □ Drain Piping: Size _____ Describe _____
   □ Drain Gates _____ □ Clean Outs _____ □ Grease Traps _____

Sanitary System: □ No □ Yes □ Site Main _____ □ Manholes _____
   □ Sump Pumps _____ □ Bilge Pumps _____ □ Ejectors _____
   □ Soils, Stacks _____ □ Wastes, Vents _____ □ _____

Domestic Cold Water: □ No □ Water Meters _____ □ Law Sprinkler Connection _____
   □ Water Softening _____ □ Water Filtering _____
   □ Boiler Feed Water _____ □ Conditioning Apparatus _____
   □ Standpipe System _____ □ Hose Bibbs _____
   □ Pressure Tank _____ □ Booster Pumps _____
   □ Reducing Valves _____ □ _____

Domestic Hot Water: □ No □ Electric □ Gas □ Oil □ Solar _____
   □ Boiler _____ □ Conditioner _____ □ Fixture Connections _____
   □ Storage Tanks _____ Capacity _____
   □ Pumps _____

Piping: □ No □ Yes Material _____
   □ Air Chambers _____ □ Escutcheons _____ □ Expansion Joints _____
   □ Shock Absorbers _____ □ Hangers _____
   □ Valves _____ □ Paint _____

Special Piping: □ No □ Compressed Air _____ □ Vacuum _____
   □ Oxygen _____ □ Nitrous Oxygen _____
   □ Carbon Dioxide _____ □ Process Piping _____

Insulation Cold: □ No □ Yes Material _____ Jacket _____
   Hot: □ No □ Yes Material _____ Jacket _____

Fixtures Bathtub: □ No □ C.I. □ Steel □ Fiberglass □ _____ Color _____
   □ Curtain □ Rod □ Enclosure □ Wall Shower _____
   Drinking Fountain: □ No □ Yes □ Wall Hung □ Pedestal _____
   Hose Bibb: □ No □ Yes Describe _____
   Lavatory: □ No □ China □ C.I. □ Steel □ _____ Color _____
   □ Wall Hung □ Legs □ Acid Resisting _____
   Shower: □ No □ Individual □ Group □ Heads □ _____ Size _____
   Compartment: □ No □ Metal □ Stone □ Fiberglass □ _____ □ Door □ Curtain
   Receptor: □ No □ Plastic □ Metal □ Terrazzo □ _____
   Sinks: □ No □ Kitchen _____ □ Janitor _____
   □ Laundry _____ □ Pantry _____
   □ _____
   Urinals: □ No □ Floor Mounted □ Wall Hung _____
   Screens: □ No □ Floor Mounted □ Wall Hung _____
   Wash Centers: □ No □ Yes Describe _____
   Wash Fountains: □ No □ Floor Mounted □ Wall Hung _____ Size _____
   Describe _____
   Water Closets: □ No □ Floor Mounted □ Wall Hung Color _____
   Describe _____
   Water Coolers: □ No □ Floor Mounted □ Wall Hung _____ Capacity _____ gph.
   □ Water Supply □ Bottle □ Hot □ Compartment _____
   Other Fixtures: _____

⚓ Means® Forms

SPEC-AID

DIVISION 15: MECHANICAL

Fire Protection: □ Carbon Dioxide System _____ □ Standpipe _____

□ Sprinkler System □ Wet □ Dry _____ Spacing _____

□ Fire Department Connection _____ □ Building Alarm _____

□ Hose Cabinets _____ □ Hose Racks _____

□ Roof Manifold _____ □ Compressed Air Supply _____

□ Hydrants _____ □ _____

Special Plumbing _____

_____

Gas Supply System: □ No □ Natural Gas □ Manufactured Gas _____

Pipe: Schedule _____ Fittings _____

Shutoffs: _____ Master Control Valve: _____

Insulation: _____ Paint: _____

Oil Supply System: □ No □ Tanks □ Above Ground □ Below Ground _____

□ Steel □ Plastic □ _____ Capacity _____

Heating Plant: □ No □ Electric □ Gas □ Oil □ Solar _____

□ Boilers _____ □ Pumps _____

□ PRV Stations _____ □ Piping _____

□ Heat Pumps _____

Cooling Plant: □ No □ Yes _____ Tons _____

Chillers: □ Steam □ Water □ Air _____

Condenser—Compressor □ Air □ Water _____

Pumps _____ Cooling Towers _____

System Type: _____

□ Single Zone _____ □ Multi-Zone _____

□ All Air _____ □ Terminal Reheat _____

□ Double Duct _____ □ Radiant Panels _____

□ Fan Coil _____ □ Unit Ventilators _____

□ Perimeter Radiation _____ □ _____

Air Handling Units: Area Served _____ Number _____

Total CFM _____ % Outside Air _____

Cooling, Tons _____ Heating, MBH _____

Filtration _____ Supply Fans _____

Economizer _____

Fans: □ No □ Return □ Exhaust □ _____

Describe _____

Distribution: Ductwork _____ Material _____

Terminals: □ Diffusers _____ □ Registers _____

□ Grilles _____ □ Hoods _____

Volume Dampers: _____

Terminal Boxes: □ High Velocity _____ □ With Coil _____

□ Double Duct _____ □ _____

Coils: _____

□ Preheat _____ □ Reheat _____

□ Cooling _____ □ _____

Piping: See Previous Page _____

Insulation: Cold: □ No □ Yes Material _____ Jacket _____

□ Hot: □ No □ Yes Material _____ Jacket _____

Automatic Temperature Controls: _____

Air & Hydronic Balancing: _____

Special HVAC: _____

_____

⚓ Means® Forms

SPEC-AID

DATE _____

DIVISION 16: ELECTRICAL

PROJECT _____ LOCATION _____

Incoming Service: ☐ Overhead ☐ Underground

	Primary	Secondary
Voltage _____		
Unit Sub-station & Size _____		
Number of Manholes _____		
Feeder Size _____		
Length _____		
Conduit _____		
Duct _____		
Concrete: ☐ No ☐ Yes _____		
Other _____		

Building Service: Size _____ Amps Switchboard _____

Panels: ☐ Distribution _____ Lighting _____ Power _____

Describe _____

Motor Control Center: Furnished by _____

Describe _____

Bus Duct: ☐ No ☐ Yes Size _____ Amps Application _____

Describe _____

Cable Tray: ☐ No ☐ Yes Describe _____

Emergency System: ☐ No ☐ Yes Allowance _____ ☐ Separate Contract

Generator: ☐ No ☐ Diesel ☐ Gas ☐ Gasoline _____ Size _____ KW

Transfer Switch: ☐ No ☐ Yes Number _____ Size _____ Amps

Area Protection Relay Panels: ☐ No ☐ Yes _____

Other _____

Conduit: ☐ No ☐ Yes ☐ Aluminum _____

☐ Electric Metallic Tubing _____

☐ Galvanized Steel _____

☐ Plastic _____

Wire: ☐ No ☐ Yes ☐ Type Installation _____

☐ Armored Cable _____

☐ Building Wire _____

☐ Metallic Sheath Cable _____

☐ _____

Underfloor Duct: ☐ No ☐ Yes Describe _____

Header Duct: ☐ No ☐ Yes Describe _____

Trench Duct: ☐ No ☐ Yes Describe _____

Underground Duct: ☐ No ☐ Yes Describe _____

Explosion Proof Areas: ☐ No ☐ Yes Describe _____

Motors: ☐ No ☐ Yes Total H.P. _____ No. of Fractional H.P. _____ Voltage _____

☐ 1/2 to 5 H.P. ☐ 7-1/2 to 25 H.P. _____ ☐ Over 25 H.P. _____

Describe _____

Starters: Type _____

Supplied by: _____

⚓ Means® Forms

SPEC-AID

DIVISION 16: ELECTRICAL

Telephone System: ☐ No ☐ Yes Service Size _____ Length _____
  Manhole: ☐ No ☐ Yes Number _____ Termination _____
  Concrete Encased: ☐ No ☐ Yes ☐ Rigid Galv. ☐ Duct ☐ _____

Fire Alarm System: ☐ No ☐ Yes Service Size _____ Length _____ Wire Type _____
  Concrete Encased: ☐ No ☐ Yes ☐ Rigid Galv. ☐ Duct ☐ _____
  ☐ Stations _____ ☐ Horns _____ ☐ Lights _____ ☐ Combination _____
  Detectors: ☐ Rate of Rise _____ ☐ Fixed _____ ☐ Smoke _____
    Describe _____ Insulation _____ Wire Size _____
  ☐ Zones _____ ☐ Conduit _____ ☐ E.M.T. _____ ☐ Empty _____
    Describe _____

Watchmans Tour: ☐ No ☐ Yes ☐ Stations _____ ☐ Door Switches _____
  ☐ Alarm Bells _____ ☐ Key Re-sets _____ ☐ _____
  ☐ Conduit _____ ☐ E.M.T. _____ ☐ Wire _____ ☐ Empty _____
    Describe _____

Clock System: ☐ No ☐ Yes ☐ Electronic ☐ Wired ☐ _____
  ☐ Single Dial _____ ☐ Double Dial _____ ☐ Program Bell _____
  ☐ Conduit _____ ☐ E.M.T. _____ ☐ Empty _____
    Describe _____

Sound System: ☐ No ☐ Yes Type _____ Speakers _____
  ☐ Conduit _____ ☐ Cable _____ ☐ E.M.T. _____ ☐ Empty _____
    Describe _____

Television System: ☐ No ☐ Yes Describe _____
  ☐ Antenna _____ ☐ Closed Circuit _____ ☐ Teaching _____ ☐ Security _____
  ☐ Learning Laboratory _____ ☐ _____
  ☐ Conduit _____ ☐ E.M.T. _____ ☐ Wire _____ ☐ Empty _____

Lightning Protection: ☐ No ☐ Yes Describe _____
Low Voltage Switching: ☐ No ☐ Yes Describe _____
Scoreboards: ☐ No ☐ Yes Describe _____ Number _____
Comfort Systems: ☐ No ☐ Electric Heat ☐ Snow Melting ☐ _____
  Describe _____

Other Systems: _____
_____
_____

Lighting Fixtures: ☐ No ☐ Yes ☐ Allowance _____ ☐ Separate Contract
  ☐ Economy ☐ Commercial ☐ Deluxe ☐ Explosion Proof ☐ _____
  ☐ Incandescent _____
    _____ Foot Candles _____
  ☐ Fluorescent _____
    _____ Foot Candles _____
  ☐ Mercury Vapor _____
    _____ Foot Candles _____
  ☐ _____
    _____ Foot Candles _____
  ☐ Step Lighting _____ ☐ Planter Lighting _____ ☐ Fountain Lighting _____
  ☐ Site Lighting _____ ☐ Poles _____ ☐ Area Lighting _____ ☐ Flood Lighting _____
  Dimming System: ☐ No ☐ Yes ☐ Incandescent ☐ Fluorescent _____
  Ceilings: ☐ T Bar ☐ Concealed Spline ☐ _____
  Emergency Battery Units: ☐ No ☐ Lead Acid ☐ Nickel Cadmium ☐ 6 Volt _____ 12 Volt _____
    Describe _____

Special Considerations: _____
_____
_____

MEANSCO FORM 103	**SYSTEMS ESTIMATE SUMMARY**						

PROJECT		NET AREA		S.F.	SHEET NO.		
LOCATION		GROSS AREA		S.F.	ESTIMATE NO.		
ARCHITECT		RATIO: NET TO GROSS			DATE		
OWNER		GROSS VOLUME		C.F.	NO. OF STORIES		
PRICES BY		EXTENSIONS BY			CHECKED BY		

NO.	SYSTEM DESCRIPTION	QUANTITY	UNIT	UNIT PRICE	TOTAL COST	COST/S.F.
1.01	SUB-STRUCTURE					
.11	Spread Footings					
.21	Strip Footings					
.31	Grade Beams					
.41	Foundation Walls					
.51	Slab on Grade					
.61	Building Excavation					
3.01	SUPERSTRUCTURE					
.11	Floor Systems					
.21	Roof Systems					
.31	Columns					
.41	Structural Walls					
.42	Shear Walls					
.51	Stairs					
4.01	EXTERIOR CLOSURE					
.11	Bearing Walls					
.21	Curtain Walls					
.31	Fenestration					
.41	Glass and Glazing					
5.01	ROOFING					
.11	Covering					
.21	Openings					
.31	Insulation					
.41	Special Systems					
.51	Gutters, Downspouts, Flashing					
6.01	INTERIOR CONSTRUCTION					
.11	Fixed Partitions					
.21	Miscellaneous Partitions					
.31	Doors					
.41	Interior Finishes					
.51	Floor Coverings					
.61	Ceilings					
7.01	CONVEYING SYSTEMS					
.11	Elevators					
.21	Escalators					
.31	Lifts and Hoists					
.32	Conveyors					
.33	Pneumatic Tubes					
.34	Other Systems					
8.01	PLUMBING SYSTEMS					
.11	Drainage Rough-In					
.21	Supply Rough-In					
.31	Fixtures and Hardware					
.41	Equipment					
.51	Fire Protection					
.61	Special Sub-Systems					
8.02	H.V.A.C. SYSTEMS					
.11	Energy Conversion					
.12	Heat Generation Equipment					
.13	Cooling Generation Equipment					
.21	Energy Distribution					
.22	Piping					
.23	Insulation					
.24	Heating Dist. Equipment with Insulation					

NO.	SYSTEM DESCRIPTION	QUANTITY	UNIT	UNIT PRICE	TOTAL COST	COST/S.F.
.25	Cooling Distribution Equipment					
.31	Air Handling System					
.32	Sheet Metal					
.34	Registers, Grilles & Diffusers					
.35	Air Handling Equipment					
.41	Temperature Control System					
.51	Special Sub-Systems					
9.01	ELECTRICAL SYSTEMS					
.11	Emergency Power					
.21	Lighting					
.31	Power					
.41	Electrical Circuits					
.51	Service and Distribution					
.61	Sub-Systems					
.71	Communications Systems					
	BASIC BUILDING SUB-TOTAL					
10.01	FIXED EQUIPMENT					
11.01	SPECIAL FOUNDATIONS					
.11	Special Excavation					
.21	Piles (Bearing/Friction)					
.31	Caissons					
.41	Mat Construction					
.51	Sheeting & Shoring					
.61	Dewatering					
.71	Special Waterproofing					
	BUILDING TOTAL COST, SUB-TOTAL					
12.01	SITE CONSTRUCTION					
.11	Site Improvement					
.12	Grading & Landscaping					
.13	Site Structures & Paving					
.21	Site Utilities					
.22	Plumbing Site Work					
.23	H.V.A.C. Site Work					
.24	Electrical Site Work					
	CONSTRUCTION COST, SUB-TOTAL					
13.01	CONSTRUCTION RELATED COSTS & CONDITIONS					
.11	General Conditions					
.21	Special Requirements					
.31	Overhead & Insurance					
.41	Profit and Fees					
	ESTIMATED CONSTRUCTION CONTRACT AWARD					
14.01	Contingencies					
.11	Construction & Design _____ %					
.12	Scope & Information Increase _____ %					
.13	Field Change Orders _____ %					
.21	Escalation to Bid Date ____/____ 19 ____ ____ %					
.31	Probable Bond Cost _____ %					
	TOTAL ESTIMATED CONSTRUCTION COST					
15.01	PROJECT RELATED COSTS					
.11	Site Costs					
.21	Design & Review Costs					
.31	Management & Inspection Costs					
.41	Furnishings & Fixtures					
	ESTIMATED TOTAL PROJECT COST					
	ESTIMATE PROJECTED TO A BID DATE OF					

APPENDIX B

APPENDIX B

The following tables have been included to assist in the estimating process. They provide man-hours, technical data and shortcuts for material takeoffs. These figures have been numbered by MasterFormat Division and are a sampling from *Means Estimating Handbook*. The tables should be used with discretion, taking into account any unique or unusual project requirements. Factors for determining quantities related to carpentry include waste allowance. However, items such as plates, double joists or studs, and corners must be taken off and added separately.

Figure 2.1 Installation Time in Man-Hours for Dewatering

Description	Man-Hours	Unit
Excavate Drainage Trench, 2' Wide		
2' Deep	.178	C.Y.
3' Deep	.160	C.Y.
Sump Pits, by Hand		
Light Soil	1.130	C.Y.
Heavy Soil	2.290	C.Y.
Pumping 8 Hours, Diaphragm or Centrifugal Pump		
Attended 2 hours per day	3.000	Day
Attended 8 hours per day	12.000	Day
Pumping 24 Hours, Attended 24 Hours, 4 Men at		
6 Hour Shifts, 1 Week Minimum	25.140	Day
Relay Corrugated Metal Pipe, Including		
Excavation, 3' Deep		
12" Diameter	.209	L.F.
18" Diameter	.240	L.F.
Sump Hole Construction, Including Excavation,		
with 12" Gravel Collar		
Corrugated Pipe		
12" Diameter	.343	L.F.
18" Diameter	.480	L.F.
Wood Lining, Up to 4'x4'	.080	SFCA
Wellpoint System, Single Stage, Install and		
Remove, per Length of Header		
Minimum	.750	L.F.
Maximum	2.000	L.F.
Wells, 10' to 20' Deep with Steel Casing		
2' Diameter		
Minimum	.145	V.L.F.
Average	.245	V.L.F.
Maximum	.490	V.L.F.

Figure 2.2 Excavating

The selection of equipment used for structural excavation and bulk excavation or for grading is determined by the following factors.

1. Quantity of material
2. Type of material
3. Depth or height of cut
4. Length of haul
5. Condition of haul road
6. Accessibility of site
7. Moisture content and dewatering requirements
8. Availability of excavating and hauling equipment

Some additional costs must be allowed for hand trimming the sides and bottom of concrete pours and other excavation below the general excavation.

When planning excavation and fill, the following should also be considered.

1. Swell factor
2. Compaction factor
3. Moisture content
4. Density requirements

A typical example for scheduling and estimating the cost of excavation of a 15' deep basement on a dry site when the material must be hauled off the site, is outlined below.

Assumptions:

1. Swell factor, 18%
2. No mobilization or demobilization
3. Allowance included for idle time and moving on job
4. No dewatering, sheeting, or bracing
5. No truck spotter or hand trimming

Number of B.C.Y. per truck

$$= 1.5 \text{ C.Y. bucket} \times 8 \text{ passes} = 12 \text{ loose C.Y.}$$

$$= 12 \times \frac{100}{118} = 10.2 \text{ B.C.Y. per truck}$$

Truck haul cycle:

Load truck 8 passes	= 4 minutes
Haul distance 1 mile	= 9 minutes
Dump time	= 2 minutes
Return 1 mile	= 7 minutes
Spot under machine	= 1 minute
	23 minute cycle

Fleet Haul Production per Day in B.C.Y.

$$4 \text{ trucks} \times \frac{50 \text{ min. hr.}}{23 \text{ min. haul cycle}} \times 8 \text{ hrs.} \times 10.2 \text{ B.C.Y.} = 4 \times 2.2 \times 8 \times 10.2 = 718 \text{ B.C.Y./day}$$

Note: B.C.Y. = Bank Measure Cubic Yards

Figure 3.1 Formwork Labor Hours

Man-hours for formwork vary greatly from one component to another. This table is convenient for planning the number of forms to be fabricated or provided, depending on the number of reuses anticipated.

Item	Unit	Hours Required			Total Hours 1 Use	Multiple Use		
		Fabricate	Erect & Strip	Clean & Move		2 Use	3 Use	4 Use
Beam and Girder, interior beams, 12" wide	100 S.F.	6.4	8.3	1.3	16.0	13.3	12.4	12.0
Hung from steel beams		5.8	7.7	1.3	14.8	12.4	11.6	11.2
Beam sides only, 36" high		5.8	7.2	1.3	14.3	11.9	11.1	10.7
Beam bottoms only, 24" wide		6.6	13.0	1.3	20.9	18.1	17.2	16.7
Box out for openings		9.9	10.0	1.1	21.0	16.6	15.1	14.3
Buttress forms, to 8' high		6.0	6.5	1.2	13.7	11.2	10.4	10.0
Centering, steel, 3/4" rib lath			1.0		1.0			
3/8" rib lath or slab form	▼		0.9		0.9			
Chamfer strip or keyway	100 L.F.		1.5		1.5	1.5	1.5	1.5
Columns, fiber tube 8" diameter			20.6		20.6			
12"			21.3		21.3			
16"			22.9		22.9			
20"			23.7		23.7			
24"			24.6		24.6			
30"	▼		25.6		25.6			
Round Steel, 12" diameter					22.0	22.0	22.0	22.0
16"					25.6	25.6	25.6	25.6
20"					30.5	30.5	30.5	30.5
24"	▼				37.7	37.7	37.7	37.7
Plywood 8" x 8"	100 S.F.	7.0	11.0	1.2	19.2	16.2	15.2	14.7
12" x 12"		6.0	10.5	1.2	17.7	15.2	14.4	14.0
16" x 16"		5.9	10.0	1.2	17.1	14.7	13.8	13.4
24" x 24"		5.8	9.8	1.2	16.8	14.4	13.6	13.2
Steel framed plywood 8" x 8"			10.0	1.0	11.0	11.0	11.0	11.0
12" x 12"			9.3	1.0	10.3	10.3	10.3	10.3
16" x 16"			8.5	1.0	9.5	9.5	9.5	9.5
24" x 24"			7.8	1.0	8.8	8.8	8.8	8.8
Drop head forms, plywood		9.0	12.5	1.5	23.0	19.0	17.7	17.0
Coping forms		8.5	15.0	1.5	25.0	21.3	20.0	19.4
Culvert, box			14.5	4.3	18.8	18.8	18.8	18.8
Curb forms, 6" to 12" high, on grade	▼	5.0	8.5	1.2	14.7	12.7	12.1	11.7
On elevated slabs		6.0	10.8	1.2	18.0	15.5	14.7	14.3
Edge forms to 6" high, on grade	100 L.F.	2.0	3.5	0.6	6.1	5.6	5.4	5.3
7" to 12" high	100 S.F.	2.5	5.0	1.0	8.5	7.8	7.5	7.4
Equipment foundations	"	10.0	18.0	2.0	30.0	25.5	24.0	23.3
Flat slabs, including drops		3.5	6.0	1.2	10.7	9.5	9.0	8.8
Hung from steel		3.0	5.5	1.2	9.7	8.7	8.4	8.2
Closed deck for domes		3.0	5.8	1.2	10.0	9.0	8.7	8.5
Open deck for pans		2.2	5.3	1.0	8.5	7.9	7.7	7.6
Footings, continuous, 12" high		3.5	3.5	1.5	8.5	7.3	6.8	6.6
Spread, 12" high		4.7	4.2	1.6	10.5	8.7	8.0	7.7
Pile caps, square or rectangular		4.5	5.0	1.5	11.0	9.3	8.7	8.4
Grade beams, 24" deep		2.5	5.3	1.2	9.0	8.3	8.0	7.9
Lintel or Sill forms		8.0	17.0	2.0	27.0	23.5	22.3	21.8
Spandrel beams, 12" wide		9.0	11.2	1.3	21.5	17.5	16.2	15.5
Stairs			25.0	4.0	29.0	29.0	29.0	29.0
Trench forms in floor		4.5	14.0	1.5	20.0	18.3	17.7	17.4
Walls, Plywood, at grade, to 8' high		5.0	6.5	1.5	13.0	11.0	9.7	9.5
8' to 16'		7.5	8.0	1.5	17.0	13.8	12.7	12.1
16' to 20'		9.0	10.0	1.5	20.5	16.5	15.2	14.5
Foundation walls, to 8' high		4.5	6.5	1.0	12.0	10.3	9.7	9.4
8' to 16' high		5.5	7.5	1.0	14.0	11.8	11.0	10.6
Retaining wall to 12' high, battered		6.0	8.5	1.5	16.0	13.5	12.7	12.3
Radial walls to 12' high, smooth		8.0	9.5	2.0	19.5	16.0	14.8	14.3
But in 2' chords		7.0	8.0	1.5	16.5	13.5	12.5	12.0
Prefabricated modular, to 8' high		—	4.3	1.0	5.3	5.3	5.3	5.3
Steel, to 8' high		—	6.8	1.2	8.0	8.0	8.0	8.0
8' to 16' high		—	9.1	1.5	10.6	10.3	10.2	10.2
Steel framed plywood to 8' high		—	6.8	1.2	8.0	7.5	7.3	7.2
8' to 16' high	▼	—	9.3	1.2	10.5	9.5	9.2	9.0

Figure 3.2 Data on Handling and Transporting Concrete

On most construction jobs, the method of concrete placement is an important consideration for the estimator and the project manager. This table is a guide for planning time and equipment for concrete placement.

Quantity	Rate
Unloading 6 cubic yard mixer truck, 1 operator	Minimum time 2 minutes, average time 7 minutes
Wheeling, using 4-1/2 cubic feet wheelbarrows, 1 laborer	
up to 100'	Average 1-1/2 cubic yards per hour
up to 200'	Average 1 cubic yard per hour
Wheeling, using 8 cubic feet hand buggies, 1 laborer	
up to 100'	Average 5 cubic yards per hour
up to 200'	Average 3 cubic yards per hour
Transporting, using 28 cubic feet power buggies, 1 laborer	
up to 500'	Average 20 cubic feet per hour
up to 1000'	Average 15 cubic feet per hour
Portable conveyor, 16" belt, 30° elevation, 1 laborer	
100 FPM belt speed	30 C.Y./Hr. max., 15 C.Y./Hr. average
200 FPM belt speed	60 C.Y./Hr. max., 30 C.Y./Hr. average
300 FPM belt speed	90 C.Y./Hr. max., 45 C.Y./Hr. average
400 FPM belt speed	120 C.Y./Hr. max., 60 C.Y./Hr. average
500 FPM belt speed	150 C.Y./Hr. max., 75 C.Y./Hr. average
600 FPM belt speed	180 C.Y./Hr. max., 90 C.Y./Hr. average
Feeder conveyors, up to 600' 5 laborers	
500 FPM belt speed	150 C.Y./Hr. max., 50 C.Y./Hr. average
600 FPM belt speed	180 C.Y./Hr. max., 60 C.Y./Hr. average
Side discharge conveyor, 1 laborer	
fed by portable conveyor	40–60 C.Y./Hr. average
fed by feeder conveyor	80–100 C.Y./Hr. average
fed by crane & bucket	35–60 C.Y./Hr. average
Mobile crane, 1 operator* 2 laborers	
1 cubic yard bucket	40 C.Y./Hr. average
2 cubic yard bucket	60 C.Y./Hr. average
Tower crane 1 operator* 2 laborers	
1 cubic yard bucket	35–40 C.Y./Hr. average
Small line pumping systems, 1 foot vertical = 6 feet horizontally 1 90 degree bend = 40 feet horizontally 1 45 degree bend = 20 feet horizontally 1 30 degree bend = 13 feet horizontally 1 foot rubber hose = 1-1/2 feet of steel tubing 1 operator*	
average output, 1000' horizontally	40–50 C.Y./Hr. Average

*In some regions an oiler or helper may be needed, according to union rules.

(*courtesy Concrete Estimating Handbook, Michael F. Kenny, Van Nostrand Reinhold Company*).

Figure 4.1 Man-Hours Required for the Installation of Brick Masonry

Description	Man-Hours	Unit
Brick Wall		
Veneer		
4" Thick		
Running Bond		
Standard Brick (6.75/S.F.)	.182	S.F.
Engineer Brick (5.63/S.F.)	.154	S.F.
Economy Brick (4.50/S.F.)	.129	S.F.
Roman Brick (6.00/S.F.)	.160	S.F.
Norman Brick (4.50/S.F.)	.125	S.F.
Norwegian Brick (3.75/S.F.)	.107	S.F.
Utility Brick (3.00/S.F.)	.089	S.F.
Common Bond, Standard Brick (7.88/S.F.)	.216	S.F.
Flemish Bond, Standard Brick (9.00/S.F.)	.267	S.F.
English Bond, Standard Brick (10.13/S.F.)	.286	S.F.
Stack Bond, Standard Brick (6.75/S.F.)	.200	S.F.
6" Thick		
Running Bond		
S.C.R. Brick (4.50/S.F.)	.129	S.F.
Jumbo Brick (3.00/S.F.)	.092	S.F.
Backup		
4" Thick		
Running Bond		
Standard Brick (6.75/S.F.)	.167	S.F.
Solid, Unreinforced		
8" Thick Running Bond (13.50/S.F.)	.296	S.F.
12" Thick, Running Bond (20.25/S.F.)	.421	S.F.
Solid, Rod Reinforced		
8" Thick, Running Bond	.308	S.F.
12" Thick, Running Bond	.444	S.F.
Cavity		
4" Thick		
4" Backup	.242	S.F.
6" Backup	.276	S.F.
Brick Chimney		
16" x 16", Standard Brick w/8" x 8" Flue	.889	V.L.F.
16" x 16", Standard Brick w/8" x 12" Flue	1.000	V.L.F.
20" x 20", Standard Brick w/12" x 12" Flue	1.140	V.L.F.
Brick Column		
8" x 8", Standard Brick 9.0 V.L.F.	.286	V.L.F.
12" x 12", Standard Brick 20.3 V.L.F.	.640	V.L.F.
20" x 20", Standard Brick 56.3 V.L.F.	1.780	V.L.F.
Brick Coping		
Precast, 10" Wide, or Limestone, 4" Wide	.178	L.F.
Precast 14" Wide, or Limestone, 6" Wide	.200	L.F.

Figure 4.1 (cont.) Man-Hours Required for the Installation of Brick Masonry

Description	Man-Hours	Unit
Brick Fireplace		
30" x 24" Opening, Plain Brickwork	40.000	Ea.
Firebox Only, Fire Brick (110/Ea.)	8.000	Ea.
Brick Prefabricated Wall Panels, 4" Thick		
Minimum	.093	S.F.
Maximum	.144	S.F.
Brick Steps	53.330	M
Window Sill		
Brick on Edge	.200	L.F.
Precast, 6" Wide	.229	L.F.
Needle Brick and Shore, Solid Brick		
8" Thick	6.450	Ea.
12" Thick	8.160	Ea.
Repoint Brick		
Hard Mortar		
Running Bond	.100	S.F.
English Bond	.123	S.F.
Soft Mortar		
Running Bond	.080	S.F.
English Bond	.098	S.F.
Toothing Brick		
Hard Mortar	.267	V.L.F.
Soft Mortar	.200	V.L.F.
Sandblast Brick		
Wet System		
Minimum	.024	S.F.
Maximum	.057	S.F.
Dry System		
Minimum	.013	S.F.
Maximum	.027	S.F.
Sawing Brick, Per Inch of Depth	.027	L.F.
Steam Clean, Face Brick	.033	S.F.
Wash Brick, Smooth	.014	S.F.

Figure 4.2 Installation Time in Man-Hours for
Block Walls, Partitions, and Accessories

Description	Man-Hours	Unit
Foundation Walls, Trowel Cut Joints, Parged 1/2" Thick, 1 Side, 8" x 16" Face		
Hollow		
8" Thick	.093	S.F.
12" Thick	.122	S.F.
Solid		
8" Thick	.096	S.F.
12" Thick	.126	S.F.
Backup Walls, Tooled Joint 1 Side, 8" x 16" Face		
4" Thick	.091	S.F.
8" Thick	.100	S.F.
Partition Walls, Tooled Joint 2 Sides 8" x 16" Face		
Hollow		
4" Thick	.093	S.F.
8" Thick	.107	S.F.
12" Thick	.141	S.F.
Solid		
4" Thick	.096	S.F.
8" Thick	.111	S.F.
12" Thick	.148	S.F.
Stud Block Walls, Tooled Joints 2 Sides 8" x 16" Face		
6" Thick and 2", Plain	.098	S.F.
Embossed	.103	S.F.
10" Thick and 2", Plain	.108	S.F.
Embossed	.114	S.F.
6" Thick and 2" Each Side, Plain	.114	S.F.
Acoustical Slotted Block Walls Tooled 2 Sides		
4" Thick	.127	S.F.
8" Thick	.151	S.F.
Glazed Block Walls, Tooled Joint 2 Sides 8" x 16", Glazed 1 Face		
4" Thick	.116	S.F.
8" Thick	.129	S.F.
12" Thick	.171	S.F.
8" x 16", Glazed 2 Faces		
4" Thick	.129	S.F.
8" Thick	.148	S.F.
8" x 16", Corner		
4" Thick	.140	Ea.

Figure 4.2 (cont.) Installation Time in Man-Hours for Block Walls, Partitions, and Accessories

Description	Man-Hours	Unit
Structural Facing Tile, Tooled 2 Sides		
5" x 12", Glazed 1 Face		
4" Thick	.182	S.F.
8" Thick	.222	S.F.
5" x 12", Glazed 2 Faces		
4" Thick	.205	S.F.
8" Thick	.246	S.F.
8" x 16", Glazed 1 Face		
4" Thick	.116	S.F.
8" Thick	.129	S.F.
8" x 16", Glazed 2 Faces		
4" Thick	.123	S.F.
8" Thick	.137	S.F.
Exterior Walls, Tooled Joint 2 Sides, Insulated		
8" x 16" Face, Regular Weight		
8" Thick	.110	S.F.
12" Thick	.145	S.F.
Lightweight		
8" Thick	.104	S.F.
12" Thick	.137	S.F.
Architectural Block Walls, Tooled Joint 2 Sides		
8" x 16" Face		
4" Thick	.116	S.F.
8" Thick	.138	S.F.
12" Thick	.181	S.F.
Interlocking Block Walls, Fully Grouted		
Vertical Reinforcing		
8" Thick	.131	S.F.
12" Thick	.145	S.F.
16" Thick	.173	S.F.
Bond Beam, Grouted, 2 Horizontal Rebars		
8" x 16" Face, Regular Weight		
8" Thick	.133	L.F.
12" Thick	.192	L.F.
Lightweight		
8" Thick	.131	L.F.
12" Thick	.188	L.F.
Lintels, Grouted, 2 Horizontal Rebars		
8" x 16" Face, 8" Thick	.119	L.F.
16" x 16" Face, 8" Thick	.131	L.F.
Control Joint 4" Wall	.013	L.F.
8" Wall	.020	L.F.
Grouting Bond Beams and Lintels		
8" Deep Pumped, 8" Thick	.018	L.F.
12" Thick	.025	L.F.
Concrete Block Cores Solid		
4" Thick By Hand	.035	S.F.
8" Thick Pumped	.038	S.F.
Cavity Walls 2" Space Pumped	.016	S.F.
6" Space	.034	S.F.

(continued on next page)

Figure 4.2 (cont.) Installation Time in Man-Hours for Block Walls, Partitions, and Accessories

Description	Man-Hours	Unit
Joint Reinforcing		
Wire Strips Regular Truss to 6" Wide	.267	C.L.F.
12" Wide	.400	C.L.F.
Cavity Wall with Drip Section to 6" Wide	.267	C.L.F.
12" Wide	.400	C.L.F.
Lintels Steel Angles Minimum	.008	lb.
Maximum	.016	lb.
Wall Ties	.762	C
Coping For 12" Wall Stock Units, Aluminum	.200	L.F.
Precast Concrete	.188	L.F.
Structural Reinforcing, Placed Horizontal,		
#3 and #4 Bars	.018	lb.
#5 and #6 Bars	.010	lb.
Placed Vertical, #3 and #4 Bars	.023	lb.
#5 and #6 Bars	.012	lb.
Acoustical Slotted Block		
4" Thick	.127	S.F.
6" Thick	.138	S.F.
8" Thick	.151	S.F.
12" Thick	.163	S.F.
Lightweight Block		
4" Thick	.090	S.F.
6" Thick	.095	S.F.
8" Thick	.100	S.F.
10" Thick	.103	S.F.
12" Thick	.130	S.F.
Regular Block		
Hollow		
4" Thick	.093	S.F.
6" Thick	.100	S.F.
8" Thick	.107	S.F.
10" Thick	.111	S.F.
12" Thick	.141	S.F.
Solid		
4" Thick	.095	S.F.
6" Thick	.105	S.F.
8" Thick	.113	S.F.
12" Thick	.150	S.F.
Glazed Concrete Block		
Single Face 8" x 16"		
2" Thick	.111	S.F.
4" Thick	.116	S.F.
6" Thick	.121	S.F.
8" Thick	.129	S.F.
12" Thick	.171	S.F.
Double Face		
4" Thick	.129	S.F.
6" Thick	.138	S.F.
8" Thick	.148	S.F.

Figure 4.2 (cont.) Installation Time in Man-Hours for Block Walls, Partitions, and Accessories

Description	Man-Hours	Unit
Joint Reinforcing Wire Strips		
4" and 6" Wall	.267	C.L.F.
8" Wall	.320	C.L.F.
10" and 12" Wall	.400	C.L.F.
Steel Bars Horizontal		
#3 and #4	.018	lb.
#5 and #6	.010	lb.
Vertical		
#3 and #4	.023	lb.
#5 and #6	.012	lb.
Grout Cores Solid		
By Hand 6" Thick	.035	S.F.
Pumped 8" Thick	.038	S.F.
10" Thick	.039	S.F.
12" Thick	.040	S.F.

Figure 5.1 Installation Time in Man-Hours for the Erection of Steel Superstructure Systems

Description	Man-Hours	Unit
Steel Columns Concrete Filled		
4" Diameter	.072	L.F.
5" Diameter	.055	L.F.
6-5/8" Diameter	.047	L.F.
Steel Pipe		
6" Diameter	6.000	ton
12" Diameter	2.000	ton
Structural Tubing		
6" x 6"	6.000	ton
10" x 10"	2.000	ton
Wide Flange		
W8 x 31	3.355	ton
W10 x 45	2.412	ton
W12 x 50	2.171	ton
W14 x 74	1.538	ton
Beams WF Average	4.000	ton
Steel Joists H Series Horizontal Bridging		
To 30' Span	6.667	ton
30' to 50' Span	6.353	ton
(Includes One Row of Bolted Cross Bridging for Spans Over 40' Where Required)		
LH Series Bolted Cross Bridging		
Spans to 96'	6.154	ton
DLH Series Bolted Cross Bridging		
Spans to 144' Shipped in 2 Pieces	6.154	ton
Joist Girders	6.154	ton
Trusses, Factory Fabricated, with Chords	7.273	ton
Metal Decking Open Type		
1-1/2" Deep		
22 Gauge	.007	S.F.
18 and 20 Gauge	.008	S.F.
3" Deep		
20 and 22 Gauge	.009	S.F.
18 Gauge	.010	S.F.
16 Gauge	.011	S.F.
4-1/2" Deep		
20 Gauge	.012	S.F.
18 Gauge	.013	S.F.
16 Gauge	.014	S.F.
7-1/2" Deep		
18 Gauge	.019	S.F.
16 Gauge	.020	S.F.

Figure 5.1 (cont.) Installation Time in Man-Hours for the Erection of Steel Superstructure Systems

Figure 5.2 Installation Time in Man-Hours for Fireproofing Structural Steel

Description	Man-Hours	Unit
Fireproofing - 10" Column Encasements		
Perlite Plaster	.273	V.L.F.
1" Perlite on 3/8" Gypsum Lath	.345	V.L.F.
Sprayed Fiber	.131	V.L.F.
Concrete 1-1/2" Thick	.716	V.L.F.
Gypsum Board 1/2" Fire Resistant,		
1 Layer	.364	V.L.F.
2 Layer	.428	V.L.F.
3 Layer	.530	V.L.F.
Fireproofing – 16" x 7" Beam Encasements		
Perlite Plaster on Metal Lath	.453	L.F.
Gypsum Plaster on Metal Lath	.408	L.F.
Sprayed Fiber	.079	L.F.
Concrete 1-1/2" Thick	.554	L.F.
Gypsum Board 5/8" Fire Resistant	.488	L.F.

Sprayed Fiber on Columns

Sprayed Fiber on Beams and Girders

Concrete Encasement on Columns

Concrete Encasement on Beams and Girders

Gypsum Board on Columns

(continued on next page)

Figure 5.2 (cont.)   Installation Time in Man-Hours for
Fireproofing Structural Steel

Gypsum Board on Beams and Girders   Plaster on Gypsum Lath — Columns

Plaster on Metal Lath — Columns   Plaster on Metal Lath — Beams and Girders

Figure 6.1   Flat Roof Framing

This table can be used to compute the amount of lumber in board feet required to frame a flat roof, based on the size lumber required.

Flat Roof Framing			
Joist Size	Inches On Center	Board Feet per Square Foot of Ceiling Area	Nails Lbs. per MBM
2" x 6"	12"	1.17	10
	16"	.91	10
	20"	.76	10
	24"	.65	10
2" x 8"	12"	1.56	8
	16"	1.21	8
	20"	1.01	8
	24"	.86	8
2" x 10"	12"	1.96	6
	16"	1.51	6
	20"	1.27	6
	24"	1.08	6
2" x 12"	12"	2.35	5
	16"	1.82	5
	20"	1.52	5
	24"	1.30	5
3" x 8"	12"	2.35	5
	16"	1.82	5
	20"	1.52	5
	24"	1.30	5
3" x 10"	12"	2.94	4
	16"	2.27	4
	20"	1.90	4
	24"	1.62	4

MBM; MFBM = Thousand Feet Board Measure

Figure 6.2 Pitched Roof Framing

This table is used to compute the board feet of lumber required per square foot of roof area, based on the required spacing and the lumber size to be used.

	Rafters Including Collar Ties, Hip and Valley Rafters, Ridge Poles							
	Spacing Center to Center							
Rafter Size	**12"**		**16"**		**20"**		**24"**	
	Board Feet per Square Foot of Roof Area	Nails Lbs. per MBM	Board Feet per Square Foot of Roof Area	Nails Lbs. per MBM	Board Feet per Square Foot of Roof Area	Nails Lbs. per MBM	Board Feet per Square Foot of Roof Area	Nails Lbs. per MBM
2" x 4"	.89	17	.71	17	.59	17	.53	17
2" x 6"	1.29	12	1.02	12	.85	12	.75	12
2" x 8"	1.71	9	1.34	9	1.12	9	.98	9
2" x 10"	2.12	7	1.66	7	1.38	7	1.21	7
2" x 12"	2.52	6	1.97	6	1.64	6	1.43	6
3" x 8"	2.52	6	1.97	6	1.64	6	1.43	6
3" x 10"	3.13	5	2.45	5	2.02	5	1.78	5

Figure 6.3 Board Feet Required for On-the-Job Cut Bridging

Based on the size of the lumber used for joists, the total lengths of lumber for various sized bridging can be obtained from this chart.

Cross Bridging—Board Feet per Square Foot of Floors, Ceiling or Flat Roof Area Nails — Pounds Per MBM of Bridging							
		1" x 3"		1" x 4"		2" x 3"	
Joist Size	Spacing	B.F.	Nails	B.F.	Nails	B.F.	Nails
2" x 8"	12"	.04	147	.05	112	.08	77
	16"	.04	120	.05	91	.08	61
	20"	.04	102	.05	77	.08	52
	24"	.04	83	.05	63	.08	42
2" x 10"	12"	.04	136	.05	103	.08	71
	16"	.04	114	.05	87	.08	58
	20"	.04	98	.05	74	.08	50
	24"	.04	80	.05	61	.08	41
2" x 12"	12"	.04	127	.05	96	.08	67
	16"	.04	108	.05	82	.08	55
	20"	.04	94	.05	71	.08	48
	24"	.04	78	.05	59	.08	39
3" x 8"	12"	.04	160	.05	122	.08	84
	16"	.04	127	.05	96	.08	66
	20"	.04	107	.05	81	.08	54
	24"	.04	86	.05	65	.08	44
3" x 10"	12"	.04	146	.05	111	.08	77
	16"	.04	120	.05	91	.08	62
	20"	.04	102	.05	78	.08	52
	24"	.04	83	.05	63	.08	42

Figure 6.4   Wood Siding Factors

This table shows the factor by which area to be covered is multiplied to determine exact amount of surface material needed.

Item	Nominal Size	Width Overall	Face	Area Factor
Shiplap	1" x 6"	5-1/2"	5-1/8"	1.17
	1 x 8	7-1/4	6-7/8	1.16
	1 x 10	9-1/4	8-7/8	1.13
	1 x 12	11-1/4	10-7/8	1.10
Tongue and Grooved	1 x 4	3-3/8	3-1/8	1.28
	1 x 6	5-3/8	5-1/8	1.17
	1 x 8	7-1/8	6-7/8	1.16
	1 x 10	9-1/8	8-7/8	1.13
	1 x 12	11-1/8	10-7/8	1.10
S4S	1 x 4	3-1/2	3-1/2	1.14
	1 x 6	5-1/2	5-1/2	1.09
	1 x 8	7-1/4	7-1/4	1.10
	1 x 10	9-1/4	9-1/4	1.08
	1 x 12	11-1/4	11-1/4	1.07
Solid Paneling	1 x 6	5-7/16	5-7/16	1.19
	1 x 8	7-1/8	6-3/4	1.19
	1 x 10	9-1/8	8-3/4	1.14
	1 x 12	11-1/8	10-3/4	1.12
Bevel Siding*	1 x 4	3-1/2	3-1/2	1.60
	1 x 6	5-1/2	5-1/2	1.33
	1 x 8	7-1/4	7-1/4	1.28
	1 x 10	9-1/4	9-1/4	1.21
	1 x 12	11-1/4	11-1/4	1.17

Note: This area factor is strictly so-called milling waste. The cutting and fitting waste must be added.

*1" lap

(from Western Wood Products Association)

Figure 6.5 Exterior Wall Stud Framing

This table allows you to compute the board feet of lumber required for each square foot of exterior wall to be framed based on the lumber size and spacing design.

Stud Size	Inches On Center	Studs Including Corner Bracing		Horizontal Bracing Midway Between Plates	
		Board Feet per Square Foot of Ext. Wall Area	Lbs. of Nails per MBM of Stud Framing	Board Feet per Square Foot of Ext. Wall Area	Lbs. of Nails per MBM of Bracing
2" x 3"	16"	.78	30	.03	117
	20"	.74	30	.03	97
	24"	.71	30	.03	85
2" x 4"	16"	1.05	22	.04	87
	20"	.98	22	.04	72
	24"	.94	22	.04	64
2" x 6"	16"	1.51	15	.06	59
	20"	1.44	15	.06	48
	24"	1.38	15	.06	43

Figure 6.6 Floor Framing

This table can be used to compute the board feet required for each square foot of floor area, based on the size of lumber to be used and the spacing design.

Floor Joists				Block Over Main Bearing	
Joist Size	Inches On Center	Board Feet per Square Foot of Floor Area	Nails Lbs. per MBM	Board Feet per Square Foot of Floor Area	Nails Lbs. per MBM Blocking
2" x 6"	12"	1.28	10	.16	133
	16"	1.02	10	.03	95
	20"	.88	10	.03	77
	24"	.78	10	.03	57
2" x 8"	12"	1.71	8	.04	100
	16"	1.36	8	.04	72
	20"	1.17	8	.04	57
	24"	1.03	8	.05	43
2" x 10"	12"	2.14	6	.05	79
	16"	1.71	6	.05	57
	20"	1.48	6	.06	46
	24"	1.30	6	.06	34
2" x 12"	12"	2.56	5	.06	66
	16"	2.05	5	.06	47
	20"	1.77	5	.07	39
	24"	1.56	5	.07	29
3" x 8"	12"	2.56	5	.04	39
	16"	2.05	5	.05	57
	20"	1.77	5	.06	45
	24"	1.56	5	.06	33
3" x 10"	12"	3.20	4	.05	72
	16"	2.56	4	.07	46
	20"	2.21	4	.07	36
	24"	1.95	4	.08	26

Figure 6.7 Board Feet of Sheathing and Subflooring

This table is used to compute the board feet of sheathing or subflooring required per square foot of roof, ceiling or flooring.

Type	Size	Board Feet per Square Foot of Area	Diagonal			
			Lbs. Nails per MBM Lumber			
			Joist, Stud or Rafter Spacing			
			12"	16"	20"	24"
Surface 4 Sides (S4S)	1" x 4"	1.22	58	46	39	32
	1" x 6"	1.18	39	31	25	21
	1" x 8"	1.18	30	23	19	16
	1" x 10"	1.17	35	27	23	19
Tongue and Groove (T&G)	1" x 4"	1.36	65	51	43	36
	1" x 6"	1.26	42	33	27	23
	1" x 8"	1.22	31	24	20	17
	1" x 10"	1.20	36	28	24	19
Shiplap	1" x 4"	1.41	67	53	45	37
	1" x 6"	1.29	43	33	28	23
	1" x 8"	1.24	31	24	20	17
	1" x 10"	1.21	36	28	24	19

Figure 6.8 Factors for the Board Foot Measure of Floor or Ceiling Joists

This table allows you to compute the amount of lumber (in board feet) for the floor or ceiling joists of a known area, based on the size of lumber and the spacing. To use this chart, simply multiply the area of the room or building in question by the factor across from the appropriate board size and spacing.

Ceiling Joists			
Joist Size	Inches On Center	Board Feet per Square Foot of Ceiling Area	Nails Lbs. per MBM
2" x 4"	12"	.78	17
	16"	.59	19
	20"	.48	19
2" x 6"	12"	1.15	11
	16"	.88	13
	20"	.72	13
	24"	.63	13
2" x 8"	12"	1.53	9
	16"	1.17	9
	20"	.96	9
	24"	.84	9
2" x 10"	12"	1.94	7
	16"	1.47	7
	20"	1.21	7
	24"	1.04	7
3" x 8"	12"	2.32	6
	16"	1.76	6
	20"	1.44	6
	24"	1.25	6

Figure 6.9 Furring Quantities

This table provides multiplication factors for converting square feet of wall area requiring furring into board feet of lumber. These figures are based on lumber size and spacing.

Size	Board Feet per Square Feet of Wall Area				Lbs. Nails per MBM of Furring
	Spacing Center to Center				
	12"	16"	20"	24"	
1" x 2"	.18	.14	.11	.10	55
1" x 3"	.28	.21	.17	.14	37

Figure 6.10 Partition Framing

This table can be used to compute the board feet of lumber required for each square foot of wall area to be framed, based on the lumber size and spacing design.

Stud Size	Studs Including Sole and Cap Plates			Horizontal Bracing in All Partitions		Horizontal Bracing in Bearing Partitions Only	
	Inches on Center	Board Feet per Square Foot of Partition Area	Lbs. Nails per MBM of Stud Framing	Board Feet per Square Foot of Partition Area	Lbs. Nails per MBM of Bracing	Board Feet per Square Foot of Partition Area	Lbs. Nails per MBM of Bracing
2" x 3"	12"	.91	25	.04	145	.01	145
	16"	.83	25	.04	111	.01	111
	20"	.78	25	.04	90	.01	90
	24"	.76	25	.04	79	.01	79
2" x 4"	12"	1.22	19	.05	108	.02	108
	16"	1.12	19	.05	87	.02	87
	20"	1.05	19	.05	72	.02	72
	24"	1.02	19	.05	64	.02	64
2" x 6"	16"	1.38	19			.04	59
	20"	1.29	16			.04	48
	24"	1.22	16			.04	43
2" x 4" Staggered	8"	1.69	22				
3" x 4"	16"	1.35	17				
2" x 4" 2" Way	16"	1.08	19				

Figure 7.1 Common Insulating Materials Used in Construction

This table lists the common types of materials used in construction, their forms and their major uses.

Physical Form	Type of Material	Major Uses
Powders	Diatomaceous earth; sawdust; silica aerogel	Filler
Loose fibrous materials	Cork granules; glass wool; mineral wool; shredded bark; vermiculite; perlite; mica	Flat areas such as air spaces above ceilings, adjacent to roof, to reduce conduction and convection
Batt or blanket insulation[a]	Glass wool; mineral wool; wood fibers, etc., enclosed by paper, cloth, wire mesh, or aluminum	Air spaces, particularly in vertical walls and flat surfaces, to reduce conduction and convection
Board, sheet, and integrant insulation[a]	Cork; fiber; paper pulp; cellular glass; glass fiber	Sheathing for walls, to increase strength as well as reduce heat loss; rigid insulation on roofs; perimeter insulation along edges of slab floors
Reflective insulation	Aluminum foil, often combined in layers with one or more adjoining air spaces or combined with sheets of paper	Used principally for all types of refrigerated or controlled environmental spaces
Special types of block and brick insulation and refractories	Insulation block made of cork, expanded glass, 85% magnesia, or vermiculite; insulating refractory block or brick made of diatomaceous earth or kaolin (clay); heavy refractories made of fire clay, magnesite, or silica	Special controlled temperature and high-temperature insulation problems; for example, refrigerator rooms, pipes, ducts, boilers, fire chambers of boilers, and chimneys
Foam-type insulation	Rigid boards; 2-component on-job application with special applicators; polystyrene and polyurethane	Interior-applied insulation for walls above or below grade; roof insulation; air space and perimeter insulation

[a]These are available with vapor barrier as part of insulation.
(*courtesy Construction Materials, Caleb Hornbostel, John Wiley & Sons*)

Figure 7.2 Installation Time in Man-Hours
for Shingle and Tile Roofing

Description	Man-Hours	Unit
Shingles		
Aluminum	3.200	Sq.
Ridge Cap or Valley	.047	L.F.
Shakes	3.478	Sq.
Fiberglass		
325 lb. per Sq.	2.000	Sq.
165 lb. per Sq.	2.286	Sq.
Hip and Ridge	8.000	C.L.F.
Asphalt Standard Strip		
Class A 210 to 235 lb. per Sq.	1.455	Sq.
Class C 235 to 240 lb. per Sq.	1.600	Sq.
Standard Laminated		
Class A 240 to 260 lb. per Sq.	1.778	Sq.
Class C 260 to 300 lb. per Sq.	2.000	Sq.
Premium Laminated		
Class A 260 to 300 lb. per Sq.	2.286	Sq.
Class C 300 to 385 lb. per Sq.	2.667	Sq.
Hip and Ridge Roll	.020	L.F.
Slate Including Felt Underlay	4.571	Sq.
Steel	3.636	Sq.
Wood		
5″ Exposure	3.325	Sq.
5-1/2″ Exposure	3.034	Sq.
Panelized 8′ Strips 7″ Exposure	2.667	Sq.
Laps Rakes or Valleys	.040	L.F.
Tiles		
Aluminum		
Mission	3.200	Sq.
Spanish	2.667	Sq.
Clay 8-1/4″ x 11″	4.848	Sq.
Spanish	4.444	Sq.
Mission	6.957	Sq.
French	5.926	Sq.
Norman	8.000	Sq.
Williamsburg	5.926	Sq.
Concrete 13″ x 16-1/2″	5.926	Sq.
Steel	3.200	Sq.

Figure 8.1 Installation Time in Man-Hours for
Exterior Doors and Entry Systems

Description	Man-Hours	Unit
Glass Entrance Door, Including Frame and Hardware		
Balanced, Including Glass		
3' x 7'		
Economy	17.780	Ea.
Premium	22.860	Ea.
Hinged, Aluminum		
3' x 7'	8.000	Ea.
3' x 7', 3' Transom	8.890	Ea.
6' x 7'	12.310	Ea.
6' x 10', 3' Transom	14.550	Ea.
Stainless Steel, Including Glass		
3' x 7'		
Minimum	10.000	Ea.
Average	11.430	Ea.
Maximum	13.330	Ea.
Tempered Glass		
3' x 7'	8.000	
6' x 7'	11.430	Ea.
Hinged, Automatic, Aluminum		
6' x 7'	22.860	Ea.
Revolving, Aluminum, 7'-0" Diameter x 7' High		
Minimum	42.667	Ea.
Average	53.333	Ea.
Maximum	71.111	Ea.
Stainless Steel, 7'-0" Diameter x 7' High	106.667	Ea.
Bronze, 7'-0" Diameter x 7' High	213.333	Ea.
Glass Storefront System, Including Frame and Hardware		
Hinged, Aluminum, Including Glass, 400 S.F.		
w/3' x 7' Door		
Commercial Grade	.107	S.F.
Institutional Grade	.123	S.F.
Monumental Grade	.139	S.F.
w/6' x 7' Door		
Commercial Grade	.119	S.F.
Institutional Grade	.139	S.F.
Monumental Grade	.160	S.F.
Sliding, Automatic, 12' x 7'-6" w/5' x 7' door	22.860	Ea.
Mall Front, Manual, Aluminum		
15' x 9'	12.310	Ea.
24' x 9'	22.860	Ea.
48' x 9' w/Fixed Panels	17.780	Ea.

Figure 8.1 (cont.) Installation Time in Man-Hours for Exterior Doors and Entry Systems

Description	Man-Hours	Unit
Tempered All-Glass w/Glass Mullions,		
up to 10' High	.185	S.F.
up to 20' High, Minimum	.218	S.F.
Average	.240	S.F.
Maximum	.300	S.F.
Entrance Frames, Aluminum, 3' x 7'	2.290	Ea.
3' x 7', 3' Transom	2.460	Ea.
6' x 7'	2.670	Ea.
6' x 7', 3' Transom	2.910	Ea.
Glass, Tempered, 1/4" Thick	.133	S.F.
1/2" Thick	.291	S.F.
3/4" Thick	.457	S.F.
Insulating, 1" Thick	.213	S.F.
Overhead Commercial Doors		
Frames Not Included		
Stock Sectional Heavy Duty Wood		
1-3/4" Thick		
8' x 8'	8.000	Ea.
10' x 10'	8.889	Ea.
12' x 12'	10.667	Ea.
Fiberglass and Aluminum Heavy Duty Sectional		
12' x 12'	10.667	Ea.
20' x 20', Chain Hoist	32.000	Ea.
Steel 24' Gauge Sectional Manual		
8' x 8' High	8.000	Ea.
10' x 10' High	8.889	Ea.
12' x 12' High	10.667	Ea.
20' x 14' High, Chain Hoist	22.857	Ea.
For Electric Trolley Operator to 14' x 14'	4.000	Ea.
Over 14' x 14'	8.000	Ea.

Glass Entrance System with Transom

Figure 8.2 Installation Time in Man-Hours for Interior Doors and Frames

Description	Man-Hours	Unit
Architectural, Flush, Interior, Hollow Core, Veneer Face		
Up to 3'-0" x 7' x 0"	1.020	Ea.
4'-0" x 7'-0"	1.080	Ea.
High Pressured Plastic Laminate Face		
Up to 2'-6" x 6'-8"	1.000	Ea.
3'-0" x 7'-0"	1.153	Ea.
4'-0" x 7'-0"	1.234	Ea.
Particle Core, Veneer Face		
2'-6" x 6'-8"	1.067	Ea.
3'-0" x 6'-8"	1.143	Ea.
3'-0" x 7'-0"	1.231	Ea.
4'-0" x 7'-0"	1.333	Ea.
M.D.O. on Hardboard Face		
3'-0" x 7'-0"	1.333	Ea.
4'-0" x 7'-0"	1.600	Ea.
High Pressure Plastic Laminate Face		
3'-0" x 7'-0"	1.455	Ea.
4'-0" x 7'-0"	2.000	Ea.
Flush, Exterior, Solid Core, Veneer Face		
2'-6" x 7'-0"	1.067	Ea.
3'-0" x 7'-0"	1.143	Ea.
Decorator, Hand Carved		
Solid Wood		
Up to 3'-0" x 7'-0"	1.143	Ea.
3'-6" x 7'-0"	1.231	Ea.
Fire Door, Flush, Mineral Core		
B Label, 1 Hour, Veneer Face		
2'-6" x 6'-8"	1.143	Ea.
3'-0" x 7'-0"	1.333	Ea.
4'-0" x 7'-0"	1.333	Ea.
High Pressure Plastic Laminate Face		
3'-0" x 7'-0"	1.455	Ea.
4'-0" x 7'-0"	1.600	Ea.
Residential, Interior		
Hollow Core or Panel		
Up to 2'-8" x 6'-8"	.889	Ea.
3'-0" x 6'-8"	.941	Ea.
Bi-Folding Closet		
3'-0" x 6'-8"	1.231	Ea.
5'-0" x 6'-8"	1.455	Ea.
Interior Prehung, Hollow Core or Panel		
Up to 2'-8" x 6'-8"	.800	Ea.
3'-0" x 6'-8"	.842	Ea.
Exterior, Entrance, Solid Core or Panel		
Up to 2'-8" x 6'-8"	1.000	Ea.
3'-0" x 6'-8"	1.067	Ea.
Exterior Prehung, Entrance		
Up to 3'-0" x 7'-0"	1.000	Ea.

Left Hand Reverse

Right Hand Reverse

Left Hand

Right Hand

Hand Designations

Figure 8.2 (cont.) Installation Time in Man-Hours for Interior Doors and Frames

Description	Man-Hours	Unit
Hollow Metal Doors Flush		
Full Panel, Commercial		
20 Gauge		
2'-0" x 6'-8"	.800	Ea.
2'-6" x 6'-8"	.888	Ea.
3'-0" x 6'-8" or 3'-0" x 7'-0"	.941	Ea.
4'-0" x 7'-0"	1.066	Ea.
18 Gauge		
2'-6" x 6'-8" or 2'-6" x 7'-0"	.941	Ea.
3'-0" x 6'-8" or 3'-0" x 7'-0"	1.000	Ea.
4'-0" x 7'-0"	1.066	Ea.
Residential		
24 Gauge		
2'-8" x 6'-8"	1.000	Ea.
3'-0" x 7'-0"	1.066	Ea.
Bifolding		
3'-0" x 6'- 8"	1.000	Ea.
5'-0" x 6'-8"	1.143	Ea.
Steel Frames		
18 Gauge		
3'-0" Wide	1.000	Ea.
6'-0" Wide	1.142	Ea.
16 Gauge		
4'-0" Wide	1.066	Ea.
8'-0" Wide	1.333	Ea.
Transom Lite Frames		
Fixed Add	.103	S.F.
Movable Add	.123	S.F.

Hollow Core Door   Solid Core Door

Figure 9.1 Partition Density Guide

This table allows you to estimate the average quantities of partitions found in various types of buildings when no interior plans are available, such as in a conceptual estimating situation. To use this chart, pick out the type of structure to be estimated from the left-most column. Moving across, choose from the second column the number of stories of the building. Read across to the "Partition Density" column. This figure represents the number of square feet of floor area for every linear foot of partition.

Example: The project to be estimated is a three-story office building of 10,000 square feet per floor (total of 30,000 square feet). To estimate the approximate quantity of interior partitions in the entire building, first look in column 1 for "Office." Reading across to the "Stories" column, find the "3-5 Story" line. The "Partition Density" column for that line indicates 20 S.F./L.F. To find the number of partitions, divide the building area by the density factor: 30,000 S.F./20 = 1,500 L.F. of partition. Note that the right-most column gives a breakdown of average partition types. For our office building, the average mix is 30% concrete block (generally found at stairwells and service area partitions) and 70% drywall. Our drywall total would then be 1,050 L.F. To determine the total square footage of partitions, multiply this linear footage by the specified (or assumed) partition height. Note that the remainder of the partitions (450 L.F.) must be added to the masonry portion of the estimate, or at least accounted for in the estimate.

Building Type	Stories	Partition Density	Description of Partition
Apartments	1 story	9 S.F./L.F.	Plaster, wood doors & trim
	2 story	8 S.F./L.F.	Drywall, wood studs, wood doors & trim
	3 story	9 S.F./L.F.	Plaster, wood studs, and wood doors & trim
	5 story	9 S.F./L.F.	Plaster, wood studs, wood doors & trim
	6–15 story	8 S.F./L.F.	Drywall, wood studs, wood doors & trim
Bakery	1 story	50 S.F./L.F.	Conc. block, paint, door & drywall, wood studs
	2 story	50 S.F./L.F.	Conc. block, paint, door & drywall, wood studs
Bank	1 story	20 S.F./L.F.	Plaster, wood studs, wood doors & trim
	2-4 story	15 S.F./L.F.	Plaster, wood studs, wood doors & trim
Bottling Plant	1 story	50 S.F./L.F.	Conc. block, drywall, wood studs, wood trim
Bowling Alley	1 story	50 S.F./L.F.	Conc. block, wood & metal doors, wood trim
Bus Terminal	1 story	15 S.F./L.F.	Conc. block, ceramic tile, wood trim
Cannery	1 story	100 S.F./L.F.	Drywall on metal studs
Car Wash	1 story	18 S.F./L.F.	Concrete block, painted & hollow metal door
Dairy Plant	1 story	30 S.F./L.F.	Concrete block, glazed tile, insulated cooler doors
Department Store	1 story	60 S.F./L.F.	Drywall, wood studs, wood doors & trim
	2–5 story	60 S.F./L.F.	30% concrete block, 70% drywall, wood studs
Dormitory	2 story	9 S.F./L.F.	Plaster, concrete block, wood doors & trim
	3–5 story	9 S.F./L.F.	Plaster, concrete block, wood doors & trim
	6–15 story	9 S.F./L.F.	Plaster, concrete block, wood doors & trim
Funeral Home	1 story	15 S.F./L.F.	Plaster on concrete block & wood studs, paneling
	2 story	14 S.F./L.F.	Plaster, wood studs, paneling & wood doors
Garage Sales & Service	1 story	30 S.F./L.F.	50% conc. block, 50% drywall, wood studs
Hotel	3–8 story	9 S.F./L.F.	Plaster, conc. block, wood doors & trim
	9–15 story	9 S.F./L.F.	Plaster, conc. block, wood doors & trim
Laundromat	1 story	25 S.F./L.F.	Drywall, wood studs, wood doors & trim
Medical Clinic	1 story	6 S.F./L.F.	Drywall, wood studs, wood doors & trim
	2–4 story	6 S.F./L.F.	Drywall, wood studs, wood doors & trim
Motel	1 story	7 S.F./L.F.	Drywail, wood studs, wood doors & trim
	2–3 story	7 S.F./L.F.	Concrete block, drywall on wood studs, wood paneling

Figure 9.1 (cont.) Partition Density Guide

Building Type	Stories	Partition Density	Description of Partition
Movie 200–600 seats Theater 601–1400 seats 1401–2200 seats	1 story	18 S.F./L.F. 20 S.F./L.F. 25 S.F./L.F.	Concrete block, wood, metal, vinyl trim Concrete block, wood, metal, vinyl trim Concrete block, wood, metal, vinyl trim
Nursing Home	1 story 2–4 story	8 S.F./L.F. 8 S.F./L.F.	Drywall, wood studs, wood doors & trim Drywall, wood studs, wood doors & trim
Office	1 story 2 story 3–5 story 6–10 story 11–20 story	20 S.F./L.F. 20 S.F./L.F. 20 S.F./L.F. 20 S.F./L.F. 20 S.F./L.F.	30% concrete block, 70% drywall on wood studs 30% concrete block, 70% drywall on wood studs 30% concrete block, 70% movable partitions 30% concrete block, 70% movable partitions 30% concrete block, 70% movable partitions
Parking Ramp (Open) Parking Garage	2–8 story 2–8 story	60 S.F./L.F. 60 S.F./L.F.	Stair and elevator enclosures only Stair and elevator enclosures only

Pre-Engineered   Store
                Office
                Shop
	1 story
	1 story
	1 story
		60 S.F./L.F.
		15 S.F./L.F.
		15 S.F./L.F.
			Drywall on wood studs, wood doors & trim
			Concrete block, movable wood partitions
			Movable wood partitions

Radio & TV Broadcasting & TV Transmitter	1 story 1 story	25 S.F./L.F. 40 S.F./L.F.	Concrete block, metal and wood doors Concrete block, metal and wood doors
Self Service Restaurant Cafe & Drive-in Restaurant Restaurant with seating Supper Club Bar or Lounge	1 story 1 story 1 story 1 story 1 story	15 S.F./L.F. 18 S.F./L.F. 25 S.F./L.F. 25 S.F./L.F. 24 S.F./L.F.	Concrete block, wood and aluminum trim Drywall, wood studs, ceramic & plastic trim Concrete block, paneling, wood studs & trim Concrete block, paneling, wood studs & trim Plaster or gypsum lath, wood studs
Retail Store or Shop	1 story	60 S.F./L.F.	Drywall wood studs, wood doors & trim

Service Station   Masonry
           Metal panel
               Frame
	1 story
	1 story
	1 story
		15 S.F./L.F.
		15 S.F./L.F.
		15 S.F./L.F.
			Concrete block, paint, door & drywall, wood studs
			Concrete block paint door & drywall, wood studs
			Drywall, wood studs, wood doors & trim

Shopping Center (strip) (group)	1 story 1 story 2 story	30 S.F./L.F. 40 S.F./L.F. 40 S.F./L.F.	Drywall, wood studs, wood doors & trim 50% concrete block, 50% drywall, wood studs 50% concrete block, 50% drywall, wood studs
Small Food Store	1 story	30 S.F./L.F.	Concrete block drywall, wood studs, wood trim
Store/Apt. Masonry above Frame Frame	2 story 2 story 3 story	10 S.F./L.F. 10 S.F./L.F. 10 S.F./L.F.	Plaster, wood studs, wood doors & trim Plaster wood studs, wood doors & trim Plaster, wood studs and wood doors & trim
Supermarkets	1 story	40 S.F./L.F.	Concrete block, paint, drywall & porcelain panel
Truck Terminal	1 story	0	
Warehouse	1 story	0	

Figure 9.2 Installation Time in Man-Hours for Wood Stud Partition Systems

Description	Man-Hours	Unit
Wood Partitions Studs with Single Bottom Plate and Double Top Plate		
2" x 3" or 2" x 4" Studs		
12" On Center	.020	S.F.
16" On Center	.016	S.F.
24" On Center	.013	S.F.
2" x 6" Studs		
12" On Center	.023	S.F.
16" On Center	.018	S.F.
24" On Center	.014	S.F.
Plates		
2" x 3"	.019	L.F.
2" x 4"	.020	L.F.
2" x 6"	.021	L.F.
Studs		
2" x 3"	.013	L.F.
2" x 4"	.012	L.F.
2" x 6"	.016	L.F.
Blocking	.032	L.F.
Grounds 1" x 2"		
For Casework	.024	L.F.
For Plaster	.018	L.F.
Insulation Fiberglass Batts	.005	S.F.
Metal Lath Diamond Expanded		
2.5 lb. per S.Y.	.094	S.Y.
3.4 lb. per S.Y.	.100	S.Y.
Gypsum Lath		
3/8" Thick	.094	S.Y.
1/2" Thick	.100	S.Y.
Gypsum Plaster		
2 Coats	.381	S.Y.
3 Coats	.460	S.Y.
Perlite or Vermiculite Plaster		
2 Coats	.435	S.Y.
3 Coats	.541	S.Y.
Wood Fiber Plaster		
2 Coats	.556	S.Y.
3 Coats	.702	S.Y.

Figure 9.2 (cont.) Installation Time in Man-Hours for Wood Stud Partition Systems

Description	Man-Hours	Unit
Drywall Gypsum Plasterboard Including Taping		
3/8" Thick	.015	S.F.
1/2" or 5/8" Thick	.017	S.F.
For Thin Coat Plaster Instead of Taping Add	.013	S.F.
Prefinished Vinyl Faced Drywall	.015	S.F.
Sound-deadening Board	.009	S.F.
Walls in Place		
2" x 4" Studs with 5/8"		
Gypsum Drywall Both Sides Taped	.053	S.F.
2" x 4" Studs with 2 Layers Gypsum Drywall		
Both Sides Taped	.078	S.F.

Wood Stud Partition, No Blocking   Wood Stud Partition with Blocking

Figure 10.1 Installation Time for Metal Lockers

Metal Lockers	Crew Makeup	Daily Output	Man-Hours	Unit
LOCKERS Steel, baked enamel, 60" or 72", single tier				
Minimum	1 Sheet Metal Worker	14	.571	Opng.
Maximum		12	.667	Opng.
2 tier, 60" or 72" total height, minimum		26	.308	Opng.
Maximum		20	.400	Opng.
5 tier box lockers, minimum		30	.267	Opng.
Maximum		24	.333	Opng.
6 tier box lockers, minimum		36	.222	Opng.
Maximum		30	.267	Opng.
Basket rack with 32 baskets, 9" x 13" x 8" basket		50	.160	Basket
24 baskets, 12" x 13" x 8" basket		50	.160	Basket
Athletic, wire mesh, no lock, 18" x 18" x 72" basket		12	.667	Ea.
Overhead locker baskets on chains, 14" x 14" baskets	3 Sheet Metal Workers	96	.250	Basket
Overhead locker framing system, add		600	.040	Basket
Locking rail and bench units, add		120	.200	Basket
Locker bench, laminated maple, top only	1 Sheet Metal Worker	100	.080	L.F.
Pedestals, steel pipe	"	25	.320	Ea.
Teacher and pupil wardrobes, enameled				
22" x 15" x 61" high, minimum	1 Sheet Metal Worker	10	.800	Ea.
Average		9	.889	Ea.
Maximum		8	1.000	Ea.
Duplex lockers with 2 doors, 72" high, 15" x 15"		10	.800	Ea.
15" x 21"		10	.800	Ea.

Figure 10.2 Installation Time for Panel Partitions

Panel Partitions	Crew Makeup	Daily Output	Man-Hours	Unit
PARTITIONS, FOLDING LEAF Acoustic, wood				
Vinyl faced, to 18' high, 6 psf, minimum	2 Carpenters	60	.267	S.F.
Average		45	.356	S.F.
Maximum		30	.533	S.F.
Formica or hardwood finish, minimum		60	.267	S.F.
Maximum		30	.533	S.F.
Wood, low acoustical type, 4.5 psf, to 14' high		50	.320	S.F.
Steel, acoustical, 9 to 12 lb. per S.F., vinyl faced				
Minimum		60	.267	S.F.
Maximum		30	.533	S.F.
Aluminum framed, acoutical, to 12' high, 5.5 psf				
Minimum		60	.267	S.F.
Maximum		30	.533	S.F.
6.5 lb. per S.F., minimum		60	.267	S.F.
Maximum		30	.533	S.F.
PARTITIONS, OPERABLE Acoustic air wall, 1-5/8" thick				
Minimum		375	.043	S.F.
Maximum		365	.044	S.F.
2-1/4" thick, minimum		360	.044	S.F.
Maximum		330	.048	S.F.
Overhead track type, acoustical, 3" thick, 11 psf				
Minimum		350	.046	S.F.
Maximum		300	.053	S.F.

Figure 11.1 Installation Time for Theater/Stage Equipment

Theater/ Stage Equipment	Crew Makeup	Daily Output	Man-Hours	Unit
STAGE EQUIPMENT Control boards				
with dimmers & breakers, minimum	1 Electrician	1	8.000	Ea.
Average	↓	.50	16.000	Ea.
Maximum		.20	40.000	Ea.
Curtain track, straight, light duty	2 Carpenters	20	.800	L.F.
Heavy duty		18	.889	L.F.
Curved sections		12	1.330	L.F.
Curtains, velour, medium weight		600	.027	S.F.
Asbestos		50	.320	S.F.
Silica based yarn, fireproof	↓	50	.320	S.F.
Lights, border, quartz, reflector, vented,				
colored or white	1 Electrician	20	.400	L.F.
Spotlight, follow spot, with transformer, 2100 watt		4	2.000	Ea.
Stationary spot, fresnel quartz, 6″ lens		4	2.000	Ea.
8″ lens		4	2.000	Ea.
Ellipsoidal quartz, 1000W, 6″ lens		4	2.000	Ea.
12″ lens		4	2.000	Ea.
Strobe light, 1 to 15 flashes per second, quartz		3	2.670	Ea.
Color wheel, portable, five hole, motorized	↓	4	2.000	Ea.
Telescoping platforms, extruded alum., straight				
Minimum	4 Carpenters	157	.204	S.F. Stg.
Maximum		77	.416	S.F. Stg.
Pie-shaped, minimum		150	.213	S.F. Stg.
Maximum		70	.457	S.F. Stg.
Band risers, steel frame, plywood deck, minimum		275	.116	S.F. Stg.
Maximum	↓	138	.232	S.F. Stg.
Chairs for above, self-storing, minimum	2 Carpenters	43	.372	Ea.
Maximum	″	40	.400	Ea.
Rule of thumb: total stage equipment, minimum	4 Carpenters	100	.320	S.F. Stg.
Maximum	″	25	1.280	S.F. Stg.
MOVIE EQUIPMENT				
Lamphouses, incl. rectifiers, xenon, 1000 watt	1 Electrician	2	4.000	Ea.
1600 watt		2	4.000	Ea.
2000 watt		1.50	5.330	Ea.
4000 watt	↓	1.50	5.330	Ea.
Projection screens, rigid, in wall, acrylic, 1/4″ thick	2 Glaziers	195	.082	S.F.
1/2″ thick	″	130	.123	S.F.
Electric operated, heavy duty, 400 S.F.	2 Carpenters	1	16.000	Ea.
Sound systems, incl. amplifier, single system				
Minimum	1 Electrician	.90	8.890	Ea.
Dolby/Super Sound, maximum		.40	20.000	Ea.
Dual system, minimum		.70	11.430	Ea.
Dolby/Super Sound, maximum		.40	20.000	Ea.
Speakers, recessed behind screen, minimum		2	4.000	Ea.
Maximum	↓	1	8.000	Ea.
Seating, painted steel, upholstered, minimum	2 Carpenters	35	.457	Ea.
Maximum	″	28	.571	Ea.

Figure 11.2 Installation Time for Loading Dock Equipment

Loading Dock Equipment	Crew Makeup	Daily Output	Man-Hours	Unit
LOADING DOCK Bumpers, rubber blocks 4-1/2" thick				
10" high, 14" long	1 Carpenter	26	.308	Ea.
24" long		22	.364	Ea.
36" long		17	.471	Ea.
12" high, 14" long		25	.320	Ea.
24" long		20	.400	Ea.
36" long		15	.533	Ea.
Rubber blocks 6" thick, 10" high, 14" long		22	.364	Ea.
24" long		18	.444	Ea.
36" long		13	.615	Ea.
20" high, 11" long		13	.615	Ea.
Extruded rubber bumpers, T section				
22" x 22" x 3" thick		41	.195	Ea.
Molded rubber bumpers, 24" x 12" x 3" thick		20	.400	Ea.
Welded installation of above bumpers	1 Welder Foreman 1 Gas Welding Machine	8	1.000	Ea.
For drilled anchors, add per anchor	1 Carpenter	36	.222	Ea.
Door seal for door perimeter				
12" x 12", vinyl covered	"	26	.308	L.F.
Levelers, hinged for trucks, 10 ton capacity, 6' x 8'	2 Skilled Workers 1 Helper	1.90	12.630	Ea.
7' x 8'		1.90	12.630	Ea.
Hydraulic, 10 ton capacity, 6' x 8'		1.90	12.630	Ea.
7' x 8'		1.90	12.630	Ea.
Lights for loading docks, single arm, 24" long	1 Electrician	3.80	2.110	Ea.
Double arm, 60" long	"	3.80	2.110	Ea.
Shelters, fabric, for truck or train, scissor arms				
Minimum	1 Carpenter	1	8.000	Ea.
Maximum	"	.50	16.000	Ea.
DOCK BUMPERS Bolts not incl. 2" x 6" to 4" x 8"				
Average	1 Carpenter Power Tools	.30	26.670	M.B.F.

Figure 12.1 Installation Time for Hospital Casework

Hospital Casework	Crew Makeup	Daily Output	Man-Hours	Unit
CABINETS				
Hospital, base cabinets, laminated plastic	2 Carpenters	10	1.600	L.F.
Enameled steel		10	1.600	L.F.
Stainless steel		10	1.600	L.F.
Cabinet base trim, 4" high, enameled steel		200	.080	L.F.
Stainless steel		200	.080	L.F.
Counter top, laminated plastic, no backsplash		40	.400	L.F.
With backsplash		40	.400	L.F.
For sink cutout, add		12.20	1.310	Ea.
Stainless steel counter top		40	.400	L.F.
Nurses station, door type, laminated plastic		10	1.600	L.F.
Enameled steel		10	1.600	L.F.
Stainless steel		10	1.600	L.F.
Wall cabinets, laminated plastic		15	1.070	L.F.
Enameled steel		15	1.070	L.F.
Stainless steel		15	1.070	L.F.
Kitchen, base cabinets, metal, minimum		30	.533	L.F.
Maximum		25	.640	L.F.
Wall cabinets, metal, minimum		30	.533	L.F.
Maximum		25	.640	L.F.
School, 24" deep		15	1.070	L.F.
Counter height units		20	.800	L.F.
Wood, custom fabricated, 32" high counter		20	.800	L.F.
Add for counter top		56	.286	L.F.
84" high wall units		15	1.070	L.F.

Figure 12.2 Installation Time for Display Casework

Display Casework	Crew Makeup	Daily Output	Man-Hours	Unit
DISPLAY CASES Free standing, all glass				
Aluminum frame, 42" high x 36" x 12" deep	2 Carpenters	8	2.000	Ea.
70" high x 48" x 18" deep	"	6	2.670	Ea.
Wall mounted, glass front, aluminum frame				
Non-illuminated, one section 3' x 4' x 1'-4"	2 Carpenters	5	3.200	Ea.
5' x 4' x 1'-4"		5	3.200	Ea.
6' x 4' x 1'-4"		4	4.000	Ea.
Two sections, 8' x 4' x 1'-4"		2	8.000	Ea.
10' x 4' x 1'-4"		2	8.000	Ea.
Three sections, 16' x 4' x 1'-4"		1.50	10.670	Ea.
Table exhibit cases, 2' wide, 3' high, 4' long, flat top		5	3.200	Ea.
3' wide, 3' high, 4' long, sloping top	↓	3	5.330	Ea.

Figure 13.1 Installation Time for
Pre-Engineered Buildings

Pre-Engineered Buildings	Crew Makeup	Daily Output	Man-Hours	Unit
HANGARS Prefabricated steel T hangars Galv. steel roof & walls, incl. electric bi-folding doors, 4 or more units, not including floors or foundations, minimum	1 Struc. Steel Foreman 4 Struc. Steel Workers 1 Equip. Oper. (crane) 1 Equip. Oper. Oiler 1 Crane, 90 Ton	1,275	.044	S.F. Flr.
Maximum		1,063	.053	S.F. Flr.
With bottom rolling doors, minimum	↓	1,386	.040	S.F. Flr.
Maximum		966	.058	S.F. Flr.
Alternate pricing method: Galv. roof and walls, electric bi-folding doors, minimum	1 Struc. Steel Foreman 4 Struc. Steel Workers 1 Equip. Oper. (crane) 1 Equip. Oper. Oiler 1 Crane, 90 Ton	1.06	52.830	Plane
Maximum		.91	61.540	Plane
With bottom rolling doors, minimum	↓	1.25	44.800	Plane
Maximum		.97	57.730	Plane
Circular type, prefab., steel frame, plastic skin, electric door, including foundations, 80' diameter, for up to 5 light planes Minimum	1 Struc. Steel Foreman 4 Struc. Steel Workers 1 Equip. Oper. (crane) 1 Equip. Oper. Oiler 1 Crane, 90 Ton	.50	112.000	Total
Maximum	"	.25	224.000	Total

Figure 13.2 Installation Time for Ground Storage Tanks

Ground Storage Tanks	Crew Makeup	Daily Output	Man-Hours	Unit
TANKS Not incl. pipe or pumps				
Wood tanks, ground level, 2" cypress, 3000 gallons	3 Carpenters 1 Building Laborer Power Tools	.19	168.000	Ea.
2-1/2" cypress, 10,000 gallons		.12	267.000	Ea.
3" redwood or 3" fir, 20,000 gallons		.10	320.000	Ea.
30,000 gallons		.08	400.000	Ea.
45,000 gallons	↓	.07	457.000	Ea.
Vinyl coated fabric pillow tanks, freestanding				
5000 gallons	4 Building Laborers	4	8.000	Ea.
Supporting embankment not included				
25,000 gallons	6 Building Laborers	2	24.000	Ea.
50,000 gallons	8 Building Laborers	1.50	42.670	Ea.
100,000 gallons	9 Building Laborers	.90	80.000	Ea.
150,000 gallons		.50	144.000	Ea.
200,000 gallons		.40	180.000	Ea.
250,000 gallons	↓	.30	240.000	Ea.

Figure 14.1 Installation Time for Elevators

Elevators	Crew Makeup	Daily Output	Man-Hours	Unit
ELEVATORS				
2 story, hydraulic, 4,000 lb. capacity, minimum	3 Elevator Constructors 1 Elevator Apprentice Hand Tools	.09	356.000	Ea.
Maximum		.09	356.000	Ea.
10,000 lb. capacity, minimum		.07	457.000	Ea.
Maximum		.07	457.000	Ea.
6 story hydraulic, 4000 lb. capacity		.03	67.000	Ea.
10,000 lb. capacity		.03	67.000	Ea.
6 story geared electric 4000 lb. capacity		.04	800.000	Ea.
10,000 lb. capacity		.03	67.000	Ea.
12 story gearless electric 4000 lb. capacity		.03	67.000	Ea.
10,000 lb. capacity		.03	67.000	Ea.
20 story gearless electric 4000 lb. capacity		.02	600.000	Ea.
10,000 lb. capacity		.02	600.000	Ea.
Passenger, 2 story hydraulic, 2000 lb. capacity		.07	457.000	Ea.
5000 lb. capacity		.07	457.000	Ea.
6 story hydraulic, 2000 lb. capacity		.03	67.000	Ea.
5000 lb. capacity		.03	67.000	Ea.
6 story geared electric, 2000 lb. capacity		.04	800.000	Ea.
5000 lb. capacity		.04	800.000	Ea.
12 story gearless electric, 2000 lb. capacity		.03	67.000	Ea.
5000 lb. capacity		.03	67.000	Ea.
20 story gearless electric, 2000 lb. capacity		.02	600.000	Ea.
5000 lb. capacity		.02	600.000	Ea.
Passenger, pre-engineered, 5 story, hydraulic 2500 lb. capacity		.04	800.000	Ea.
For less than 5 stops, deduct		.29	110.000	Stop
10 story, geared traction, 200 FPM 2500 lb. capacity		.02	600.000	Ea.
For less than 10 stops, deduct		.34	94.120	Stop
For 4500 lb. capacity, general purpose		.02	600.000	Ea.
For hospital		.02	600.000	Ea.
Residential, cab type, 1 floor, 2 stop, minimum	2 Elevator Constructors	.20	80.000	Ea.
Maximum		.10	160.000	Ea.
2 floor, 3 stop, minimum		.12	133.000	Ea.
Maximum		.06	267.000	Ea.
Stair climber (chair lift) single seat, minimum		1	16.000	Ea.
Maximum		.20	80.000	Ea.
Wheelchair, porch lift, minimum		1	16.000	Ea.
Maximum		.50	32.000	Ea.
Stair lift, minimum		1	16.000	Ea.
Maximum		.20	80.000	Ea.

Figure 14.2 Installation Time for Electric Dumbwaiters

Electric Dumbwaiters	Crew Makeup	Daily Output	Man- Hours	Unit
DUMBWAITERS 2 stop, electric, minimum	2 Elevator Constructors	.13	123.000	Ea.
Maximum	↓	.11	145.000	Ea.
For each additional stop, add		.54	29.630	Stop

Figure 15.1 Pipe Sizing for Heating

Heating Load, BTU/HR.	GPM Circulated (20°T.D.)	Recommended Connecting Tubing Size (Type M) for Various Heating Loads and Connecting Tubing Lengths. (Figures based on 10,000 BTU per GPM, or on temperature drop of 20° thru the circuit.)				
		Total Length Ft. Connecting Tubing				
		0–50	50–100	100–150	150–200	200–300
		Tubing, Nominal O.D., Type M				
5,000	0.5	3/8	3/8	1/2	1/2	1/2
10,000	1.0	3/8	3/8	1/2	1/2	1/2
15,000	1.5	1/2	1/2	1/2	1/2	3/4
20,000	2.0	1/2	1/2	1/2	3/4	3/4
30,000	3.0	1/2	1/2	3/4	3/4	3/4
40,000	4.0	1/2	3/4	3/4	3/4	3/4
50,000	5.0	3/4	3/4	3/4	1	1
60,000	6.0	3/4	3/4	1	1	1
75,000	7.5	3/4	1	1	1	1
100,000	10.0	1	1	1	1-1/4	1-1/4
125,000	12.5	1	1	1-1/4	1-1/4	1-1/4
150,000	15.0	1	1-1/4	1-1/4	1-1/4	1-1/2
200,000	20.0	1-1/4	1-1/4	1-1/2	1-1/2	1-1/2
250,000	25.0	1-1/4	1-1/2	1-1/2	2	2
300,000	30.0	1-1/2	1-1/2	2	2	2
400,000	40.0	2	2	2	2	2
500,000	50.0	2	2	2	2-1/2	2-1/2
600,000	60.0	2	2	2-1/2	2-1/2	2-1/2
800,000	80.0	2-1/2	2-1/2	2-1/2	2-1/2	3
1,000,000	100.0	2-1/2	2-1/2	3	3	3
1,250,000	125.0	2-1/2	3	3	3	3-1/2
1,500,000	150.0	3	3	3	3-1/2	3-1/2
2,000,000	200.0	3	3-1/2	3-1/2	4	4
2,500,000	250.0	3-1/2	3-1/2	4	4	5
3,000,000	300.0	3-1/2	4	4	4	5
4,000,000	400.0	4	4	5	5	5
5,000,000	500.0	5	5	5	6	6
6,000,000	600.0	5	6	6	6	8
8,000,000	800.0	8	6	8	8	8
10,000,000	1,000.0	8	8	8	8	10

Figure 15.2 Installation Time in Man-Hours for Plumbing Fixtures

Description	Man-Hours	Unit
For Setting Fixture and Trim		
Bath Tub	3.636	Ea.
Bidet	3.200	Ea.
Dental Fountain	2.000	Ea.
Drinking Fountain	2.500	Ea.
Lavatory		
Vanity Top	2.500	Ea.
Wall Hung	2.000	Ea.
Laundry Sinks	2.667	Ea.
Prison/Institution Fixtures		
Lavatory	2.000	Ea.
Service Sink	5.333	Ea.
Urinal	4.000	Ea.
Water Closet	2.759	Ea.
Combination Water Closet and Lavatory	3.200	Ea.
Shower Stall	8.000	Ea.
Sinks		
Corrosion Resistant	5.333	Ea.
Kitchen, Countertop	3.330	Ea.
Kitchen, Raised Deck	7.270	Ea.
Service, Floor	3.640	Ea.
Service, Wall	4.000	Ea.
Urinals		
Wall Hung	5.333	Ea.
Stall Type	6.400	Ea.
Wash Fountain, Group	9.600	Ea.
Water Closets		
Tank Type, Wall Hung	3.019	Ea.
Floor Mount, One Piece	3.019	Ea.
Bowl Only, Wall Hung	2.759	Ea.
Bowl Only, Floor Mount	2.759	Ea.
Gang, Side by Side, First	2.759	Ea.
Each Additional	2.759	Ea.
Gang, Back to Back, First Pair	5.520	Pair
Each Additional Pair	5.520	Pair
Water Conserving Type	2.963	Ea.
Water Cooler	4.000	Ea.

Figure 16.1 Installation Time in Man-Hours for Conduit

Description	Man-Hours	Unit
Rigid Galvanized Steel 1/2" Diameter	.089	L.F.
1-1/2" Diameter	.145	L.F.
3" Diameter	.320	L.F.
6" Diameter	.800	L.F.
Aluminum 1/2" Diameter	.080	L.F.
1-1/2" Diameter	.123	L.F.
3" Diameter	.178	L.F.
6" Diameter	.400	L.F.
IMC 1/2" Diameter	.080	L.F.
1-1/2" Diameter	.133	L.F.
3" Diameter	.267	L.F.
4" Diameter	.320	L.F.
Plastic Coated Rigid Steel 1/2" Diameter	.100	L.F.
1-1/2" Diameter	.178	L.F.
3" Diameter	.364	L.F.
6" Diameter	.800	L.F.
EMT 1/2" Diameter	.047	L.F.
1-1/2" Diameter	.089	L.F.
3" Diameter	.160	L.F.
4" Diameter	.200	L.F.
PVC Nonmetallic 1/2" Diameter	.042	L.F.
1-1/2" Diameter	.080	L.F.
3" Diameter	.145	L.F.
6" Diameter	.267	L.F.

Rigid Steel, Plastic Coated Coupling

PVC Conduit

PVC Elbow

Aluminum Conduit

EMT Set Screw Connector

Aluminum Elbow

EMT Connector

Rigid Steel, Plastic Coated Conduit

EMT to Conduit Adapter

Rigid Steel, Plastic Coated Elbow

EMT to Greenfield Adapter

Figure 16.2 Installation Time in Man-Hours for Wiring Devices

Description	Man-Hours	Unit
Receptacle 20A 250V	.290	Ea.
Receptacle 30A 250V	.530	Ea.
Receptacle 50A 250V	.720	Ea.
Receptacle 60A 250V	1.000	Ea.
Box, 4″ Square	.400	Ea.
Box, Single Gang	.290	Ea.
Box, Cast Single Gang	.660	Ea.
Cover, Weatherproof	.120	Ea.
Cover, Raised Device	.150	Ea.
Cover, Brushed Brass	.100	Ea.

30 Amp, 125 Volt, Nema 5

50 Amp, 125 Volt, Nema 5

20 Amp, 250 Volt, Nema 6

Box, Single Gang

Cover

Duplex Receptacle

Receptacle, Including Box and Cover

Receptacles

INDEX